MW00560604

Complete Book of Equipment Leasing Agreements, Forms, Worksheets & Checklists

Complete Book of Equipment Leasing Agreements, Forms, Worksheets & Checklists

Richard M. Contino

AMACOM
American Management Association
New York • Atlanta • Boston • Chicago • Kansas City • San Francisco • Washington, D.C.
Brussels • Mexico City • Tokyo • Toronto

This book is available at a special
discount when ordered in bulk quantities.
For information, contact Special Sales Department,
AMACOM, a division of American Management Association,
1601 Broadway, New York, NY 10019.

Library of Congress Cataloging-in-Publication Data

Contino, Richard M.
Complete book of equipment leasing agreements, forms, worksheets & checklists / Richard M. Contino.
p. cm.
Includes index.
ISBN 0-8144-0338-7
1. Industrial equipment leases—United States—Forms.
I. Title.
KF946.A65C66 1997
346.7304'7—dc21 96-52974
CIP

Printing number

10 9 8 7 6 5 4 3 2 1

To
Penelope,
May-Lynne,
Matthew,
my **Mother,**
and
my **Father**

Contents

Introduction

General

The *Complete Book of Equipment Leasing Agreements, Forms, Worksheets & Checklists* provides examples of virtually every type of document, worksheet, checklist, notification, and letter to assist anyone involved, or intending to become involved, in equipment leasing or lending. In total, there are 117 documents. So, if you're a prospective or existing lessor, lessee, or equipment lender, or a lease or loan advisor, this book will provide a handy and invaluable state-of-the-art document reference for small to multi-million dollar equipment financing (and equipment-financing related) transactions. For example, there are forms for:

- Preparing lessor lease proposals and lessee requests for lease proposals, such as lessor underwritten lease proposals and lessee RFQs
- Evaluating lessor proposals or prospective lessee deals, such as transactions summaries
- Documenting equipment lease or loan transactions, such as single deal or master lease and loan agreements
- Starting and operating a leasing business, such as lessee marketing materials, internal deal and operations worksheets, and collection notices
- Setting up equipment vendor financing arrangements, such as vendor program and remarketing agreements

All documents, where relevant, are fully integrated with cross references to other documents necessary, which may be integral with the document being used, thereby enabling you to quickly access these collateral forms. For example, lease agreements are integrated with opinions of counsel, guaranties, corporate resolutions, and various lessee and lessor lease options so you have a complete package. In addition, the book comes with a computer disk containing the agreements, forms, worksheets, checklists, notifications, and letters.

Each form is preceded by a page that states the respective form number, computer disk file name identification, summary of the form's purpose, an identification of who the executing parties are, and cross references to other pertinent forms. Other than the computer disk file name identification, that information appears only in this volume; the computer files contain only information that is part of the respective document.

Specific Tips of Using Your Form Book

Provided below are some tips on getting the most out of this book.

- *Do you need a particular lease or loan provision?* The 117 agreements, forms, worksheets, and checklists available to you in this book are based upon, and have been honed through, the author's equipment financing experience with hundreds of transactions and situations, both as a legal and business advisor and as a business principal, during his fifteen-year involvement with the business of equipment leasing and lending. With these documents at your fingertips, you have immediate access to a unique wealth of equipment lease and loan provisions to help you gain every advantage, avoid the many pitfalls, and assist you in developing negotiating compromises when necessary. Many form categories provide you with drafting approach choices to enable you to select the most appropriate provision style for your particular situation. For example, in a small-ticket financing, a less detail-specific approach may be the most appropriate. Also, many provisions reflect the give-and-take of actual deal negotiations. These provisions will provide you with winning insights—ones, for example, that can increase your bargaining power, help you win profitable business deals or obtain cost-effective equipment financing, enhance your ability to effectively make reasonable negotiating compromises, and assist you in closing beneficial equipment financing deals.

• *Do you need a particular form?* When you need a particular form, simply check the Table of Contents for what you want. Where relevant, a selection of forms within a particular category has been provided. For example, if you are looking for an equipment lease agreement, you will find that there are three lease agreements to choose from: a long-form master lease agreement, a short-form lease agreement, and a lease agreement used in a leveraged transaction. If you are involved with a small-ticket, nontax sensitive lease transaction, you will not need, or want, a fifty-page document, so the short-form lease agreement is the place to start. If, on the other hand, you are involved with a multimillion dollar lease transaction, you should refer to one of the more comprehensive lease agreements, which will contain provisions that address the needs found in major equipment financings. If there are specific lease agreement provisions you need assistance on, refer to all the lease agreements for guidance; each document contains valuable deal nuances. In using all these documents, keep in mind that no matter what type of equipment you are involved with, the basic forms can be easily adapted by making the appropriate equipment type changes.

• *Are you putting together an entire transaction?* Equipment lease and loan transactions involve multiple documents, which, in many cases, must interrelate. For example, if you are involved with an equipment lending transaction, you will not only need the loan and security agreement, but you will also need all the collateral forms typically used in a loan transaction, such as a form legal opinion. By referencing the Loan Document Section of the Table of Contents, you can identify which loan and security agreement forms are packaged specifically to provide you with fully integrated collateral documents, so important and critical deal aspects and collateral documents are not inadvertently overlooked. Using these fully integrated forms will save you drafting time. Additionally, the page proceeding each form has cross references, where relevant, to other documents that you might want or need to consider.

• *Are you proposing a deal?* If you are an equipment lessor or lease underwriter, this book can save you time in putting together the best possible proposal for you and your prospective lessee. The relevant checklists, worksheets, and letters will get you off on the right track—quickly. For example, the book contains forms in single-investor and multiple-investor proposal formats. Additionally, if you are proposing on an equipment loan, these forms can be readily adapted to loan proposals.

• *Are you looking for equipment financing offers?* If you're a prospective equipment lender or borrower, and want financing bids on equipment you need, the documents available will ensure that you don't miss out on the many possible benefits, that you put together a professional-looking request for bids, and that you are able to quickly analyze financing offers when they come in. For example, there is a time-saving request for lease proposals (RFQ-Deal Sheet Format, Form r-01) developed by the author that sets up the bidding parameters so offer comparisons can be done simply and meaningfully.

- *Are you concerned about missing an important deal point?* Unless you are thoroughly experienced in equipment leasing or lending, it's often difficult, and sometimes impossible, to know what you should ask for and what may be available. Even when you *do* know, in the rush of a deal it's easy to inadvertently miss an important point. The worksheets and checklists available will ensure that you're never in that situation—whether you are on the lessor's or lessee's side. For example, a handy lease proposal evaluation worksheet and an invaluable lease negotiation and drafting checklist gives you expert guidance.
- *Are you negotiating a deal?* In negotiating any equipment lease or loan financing, a ready reference to comprehensive provisions and forms can assist you in documenting or negotiating difficult points—and in formulating possible solutions when transaction impasses occur. And they will. The documents provided in this book come from the negotiating trenches. If you need assistance, they will help you solve difficult problems and gain protection.
- *Are you starting or running a leasing or lending business?* Not only does this book contain all the basic agreements that you need to document an equipment lease or loan transaction, but it contains worksheets, checklists, and time-saving form letters that you can use in the day-to-day running of a leasing business. For example, there are lessee marketing materials, such as a form rate sheet and a form proposal letter, transaction audit worksheets, and collection letters. All are based upon documents in actual use by equipment lessors and lenders.

In summary, whatever your equipment financing needs, this book offers you a unique and ready source for invaluable state-of-the-art agreements, forms, worksheets, and checklists that are not available in any other publication.

If you have any questions about the forms, you may contact the author by e-mail at rlegal@ix.netcom.com, or by postal mail at Contino & Partners, 70 Red Oak Lane, White Plains, New York 10604

About the Disk

The computer disk contains 118 files: a README file and 117 compressed files. The README file contains information about the disk files and how to install and use them. README is an ASCII file that can be read through MS-DOS or any MS-DOS word processor.

The compressed form files on the computer disk cannot be used until they are installed on the hard drive of a personal computer (PC) through the automatic installation procedure described in the instructions accompanying the disk. These files were prepared in Microsoft Word, version 5, and are presented on a 3.5″ high density (DSHD) disk (1.44 MB).

Microsoft Word for Windows can import these files, but you must inform the program that they are rich text format files to enable the conversion. Macintosh computers equipped to convert MS-DOS files should be able to read these files without difficulty.

Acknowledgment Documents

Form: a-01
Disk File Name: a-01.rtf

Acknowledgment of Receipt of Certificate of Deposit

Form Purpose

Acknowledgment for use by an equipment leasing company or equipment lender of the receipt and acceptance of a certificate of deposit as collateral security for equipment lease or loan obligations.

Executing Parties

The equipment leasing company or lender, as applicable.

See:

Assignment of Certificate of Deposit, Form a-02

Acknowledgment of Receipt of Certificate of Deposit

Lessee (or Borrower, as applicable) Name: ______________________

Lessee (or Borrower, as applicable) Address: ______________________

____

Lease (or Loan, as applicable) Number: __________

Certificate of Deposit Identification No.: __________

To Whom It May Concern:

I hereby certify that I am a duly elected officer of (insert name of leasing company or lender) (the "Company"), and as said officer, I am duly authorized to acknowledge and accept receipt of original Certificates of Deposit on behalf of the Company.

The Certificate of Deposit referenced above has been tendered by the above-referenced lessee (or borrower, as applicable) in accordance with the terms and conditions of the above-referenced lease (or loan, as applicable), and in accordance with the Assignment of Certificate of Deposit, a copy of which is attached hereto as Exhibit A.

This letter is to acknowledge the receipt and acceptance of one original Certificate of Deposit, identified above, issued by (insert name of issuing institution) in the amount of $ __________.

(Insert name of leasing company or lender.)

By: ______________________

Title: ______________________

Date: ______________

Exhibit A

[Copy of Assignment of Certificate of Deposit.]

Assignment Documents

Form a-02
Disk File Name: a-02.rtf

ASSIGNMENT OF CERTIFICATE OF DEPOSIT

Form Purpose

Assignment to an equipment leasing company or lender of one or more certificates of deposit as collateral security for equipment lease or loan obligations.

Executing Parties

The equipment lessee (assignor), or borrower, as applicable.
The equipment lessor (assignee), or lender, as applicable.

See:

Acknowledgment of Receipt of Certificate of Deposit, Form a-01

Assignment of Certificate of Deposit

This Assignment of Certificate of Deposit (the "Agreement"), dated ________________, XXXX, is entered into by and between ________________ (the "Assignor"), having its principal place of business at ________________________________, and ________________________________ (the "Assignee"), having its principal place of business at ________________________________.

1. Collateral. As collateral security for the payment of any and all indebtedness and liabilities of Assignor to Assignee, howsoever evidenced or acquired, whether now existing or hereafter arising, whether direct or indirect, absolute or contingent, or joint and several, Assignor hereby assigns, pledges, and transfers to Assignee all of Assignor's right, title, and interest in and to the certificate(s) of deposit (collectively, the "Certificate") described as follows:

Certificate No.	*Institution Name/Address*	*Amount*
________________	________________________	$__________
	________________________	
	________________________	
	________________________	
________________	________________________	$__________
	________________________	
	________________________	
	________________________	

2. Assignor Representations and Warranties. With respect to the Certificate, Assignor represents and warrants that:

a. Assignor is the lawful owner of the Certificate, free and clear of all loans, liens, encumbrances, and claims except as disclosed in writing to Assignee on Annex A hereto;
b. Assignor has full right, power, and authority to enter into this Agreement and to assign the Certificate to Assignee;
c. The Certificate is genuine and the amount(s) of the Certificate stated above is the true amount(s) of the Certificate as of the date of this Agreement;
d. Assignor will not sell, assign, encumber, or otherwise dispose of any of Assignee's rights to the Certificate except as provided for in this Agreement.

3. Assignee Rights and Obligations. Assignor hereby appoints Assignee as its true and lawful attorney-in-fact, with full power of substitution, and agrees that Assignee shall have full and irrevocable right, power, and authority, in the name of Assignor or in Assignee's own name, to demand, collect, withdraw, receipt for, or sue for all amounts due or to become due and payable upon the Certificate, including any interest accrued or payable thereon and any renewals, extensions, or reinvestments thereof. Assignee may execute withdrawal receipts respecting the Certificate and endorse the name of Assignor on any or all commercial paper given in payment thereof, and, at Assignee's discretion, take any other action, including without limitation the transfer of the Certificate into its

own name or the name of its nominee which it may deem necessary or appropriate to preserve or protect its interest in the Certificate.

While this Agreement is in effect, Assignee may retain the rights to possession of the Certificate. Assignee may notify the institution that issued the Certificate of this Agreement. Assignor agrees that such institution will not pay any amount on the Certificate, other than to Assignee, so long as this Agreement is in effect. This Agreement will remain in effect until (i) there is no longer any indebtedness owing to Assignee, or (ii) Assignor has received, in writing from Assignee, a release of this Agreement.

Assignor hereby agrees that the Certificate-issuing institution may act, and in doing so shall be fully protected from liability to Assignor when so acting, on any order or direction by Assignee respecting the Certificate without making any inquiry as to Assignee's right or authority to give such order or direction or as to the application of any payment made pursuant thereto; and any payment of the Certificate made to Assignee pursuant to any such order or direction shall satisfy and discharge any liability of such institution to Assignor to the extent of such payment.

In addition to its rights under this Agreement, Assignee shall have all rights of a secured party under the Uniform Commercial Code in effect in the State of ____________________, and Assignor will execute required financing statements to give notice of such rights.

4. Limitations of Assignee. Assignee shall use reasonable care in the physical preservation and custody of the Certificate, but shall have no other obligation to protect the Certificate or its value, including but not limited to collection or protection of any income on the Certificate or the preservation of rights against issuers of the Certificate or third parties.

5. Events of Default and Remedies. An event of default (an "Event of Default") will exist under this Agreement if Assignor (i) fails to make any payment when due on any indebtedness and/or obligations secured by the Certificate, or (ii) dies (*Author's Note:* Delete "dies" if a corporate Assignor), becomes insolvent, appoints a receiver to any part of Assignor's property, makes any assignment for the benefit of creditors, or commences any bankruptcy proceedings.

Upon the occurrence of an Event of Default, and upon prior notice to Assignor, Assignee may present the Certificate to the issuing institution, obtain all funds deposited or accrued under the Certificate, and apply such funds to the indebtedness. If the Certificate is subject to an early withdrawal penalty, such penalty shall be deducted from the funds prior to application against the indebtedness. Any excess funds remaining after the indebtedness is satisfied will be paid to Assignor.

6. Assignment by Assignee. Assignee shall have the right, upon prior notice to Assignor, to assign its right and interest in the Certificate and to grant an assignee a first security interest in the Certificate.

7. Severability. Any provision of this Agreement which is prohibited or unenforceable in any jurisdiction shall, as to such jurisdiction, be ineffective to the extent of such prohibition or unenforceability without invalidating the remaining provisions hereof, and any such prohibition or unenforceability in any jurisdiction shall not invalidate or render unenforceable such provision in any other jurisdiction.

8. Binding Agreement. This Agreement and all representations and warranties herein contained are binding upon and shall inure to the benefit of the parties hereto and to their respective successors and assigns.

IN WITNESS WHEREOF, the parties hereto have caused this Agreement to be executed by their duly authorized officers on the date and year first written above.

_______________________, Assignee

By: _______________________

Title: _______________________

_______________________, Assignor

By: _______________________

Title: _______________________

Annex A

[List any loans, liens, encumbrances, and/or claims affecting the Certificates of Deposit(s).]

Acknowledgment

The undersigned, being the institution referred to in the foregoing Agreement, hereby acknowledges receipt of a copy of, and consents to, this Agreement and certifies that the amount owing on the Certificate listed in the Agreement is not less than the amount(s) set forth above, and that parties executing the Agreement are the only parties having interest in the Certificate as appears on the record of undersigned, and that the undersigned has not received notice of any assignment, other than this Agreement, of the Certificate.

(Insert name of institution.)

By: ______________________________

Title: ______________________________

Date: ______________________________

Form: a-03
Disk File Name: a-03.rtf

Assignment of Savings Account and/or Stock Certificate

Form Purpose

Assignment to an equipment leasing company or lender of a savings account and/or stock certificate as collateral security for equipment lease or loan obligations.

Executing Parties

The equipment lessee or borrower, as applicable (assignor).
The equipment lessor or lender, as applicable (assignee).

Assignment of Savings Account and/or Stock Certificate

Date: ______________________

[Insert name and address of Assignee.]

Gentlemen:

For value received, I/we (Assignor) hereby assign and transfer to and pledge to [insert name of Assignee] ("Assignee") my/our savings account and/or stock certificate number __ as collateral for my/our obligations ("Obligation") under that certain [insert the identification of the document giving raise to this assignment, such as "that certain equipment lease agreement, dated April 5, XXXX, by and between Assignor and Assignee."].

This assignment shall be a continuing one and shall be effective until canceled, and shall operate as security for payment of any other debts or liabilities of the undersigned to Assignee now in existence or hereafter contracted.

You are hereby authorized to charge against the above savings account and/or stock certificate, for Obligation monies not paid when due, and, in this regard, I/we do hereby irrevocably constitute and appoint Assignee as attorney-in-fact to effect transfers of said stock and/or withdrawals and transfers of said savings account.

Assignor warrants the savings account and/or stock certificate is genuine and in all respects what it purports to be; that Assignor is the owner thereof free and clear of all liens and encumbrances of any nature whatsoever; and that Assignor has full power, right, and authority to execute and deliver this assignment.

______________________, Assignor

By: ______________________

Title: ______________________

Accepted this ______ day of ______________, XXXX.

______________________, Assignee

By: ______________________

Title: ______________________

Form: a-04
Disk File Name: a-04.rtf

ASSIGNMENT OF LEASE TO LENDER—SINGLE TAKEDOWN

Form Purpose

Assignment to a leasing company's equipment lender of the leasing company's rights under an equipment lease, as collateral security for a loan to be used by the leasing company to pay, at least in part, for the cost of the equipment to be leased. This form contemplates a one-time loan takedown.

Executing Parties

The equipment lessor.
The equipment lender.

See:

Loan and Security Agreements Forms
Promissory Note Forms

Assignment of Lease

This ASSIGNMENT made as of ______________________, XXXX [insert name of leasing company], a ______________ corporation, with offices at ______________ ____________________________ (hereinafter referred to as the "Borrower"), to ____________________ corporation, with offices at ______________________ ______________________________ (hereinafter referred to as the "Lender").

WITNESSETH:

WHEREAS, Borrower and (insert name of lessee) (the "Lessee") are parties to an equipment lease agreement dated as of ____________________, XXXX, (the "Lease") that provides for the leasing by Borrower to Lessee of certain equipment (the "Equipment") described in Schedule A attached hereto;

WHEREAS, Borrower desires to borrow from (insert name of lender) (the "Lender") the principal sum of $ ______________, such borrowing to be evidenced by a promissory note of Borrower in said principal amount payable to Lender or to its order (the promissory note, together with any extension and renewal thereof, hereinafter referred to as the "Note");

WHEREAS, such borrowing (the "Loan") is to be made at a closing at which Borrower has agreed to deliver to Lender (i) this Assignment (the "Assignment"), and (ii) a Loan and Security Agreement, dated the same date as this Assignment, by and between Borrower and Lender (the "Security Agreement"); and

WHEREAS, this Assignment and the Security Agreement are being delivered to Lender as security for the payment of the Note and the performance by Borrower of its obligations under the Note, the Assignment and the Security Agreement (all such sums and obligations hereinafter referred to as the "Indebtedness").

NOW, THEREFORE, to induce Lender to make the Loan and for other good and valuable consideration, the receipt of which is hereby acknowledged, the parties hereto agree as follows:

1. As security for the Indebtedness, Borrower hereby assigns, transfers, and sets over unto Lender all Borrower's right, title, and interest as lessor under the Lease, together with all rights, powers, privileges, and other benefits of Borrower as lessor under the Lease, including, without limitation, the immediate right to receive and collect all rentals, insurance proceeds, net proceeds from the sale of all the Equipment, profits and other sums payable to or receivable by Borrower under or pursuant to the provisions of the Lease, and the right to make all waivers and agreements, to give all notice, consents, and releases, to take all action upon the happening of a default or an event of default under the Lease, and to do any and all other things whatsoever which Borrower is or may become entitled to do under the Lease. In furtherance of the foregoing assignment, Borrower hereby irrevocably authorizes and empowers Lender in its own name, or in the name of its nominee, if any, or in the name of Borrower or as its attorney, to ask, demand, collect, and receive any and all sums to which Borrower is or may become

entitled under the Lease to enforce compliance by Lessee with all the terms and agreements of the Lease.

2. The assignment made hereby is executed only as security, and, therefore, the execution and delivery of this Assignment shall not subject Lender to, or transfer, or pass, or in any way affect or modify, the liability of Borrower under the Lease, it being understood and agreed that notwithstanding such assignment, or any subsequent assignment, all obligations of Borrower to Lessee under the Lease shall be and remain enforceable by Lessee, its successors and assigns, against Borrower.

3. Borrower covenants and agrees that it will perform all of its obligations to be performed under the terms of the Lease, and hereby irrevocably authorizes and empowers Lender, in its own name, or in the name of its nominee, if any, or in the name of Borrower, or its attorney, on the happening of any failure by Borrower, to perform, or cause to be performed, any such obligation, all at Borrower's expense.

4. Upon (i) the full discharge and satisfaction of the Indebtedness, or (ii) the failure on the part of Lender to diligently exercise any right or remedies to which Lender is entitled by virtue of this Assignment and which arise out of the happening of a default or an event of default under the Lease, the assignment made hereby and all rights herein assigned to Lender shall cease and terminate, and all estate, right, title, and interest of Lender in and to the Lease shall revert to Borrower.

5. Borrower warrants and covenants that: (a) the Lease is valid, is in full force and effect, is not in default, and is enforceable in accordance with its terms (subject only to bankruptcy, insolvency, and reorganization laws and other laws governing the enforcement of lessor's or creditor's rights), (b) the execution and delivery of the Assignment, the Security Agreement and the Note have been duly authorized, and the Assignment, the Security Agreement and the Note are and will remain the valid and enforceable obligations of Borrower in accordance with their terms, (c) Borrower has not executed, and will not execute, any other assignment of the Lease and its right to receive all payments under the Lease is and will continue to be free and clear of any and all liens or encumbrances created or suffered by any act or omission on the part of Borrower, except as encumbered hereunder, (d) Borrower has delivered to Lender its only executed counterpart of the Lease, and (e) notwithstanding the Assignment, Borrower will perform and comply with each and all of the covenants and conditions in the Lease set forth to be complied with by it.

6. Borrower covenants and agrees with Lender that in any suit, proceeding, or action brought by Lender under the Lease for any sum owing thereunder, or to enforce any provisions of such Lease, Borrower will save, indemnify, and keep Lender harmless from and against all expense, loss, or damage suffered by reason of any defense, setoff, counterclaim, or recoupment whatsoever of Lessee thereunder or its successors, arising out of a breach by Borrower of any obligation in respect of the Equipment covered by the Lease or arising out of any other indebtedness or liability at any time owing to Lessee or its successors from Borrower.

7. Borrower will from time to time execute all such financing statements and supplemental instruments as Lender may from time to time reasonably request in order to confirm or further assure the assignment made hereby and the provisions hereof.

8. Lender may assign all or any of its rights under the Lease, including the right to receive any payments due or to become due to it from Lessee. In the event of any such assignment, any such subsequent or successive assignee or assignees shall, to the extent

of such assignment, enjoy all rights and privileges and be subject to all the obligations of Lender.

9. Borrower agrees that it will not, without the prior written consent of Lender, enter into any agreement amending, modifying, or terminating the Lease and that any attempted amendment, modification, or termination without such consent shall be void.

10. Borrower hereby constitutes Lender, its successors and assigns, its true and lawful attorney, irrevocably, with full power (in its name or otherwise) to ask, require, demand, receive, and compound any and all rents and claims for money due and to become due under, or arising out of this Assignment, to endorse any checks or other instruments or orders in connection therewith and to file any claims or take any action or institute any proceedings which to Lender or any subsequent assignee seem necessary or advisable, all without affecting Borrower's liability in any manner whatsoever.

11. Borrower shall have no authority, without Lender's prior written consent, to accept payments or other collections, repossess or consent to the return of the property described in the Lease, or modify the terms of said Lease.

12. The Assignment shall be governed by the laws of the State of ______________.

13. The Assignment shall be binding upon and inure to the benefit of the parties hereto and their respective successors and assigns.

14. Borrower shall cause copies of all notices received in connection with the Lease to be promptly delivered to Lender at ________________________________,
or at such other address as Lender shall designate in writing.

IN WITNESS WHEREOF, the parties hereto have caused this instrument to be duly executed as of the date first above written.

____________________________________, Borrower

By: ______________________________

Title: ____________________________

Accepted this __________ day of __________ XXXX:

____________________________________, Lender

By: ______________________________

Title: ____________________________

Schedule A

[Insert equipment description.]

Form: a-05
Disk File Name: a-05.rtf

ASSIGNMENT OF LEASE TO LENDER—MULTIPLE TAKEDOWN

Form Purpose

Assignment to a leasing company's equipment lender of the leasing company's rights under an equipment lease, as collateral security for a loan to be used by the leasing company to pay, at least in part, for the cost of the equipment to be leased. This form contemplates multiple equipment deliveries, and multiple equipment loan takedowns by the leasing company, and has been intergrated with a Loan and Security Agreement, Form l-05, a Promissory Note, Form p-02, and an Assignment Amendment, Form a-10.

Executing Parties

The equipment lessor.
The equipment lender.

See:

Loan and Security and Loan Agreement, Form l-05
Promissory Note, Form p-02
Assignment Amendment, Form a-10

Assignment

This ASSIGNMENT made as of ________________, XXXX, from ________________ ________________________, a ________________________ corporation, with offices at ____ (hereinafter referred to as the "Company"), to ________________________, with offices at ____ (hereinafter referred to as the "Lender").

WITNESSETH:

WHEREAS the Company and ________________________ (hereinafter referred to as the "Lessee") are parties to a Lease Agreement dated as of ____________ XXXX, including as a part thereof, Schedule No. ____________ dated as of ____________, XXXX, and the Acceptance Certificate executed between the Company and Lessee, dated as of ________________, XXXX, (said Lease, Schedule, and Acceptance Certificate being hereinafter referred to collectively as the "Lease") providing for the leasing by the Company to Lessee of certain newly manufactured equipment (as further described in Schedule A attached hereto and hereinafter referred to as the "Units");

WHEREAS, the Company desires to borrow from Lender an aggregate amount (hereinafter referred to as the "Loan") equal to ______ % of the purchase price of the Units, said Loan to be evidenced by one or more promissory notes of the Company payable to Lender or to its order (the promissory notes, together with any extension and renewal thereof, are hereinafter referred to as the "Notes");

WHEREAS, the Loan is to be made in a number of installments, each pursuant to a closing prior to which the Company has agreed to deliver to Lender (i) this Assignment (hereinafter referred to as the "Assignment") covering the Lease and (ii) a Loan and Security Agreement (hereinafter referred to as the "Security Agreement") on the Units; and

WHEREAS, the Assignment and the Security Agreement are being delivered to Lender as security for the payment of the Notes and the performance by the Company of its obligations under the Notes, the Assignment and the Security Agreement (all such sums and obligations being hereinafter referred to as the "Indebtedness").

NOW, THEREFORE, to induce Lender to make the Loan and for other good and valuable consideration, the receipt of which is hereby acknowledged, the parties hereto agree as follows:

1. As security for the Indebtedness, the Company hereby assigns, transfers, and sets over unto Lender all the Company's right, title, and interest as lessor under the Lease to receive and collect all rentals, insurance proceeds, net proceeds from the sale of the Units, profits and other sums payable to or receivable by the Company under or pursuant to the provisions of the Lease (except payments and reimbursements by Lessee to the Company for taxes and payments and reimbursements to the Company in the nature of indemnification to the Company, all of which shall be retained by the Company), and the right to make all waivers and agreements permitted under the Security Agreement, to

give all notice, consents, and releases permitted under the Security Agreement, to take all action upon the happening of a default or an event of default under the Lease, and to do any and all other things whatsoever which the Company is or may become entitled to do under the Lease; provided, however, that no assignment is hereby made of the rights and options granted to the Lessee in Section ____________ of the Lease and, in connection therewith, the Company reserves the right to give all such notices and take all such acts as are required or incident to the exercise of such rights and options, and the Company further reserves the right to receive all financial and other information which the Lessee is required to furnish to the Company pursuant to the Lease, provided that the Company, if requested by Lender, will deliver copies of all such information received by it to Lender. In furtherance of the foregoing assignment, the Company hereby irrevocably authorizes and empowers Lender in its own name, or in the name of its nominee, if any, or in the name of the Company or as its attorney, to ask, demand, collect, and receive any and all sums to which the Company is or may become entitled under the Lease and to enforce compliance by Lessee with all the terms and agreements of the Lease.

2. The assignment made hereby is executed only as security, and therefore, the execution and delivery of this Assignment shall not subject Lender to, or transfer, or pass, or in any way affect or modify, the liability of the Company under the Lease, it being understood and agreed that notwithstanding such assignment, or any subsequent assignment, all obligations of the Company to Lessee under the Lease shall be and remain enforceable by Lessee, its successors and assigns, against the Company.

3 . The Company covenants and agrees that it will perform all of its obligations to be performed under the terms of the Lease, and hereby irrevocably authorizes and empowers Lender, in its own name, or in the name of its nominee, if any, or in the name of the Company, or its attorney, on the happening of any failure by the Company, to perform, or cause to be performed, any such obligation, all at the Company's expense.

4. Upon the full discharge and satisfaction of the Indebtedness, the assignment made hereby and all rights herein assigned to Lender will cease and terminate, and all estate, right, title, and interest of Lender in and to the Lease shall revert to the Company. Lender will forthwith execute and file all such termination statements and such other documents as may be necessary or appropriate to make clear upon the public record the termination of such assignment hereunder.

5. The Company warrants and covenants that (a) the Lease is valid, in full force and effect, is not in default, and is enforceable in accordance with its terms against the Company (subject only to bankruptcy, insolvency, and reorganization laws and other laws governing the enforcement of lessor's or creditor's rights), (b) the execution and delivery of the Assignment, the Security Agreement and the Notes have been duly authorized, and the Assignment and Security Agreement are and the Notes will be, the valid and enforceable obligations of the Company in accordance with their terms, (c) the Company has not executed, and will not execute, any other assignment of the Lease and its right to receive all payments under the Lease is and will continue to be free and clear of any and all liens or encumbrances created or suffered by any act or omission on the part of the Company, except as encumbered hereunder, (d) the Company has delivered to Lender the Company's only executed counterpart of the Lease, and notwithstanding the assignment, the Company will perform and comply with each and all of the covenants and conditions in the Lease set forth to be complied with by it, and (e) notice pursuant to Section ____________ of the Lease has been given to Lessee (*Author's Note:* Include if Lessor is obligated under the Lease to notify Lessee of a Lease assignment).

6. The Company covenants and agrees with Lender that in any suit, proceeding, or action brought by Lender under the Lease for any sum owing thereunder, or to enforce any provisions of such Lease, the Company will save, indemnify, and keep Lender harmless from and against all expense, loss, or damage suffered by reason of any defense, setoff, counterclaim, or recoupment whatsoever of Lessee hereunder or its successors, arising out of a breach by the Company of any obligation in respect of the Units covered by the Lease or arising out of any other indebtedness or liability at any time owing to Lessee or its successors from the Company.

7. The Company will from time to time execute all such instruments and supplemental instruments and cooperate in the filing or recording of such documents, as Lender may from time to time reasonably request in order to confirm and perfect the assignment made hereby and the provisions hereof.

8 . Lender may assign all or any of its rights under the Lease, including the right to receive any payments due or to become due to it from Lessee. In the event of any such assignment, any such subsequent or successive assignee or assignees shall, to the extent of such assignment, enjoy all rights and privileges and be subject to all the obligations of Lender.

9 . The Company agrees that it will not, without prior written consent of Lender, enter into any agreement materially amending, modifying, or terminating the Lease, and any such attempted amendment, modification, or termination without such consent shall be void.

10. The Company hereby constitutes Lender, its successors and assigns, its true and lawful attorney, irrevocably, with full power, (in its name or otherwise) to ask, require, demand, receive, and compound any and all rents and claims for money due and to become due under, or arising out of this Agreement, to endorse any checks or other instruments or orders in connection therewith, and to file any claims or take any action or institute any proceedings which to Lender or any subsequent assignee seem necessary or advisable, all without affecting the Company's liability in any manner whatsoever.

11. The Company shall have no authority, without Lender's prior written consent, to accept payments or other collections assigned to Lender hereunder, or to repossess or consent to the return of the property described in the Lease, or materially modify the terms of said Lease.

12. The Assignment shall be governed by the laws of the State of ______________.

13. The Assignment shall be binding upon and inure to the benefit of the parties hereto and the respective successors and assigns.

14. The Company shall cause copies of all notices received in connection with the Lease to be promptly delivered to Lender at ____________________________________
____, Attn.: ___________________________,
or at such other address as Lender shall designate in writing.

IN WITNESS WHEREOF, the parties hereto have caused this instrument to be duly executed as of the date first written above.

(Insert name of Company.)

By: ______________________________

Title: ______________________________

Accepted:

(Insert name of Lender)

By: ______________________________

Title: ______________________________

Schedule A

Description of Equipment

Description of Unit and Manufacturer	*No. of Units*	*Location*	*Supplier or Vendor*	*Identification or Serial No.*

Form: a-06
Disk File Name: a-06.rtf

ASSIGNMENT OF LEASE—SALE BY LESSOR (LIMITED RECOURSE)

Form Purpose

Sale assignment, limited recourse, by one leasing company to another leasing company of an equipment lease and the underlying equipment.

Executing Parties

The selling equipment lessor.
The purchasing equipment lessor.

See:

Bill of Sale, Forms b-01 and b-02

Assignment of Lease

(Limited Recourse)

[Insert name of assigning leasing company] (the "Assignor") hereby sells, assigns, transfers, and conveys to (insert name of equipment lender) (the "Assignee"), its successors and assigns, without recourse except as hereinafter provided, the lease agreement (the "Lease"), covering

(insert equipment description here),

dated _______________, XXXX, between Assignor and (insert name and address of Assignor of the lease), and ______________________________, as lessee, ("Lessee") and all payments due and to become due thereunder and all right, title, and interest of Assignor in and to the property described in the Lease (the "Property") and all Assignor's rights and remedies thereunder, and the right either in Assignee's own behalf or in Assignor's name to take all such proceedings, legal, equitable, or otherwise, that we might take, save for this assignment.

Assignor warrants that the Lease and all related instruments are genuine, enforceable, and the Lease is the only one executed with respect to said property; all statements therein contained are true; the Property has been delivered to, and accepted by, Lessee in condition satisfactory to Lessee, and Assignor will comply with all its warranties and other obligations to Lessee.

Assignor hereby agrees to indemnify, hold safe and harmless from and against and covenant to defend Assignee against any and all claims, costs, expenses, damages, and all liabilities arising from or pertaining to the use, possession, or operation of the Property.

Assignor warrants and represents that the Lease is in full force and effect and that Assignor has not assigned or pledged, and hereby covenants that it will not assign or pledge, so long as this instrument of assignment shall remain in effect, the whole or any part of the rights hereby assigned, to anyone other than Assignee, its successors or assigns.

Assignee shall have no obligations of Assignor under the Lease.

All Assignor's right, title and interest assigned hereunder may be reassigned by Assignee and any subsequent assignee. It is expressly agreed that, anything herein contained to the contrary notwithstanding, Assignor's obligations under the Lease may be performed by Assignee or any subsequent assignee without releasing Assignor therefrom, and that Assignee shall not, by reason of this assignment, be obligated to perform any of our obligations under the Lease or to file any claim or take any other action to collect or enforce any payment assigned hereunder.

Assignor waives presentment and demand for payment, protest or notice of nonpayment and notice as to the Lease and all related documents now and hereafter assigned or endorsed and subordinate to any rights Assignee may now or hereafter have against Lessee any rights we may now or hereafter have or acquire by reason of payment to Assignee of any payments under the Lease or otherwise.

Assignor hereby constitutes Assignee, its successors and assigns, its true and lawful attorney, irrevocably, with full power (in our name or otherwise) to ask, require, demand, receive, compound, and give acquittance for any and all rents and claims for money due and to become due under, or arising out of this assignment agreement, to endorse any checks or other instruments or orders in connection therewith, and to file any claims or take any action or institute any proceedings which to Assignee or any subsequent assignee seem necessary or advisable, all without affecting our liability in any manner whatsoever.

Assignor shall have no authority, without Assignee's prior written consent, to accept payments or other collections, repossess or consent to the return of the Property described in said Lease, or modify the terms of said contract.

Dated this ______ day of ______________________ XXXX

WITNESS, our hand and seal.

______________________________, Assignor

By: ______________________________

Title: ______________________________

Accepted this ______ day of __________________ XXXX:

______________________________, Assignee

By: ______________________________

Title: ______________________________

Form: a-07
Disk File Name: a-07.rtf

Assignment of Lease—Sale by Lessor Integrated (Limited Recourse)

Form Purpose

Sale assignment, without recourse, by one leasing company to another leasing company of an equipment lease and the underlying equipment. This form is integrated with Lease Agreement Form l-03.

Executing Parties

The selling equipment lessor.
The purchasing equipment lessor.

See:

Lease Agreement, Form l-03; Bill of Sale, Forms b-01 and b-02

_______________, Lessor

Home Office Address: _______________

Phone ( ) _______________

Assignment and Assumption of Agreement to Lease Equipment

ASSIGNMENT AND ASSUMPTION ("Assignment") made this _______ day of _______________, between _______________, a _______________ corporation ("Assignor"), and _______________ a _______________ corporation ("Assignee").

WHEREAS, Assignor has entered into a certain Master Agreement to Lease Equipment ("Master Agreement"), dated as of _______________, between Assignor, as Lessor, and _______________, as Lessee ("Lessee"), pursuant to which Assignor has agreed to lease equipment to Lessee by means of Schedules entered into by the parties with respect to certain items of equipment ("Units"); and

WHEREAS, Assignor desires to sell and assign to Assignee the Master Agreement and/or certain Schedules.

NOW, THEREFORE, for good and valuable consideration, the receipt of which is hereby acknowledged, the parties hereto agree as follows:

1. Assignor hereby assigns, transfers, and sets over unto Assignee all of Assignor's rights and interests in and to the Master Agreement and/or the Schedules identified in Exhibit A hereto (collectively "Assigned Contracts"), including all rights, powers, privileges, and other benefits of Assignor as lessor under the Assigned Contracts. Assignee, for itself and its successors and assigns, hereby expressly assumes and agrees to satisfy all obligations and liabilities existing or arising on or after the date of this Assignment out of or relating to the Assigned Contracts. From and after the date of this Assignment, Assignor shall have no further liability or obligations under the Assigned Contracts as lessor, or otherwise, of any nature whatsoever.

2. Assignor warrants and covenants that (a) the execution and delivery of this Assignment has been duly authorized, and this Assignment is and will remain the valid and binding obligation of Assignor enforceable against Assignor in accordance with its terms (subject only to bankruptcy, insolvency, and reorganization laws and other laws governing the enforcement of lessor or creditor rights), (b) Assignor has not executed any other assignment of the Assigned Contracts or any of them and any right to receive payments under the Assigned Contracts is free and clear of any and all liens or encumbrances created or suffered by any act or omission on the part of Assignor, and (c) Assignor has delivered to Assignee all executed counterparts of the Assigned Contracts in its possession.

3. Assignee covenants and agrees with Assignor on behalf of itself and its successors and assigns that from and after the date of this Assignment it shall save and hold As-

signor harmless from and against and indemnify and defend Assignor with respect to any and all damages, losses, liabilities, claims, and expenses suffered or incurred by Assignor arising directly or indirectly out of or in connection with the Assigned Contracts, the Units and any other matter arising out of or relating to any transaction contemplated by, or effected pursuant to, the Assigned Contracts.

4. Assignor and Assignee agree that each will execute all such supplemental instruments as Assignor or Assignee may from time to time reasonably request in order to confirm or further assure the assignment made hereby and the provisions hereof and to evidence and provide for the specific assumption by Assignee, its successors or assigns, of the obligations and liabilities of Assignor relating to the Assigned Contracts.

5. Assignee may not assign all or any of its rights under the Assigned Contracts, including the right to receive any payments due or to become due to it from Lessee, without the prior written consent of Assignor.

6. This Assignment shall be governed by the laws of the State of ____________.

7. This Assignment shall be binding upon and inure to the benefit of the parties hereto and their respective successors and assigns.

IN WITNESS WHEREOF, the undersigned have duly executed this Assignment as of the date first above written.

______________________________, Assignor

By: ______________________________

Title: ______________________________

______________________________, Assignee

By: ______________________________

Title ______________________________

Exhibit A to Assignment and Assumption of Agreement to Lease Equipment

Description of Assigned Contracts

1. Master Agreement: Yes ____ No ____
2. Schedules: Yes ____ No ____

If Yes,

Schedule No	*Lessee*	*Date of Schedule*

Form: a-08
Disk File Name: a-08.rtf

Assignment of Lease With Bill of Sale Incorporated (Without Recourse)

Form Purpose

Sale assignment, without recourse, by one leasing company to another leasing company of an equipment lease and the underlying equipment. This form incorporates a "bill of sale" into the assignment provisions.

Executing Parties

The selling equipment lessor.
The purchasing equipment lessor.

Assignment of Equipment Lease and Equipment Bill of Sale

FOR VALUE RECEIVED, the undersigned, (insert name of Assignor), having a place of business at (insert address), (the "Assignor") hereby sells, assigns, transfers and conveys all right, title, and interest, to (insert name of Assignee), having a place of business at (insert address), its assigns and successors (the "Assignee") pursuant to this Assignment of Equipment Lease and Equipment Bill of Sale in and to (i) Equipment Lease No. ________, dated ______________________, XXXX, between Assignor, as Lessor, and (insert name of Lessee), as Lessee, together with all schedules, amendments, modifications, and supplements thereto (the "Lease"), (ii) the machinery and equipment covered by the Lease (collectively, the "Equipment"), including all reversionary rights to the Equipment arising in favor of Lessor under the Lease upon the expiration or termination of the Lease; (iii) all contracts of guaranty, suretyship, and insurance pertaining to the Lease; (iv) all rental charges and other monies which are payable, due, or to become due under the Lease or any such contract; and (v) proceeds of the foregoing including residuals, lease renewal payments, sale proceeds, or any exchange or trade-in values.

A. In order to induce Assignee to accept this Assignment of Equipment Lease and Equipment Bill of Sale (this "Assignment"), Assignor represents and warrants to Assignee, as follows:

1. Assignor is qualified to do business, either as a domestic or foreign corporation, in all states and other jurisdictions wherein such qualification is legally required in order to enable Assignor, as Lessor, to enforce the Lease against Lessee.

2. All signatures on the Lease are the genuine signatures of persons duly authorized and having legal capacity to contract on behalf of the respective parties.

3. The Lease is genuine and is in all respects a valid, binding, and enforceable obligation arising out of the bona fide rental of the Equipment to Lessee in the ordinary course of Assignor's business.

4. The Equipment is not currently under lease to any other party.

5. The Equipment is being leased to Lessee for business, commercial, or agricultural purposes only and not for the personal, family, or household purposes of any natural person.

6. Assignor is the lawful owner and has good title to the Lease and to the Equipment free of all liens, claims, or encumbrances, other than the leasehold interest of Lessee in the Equipment; none of the rights sold and assigned hereby have previously been alienated, transferred, assigned, or otherwise encumbered; no financing statement covering any of the Equipment is on file in any public office, except financing statements filed by Assignor against Lessee showing Assignor as lessor; and all such financing statements are sufficient in form and substance to protect Assignor against loss of the Equipment to a trustee in bankruptcy or other creditor representative of Lessee.

7. The Lease contains or describes the entire agreement between Assignor and Lessee, and all instruments or documents made or given in favor of Assignor in connection therewith have been delivered to Assignee; and the obligations of Lessee are not, nor will they at any time become, contingent upon the fulfillment of any condition precedent,

nor are they evidenced by any note or other negotiable instrument, except as has been assigned or endorsed or delivered by Assignor to Assignee.

8. All statements and figures contained in the Lease or given in connection with the sale thereof to Assignee are true and correct in all material respects, and the Lease accurately reflects the terms and conditions of Assignor's agreement with Lessee; Lessee has paid to Assignor the sum of $ ____ (no part of which has been loaned directly or indirectly by Assignor) on account of the aggregate rental charges under the Lease, leaving an unpaid balance of $ ______ owing by Lessee (or other parties obligated or shown to be obligated thereon). The Lease is free from all defenses, counterclaims, setoffs, rights of recoupment, and disputes of any kind; and no event of default as set forth in the Lease has ever occurred.

9. The Equipment has been delivered and, where necessary, installed at the location specified in the Lease, delivery and installation having occurred prior to, or contemporaneously with the commencement of the term of the Lease; and Lessee has not communicated to Assignor, either orally or in writing, any expression of dissatisfaction with or any complaint concerning the condition of any of the Equipment or, where applicable, the manner of its installation, which has not been disclosed in writing to Assignee.

B. In order further to induce Assignee to accept the Assignment, Assignor agrees as follows:

1. Assignor will promptly notify Assignee in writing of each of the following matters of which it acquires knowledge: (a) the occurrence of any of the events of default described in the Lease; (b) the loss, theft, damage, and destruction of any of the Equipment; (c) any change in either the principal place of business of Lessee or in the location of any of the Equipment; and (d) any complaint by Lessee or other expression of dissatisfaction concerning the condition of any of the Equipment or, where applicable, the manner of its installation.

2. Should Assignor receive any of the rental charges or other monies payable, due, or to become due to Assignee under the Lease, on any Equipment, Assignor will receive said monies and Equipment as an agent of Assignee and will immediately deliver same to Assignor without commingling with Assignor's own funds and Equipment.

3. Assignor hereby irrevocably constitutes and appoints Assignee as its true and lawful attorney with full power or substitution for it, and in its name, place, and stead, without notice to Assignor and without affecting Assignor's liability hereunder, to ask, demand, collect, receive, receipt for, sue for, compound, and give acquittance for any and all amounts which may be or become due or payable under the Lease, with full power to settle, adjust, or compromise any claim thereunder as fully as Assignor could itself do, otherwise to enter into any settlement, extension, forbearance, or other modification with respect to the Lease, or discharge or release Lessee or any other person from its obligations thereunder.

4. Assignor shall hold Assignee harmless and defend Assignee's title to the Lease and the Equipment against all claims of any person, firm, or corporation whatsoever in any manner arising out of the alleged rights existing prior to the date hereof or rights resulting from acts of Assignor subsequent thereto.

5. Assignor hereby agrees to execute such additional documents and to do such things as may be reasonably required by Assignee to implement the purposes of the Assignment.

6. Assignor hereby assigns to Assignee its rights in any and all warranties of and other claims against dealers, manufacturers, vendors, contractors and subcontractors relating to the Equipment and all indemnities with respect to patent infringements and other related general intangibles.

7. The Equipment is of merchantable quality, in new condition, ordinary wear and tear excepted, and is free of defects.

8. This Assignment is absolute and irrevocable.

This Assignment has been executed on this ______ day of __________________, XXXX, by the duly authorized officer set forth below.

(Insert name of Assignor), Assignor

By: ______________________________

Title: ______________________________

Accepted this ____ day of ______________, XXXX.

(Insert name of Assignee), Assignee

By: ______________________________

Title: ______________________________

Form: a-09
Disk File Name: a-09.rtf

ASSIGNMENT OF LEASE—SALE BY LESSOR (WITH RECOURSE)

Form Purpose

Sale assignment, with recourse, by one leasing company to another leasing company of an equipment lease and the underlying equipment.

Executing Parties

The selling equipment lessor.
The purchasing equipment lessor.

See:

Bill of Sale, Forms b-01 and b-02

Assignment of Lease With Recourse

TO: [Insert name and address of Assignee]

RE: Equipment Lease Agreement ("Lease") by and between [insert name of lessee] (the "Lessee"), and undersigned (the "Assignor"), as lessor, dated ________, XXXX, having aggregate unpaid rentals of $ ________________.

FOR VALUE RECEIVED, Assignor hereby sells, assigns, and transfers to [insert name of assignee] (the "Assignee"), Assignor's right, title, and interest in and to the Lease, the property therein leased, and all monies to become due thereunder. In consideration of the purchase of the Lease, Assignor agrees, in the event Lessee defaults in making any payment due under the Lease, at the time and in the manner therein specified, to pay on demand to Assignee such payments due, or to become due under the Lease.

Assignor further agrees to reimburse Assignee for any failure or refusal of Lessee to perform the conditions and assignments of the Lease.

Assignor hereby consents that Assignee, its successors and assigns, may, without notice, extend the time for payment under said Lease, waive the performance of the terms and conditions as it may determine appropriate, and make any reasonable settlement thereunder without affecting or limiting Assignor's liability hereunder.

Assignor warrants that (i) Assignor is the owner of the property described in the Lease free from all liens and encumbrances except the Lease, (ii) the Lease and any accompanying guaranties, waivers, and/or other instruments are genuine, enforceable, (iii) the Lease is the only lease executed concerning the property described in the Lease, (iv) the Lease rentals and other payments due and to be become due are and will continue to be free from defenses, setoffs, and counterclaims, (v) all signatures, names, addresses, amounts, and other statements and facts contained in the Lease and related documents are true and correct, (vi) the aggregate unpaid Lease rentals shown above is correct, (vii) the property has been delivered to Lessee under the Lease on the date set forth below in satisfactory condition and has been accepted by Lessee, (viii) Assignor will comply with all its warranties and other obligations with respect to the Lease transaction, and (ix) the Lease constitutes and will continue to constitute a valid reservation of unencumbered title to or first lien upon or security interest in the property covered thereby, effective against all persons, and if filing, recordation, or any other action or procedure is permitted or required by statute or regulation to perfect such reservation of title or lien or security interest, the same has been accomplished. If Assignor breaches any of the foregoing, it will, upon Assignee's request, promptly repurchase the Lease for an amount equal to the unpaid rentals thereon, including accrued interest plus any expenses of collection, repossession, transportation, and storage incurred by Assignee, less any customary refund by Assignee of unearned charges. Assignor agrees that Assignee may, in Assignor's name, endorse all remittances received, and Assignor gives express permission to Assignee to release, on terms satisfactory to Assignee or by operation of law or otherwise, or to compromise or adjust any and all rights against and grant extensions of time of payment to Lessee or any other persons obligated on the Lease or on any accompanying guaranty, or to agree to the substitution of a Lessee, without notice to Assignor and without affecting Assignor's obligations hereunder. Assignor shall have no authority to, and will not, without Assignee's prior written consent, accept payments of rents or of option prices, repossess, or consent to the return of the property described in the Lease, or modify the terms thereof or of any accompanying guaranty. Assignee's knowledge at any time of any breach or of noncompliance with any of the foregoing shall not constitute any waiver by Assignee. Assignor waives notice of acceptance hereof.

The property covered by the Lease was delivered to, and accepted by Lessee on ____________________, XXXX.

Date: ____________________________

___________________________________, Assignor

By: ____________________________

Title: ____________________________

___________________________________, Assignee

By: ____________________________

Title: ____________________________

Form: a-10
Disk File Name: a-10.rtf

ASSIGNMENT AMENDMENT—EQUIPMENT LOAN

Form Purpose

Amendment of a loan and security agreement equipment lease assignment. This form has been integrated with Loan and Security Agreement Form l-05.

Executing Parties

The equipment lessor.
The equipment lender.

See:

Assignment of Lease, Forms a-05
Loan and Security Agreement, Form l-05
Promissory Note, Form p-02

Amendment No. ____ to Assignment

This Amendatory Agreement, dated this ______ day of ________________, XXXX ("Amendment") by and between ________________________________, with a place of business at ____, (the "Company") and ____, with a place of business at ____, (the "Lender").

WITNESSETH:

WHEREAS, as security for the repayment of a Note, dated ____________, XXXX, in the principal amount of $ __________, issued by the Company to Lender, the Company and Lender entered into (i) a Loan and Security Agreement dated as of ______________, XXXX (the "Security Agreement") granting to Lender a security interest in the items of equipment described therein (the equipment being referred to as "Units" in the Security Agreement) and (ii) a related assignment dated as of __________________, XXXX, granting a security interest to Lender in certain rights of the Company as lessor of the Equipment under a Lease Agreement dated as of ________________________, XXXX (the "Lease") by and between the Company and _________________ (the "Lessee"); and

WHEREAS, pursuant to the Acceptance Certificate referenced below, (the "Acceptance Certificate") Lessee has leased certain additional items of equipment from the Company under the Lease and the Company desires to borrow the additional principal amount of $ _______________ from Lender to partially finance the purchase of these additional Units, the borrowing to be evidenced by a promissory note, of even date herewith, to be issued by the Company to Lender in said principal amount (the "Note") and secured by the additional items of equipment under the Security Agreement and the Acceptance Certificate under the Assignment.

NOW, THEREFORE, in consideration of the premises and the mutual covenants herein contained, the parties hereto agree as follows:

1. The Note and the Units described in Annex A hereto shall be included as a "Note" and as "Units" respectively under the Security Agreement and for all purposes thereof be considered a "Note" and "Units" respectively as defined therein.

2. The Acceptance Certificates listed in Annex A hereto shall be included under the Assignment and shall for all purposes thereof be considered a part of the "Lease" (as defined in the Assignment),

IN WITNESS WHEREOF, the parties hereto have executed this Amendment as of the day and year first above written.

(Insert name of the Company)

By: ________________________________

Title: ______________________________

(Insert name of Lender)

By: ________________________________

Title: ______________________________

Annex A

Acceptance Certificate dated ______________________________

Identification or Description of Unit	*No. of Units*	*Serial Number*

Form: a-11
Disk File Name: a-11.rtf

ASSIGNMENT OF EQUIPMENT PURCHASE CONTRACT

Form Purpose

Assignment by an equipment lessee to an equipment leasing company of the rights, but not the obligations, to purchase equipment from its equipment vendor, which will be the subject of the lease agreement.

Executing Parties

The equipment lessor.
The equipment lessee.

Equipment Purchase Contract Assignment

Equipment Purchase Contract Assignment, dated ______________________, XXXX, by and between ______________________________ ("the Assignee"), with a place of business at ______________________________ and ______________________________ ("the Assignor"), with a place of business at ____ (the "Assignment").

WITNESSETH:

WHEREAS, the Assignor has entered into certain equipment purchase contracts, copies of which are annexed as Exhibit A hereto (the "Purchase Contracts"), with certain manufacturers, dealers, or distributors (the "Vendors") pursuant to which the Vendors agreed to sell to the Assignor the Equipment described therein (the "Equipment");

WHEREAS, the Assignor wishes to lease said Equipment subject to the Purchase Contracts from the Assignee instead of purchasing the Equipment; and

WHEREAS, the Assignor, as Lessee, and the Assignee, as Lessor, have entered into an Equipment Lease Agreement, dated as of ______________________, XXXX, (the "Lease") whereby the Assignee will lease, subject to the terms of the Lease, the Equipment described in the Lease as it is delivered to and accepted for lease by the Assignor and the Assignee.

NOW, THEREFORE, in consideration of the premises and the mutual covenants herein contained, the parties hereto agree as follows:

1. For purposes of this Assignment, the terms used hereafter which are not specifically defined herein shall have the meanings that are attributed to them in the Lease, unless the context otherwise requires.

2. The Assignor does hereby sell, assign, transfer, and set over unto the Assignee all of the Assignor's rights and interest in and to the Purchase Contracts as and to the extent that the same relate to such Equipment and the purchase and operation thereof. This Assignment, except to the extent reserved below shall include, without limitation, (a) in respect of the Assignee, the right, upon valid tender by the Vendors, to purchase the Equipment pursuant to the respective Purchase Contracts, and the right to take title to such Equipment and to be named the purchaser in the bills of sale to be delivered by the Vendors in respect of said Equipment, and (b) any and all rights of the Assignor to compel performance of the terms of the Purchase Contracts in respect to the Equipment; reserving to the Assignor, however, so long, and only so long, as such Equipment shall be subject to the Lease (i) the rights to demand, accept, and retain all rights in and to all property (other than the Equipment), data, technical publications, and service which the Vendors are obligated to provide or do provide pursuant to the Purchase Contacts and (ii) the right to any services, training, data, demonstrations, and testing pursuant to the Purchase Contracts.

Notwithstanding the foregoing, so long as the Assignee shall not have declared the Assignor to be in default under the Lease, the Assignee authorizes the Assignor, to the exclusion of the Assignee, to exercise in its own name all rights and powers of the buyer under the Purchase Contracts in respect to said Equipment and to retain any recovery or benefit resulting from the enforcement of any warranty or indemnity under the Purchase Contracts in respect to said Equipment, or otherwise, except that (a) the Assignor may not enter into any change order or other amendment, modification, or supplement to any of the Purchase Contracts without the consent or countersignature of the Assignee if such change order, amendment, modification, or supplement would result in any rescission, cancellation, termination, or modification of any of the Purchase Contracts.

3. It is expressly agreed that, anything herein contained to the contrary, (a) the Assignor shall at all times remain liable to the Vendors under the Purchase Contracts to perform all the duties and obligations of the buyers thereunder to the same extent as if this Assignment had not been executed and (b) the exercise by the Assignee of any of the rights assigned hereunder shall not release the Assignor from any of its duties or obligations to the Vendors under the Purchase Contracts except to the extent that such exercise by the Assignee shall constitute performance of such duties and obligations.

4. The Assignor does hereby constitute, effective at any time after the time the Assignee has declared the Assignor to be in default under the Lease, the Assignee, its successors and assigns, the Assignor's true and lawful attorney, irrevocably, with full power (in the name of the Assignor or otherwise) to ask, require, demand, receive, compound, and give acquittance for any and all monies and claims for monies due and to become due under, or arising out of, the Purchase Contracts to the extent that the same have been assigned by this Assignment and, for such period as the Assignee may exercise rights with respect thereto under this Assignment, to endorse any checks or other instruments or orders in connection therewith and to file any claims or take any action or institute (or, if previously commenced, assume control of) any proceedings and to obtain any recovery in connection therewith which the Assignee may deem to be necessary or advisable in the premises.

5. Notwithstanding the foregoing Assignment, the Assignee hereby designates the Assignor to perform all obligations and duties of the Assignee under the Purchase Contracts except the purchase of the Equipment and the payment of monies due the Vendors under the Purchase Contracts as of the time of the completion of delivery and acceptance of Equipment and making same subject to the Lease by and between Assignee, as lessor and Assignor, as lessee. The only obligations of the Assignee under this Assignment shall be, on the dates of acceptance of the Equipment by Assignor, as lessee, and Assignor, as lessor, pursuant to the Lease, to purchase said Equipment from the respective Vendors and to pay the Vendors an amount equal to the purchase price due and owing, taking advantage of applicable discounts, subject to the limitations as set forth in the Lease. In the event that any of the Vendors have heretofore or may hereafter require the making of any down payments, progress payments, or other advances, same shall be (or have heretofore been) made by the Assignor. Any such payments and/or advances shall be reimbursed to the Assignor by the Assignee upon proof of payment therefor when and if the Assignee is required to make payment of the purchase price therefor pursuant to the Lease including all attachments thereto.

6. In the event that the Assignor or the Assignee determines not to accept for lease any of said Equipment, the Assignee shall reassign to the Assignor the appropriate contract rights governing said Equipment and release the Assignee's interests therein. The Assignee shall thereupon have no further obligations, or liabilities in connection with said contract rights and Equipment, and the Assignor hereby agrees to indemnify the Assignee and hold the Assignee harmless from and against any and all claims, demands, actions, or proceedings arising out of or in any way relating to said contract rights and Equipment, by whomsoever asserted, and any and all losses, damage, obligations, liabilities, costs, expenses (including attorneys' fees) suffered, paid, or incurred by the Assignee in connection therewith.

7. The Assignor agrees that at any time and from time to time, upon written request of the Assignee, the Assignor will promptly and duly execute and deliver any and all

such further instruments and documents and take such further action as the Assignee may reasonably request in order to obtain the full benefit of this Assignment and of the rights and powers herein granted.

8. The Assignor does hereby represent and warrant that the Purchase Contracts are in full force and effect and the Assignor is not in default thereunder. The Assignor does hereby further represent and warrant that the Assignor has not assigned or pledged, and hereby covenants that it will not assign or pledge, so long as this Assignment shall remain in effect, the whole or any part of the rights hereby assigned or any of its rights with respect to the Equipment under the Purchase Contracts not assigned hereby, to anyone other than the Assignee.

9. The Assignee agrees that, except as otherwise expressly provided herein, it will not enter into any agreement with any of the Vendors that would amend, modify, supplement, rescind, cancel, or terminate any of the Purchase Contracts in respect to the Equipment without the prior written consent of the Assignor.

10. All notices, requests, demands, or communications to or upon the Assignee and the Assignor shall be deemed to have been given or made when deposited in the U.S. mail, postage for certified mail prepaid, or in the case of telegraphic notice, when delivered to the telegraph company, addressed to respective addresses contained in the Lease.

11. The Assignor shall notify the Vendors of this assignment, such notice to be in the form of Exhibit B hereto.

12. Neither this Assignment nor any provision hereby may be changed, waived, discharged, or terminated orally, but only by an instrument in writing signed by the party against whom enforcement of the change, waiver, discharge, or termination is sought.

13. This Assignment shall be binding upon the Assignor and its successors and assigns and shall be binding upon and inure to the benefit of the Assignee and its successors and assigns.

14. This Assignment and the rights and obligations of the parties hereunder shall be construed in accordance with and governed by the laws of the State of __________.

IN WITNESS WHEREOF, the parties here to have caused this Assignment to be duly executed this ____ day of __________________, XXXX.

____________________________________, Assignor

By: ____________________________

Title: __________________________

____________________________________, Assignee

By: ____________________________

Title: __________________________

Exhibit A

[Copies of Purchase Contracts]

Exhibit B

Form of Notification of Assignment
[See Form a-12.]

Form: a-12
Disk File Name: a-12.rtf

ASSIGNMENT OF PURCHASE CONTRACT NOTIFICATION TO VENDOR

Form Purpose

Notification to, and acknowledgment by, an equipment vendor of the assignment by an equipment lessee to an equipment leasing company of the rights, but not the obligations, to purchase equipment, from its equipment vendor, which will be the subject of the lease agreement.

Executing Parties

The equipment lessee.
The equipment vendor.

See:

Assignment of Equipment Purchase Contract, Form a-11

Notification of Purchase Contract Assignment

Date ___________

(Insert name and address of equipment vendor)

Re: Purchase Contract, dated _________________________________, XXXX.

(Insert name of assignor) ("Lessee") has assigned its position under this purchase contract to (Insert name of assignee), as lessor, who will lease the equipment which is the subject of the above-referenced purchase contract to Lessee. Notwithstanding such assignment, Lessee hereby guarantees performance of all of buyer's obligations under this purchase contract and expects you to permit Lessee to continue to exercise and permit the enforcement of buyer's rights in relation to warranties and/or representations provided by, or through, you the seller.

Please prepare your invoices to show the equipment as billed, and shipped, to Lessor in care of Lessee. Any additional title papers or bills of sale should be prepared to show as owner:

[Insert Lessor's name and address].

We request your written acknowledgment that these changes will be made as requested, by signing and returning to us the enclosed copy of this notification.

Thank you.

(Insert name of Lessee)

By: ____________________________________

Title: __________________________________

Accepted this ______ day of ____________, XXXX.

(Insert name of equipment vendor), Vendor

By: ____________________________________

Title: __________________________________

Assumption Documents

Form: a-13
Disk File Name: a-13.rtf

ASSUMPTION AGREEMENT

Form Purpose

When one equipment leasing company sells an equipment lease, and the equipment subject to the lease, to another equipment leasing company, if some or all of the equipment purchase funds have been borrowed from a third-party lender, an assumption agreement can be used to, in effect, transfer the loan obligation to the second leasing company. The following assumption is a recourse assumption, obligating the selling leasing company to pay any transferred obligations not paid by the purchasing leasing company. If the equipment loan had been guaranteed, the guarantor must also consent to the assumption agreement.

Executing Parties

The selling equipment lessor.
The purchasing equipment lessor.
The selling equipment lessor's loan guarantor.
The equipment lender (secured party).

See:

Assignment of Lease, Forms a-06, a-07, a-08, and a-09
Assumption Consent–Guarantor, Form a-14

Assumption Agreement

This Assumption Agreement ("Agreement") is made this ____ day of ______________ XXXX, by and among ____________________________________ ("Transferor"), with a place of business at ____; ____________________________________ ("Transferee"), with a place of business at ____________________________; and ______________________ ("Secured Party"), with a place of business at ____.

WHEREAS, Transferor has entered into a Loan and Security Agreement ("Security Agreement") with Secured Party covering the following equipment ("Equipment")

[insert equipment description here]

which is subject to an equipment lease, dated ______________________, XXXX, by and between Transferor, as lessor, and ______________________________________, as lessee, (the "Lease").

WHEREAS, Transferor wishes to sell, assign, and/or transfer all of its right, title, and interest in and to the Lease, the Equipment, and the Security Agreement thereof to Transferee, and

WHEREAS, the Equipment and the Lease is subject to the security interest of Secured Party, and Secured Party is willing to consent to such sale, assignment, and transfer, subject, however, to the terms and conditions hereinafter set forth.

NOW, THEREFORE, in consideration of the mutual covenants contained herein, this Agreement the parties hereto agree as follows:

1. Transferor hereby sells, assigns, and/or transfers to Transferee all of its right, title, and interest in and to the Security Agreement, the Lease, and the Equipment.

2. Transferee hereby:

(a) promises to pay to Secured Party all monies due and to become due pursuant to the terms and conditions of the Security Agreement and in the manner set forth therein;

(b) hereby assumes and covenants to perform all obligations of Transferor;

(c) agrees that it shall stand in the place and stead of Transferor and shall be subject to all of the terms and provisions contained in the original Security Agreement, as though it were the original Security Agreement named therein; and

(d) agrees to pay as they become due the remaining monthly rentals numbering ________ at $ ______________ each.

3. In consideration of the consent of Secured Party to the foregoing sale, assignment, transfer, and assumption, Transferor does hereby absolutely, irrevocably, and unconditionally guarantee to Secured Party and its successors and assigns that all warranties and representations made by Transferor to Secured Party to induce Secured Party to consent to this transfer and assumption are true and correct. Upon any default by Transferee, Transferor shall pay to Secured Party or its successors or assigns the full unpaid

amounts of any and all the obligations then owed by Transferee to Secured Party pursuant to the aforementioned Security Agreement.

IN WITNESS WHEREOF, the parties have executed this Agreement on the day and year first above written.

(Insert name of Transferor), Transferor

By: ______________________________

Title: ______________________________

(Insert name of Transferee), Transferee

By: ______________________________

Title: ______________________________

(Insert name of Secured Party), Secured Party

By: ______________________________

Title: ______________________________

Form a-14
Disk File Name: a-14.rtf

ASSUMPTION CONSENT—GUARANTOR

Form Purpose

When one equipment leasing company sells an equipment lease, to another leasing company, if some or all of the equipment purchase funds have been borrowed from a third-party lender, an assumption agreement can be used to, in effect, transfer the loan obligation to the second leasing company. If the equipment loan had been guaranteed, the gurantor must also consent to the assumption agreement. The following agreement provides for such a guarantor consent and should be attached to the assumption agreement as an exhibit.

Executing Parties

The selling equipment lessor's guarantor.

See:

Assumption Agreement, Form a-13

Agreement of Guarantor

Lease Agreement dated ____________________

Selling Lessor ______________________________

Lessee __________________________________

Purchasing Lessor ________________________

The undersigned, as a guarantor of Selling Lessor's obligations under the Lease, does hereby represent and warrant that the undersigned has read and understands the foregoing Assumption Agreement, does hereby consent to the execution thereof, and covenants and agrees that any oblligation or liability, which it may have by virtue of the undersigned's guaranty, will remain in full force and effect upon and after the execution of these presents and shall secure the full and timely performance of the obligations of both the Selling Lessor and Purchasing Lessor.

_________________________________, Guarantor

By: ____

Title: _______________________________________

Amendment to Lease Documents

Form: a-15
Disk File Name: a-15.rtf

AMENDMENT TO LEASE AGREEMENT

Form Purpose

Lease amendment. This form has been integrated with the short form net finance master lease agreement, Equipment Lease Agreement Form l-03.

Executing Parties

The equipment lessor.
The equipment lessee.

See:

Equipment Lease Agreement, Form l-03

RIDER ______ to Schedule No. ______ dated as of ______________________________ to

Master Agreement to Lease Equipment, dated as of ______________________________,

between ______________________________, Lessor, and ______________________________,

Lessee.

Amendment to Lease

The terms and conditions of the Schedule designated above are modified and amended as follows:

______________________________, Lessor

By: ______________________________

Title: ______________________________

______________________________, Lessee

By: ______________________________

Title: ______________________________

Bill of Sale Documents

Form: b-01
Disk File Name: b-01.rtf

Bill of Sale—Warranty

Form Purpose

A warranty equipment bill of sale.

Executing Parties

The equipment seller.

Bill of Sale

____________________________________ ("Seller"), with a principal place of business at ____ for and in consideration of the sum of dollars received from ____________________________ ("Buyer") with a principal place of business at ________________________________, the receipt and sufficiency of which is hereby acknowledged as payment in full for the purchase price of the equipment described on Annex A hereto (the "Equipment"), has bargained, sold, transferred, assigned, set over, and conveyed, and by these presents does bargain, sell, transfer, assign, set over, and convey unto Buyer, its successors and assigns forever all of the Equipment.

TO HAVE AND TO HOLD, all and singular the Equipment unto the Buyer, its successors and assigns, for its and their own use and behalf forever.

Seller shall indemnify, defend, and hold Buyer harmless from and against any and all claims or liabilities resulting from any misrepresentation by, or breach of warranty, covenant, or agreement of Seller.

Seller, for itself and its successors and assigns, further covenants and agrees to do, execute, and deliver, or to cause to be done, executed, and delivered, all such further reasonable acts, transfers, and assurances, for the better assuring, conveying, and confirming unto Buyer and its successors and assigns, all and singular, the Equipment hereby bargained, sold, assigned, transferred, set over, and conveyed as Buyer and its successors and assigns shall reasonably request.

Seller hereby warrants to Buyer, its successors and assigns, that at the time of this sale to Buyer, Seller is the lawful owner of the Equipment; that title to said Equipment is free from all prior claims, liens, and encumbrances suffered by or through Seller; that Seller has good right to sell the same as aforesaid; and that Seller covenants that it will warrant and defend such title against all claims and demands whatsoever.

This Bill of Sale and the representations, warranties, and covenants herein contained shall inure to the benefit of Buyer and its successors and assigns, shall be binding upon Seller and its successors and assigns, and shall survive the execution and delivery hereof.

IN WITNESS WHEREOF, Seller has caused this Bill of Sale to be executed on the ____ day of ______________________, XXXX.

By: ____________________________________

Title: ___________________________________

Annex A

Form: b-02
Disk File Name: b-02.rtf

Bill of Sale—"As Is, Where Is"

Form Purpose

An "as is, where is" equipment bill of sale.

Executing Parties

The equipment seller.

Bill of Sale

This Bill of Sale, dated the ____ day of ______________________________, XXXX, from ____ ("Seller"), with a place of business at ____.

WITNESSETH

In consideration of the receipt of $ ____________ and other valuable consideration, the receipt of which is hereby acknowledged, Seller does hereby sell, assign, transfer, convey, and deliver, on an "as is, where is" basis to ______________________________ (the "Buyer"), with a place of business at ______________________________ ____ all the property and equipment of whatsoever kind of character listed, described, or otherwise referred to on its attached invoice, a copy of which is attached hereto and incorporated herein by this reference with the same force and effect as set forth herein full as Annex A.

Seller covenants and warrants that:

A. It is the owner of, and has absolute title to each and every item of said property free and clear of all claims, liens, encumbrances, and all other defects of title, of any kind whatsoever.

B. It has not made any prior sale, assignment, or transfer of any item of said property to any person, firm, or corporation.

C. It has the present power and authority to sell, assign, and transfer each and every item of said property to Buyer.

D. All acts, proceedings, and things necessary and required by law and the articles of incorporation and by-laws of Seller to make this Bill of Sale a valid, binding, and legal obligation of Seller have been done, taken, and have happened; and the execution and delivery hereof have in all respects been duly authorized in accordance with the law, and said articles of incorporation and by-laws.

Seller shall forever warrant and defend the sale, assignment, transfer, conveyance, and delivery of each and every item of said property to Buyer and its successors and assigns, against each and every person whomsoever lawfully claiming the same.

This Bill of Sale is binding upon the successors and assigns of Seller and insures to the benefit of the successors and assigns of Buyer.

IN WITNESS WHEREOF, the undersigned Seller has caused this instrument to be executed on the day and year first above appearing, by and through an officer thereunto duty authorized.

(Seller)

By: ________________________________

Title: ______________________________

Annex A

Casualty Value Schedules

[See Casualty Value Schedule, Form I-02c.]

Certificates of Acceptance

[See Certificate of Acceptance, Forms I-02b and I-06d.]

Checklists

Form: c-01
Disk File Name: c-01.rtf

CHECKLIST—LESSEE PROPOSAL STAGE

Form Purpose

A lessee proposal stage checklist.

See:

Request for Lease Quotations, Forms r-01 through r-04

A Lessee Proposal Stage Checklist

The following lists the issues that a prospective lessee should address in considering its negotiation objectives and in preparing its request for bids letter.

Equipment Description

- What type will be involved?
- Who is the manufacturer?
- What is the model?
- How many units will be involved?

Equipment Cost

- What is the total cost involved?
- What is the cost per item?
- Is the cost per item fixed?

  (1) If not, what is the probable cost escalation?

Equipment Payment

- When must the equipment be paid for?
- Must the entire purchase price be paid at once?

Equipment Delivery

- What is the anticipated delivery date?
- How long should the lessor's lease commitment run past the anticipated delivery date?

Equipment Location

- Where will the equipment be located?

  (1) At the lease inception
  (2) During the lease term

Equipment Lease

- What type of lease is desired?

  (1) Net finance lease
  (2) Service lease
  (3) Other

Lease Period

- How long must the lease term run?
- Will an interim lease period be acceptable?

  (1) If so, what is the latest point in time when the primary term must begin?

- How long a renewal period is desired?
- How will the renewal right be structured? (For example, five one-year periods, one five-year period, etc.)

Rent Program

- When should the rent be payable?

  (1) Annually
  (2) Semiannually
  (3) Quarterly
  (4) Monthly
  (5) Other

- Should the payments be "in advance" or "in arrears?"
- If there is an interim period, how should the interim rent be structured?

  (1) Based on the primary rent (For example, the daily equivalent of the primary rent.)
  (2) Based on the long-term debt interest rate
  (3) Other

- If there will be a renewal period, how should the renewal rent be structured?

  (1) Fixed
  (2) Fair rental value

Options

- What type of options are desired

  (1) Fair market value purchase right
  (2) Fixed price purchase right
  (3) Fair market rental value renewal right
  (4) Fixed price renewal right
  (5) Right of first refusal
  (6) Termination right
  (7) Upgrade financing right
  (8) Other

- Is a right of first refusal specifically unacceptable?

Casualty and Termination Values

- If a termination right is required, will the termination value be a primary consideration in the lease decision?
- Must the termination and casualty values be submitted at the time of the lessor's proposal?

Maintenance and Repair

- Who will have the equipment maintenance and repair obligations?
- Are third-party maintenance contract requirements acceptable?

Tax Indemnifications

- What tax indemnifications will be acceptable, if any?

Insurance

- Is the right of self-insurance desired?

Taxes

- What taxes will be assumed?

  (1) Sales
  (2) Rental
  (3) Other

Transaction Expenses

- What expenses other than lessee's legal fees, if any, will be assumed if the transaction is completed? (Usually only a concern in underwritten transactions.)

  (1) Counsel fees for any lenders and their representatives
  (2) Acceptance and annual fees of any lender representative (trust arrangement)
  (3) Counsel fees for the lessor-investors and any representative
  (4) Counsel fees for the lessor-investor's representative (trust arrangement)
  (5) IRS private ruling letter fees
  (6) Documentation expenses
  (7) Debt placement fees
  (8) Other

- What expenses, if any, will be assumed if the transaction collapses?

Tax Ruling

- Is an IRS private letter ruling necessary or desirable?
- Can a favorable letter ruling be a prerequisite to any obligations to the lessor under the lease, such as a nonutilization fee?
- Should a private letter ruling relieve any tax indemnification obligations to the lessor?

Submission Date

- When is the latest date on which a lessor proposal may be submitted?

Award Date

- On what date will the transaction be awarded?

Type of Proposals

- Is a leverage lease or single source preferred?
- Is an underwritten Transaction acceptable? If, so:

(1) Will "best efforts" as well as "firm" proposals be accepted?
(2) If "best efforts" proposals are acceptable, how long after the awards will the underwriter have to firm up the prospective lessor-investors and any lenders?

Prospective Equity and Debt Participants—Underwritten Transaction

- Are any prospective lessor-investors or lenders not to be approached?

Form: c-02
Disk File Name: c-02.rtf

CHECKLIST—LEASE NEGOTIATION AND DRAFTING

Form Purpose

A checklist for drafting and negotiating a lease agreement.

See:

Lease Agreements, Forms l-02 through l-04

A Checklist for Drafting and Negotiating a Lease Agreement

In preparing a well-drafted lease agreement, the parties should cover all the important issues involved in a transaction. The following checklist pinpoints the issues frequently encountered.

What form of lease is appropriate?

- A single transaction lease
- A master lease
- Does the lease agreement cover the following issues?

- Has a page index of all topic headings been included?
- Have the parties been properly identified?

  (1) Lessor
  (2) Lessee

    A. Is the lessee a valid legal entity?
    B. Has a factual summary of the circumstances giving rise to the transaction been included?

- Has the consideration for the transaction been stated?
- Have the key terms been defined in a definition section? For example:

  (1) Affiliate
  (2) Business day
  (3) Buyer-furnished equipment
  (4) Equipment delivery date
  (5) Equipment manufacturer
  (6) Event of default
  (7) Event of loss
  (8) Fair market value
  (9) Indenture
  (10) Interim rent
  (11) Lease
  (12) Lease period
  (13) Lease supplement
  (14) Lessor's cost
  (15) Lien
  (16) Loan certificates
  (17) Loan participant
  (18) Overdue interest rate
  (19) Primary rent
  (20) Casualty loss value

- If equipment will be delivered after the lease is signed, has a procedure for adding it been established?

  (1) Can the lessee decide not to lease future delivered equipment when it arrives? If so, will the lessee be obligated to pay:

A. A nonutilization fee?
B. A commitment fee?

(2) Can future delivered equipment be accepted for lease as it arrives or must the lessee aggregate a minimum dollar amount?

- The lease period should be defined.

(1) Will there be an interim lease term? If so, when will it begin and end?
(2) When will the primary term begin?
(3) How long will the primary term run?
(4) Will the lessee be permitted to renew the lease? If so, what is the renewal period arrangement?

- The rent structure must be defined.

(1) Will a percentage rent factor be used? If so, what may be included in the equipment cost base?

A. Sales tax
B. Transportation charges
C. Installation charges
D. Other

(2) How much rent must be paid?
(3) When will the rent be due?
(4) How must the rent be paid?

A. Check
B. Wire transfer
C. Other

(5) Where must the rent be paid?

A. Has a post office box or other address been specified?

(6) Can or must the lessor adjust the rent charge if there is a tax law change affecting, favorably or unfavorably, the lessor's economic return?

A. If a rent adjustment is provided for, has the exact criterion for making it been clearly specified?
B. If the tax law change applies to future delivered equipment and a rent adjustment is not acceptable, can the party adversely affected elect to exclude the equipment?

(7) Will the rent obligation be a hell or high water obligation?

- What is the lessor's total dollar equipment cost commitment?

(1) Will a percentage variance be permitted?

- Will the lessee be required to submit reports? For example:

(1) Financial reports

A. Profit and loss statements
B. Balance sheets
C. Other

(2) Accident reports

A. Has a minimum estimated accident dollar amount been agreed upon below which a report is not required? .

B. Will the lessee be obligated to immediately telephone if a accident occurs?

(3) Lease conformity reports

(4) Equipment location reports

(5) Third-party claim reports

- Has a time been established for when lessee reports are due?
- Has a general lessee reporting requirement been imposed as to reports that may be deemed necessary by the lessor in the future?
- Equipment maintenance

(1) Who has the responsibility for ensuring proper maintenance?

A. Lessor

B. Lessee

C. A third party

(2) Who must bear the cost of the maintenance?

A. Lessor

B. Lessee

(3) Will maintenance records be required?

A. Will the lessor be permitted access to the maintenance records?

(1) If so, at what times:

(A) Normal business hours

(B) Any time requested

- Will equipment alterations be permitted? If so,

(1) Will the lessor's consent be required before:

A. An addition that may impair the equipment's originally intended function or that cannot be removed without so impairing such function?

B. Any change?

(2) Who will have title to any addition or other alteration:

A. If it can be easily removed without equipment damage?

B. If it cannot be removed without function impairment?

C. What rights will the lessor have to buy the alteration?

- Will certain lessor ownership protection filings be necessary?

(1) Federal regulatory agencies, such as the Federal Aviation Administration

(2) Uniform Commercial Code

(3) Other

- If lessor ownership protection filings will be made, who has the responsibility for making them and who must bear the expense?

(1) Lessor

(2) Lessee

- If the lessee must make required filings for the lessor, will the lessee have to confirm they have been made?
- Will the equipment be marked with the lessor's name and address? If so, who will have the marking responsibility and expense?
    - (1) Lessor
    - (2) Lessee
- Has the lessee been specifically prohibited from using, operating, storing, or maintaining the equipment carelessly, improperly, in violating the law, or in a manner not contemplated by the manufacturer?
    - (1) If the lessee must use the equipment for a purpose other than intended, an exception should be negotiated
    - (2) If certain key lessee representations are required, can they be validly made?
        - (1) That the lessee is properly organized, validly existing, and in good standing
        - (2) That it has proper authorization to do business in the state where the equipment will be located
        - (3) That the lessee has the transactional authority to enter into the lease
            - A. That necessary board of director approvals have been obtained covering the transaction and the person signing the lease on behalf of the lessee
            - B. That any other required approvals have been obtained
        - (4) That there are not conflicting agreements
            - A. Bank credit agreements
            - B. Other loan agreements
            - C. Mortgages
            - D. Other leases
        - (5) That all necessary regulatory approvals have been obtained
        - (6) That there are no pending or threatened adverse legal or administrative proceedings that would affect the lessee's operations or financial condition
        - (7) That there have been no adverse changes as of the lease closing in the lessee's financial condition since the latest available financial statements
- The lessor must be required to provide certain key representations
    - (1) That the lessor has the transactional authority to lease the equipment
        - A. That any necessary board of director approval has been obtained
        - B. That any other approvals have been obtained or, if none are required, a statement that none are required
    - (2) That the lessor will pay for the equipment in full
    - (3) That the lessor will not interfere with the lessee's use of the equipment
        - A. Has an exception when the lessee is in default been negotiated by the lessor?
- The lessee should require product warranties to be assigned if the lessor has no equipment defect responsibility
    - (1) If the warranties are not assignable, the lessor should be required to act on the lessee's behalf

- Who has the responsibility for equipment casualty losses?

  (1) Lessor
  (2) Lessee

- Are the casualty loss values competitive from the lessee's viewpoint?
- As of what time will a casualty loss be deemed to have occurred—has a "loss date" been defined?

  (1) What obligations change or come into effect on the loss date?

- When is the casualty loss value payable and when does interest on the amount payable begin to run?
- What taxes must be paid?

  (1) Sales tax
  (2) Property taxes
  (3) Rental taxes
  (4) Withholding taxes
  (5) Income taxes
  (6) Other

- Who must pay the taxes?

  (1) The lessor
  (2) The lessee

- For any taxes that a lessee must reimburse a lessor for payment, does the lessee have the right to have the taxes contested?

  (1) What happens if the lessor does not fully pursue its contest remedies?

- Is each party required to immediately notify the other of any tax imposition for which they will be responsible?
- Do the parties intend a true tax lease? If so,

  (1) Inconsistent actions and filings should be prohibited
  (2) Will tax loss indemnifications be required?
  (3) Will any tax indemnity cover all lessor tax losses or only those resulting from the lessee's acts or omissions?

- Who has the economic risk of a change in tax law?

  (1) For past delivered equipment
  (2) For future delivered equipment

    A. Can either party elect not to lease if the economics are no longer favorable?

- Has a formula been agreed on for measuring the amount of any tax benefit loss and the amount of any required reimbursement?

  (1) Does the formula make the indemnified party whole?
  (2) is the formula absolutely clear?

- Has the tax loss date been determined?

- Who has the expense responsibility for the equipment return and where must it be returned to:

  (1) If the lease ends normally?
  (2) If the lease ends prematurely?

- May either party designate an alternate return location? If so, what is the expense responsibility?

- The lessor may be able to terminate the lease early or take other protective action in certain situations
  (1) When the rent is not paid
  (2) When the lessee makes an unauthorized transfer of the equipment or any of its rights under the lease
  (3) When there is a general failure to perform the obligations under the lease
  (4) When the lessor discovers the lessee has made a material misrepresentation
  (5) When there is a bankruptcy or similar event that would jeopardize the lessor's position

- The actions that the lessor may take in the event of default must be specified:

  (1) Court action
  (2) Terminate the lease
  (3) Cause a redelivery of the equipment
  (4) Cause the lessee to store the equipment
  (5) Sell the equipment under its own terms
  (6) Be able to hold or re-lease the equipment
  (7) Be entitled to a predetermined amount of money as damages for a lease default

- Certain lessor assignment rights may be required:

  (1) To a lender as security
  (2) To an investor

- Will the lessee be able to sublease the equipment? If so,

  (1) Will the lessee remain primarily liable under the lease during the sublease period?
  (2) Will the lessor have any control over who the sublessee will be?

- Have any lessor options been included? For example:

  (1) Right to terminate the lease
  (2) Right to force a sale of the lessee
  (3) Right to abandon the equipment
  (4) Right to force a lease renewal

- Have all lessee's options been included? For example:

  (1) A purchase right

    A. Fair market purchase value
    B. Fixed purchase price

(2) A renewal right

A. Fair market purchase value
B. Fixed price rental

(3) A termination right
(4) A right of first refusal
(5) An upgrade financing right

- Will a defaulting party retain any of its option rights under the lease?
- Has the law of a jurisdiction been specified to control any issues that arise under the lease?
- Is there a severability clause?
- Is there any interest penalty for overdue payments?
- Has each side specified how and where any required notifications and payments will be made?

(1) The address where notifications and payments must be sent
(2) The manner in which the notifications and payments must be made

A. U.S. mail
B. Other

- Has the signature section been set up properly for:

(1) An individual
(2) A corporation
(3) A partnership
(4) A trust
(5) Other

- Has the signature been made in the proper capacity?

Form: c-03
Disk File Name: c-03.rtf

Checklist—Lessor Proposal Stage

Form Purpose

A lessor proposal stage checklist.

See:

Proposal Documents–Lessor, Forms p-04 through p-05

A Lessor Proposal Stage Checklist

The following checklist will serve as a guide to the prospective lessor in identifying issues, and in preparing and negotiating a proposal letter.

The Offer

- Will an underwritten or direct lessor proposal be involved?
- If an underwritten offer is involved,

  (1) Will it be on a "best efforts" or "firm" basis?
  (2) Must there be more than one equity participant?
  (3) If it can be on a "best efforts" basis, is there any deadline when the equity participants must give their formal commitment?
  (4) Will the transaction be leveraged with third-party debt?

The Lessee

- Has the lessee been accurately identified?
- Has the lessee's financial condition been reviewed?

Credit Support

- Can the lessee's financial condition support the entire lease obligation?
- If the lessee's "credit" is not sufficient, are there additional credit support alternatives available?

  (1) Parent company guarantee
  (2) Affiliated company guarantee
  (3) Unrelated third-party guarantee
  (4) Deficiency guarantee
  (5) Bank support
  (6) Other

- If credit support is necessary, has the financial condition of the entity giving the support been reviewed?

The Equipment Description

- What type will be involved?
- Who is the manufacturer?
- What is the model?
- How many units will be involved?

The Equipment Cost

- What is the total cost involved?
- What is the cost per item?
- Is the cost per item fixed?

  (1) If not, what is the probable cost escalation?

The Equipment Delivery

- What is the anticipated delivery date?
- Must the lease commitment run past the anticipated delivery date? If so, for how long?

  (1) Will a fee be charged for the commitment to lease future delivered equipment?

The Equipment Location

- Where will the equipment be located?

  (1) At the lease inception?
  (2) During the lease term?

The Rent Program

- What is the primary rent payment program structure?

  (1) Will the rent be payable "in advance" or "in arrears"?
  (2) Will the rent be payable annually, semiannually, quarterly, monthly, or other?

- Will interim rent be involved? If so,

  (1) Will it be based upon the primary rent, the long-term debt interest rate (if leveraged), or other?
  (2) When will the payments be due?

The Term of the Lease

- How long will the lease run?

  (1) Primary lease term
  (2) Renewal period

- Will an interim lease term be involved? If so,

  (1) When will the interim term lease term start?
  (2) When will the primary lease term start?

The Lessor

- How will the equipment be owned?

  (1) Directly
  (2) Indirectly through a partnership, trust, or corporation

- Will the ownership structure satisfy any tax and liability criteria?

  (1) Flow-through of tax benefits
  (2) Corporate-like liability protection
  (3) Other

The Debt—if the Transaction Is Leveraged

- What is the loan repayment program?

  (1) "In advance or "in arrears"?
  (2) Debt service to be payable annually, semiannually, quarterly, monthly, or other?

- Who will be responsible for arranging for the placement of the debt?
- Will the rent be quoted on the basis of an assumed debt principal amount, per annum interest charge, etc.?

  (1) If so, will the rent quoted be subject to adjustment if other than assumed?

- If the rent is subject to a debt assumption adjustment, what adjustment criteria will be used?

  (1) After-tax yield
  (2) Cash flow
  (3) Net return
  (4) Other

- Who will be responsible for fees related to the debt?

  (1) Placement fee
  (2) Lender's commitment fee
  (3) Other

Options

- What special rights will the lessee have?

  (1) Fixed price purchase right
  (2) Fair market value purchase right
  (3) Fixed price renewal right
  (4) Fair market rental value renewal right
  (5) Right of first refusal
  (6) Termination right
  (7) Upgrade right
  (8) Other

- What special rights will the lessor have?

  (1) Fixed price sale right
  (2) Fixed price renewal right
  (3) Termination right
  (4) Other

Casualty Loss

- What financial responsibilities will the lessee have in the event of a casualty loss?

Casualty and Termination Values

- What amounts are to be used?

Tax Aspects

- What are the relevant tax assumptions?
- What tax assumptions, if any, will the lessee have to indemnify the lessor for, in the event of loss or inability to claim?
- If there are lessee tax indemnifications, what events that result in tax benefit unavailability will trigger an indemnification payment?

  (1) Any reason
  (2) Acts or omissions of lessee
  (3) Acts or omissions of lessor
  (4) Change in law
  (5) Other

Tax Ruling

- Will a tax ruling be involved?
- If so, will a *favorable* ruling:

  (1) Relieve the lessee from any tax indemnifications?
  (2) Be a prerequisite to the lessor's obligation to lease the equipment?

Transaction Expenses

- Who must pay for the expenses if:

  (1) The transaction goes through without problems?
  (2) The transaction collapses before the lease documents are executed?
  (3) The transaction collapses after the lease documents are executed but before the equipment is delivered?

Type of Lease

- What type of lease will be involved?

  (1) Net finance lease
  (2) Service lease
  (3) Other

Conditions

- What conditions must be satisfied before the lessor is committed?

  (1) Governmental or regulatory approvals
  (2) Licenses or authorizations
  (3) Favorable opinions of counsel
  (4) Maintenance or achievement of certain financial tests
  (5) Satisfactory audited financial statements

(6) Acceptable documentation
(7) Approvals by prospective lessor or equity participants
(8) Minimum dollar participation by equity and debt participants
(9) Favorable equipment appraisals justifying equipment residual value
(10) Other

Form of Proposal

- Will a written proposal be used? If so,

  (1) How should acceptance be acknowledged?

Submission and Award Dates

- When is the latest date on which the proposal can be submitted?
- What is the anticipated transaction award date?

  (1) Is there adequate time to do the deal?

Offer Termination Date

- How long will the prospective lessee have to accept the offer?

Form: c-04
Disk File Name: c-04.rtf

CHECKLIST—SUPPLEMENTAL LEASE DOCUMENT CLOSING

Form Purpose

A supplemental lease document closing checklist.

Supplemental Lease Document Closing Checklist

Although the type of additional closing documents required in a lease transaction will vary with each situation, the following checklist can be used as a general guideline.

Legal opinions:

- Is the lawyer rendering the legal opinion thoroughly experienced in the area to be covered by the opinion? Fox example, if an opinion is required on complex tax issues, is he or she fully knowledgeable on all the relevant aspects?
- How much has the legal opinion been conditioned? In other words, has the lawyer left so many outs as to his or her position that he or she really has provided little comfort?
- To the extent that the legal opinion is based on facts supplied to the lawyer, are the facts accurate and complete?

Does the opinion of the lessee's lawyer, to be delivered to the lessor, address the following issues?

- Proper organization, valid existence, and good standing of the lessee.
- The lessee's full authority to enter into the lease.
- The lessee's complete and unrestricted ability to perform all obligations.
- Whether all the lessee's lease commitments are legally binding.
- Whether all necessary consents have been obtained.
- Whether all necessary regulatory approvals have been obtained.
- Whether there are any pending or threatened adverse court or administrative proceedings. If so, what the potential impact may be.
- Whether any law, rule, or collateral agreement will be violated by the lessee entering the lease transaction.

Does the opinion of the lessor's lawyer, to be delivered to the lessee, address the following issues?

- Whether the lessor is properly organized, validly existing, and in good standing.
- Whether the lessor is properly authorized to do business in the jurisdiction where the equipment will be located.
- Whether the transaction has been fully authorized by the lessor. For example, have all necessary committee and board of director approvals been secured?
- Whether all the lessor's commitments are binding.
- Whether the lessor's ability to perform its obligations is unrestricted.
- Whether any shareholder, lender, etc., consents are necessary. If so, have they been obtained?
- Whether the transaction will violate any law, rule, or collateral agreement as to the lessor.

Does the opinion of the lessor's lawyer, to be delivered to a third-party lender, address the following issues:

- Whether the lessor is properly organized, validly existing, and in good standing.
- Whether all necessary authorizations, both as to the lease financing and the loan financing, have been obtained.
- Whether the loan obligations are fully enforceable against the lessor.
- Whether the lessor has good and marketable title to the leased equipment.
- Whether the equipment has any liens or encumbrances on it.
- Whether the lessor's rights under the lease are unencumbered, including its right to receive the rent payments.

Does the opinion of the guarantor's lawyer, to be delivered to the lessor, address the following issues:

- Whether the guarantor is properly organized, validly existing, and in good standing.
- Whether all necessary authorizations as to the lease financing have been obtained.
- Whether the lease obligations are fully enforceable against the guarantor.

Does the opinion of the vendor's lawyer, to be delivered to the lessor, address the following issues:

- Whether the title of the equipment will be delivered free and clear to the lessor.
- Whether all necessary internal authorizations have been obtained.

Has the lessor been supplied with the required lessee, lessee controlling corporation, and guarantor financial statements?

- Profit and loss statements.
- Balance sheets.
- Officer's certificate updating the prior financial statements to the closing.

Have adequate lessor financial statements or information been obtained?

- Profit and loss statements.
- Balance sheets.
- Officer's certificate updating the prior financial statements to the closing.
- Have all the critical financial statements been certified by an independent certified public accounting firm?
- Has a certified copy of any relevant corporate board of director resolutions been delivered?
- If the lease obligations will be guaranteed by a third party, will it be a full and unconditional guarantee? If not, is the limited extent of the guarantee understood?
- If personal injury and property damage insurance is required, does the insurance company's certificate of insurance properly represent the required insurance?
- If the lessor must enter into an equipment purchase agreement directly with the vendor, is it prepared to buy the equipment if the lessee backs away? If not, can a purchase agreement assignment be used?

- Does any equipment purchase agreement assignment specifically provide that only the rights, not the obligations, will be transferred to the lessor?
- Under an equipment purchase agreement assignment, will the lessor be entitled to all vendor supplied services, training, information, warranties, and indemnities?
- Has the vendor's consent been obtained as to the purchase agreement assignment? If so, does it:

  (1) Acknowledge the assignment?
  (2) Acknowledge that the lessor will not have to buy the equipment if the lessee backs out before the lease is executed?

- Has an equipment bill of sale been included? If so,
- Is it a warranty bill of sale?
- Does it contain a representation that the seller has the lawful right and authority to sell the equipment?
- If the equipment will be located on leased or mortgaged property, has the landowner or mortgagee supplied a written waiver of any present or future claim to the leased equipment?
- Have appropriate UCC financing statements (UCC-1's) been prepared for filing?
- If the transaction is underwritten:
- Has a participation agreement been prepared?
- Will the lenders and the equity participants each act through:

  (1) A trust arrangement?
  (2) A partnership arrangement?

- Has a fee agreement been prepared to formalize the underwriter's fee arrangement?

Collection Documents

Form: c-05
Disk File Name: c-05.rtf

Collection Notification—Initial Lessee Nonpayment

Form Purpose

A lessee lease payment default notification letter.

Executing Parties:

The equipment lessor.

See:

Collection Notification–Follow-up Lessee Nonpayment, Form c-06
Collection Notification–Lawsuit, Form c-07
Collection Notification–Repossession, Form c-08

[Letterhead of Leasing Company]

Date: ______________________

(Insert name and address of Lessee.)

Re: Equipment Lease Agreement, dated ______________________, XXXX.

Lease Account No.: ______________

Have you forgotten "our date"?

The one on which you promised to make regular payments on your account.

Of course, if you have put your remittance in the mail, please accept our thanks and disregard this reminder. But, if the date merely slipped your mind, won't you send us a check today? Payments made on time avoid additional charges and maintain a good credit record.

If there is some reason you cannot make this payment now, please come into our office or call us.

****

Have you changed your address?

If so, kindly fill in the information requested below. Then, enclose this notice in the envelope with your account statement and payment when mailing to us.

Name: ____

New Address: ____

City: ______________________ State: ______________ Zip: __________

Phone: (______) ______________________ Account Number: ______________

Your cooperation is appreciated.

Thank you.

Form: c-06
Disk File Name: c-06.rtf

Collection Notification—Follow-Up Lessee Nonpayment

Form Purpose

A follow-up lessee lease payment default notification letter.

Executing Parties:

The equipment lessor.

See:

Collection Notification–Initial Lessee Nonpayment, Form c-05
Collection Notification–Lawsuit, Form c-07
Collection Notification–Repossession, Form c-08

[Letterhead of Leasing Company]

(Insert name and address of Lessee.)

Re: Equipment Lease Agreement, dated ______________________, XXXX.

Lease Account No.: _______________

Dear

The delinquency on your account has become an extremely serious matter. As of today's date your account remains past due for its _____ payment of $ ____________, plus late charges of $ ______________. We very much want to work with you in this matter and understand that these situations do occur. However, you should also be aware that your obligation to us needs to be paid promptly.

If we do not receive your past due payments or work out alternate arrangements within seven days from the date of this letter, you leave us no alternative but to accelerate the entire balance owing under your lease, which totals $ ______________. Failure to pay that balance will result in the loss of the leased equipment and a subsequent costly legal action.

We would like to cooperate with you as much as much as we reasonably can, but our cooperation requires immediate attention. Please contact our office immediately upon receipt of this letter.

Sincerely,

Form: c-07
Disk File Name: c-07.rtf

COLLECTION NOTIFICATION—LAWSUIT

Form Purpose

A follow-up leasing company notification letter of intent to file a lawsuit for payment default.

Executing Parties:

The equipment lessor.

See:

Collection Notification–Initial Lessee Nonpayment, Form c-05
Collection Notification–Follow-Up Lessee Nonpayment, Form c-06
Collection Notification–Repossession, Form c-08

[Letterhead of Leasing Company]

(Insert name and address of Lessee.)

Re: Equipment Lease Agreement, dated ______________________, XXXX.

Lease Account No.: ____________________

Dear

This letter is to inform you that we are about to file a lawsuit against you due to nonpayment on the above referenced lease. At this time your account balance is $____________ plus accrued late charges.

If you wish to avoid this expensive court proceeding, we demand that you forward your check for this balance, or contact our office to make suitable payment arrangements, within the next ten days. The choice is yours. We wish to resolve this with you.

If no action is taken on your part, we will immediately begin to pursue all legal remedies available to us.

Very truly yours,

Form: c-08
Disk File Name: c-08.rtf

Collection Notification—Repossession

Form Purpose

A follow-up leasing company notification letter of intent to repossess leased equipment for payment default.

Executing Parties:

The equipment lessor.

See:

Collection Notification–Initial Lessee Nonpayment, Form c-05
Collection Notification–Follow-Up Lessee Nonpayment, Form c-06
Collection Notification–Lawsuit, Form c-07

[Letterhead of Leasing Company]

Date: ______________________________

SENT CERTIFIED AND REGULAR MAIL

(Insert name and address of Lessee.)

RE: Notice of Intention to Repossess Equipment

Under Equipment Lease Agreement, Dated ______________________.

Lease Account No.: ____________.

Dear

As of today's date the above referenced lease is past due for $ ____________________.

We must have the above account brought current immediately. In the event payment is not made within ten days from the date of this letter, it is the intention of the holder of the lease to institute legal action.

All payments referred to in this notice must be in the form of cash, cashier's check, certified check, or money order, and must be received at our office no later than __________ XXXX.

If you wish to cure the default within ten days from the date of this letter you must pay the total amount due as stated above.

If payment is made after ten days from the date of this notice, you will have to pay, in addition to the regular monthly installments then due, all attorney's fees incurred.

Sincerely,

Corporate Secretary Certification Documents—Lessee

[Also see Forms I-02e and I-02f.]

Form: c-09
Disk File Name: c-09.rtf

CERTIFIED CORPORATE GUARANTOR's RESOLUTIONS

Form Purpose

Secretary's certificate incorporating corporate resolutions for an equipment lessee's guarantor. This form has been integrated with the short form net finance master lease agreement, Lease Agreement Form l-03.

Executing Parties

Corporate secretary, or assistant secretary, of the equipment lessee's guarantor.

See:

Lease Agreement, Form l-03

Form of Guarantor's Resolutions

Secretary's Certificate

I, ______________________________, the duly elected and qualified Secretary of ______________________________, a ______________ corporation (the "Corporation"), hereby certify that set forth below is a true and complete copy of certain resolutions duly adopted by the Board of Directors of the Corporation, at a meeting duly held on ______________, XXXX, at which a quorum was present and acting throughout, and such resolutions have not been amended or rescinded, are in full force and effect on the date hereof, and are the only resolutions adopted by said Board which relate to the matters referred to therein:

"RESOLVED, that the form, terms, and provisions of a proposed Guaranty (the "Guaranty") to be made and given by this Corporation to ______________ or its assignee or designee (collectively "Lessor") in order to induce Lessor to purchase and lease certain equipment to ______________, a ______________ corporation ("Lessee"), pursuant to the (proposed) Master Agreement to Lease Equipment between Lessee and Lessor (the "Agreement"), and proposed Schedule No. ________ between Lessee and Lessor (the "Schedule"), all as submitted to this meeting and filed with the records of this Corporation, be, and the same hereby are, approved in all respects; and that the ______________ (officer) and ______________ (officer) of this Corporation or any one of them be, and each such officer hereby is, authorized and directed to execute and deliver to Lessor the Guaranty, substantially in the form presented to this meeting, together with such changes, additions, and modifications as may be approved by any such officer, such approval to be conclusively evidenced by an authorized officer's execution of the Guaranty; and

RESOLVED, that the officers of this Corporation be, and each and any such officer hereby is, authorized and directed to execute and deliver all documents and to take or cause to be taken all other action, in the name and on behalf of this Corporation, as may be required by Lessor or otherwise be deemed by such officers or any of them necessary or desirable to fully effectuate the purposes and intent of, and consummate the transactions authorized by, the foregoing resolution and to comply with the terms and provisions of the Guaranty and, if required, the terms and provisions of the Schedule and the Agreement."

IN WITNESS WHEREOF, I have hereunto signed my name this ____ day of ________, XXXX.

____

Secretary

Form: c-10
Disk File Name: c-10.rtf

Certified Corporate Resolutions—Loan/Lease (With Incumbency Certification)

Form Purpose

Certified corporate resolutions, with incumbency certification, authorizing the entering into of an equipment lease/loan agreement.

Executing Parties

Corporate secretary, or assistant secretary, of the equipment lessee/borrower.

Resolutions of Corporate Board

Authority to Procure Loans or Leases
(Certified Copy)

I HEREBY CERTIFY that I am the duly elected and qualified secretary, and the keeper of the records and corporate seal, of (insert name of corporation); that the following is a true and correct copy of resolutions duly adopted at a meeting of its Board of Directors held in accordance with its by-laws at its offices at ______________________________ ______________________________, on the ____ day of ________________, XXXX, and that the following resolutions are now in full force.

Resolutions

"BE IT RESOLVED, that the (insert titles) of this corporation, or their/his/her successors in office, or any (insert number required to sign) of them be and they/he/she hereby are/is authorized for, on behalf of, and in the name of this corporation to:

(a) Negotiate and procure loans or leases from (insert name of lessor or lender) up to an amount not exceeding $ ____________ in the aggregate at any one time outstanding (*Author's Note*: If there is no limit, so indicate);

(b) Give security for any liabilities of this corporation to (insert name of lessor or lender) in connection therewith, including the pledge, sale, or assignment, or the granting of a lien, upon any personal property, tangible or intangible, of this corporation; and

(c) Execute in such form as may be required by (insert name of lessor or lender), all notes or lease agreements and other evidences of such loans or lease agreements, all instruments of pledge, assignment or lien, and that none of the same shall be valid unless signed or endorsed by the above-mentioned officers of this corporation; and

"RESOLVED FURTHER, that this resolution shall continue in force, and (insert name of lessor or lender) may consider the holders of said offices and their signatures, respectively, to be and continue as set forth in the certificate of the secretary of this corporation accompanying a copy of this resolution shown delivered to (insert name of lessor or lender) or in any similar subsequent certificate, until notice to the contrary in writing is duly served on (insert name of lessor or lender).

I HEREBY FURTHER CERTIFY that the following named persons have been duly elected to the offices set opposite their respective names, that they continue to hold these offices at the present time, and that the signatures appearing hereon are the genuine, original signatures of each respectively (insert name of those with signing authority, such as):

______________________________ President

______________________________ Vice President

______________________________ Secretary

______________________________ Asst. Secretary

______________________________ Director

IN WITNESS WHEREOF, I have hereunto affixed my name as secretary and have caused the corporate seal of said corporation to be hereto affixed this ____ day of __________, XXXX.

____ (CORPORATE SEAL)

Secretary

I hereby certify that I am a director of said corporation and that the foregoing is a correct copy of resolutions passed as therein set forth, and that the same are now in full force.

____

Director (*Author's Note:* This should be an individual other than the individual who is the Secretary)

Form: c-11
Disk File Name: c-11.rtf

CERTIFIED CORPORATE RESOLUTIONS—LOAN (WITH INCUMBENCY CERTIFICATION)

Form Purpose

Certified corporate resolutions, with incumbency certification, authorizing the entering into of an equipment loan agreement.

Executing Parties

Corporate secretary, or assistant secretary, of the equipment borrower.

Certified Copy of Resolutions of Board of Directors
of
(Insert name of corporation.)

RESOLVED, that the Board of Directors of the Corporation hereby deems it to be in the best interest of the Corporation to borrow money from ________ ("Creditor") in the principal amount of $ ____ (the "Indebtedness") and issue a note and enter into such other agreements as Creditor may require (collectively the "Agreement"), such Agreement being substantially in the form or forms submitted to the Directors of the Corporation and attached as Annex A to these Resolutions, which form(s) is (are) hereby approved; and it is

FURTHER RESOLVED, that the President, Vice President, Treasurer and/or ________ of this Corporation be and any one of them hereby is authorized, directed, and empowered to execute and deliver the Agreement to Creditor; and it is

FURTHER RESOLVED, that the President, Vice President, Treasurer and/or ________ of this Corporation be and any one of them hereby is authorized, directed, and empowered to execute, issue, and deliver to Creditor, for and on behalf of and in the name of the Corporation, the Corporation's note or notes evidencing the Indebtedness or any part therefor, at such rate(s) of interest and upon such other terms and conditions as are required by Creditor, and any and all other documents, and to do or cause to be done all such further acts and things as shall be deemed necessary, advisable, convenient, or proper in connection with the execution and delivery of any documents or instruments and in connection with or incidental to the carrying of these resolutions into effect, including, but not limited to, the execution, acknowledgment, and delivery of any and all instruments and documents which may reasonably be required by Creditor under or in connection with the Agreement, which acts and things heretofore done to effectuate the purpose or purposes of these resolutions are hereby in all respects ratified, confirmed, and approved as the act or acts of this Corporation; and it is

FURTHER RESOLVED, that the present and future officers of this Corporation are and shall be bound by these resolutions, as too shall this Corporation; and it is

FURTHER RESOLVED, that Creditor is hereby authorized to rely upon these resolutions and the Certificate of the Secretary or Assistant Secretary of this Corporation, and that these resolutions shall be in full force and effect and binding on this Corporation until they shall have been repealed and until written notice of such repeal shall have been delivered to and received by Creditor.

I, (insert name of Secretary), do hereby certify that I am the Secretary of this Corporation; that I am keeper of the corporate records and seal of said Corporation; that the foregoing is a true and correct copy of resolutions duly adopted at a meeting of the Board of Directors of the above-named Corporation duly called and held on ________________ ________________________ (or, where permitted by law, by unanimous written consent of all Directors of the above-named Corporation dated ____________________); that a quorum was present and acted throughout the meeting; that such resolutions have not been rescinded, annulled, revoked, or modified and are still in full force and effect; that neither the said resolutions nor any action taken or to be taken pursuant thereto are or will be in contravention of any provision or provisions of the Certificate of Incorporation or By-Laws of such Corporation or any agreement, indenture, or other instrument to which such Corporation is a party; and that the Certificate of Incorporation of such Corporation, and all amendments thereto, do not contain any provisions requiring any vote or consent of shareholders of such Corporation to authorize any lease, indebtedness, assignment, or any creation of a security interest in all or any part of such Corporation's property, or any interest therein, or to authorize any other action taken or to be taken pursuant to such resolutions. The persons whose names, titles, and signatures appear on the Incumbency and Signature Schedule of the Corporation hereto attached as Annex B are duly elected, qualified, and acting officers of this Corporation and hold on the date hereof the offices set forth opposite their respective names.

IN WITNESS WHEREOF, I have hereunto set my hand and seal of such Corporation on this ____ day of ______________________, XXXX

(CORPORATE SEAL)

By: ______________________________
Secretary

Annex A

(Attach copy of loan agreement.)

Annex B

Incumbency and Signature Schedule
of
(Insert name of corporation.)

Name	*Title*	*Signature*
____________	President	____________
____________	Vice President	____________
____________	Treasurer	____________
____________	Secretary	____________

Form: c-12
Disk File Name: c-12.rtf

CERTIFIED CORPORATE RESOLUTION—LEASE (WITH INCUMBENCY CERTIFICATION—ALTERNATE FORM)

Form Purpose

Certified corporate resolutions, with incumbency certification, authorizing the entering into of an equipment lease agreement—Alternate Form.

Executing Parties

Corporate secretary, or assistant secretary, of the equipment lessee.

Secretary's Certificate
Corporate Resolutions

The undersigned, ______________________, Secretary of (insert name of corporation), a (insert state of incorporation) corporation (the "Corporation"), does hereby certify:

1. That he/she is the duly elected, qualified, and acting Secretary of the Corporation and has the custody of the corporate records, minutes, and corporate seal.

2. That the following named person(s) has/have been properly designated, elected, and assigned to the office in such Corporation as indicated below; that such person(s) hold(s) such office at this time and that the specimen signature appearing beside the name of such officer is his/her true and correct signature.

Name	*Title*	*Specimen Signature*
____________________	____________________	____________________
____________________	____________________	____________________
____________________	____________________	____________________
____________________	____________________	____________________

3. That at a meeting of the Board of Directors of the Corporation, duly called, convened, and held on ____, at which meeting a quorum was present and voted throughout, the following resolution(s) were duly adopted by said Board and said resolution(s) have not been amended, altered, or repealed, and remain in full force and effect on the date hereof:

RESOLVED, that this Corporation be and hereby is authorized to enter into a lease with ______________________________ for a period of ____ months and that (insert below name and/or titles of authorized individuals)

Name	*Title*
______________________________	______________________________
______________________________	______________________________

of this Corporation be authorized for and on behalf of this Corporation as its corporate act and deed to execute and deliver the lease and such ancillary and supporting documents and instruments as may be necessary or desirable and to do any and all things necessary or desirable to execute the full intent and purpose of this resolution.

4. That he/she is one of the duly authorized and proper officers of such Corporation to make certificates in its behalf and that he/she has caused this certificate to be executed

and the seal of the Corporation to be hereunto appended this ______________ day of ________________________, XXXX.

(CORPORATE SEAL)

Dated: ______________________________

____
Secretary

Form: c-13
Disk File Name: c-13.rtf

CERTIFIED CORPORATE RESOLUTIONS—LEASE (WITH CHAPTER, BY-LAWS, INCUMBENCY CERTIFICATION)

Form Purpose

Certified corporate resolutions, with charter, by-laws, and incumbency certification, authorizing the entering into of an equipment lease agreement.

Executing Parties

Corporate secretary, or assistant secretary, of the equipment lessee.

Certificate of Corporate Resolutions Charter, By-Laws, and Incumbency of [Insert name of corporation]

I, ____________________, Secretary of (insert name of corporation) hereby certify that:

1. I am the duly elected and acting Secretary of (insert name of corporation), a corporation duly organized and existing in good standing under the laws of the State of (insert jurisdiction of incorporation) (hereafter, the "Corporation").

2. The resolutions set forth on Exhibit A, attached hereto, were duly adopted by the Board of Directors of the Corporation at a meeting duly called and held on ________, at which meeting a quorum was present and acting throughout, or by the unanimous written consent of all directors, dated ______________.

3. The resolutions set forth on Exhibit A, attached hereto, have not been amended, rescinded, or modified and are in full force and effect on the date hereof.

4. Attached hereto as Exhibit B is a true, correct and complete copy of the Articles of Incorporation of the Corporation and any amendments thereto as in effect on the date hereof.

5. Attached hereto as Exhibit C is a true, correct, and complete copy of the By-Laws of the Corporation and any amendments thereto as in effect on the date hereof.

6. The following persons are the duly elected, qualified, and acting officers of the Corporation in the capacity set forth after their names, are the officers of the Corporation who have been authorized by the Corporation to generally act for and on behalf of the Corporation with respect to the transaction contemplated by these resolutions, and the signatures set forth after their names and titles are their true and genuine signatures.

Title	*Name*	*Signature*
____________________	____________________	____________________
____________________	____________________	____________________
____________________	____________________	____________________
____________________	____________________	____________________

7. The undersigned further certifies that the following individuals are the directors of the Corporation and that each of the following individuals was duly elected as a director by proper corporate action and is eligible to serve and act as a director until the successor director has been duly elected and has qualified as such.

Name	*Signature*
____________________	____________________
____________________	____________________
____________________	____________________
____________________	____________________

WITNESS my signature under seal of the Corporation this ____ day of ____________, XXXX.

(Corporate Seal)

By: ____________________________
Secretary

I, __________________, hereby certify that:

(a) I am the duly elected, qualified, and acting President of the Corporation; and

(b) _________________________ is the duly elected, qualified, and acting Secretary of the Corporation, and

(c) The signature of ______________________ set forth above is his/her true and genuine signature.

WITNESS my signature this ____ day of ____________________________, XXXX.

(CORPORATE SEAL)

By: ____________________________
President

Form: c-14
Disk File Name: c-14.rtf

CERTIFIED CORPORATE RESOLUTION—SHORT FORM

Form Purpose

Certified corporate resolutions, short form, authorizing the entering into of an equipment lease agreement.

Executing Parties

Corporate secretary, or assistant secretary, of the equipment lessee.

Certified Copy of Resolution

This is to certify that a special meeting of the Board of Directors of (insert name of corporation), duly called and held on the ____ day of ______________, XXXX, at the principal office of the corporation in (insert location where meeting held) at which a quorum was present, the following resolution was unanimously and duly adopted, as shown by the minute book of said corporation, to wit:

"WHEREAS, the (insert name and title of individual(s) executing lease agreement) of this corporation has executed or is about to execute an equipment lease agreement with (insert here the name of the leasing company) and approve the terms thereof."

"NOW, THEREFORE, BE IT RESOLVED, that the execution and delivery of said equipment lease agreement for this corporation by its [insert name and title of the individual(s) that will sign or has signed the equipment lease agreement] be and the same are hereby authorized, approved and ratified as the act and deed of this corporation."

IN WITNESS WHEREOF, I have hereunto set my hand and the seal of this corporation this ____ day of ______________________, XXXX.

(CORPORATE SEAL)

____

Corporate Secretary

Form: c-15
Disk File Name: c-15.rtf

CERTIFIED RESOLUTION—CORPORATE—INTEGRATED

Form Purpose

Secretary's certificate incorporating corporate resolutions for an equipment lessee. This form has been integrated with the short form net finance master lease agreement, Lease Agreement Form l-03.

Executing Parties

Corporate secretary, or assistant secretary, of the equipment lessee.

See:

Lease Agreement, Form l-03.

Form of Guarantor's Resolutions

Secretary's Certificate

I, ______________________________, the duly elected and qualified Secretary of ______________________________, a ______________________________ corporation (the "Corporation"), hereby certify that set forth below is a true and complete copy of certain resolutions duly adopted by the Board of Directors of the Corporation, at a meeting duly held on ______________________________, XXXX, at which a quorum was present and acting throughout, and such resolutions have not been amended or rescinded, are in full force and effect on the date hereof, and are the only resolutions adopted by said Board, which relate to the matters referred to therein:

"RESOLVED, that the form, terms, and provisions of the proposed Master Agreement to Lease Equipment to be entered into between this Corporation and ______________, Lessor (the "Agreement"), and proposed Schedule No. ______ between Lessee and Lessor (the "Schedule"), all as submitted to this meeting and filed with the records of this Corporation, be, and the same hereby are, approved in all respects; and that the ______________________ (officer) and ______________________ (officer) of this Corporation or any one of them be, and each such officer hereby is, authorized and directed to execute and deliver to Lessor the Agreement and the Schedule, substantially in the forms presented to this meeting, together with such changes, additions, and modifications as may be approved by any such officer, such approval to be conclusively evidenced by an authorized officer's execution thereof; and

RESOLVED, that the officers of this Corporation be, and each and any such officer hereby is, authorized and directed to execute and deliver all documents and to take or cause to be taken all other action, in the name and on behalf of this Corporation, as may be required by Lessor or otherwise be deemed by such officers or any of them necessary or desirable to fully effectuate the purposes and intent of, and consummate the transactions authorized by, the foregoing resolution and to comply with the terms and provisions of the Schedule and the Agreement."

IN WITNESS WHEREOF, I have hereunto signed my name this ____ day of ________, XXXX.

____

Secretary

Form: c-16
Disk File Name: c-16.rtf

Certification of Incumbency

Form Purpose

A secretary's certificate verifying the incumbency of named corporate officers.

Executing Parties

Corporate secretary, or assistant secretary, of the equipment lessee.

See:

Incumbency Certificate, Form x-02

Incumbency Certificate

Name of Corporation: ______________________________

Date: ______________

I certify that, as of the date written above, the following are the names and signatures of the duly elected officers of this Corporation:

Name: __________ Signature: ______________ Title: __________

Name: __________ Signature: ______________ Title: __________

Name: __________ Signature: ______________ Title: __________

Name: __________ Signature: ______________ Title: __________

____

Secretary

(CORPORATE SEAL)

Corporate Resolutions—Lessee

[See Forms c-09 through c-15 and l-02f.]

Deficiency Agreement Documents

Form: d-01
Disk File Name: d-01.rtf

DEFICIENCY AGREEMENT

Form Purpose

To protect a lessor from any loss incurred in the disposition of equipment. Although this form covers aircraft equipment, it may be easily modified to cover any type of equipment.

Executing Parties

The equipment lessor.
The deficiency loss guarantor.

Deficiency Agreement

This Agreement, made and executed as of the ______ day of ____________________, by and between ____________________, a ____________________ corporation, having its principal place of business at ____ (herein called "Deficiency Guarantor), and ____, a ____ corporation, having its principal place of business at ____ (herein called "Lessor").

WITNESSETH:

WHEREAS, Lessor and Jet Aircraft Corporation, a ____________________ corporation, having a place of business at ____ (herein called "JAC") contemplate executing a Purchase Agreement of even date herewith (herein called the "Purchase Agreement") bearing JAC Document No. ____________, whereby Lessor will agree to purchase and JAC will agree to sell two JAC Model TC-60 jet aircraft (herein called the "Aircraft"), together with installed Pratt & White Model RX–20 jet engines; and

WHEREAS, Lessor and New Airlines, Inc., a ____________________ corporation, having its principal place of business at ____ (hereinafter called "NAI"), as lessee, contemplate executing a lease of even date herewith (hereinafter called the "Lease") whereby Lessor will agree to lease and NAI will agree to hire the Aircraft with such installed engines and in addition two spare Pratt & White Model RX–20 jet engines; and

WHEREAS, Lessor and Deficiency Guarantor desire to enter into this Agreement in order to partially protect Lessor against any loss which may arise out of the disposition of the Equipment (as hereinafter defined) after its delivery to Lessor.

NOW THEREFORE, in order to induce Lessor to enter into the Lease and in consideration of the mutual covenants contained herein, the parties hereto agree as follows:

1. For the purpose of this Agreement, the following terms shall have the following meanings:

1.1 "Equipment" shall mean all equipment subject to the Lease including the Aircraft, installed engines and spare engines, each Aircraft and engine hereinafter separately referred to as an "Item of Equipment."

1.2 "Original Cost" shall mean in respect of each Item of Equipment the purchase price of such Item of Equipment.

1.3 "Receipts" shall mean in respect of each Item of Equipment all amounts received by Lessor from the sale, lease (including the Lease, but excluding all tax benefits arising from ownership of the Equipment) or other disposition, insurance or other contracts relating to the Equipment, but not including any amounts received by Lessor upon the mortgage or other pledge of such Item of Equipment.

1.4 "Expenses" shall mean in respect of each Item of Equipment payments made by Lessor for reasonable attorneys' fees and other expenses incurred and paid by Lessor to third parties arising out of removing, storing and re-leasing, or selling such Equipment and in overhauling, repairing, or modifying such Equipment in condition for such release or sale or other disposition.

1.5 "Unamortized Cost" in respect of each Item of Equipment shall be the sum of (i) the Original Cost of such Equipment, together with interest thereon from the date such Equipment becomes subject to the Lease to the date as of which the computation is made, at the rate of 6% per annum, compounded quarterly, plus (ii) Expenses in respect of such Equipment, together with interest thereon from the date paid to the date as of which the computation is made, at the rate of 6% per annum, compounded quarterly, less (iii) Receipts in respect of such Equipment, together with interest thereon from the date received to the date as of which the computation is made, at the rate of 6% per annum, compounded quarterly.

1.6 "Divestiture" in respect of each Item of Equipment shall mean disposition by Lessor, whether voluntary or involuntary, of all of its right, title, and interest in such Equipment.

2. On the date of Divestiture in respect of each Item of Equipment, provided such Divestiture occurs within fifteen years from the date such Equipment becomes subject to the Lease, Deficiency Guarantor agrees to pay to Lessor the lesser of (i) the Unamortized Cost of such Equipment at the date of Divestiture in respect of such Equipment, or (ii) 20% of the Unamortized Cost of such Equipment at the date of Divestiture in respect of such Equipment excluding from the calculation of Unamortized Cost any Receipts in respect of such Equipment which arise from such Divestiture.

3. Lessor shall have the right to terminate this Agreement at any time prior to Deficiency Guarantor making any payment hereunder. Upon any such termination, neither party shall have any further liability hereunder.

4. This Agreement shall be construed and performance thereof shall be determined according to the laws of the State of ____________________. This Agreement shall not be varied in its terms by oral agreement or representation or otherwise than by an instrument in writing of even or subsequent date hereto, executed by both parties by their duly authorized representatives.

IN WITNESS WHEREOF, the parties have caused this Agreement to be executed as of the date first above written by their officers or agents thereunto duly authorized

______________________________________,

Deficiency Guarantor

By: ______________________________

Title: _____________________________

ATTEST:

By: ______________________________

Title: ______________________________

______________________________, Lessor

By: ______________________________

Title: ______________________________

Equipment Schedules

[See Equipment Schedule, Form I-02a.]

Guaranty Documents

Form: g-01
Disk File Name: g-01.rtf

GUARANTY OF LEASE—INTEGRATED

Form Purpose

A guaranty for the lessee's obligations under an equipment lease. This form is integrated with the short-form net finance master lease agreement, Lease Agreement Form l-03.

Executing Parties

The equipment lease guarantor.

See:

Lease Agreement, Form l-03

Guaranty

GUARANTY, dated as of ____________________, from ____________________, a ____________________ corporation ("Guarantor") to ______________, a ____________________ corporation ("Lessor").

WHEREAS, Guarantor desires that ____________________, a ____________________ corporation ("Lessee"), pursuant to a Master Agreement to Lease Equipment ("Master Agreement"), dated as of ____ XXXX, between Lessor and Lessee, enter into one or more leases of personal property in the form of Schedule No. ____, dated as of the date hereof (collectively the "Lease"); and

WHEREAS, as a condition to entering into the Lease, Lessor requires that all the obligations of Lessee under the Lease be guaranteed by Guarantor;

NOW, THEREFORE, in order to induce Lessor to enter into the Lease, Guarantor hereby agrees as follows:

1. Guarantor does hereby acknowledge that it is fully aware of the terms and conditions of the Lease and does hereby irrevocably and unconditionally guarantee, as primary obligor and not as a surety merely, without offset or deduction, the due and punctual payment when due by Lessee of all Rent (as defined in the Lease) which may from time to time become due and payable in accordance with the terms of the Lease and the performance by Lessee of all of its other obligations under the Lease (the payment of Rent and each other obligation of Lessee guaranteed hereby being hereinafter referred to as an "Obligation" and collectively as the "Obligations"). Guarantor does hereby agree that in the event that Lessee fails to perform any Obligation for any reason, Guarantor will perform or otherwise provide for and bring about promptly when due the performance of each such Obligation. This Guaranty of the Obligations shall constitute a guaranty of payment and performance and not of collection. Guarantor specifically agrees that it shall not be necessary or required, and that Guarantor shall not be entitled to require, that Lessor (a) file suit or proceed to obtain or assert a claim for personal judgment against Lessee or any other person for any Obligation, (b) make any effort at collection or other enforcement of any Obligation from or against Lessee or any other person, (c) foreclose against or seek to realize upon any security now or hereafter existing for any Obligation or upon any balance of any deposit account or credit on the books of Lessor or any other person in favor of Lessee or any other person, (d) exercise or assert any other right or remedy to which Lessor is or may be entitled in connection with any Obligation or any security or other guaranty therefor, or (e) assert or file any claim against the assets of Lessee or any other guarantor of other person liable for any Obligation, or any part thereof, before or as a condition of enforcing the liability of Guarantor under this Guaranty or requiring payment or performance of any Obligation by Guarantor hereunder, or at any time thereafter.

2. Guarantor waives notice of the acceptance of this Guaranty and of the performance or nonperformance by Lessee, presentment to or demand for payment or other perfor-

mance from Lessee or any other person and notice of nonpayment or failure to perform on the part of Lessee. The obligations of Guarantor hereunder shall be absolute and unconditional and shall remain in full force and effect and shall not be subject to any reduction, limitation, impairment, or termination for any reason.

3. No right, power, or remedy herein conferred upon or reserved to Lessor is intended to be exclusive of any other right, power, or remedy or remedies and each and every right, power, and remedy of Lessor pursuant to this Guaranty now or hereafter existing at law or in equity or by statute or otherwise shall, to the extent permitted by law, be cumulative and concurrent and shall be in addition to each other right, power, or remedy pursuant to this Guaranty, and the exercise by Lessor of any one or more of such rights, powers, or remedies shall not preclude the simultaneous or later exercise by Lessor of any or all such other rights, powers, or remedies.

4. No failure or delay by Lessor to insist upon the strict performance of any term, condition, covenant, or agreement of this Guaranty or to exercise any right, power, or remedy hereunder or consequent upon a breach hereof shall constitute a waiver of any such term, condition, covenant, agreement, right, power, or remedy or of any such breach, or preclude Lessor from exercising any such right, power, or remedy at any later time or times.

5. In case any one or more of the provisions contained in this Guaranty should be invalid, illegal, or unenforceable in any respect, the validity, legality, and enforceability of the remaining provisions contained herein shall not in any way be affected or impaired thereby.

6. This Guaranty (a) constitutes the entire agreement, and supersedes all prior agreements and understandings, both written and oral, among Lessee, Lessor, and Guarantor with respect to the subject matter hereof, (b) may be executed in several counterparts, each of which shall be deemed an original, but all of which together shall constitute one and the same instrument, and (c) shall be binding upon Guarantor and its successors and assigns and shall inure to the benefit of, and shall be enforceable by, Lessor and its successors and assigns.

7. Unless otherwise specifically provided herein, all notices, instructions, requests, and other communications required or permitted hereunder shall be in writing and shall become effective when received or if mailed when deposited in the United States mail, postage prepaid, registered or certified mail, return receipt requested. Notices shall be directed to Lessor at its address set forth in the Lease, and to Guarantor at its address set forth below, or at such other address as such party may from time to time furnish to the other by notice similarly given.

8. This Guaranty shall be governed by, and construed in accordance with, the laws of the State of ____________________.

IN WITNESS WHEREOF, Guarantor has caused this Guaranty to be duly executed as of the date first hereinabove set forth.

______________________________, Guarantor

By: ____________________________

Title: ___________________________

Address ___________________________

____

____

Telephone: _________________________

Form: g-02
Disk File Name: g-02.rtf

GUARANTY OF LEASE—CORPORATE

Form Purpose

Corporate guaranty for lease obligations–short form.

Executing Parties

The equipment lease guarantor.

Corporate Guaranty

Lessee: ______________________________

Lessor: ______________________________

Date: ______________________________

Lease No: ______________________________

In consideration of the making of the above lease by Lessor, with Lessee, at the request of the undersigned and in reliance on this guaranty, the undersigned (if more than one, then jointly and severally) as a direct and primary obligation, absolutely and unconditionally, guaranties to Lessor and any assignee of Lessor (either of whom are hereinafter called "Holder"), the prompt payment of all rent to be paid and the performance of all terms, conditions, covenants, and agreements of the Lease, irrespective of any invalidity or unenforceability thereof or the security thereof. The undersigned promises to pay all of the Holder's expenses, including reasonable attorney fees incurred by or in enforcing all obligations under the Lease or incurred by the Holder in connection with enforcing this guaranty. The undersigned waives notice of acceptance hereof, presentment, demand, protest, notice of protest, or of any defaults, and consents that Holder may without affecting the obligation hereunder, grant Lessee any extension or indulgence under the Lease, and may proceed directly against the undersigned without first proceeding against Lessee or liquidation or otherwise disposing of any security afforded Holder under the Lease.

This guaranty shall be binding upon the respective heirs, executors, administrators, successors and assigns of the undersigned. This guaranty shall be construed according to the laws of the State of the organization of Lessor.

Witness our hands and seals this ____ day of __________________, XXXX.

______________________________, Guarantor

(CORPORATE SEAL)

By: ______________________________

Title: ______________________________

Form: g-03
Disk File Name: g-03.rtf

Guaranty of Lease—Individual

Form Purpose

Individual guaranty for lease obligations–short form.

Executing Parties

The equipment lease guarantor.

Personal Guaranty

Lessee: ______________________________

Lessor: ______________________________

Lease No.: ___________________________

Lessor: ______________________________

Date: ________________________________

In consideration of the making of the above Lease by Lessor with Lessee, the undersigned (if more than one, then "jointly and severally"), as a direct and primary obligation, absolutely and unconditionally guaranties to Lessor and any assignee of Lessor (either of whom are called "Holder"), the prompt payment of all Lease rent to be paid and the performance of all terms, conditions, covenants, and agreements of the Lease, irrespective of any invalidity or unenforceability thereof or security thereof. The undersigned promises to pay all of the Holder's expenses, including reasonable attorney fees, incurred by Holder in enforcing all obligations under the Lease or incurred by Holder in connection with enforcing this Guaranty. The undersigned waives notice of protest or of any defaults, and consents that Holder may, without affecting the obligation hereunder, grant Lessee any extension or indulgence under the Lease, and may proceed directly against the undersigned without first proceeding against Lessee or liquidation or otherwise disposing of any security afforded Holder under the Lease.

This Guaranty shall be binding upon the respective heirs, executors, administrators, successors and assigns of the undersigned. This Guaranty shall be construed according to the laws of the State of ________________.

Witness my/our hand and seal this ____ day of ________________, XXXX.

(Insert name of individual),
Individual Guarantor

____

(signature without title)

Name: ______________________________

Home Address: _______________________

City: ________ State: ________ Zip: ________

Home Telephone No.: __________________

(Insert name of individual),
Individual Guarantor

____

(signature without title)

Name: ______________________________

Home Address: _______________________

City: ________ State: ________ Zip: ________

Home Telephone No.: __________________

Form: g-04
Disk File Name: g-04.rtf

GUARANTY—GENERAL OBLIGATION

Form Purpose

General credit extension guaranty. This form is set up for use by an individual or corporate guarantor.

Executing Parties

The credit guarantor.

Guaranty

WHEREAS, (insert name of company asking for a credit arrangement) (hereinafter referred to as "Obligor") desires to transact business and to make credit arrangements with (insert name of company for whose benefit this Guaranty is provided), with a principal place of business at ________________________________ (hereinafter referred to as "Creditor"); and

WHEREAS, Creditor is unwilling to transact business with Obligor unless it receives the guaranty of the undersigned (hereinafter referred to as "Guarantor") covering the indebtedness of the Obligor to Creditor.

NOW, THEREFORE, in consideration of the premises and of other good and valuable consideration and in order to induce Creditor to transact business with Obligor by providing credit arrangements for the Obligor, Guarantor hereby guarantees, absolutely and unconditionally to Creditor the payment of all indebtedness of Obligor to Creditor of whatever nature, whether now existing or hereafter incurred, whether created directly or acquired by Creditor by assignment or otherwise, whether matured or unmatured and whether absolute or contingent.

The term "credit" is used throughout this guaranty in its broadest and most comprehensive sense and shall include, without limiting the generality of the foregoing (a) all sums of money which Creditor heretofore has advanced or loaned or hereafter advances or lends to Obligor, whether such sums have been or hereafter are drawn from or paid out by Creditor by or on promissory notes, leases or other evidences of indebtedness, made, endorsed, or guaranteed by Obligor, either alone or with others; (b) all other obligations of Obligor, alone or with others, absolute or contingent, joint or joint and several, arising from any other financial accommodation given or continued or from any guaranty, acceptance, or paper discounted, purchased, or held by Creditor or taken as security for any loan or advance of any sort whatever or arising in any other manner; (c) any indebtedness of Obligor to Creditor on account of collections or paper received for collection and all expenses, including attorney fees and costs of collection, incurred by Creditor in connection therewith, and (d) interest, if any, on the foregoing items.

The word "indebtedness" is used throughout this guaranty in its most comprehensive sense and includes any and all advances, leases, debts, obligations, and liabilities of Obligor heretofore, now, or hereafter made, incurred, or created, whether voluntary or involuntary and however arising, whether due or not due, absolute or contingent, liquidated or unliquidated, determined or undetermined, and whether Obligor may be liable individually or jointly with others, or whether recovery on such indebtedness may be or hereafter become otherwise unenforceable.

Guarantor agrees that, with or without notice or demand, Guarantor will reimburse Creditor, to the extent that such reimbursement is not made by Obligor, for all expense (including attorney fees) incurred by Creditor in collection from Obligor of any credit hereby guaranteed or in the enforcement of this guaranty.

Guarantor further agrees that Creditor may renew or extend any indebtedness of Obligor, or accept partial payment thereon, or settle, release, compound, or compromise any of the same or collect on or otherwise liquidate any claims held by Creditor in such manner as Creditor may deem advisable, without impairing the liability of Guarantor. Extensions of the times of payment, renewal of indebtedness, extensions of the times of performance of agreements, and any other compromises, adjustments, or indulgences may be granted to Obligor without notice to Guarantor. Creditor may also release, substitute, or modify any collateral securing any of the obligations of Obligor without the consent of Guarantor.

In the event of any default by Obligor on any indebtedness hereby guaranteed, Guarantor agrees, without Creditor being first required to liquidate any lien or any other form of security, instrument or note held by Creditor, to pay on demand (either oral or written) any and all sums due to Creditor from Obligor. This is a guaranty of payment and not of collection and Guarantor further waives any right to require that any action be brought against Obligor or any other person or to require that resort be first had to any security.

In any right of action which shall accrue to Creditor by reason of indebtedness of Obligor, Creditor at its election may proceed (1) against Guarantor together with the Obligor, (2) against Guarantor and the Obligor individually, or (3) against Guarantor only without having commenced any action against or having obtained any judgment against Obligor. If any claim against Guarantor is referred to an attorney for collection, then Guarantor shall pay such attorney's reasonable fee as determined by state law.

Guarantor hereby waives (a) notice of acceptance of this guaranty and of creations of Obligor to Creditor; (b) presentment and demand for payment of any indebtedness of Obligor; (c) protest, notice of protest, and notice of dishonor or default to Guarantor or to any other party with respect to any of the indebtedness of Obligor; (d) all other notices to which Guarantor might otherwise be entitled; (e) any demand for payment under this guaranty; (f) any defense arising by reason of any disability or other defense of Obligor or by reason of the cessation from any cause whatsoever of the liability of the Obligor; (g) any rights to extension, composition or otherwise under bankruptcy law, or under any state or other federal statute; (h) any rights which the Obligor may assert against Creditor under the Uniform Commercial Code of any state or the laws of the State of ________________ regarding disposition of any collateral, including but not limited to the "commercial reasonableness" of such disposition; and (i) all exemptions and any rights under any homestead laws.

Until all credit and indebtedness hereby guaranteed have been paid in full, Guarantor shall have no right of subrogation and waives any benefit of and any right to participate in the collateral, if any there be.

Any indebtedness of Obligor now or hereafter held by Guarantor is hereby subordinated to the indebtedness of Obligor to Creditor; and such indebtedness of Obligor to Guarantor if Creditor so requests and upon default by Obligor to Creditor shall be collected, enforced, and received by Guarantor as trustee for Creditor and shall be paid over to Creditor on account of the indebtedness of Obligor to Creditor but without impairing or affecting in any manner the liability of Guarantor under the other provisions of this guaranty.

Guarantor declares to and covenants with Creditor, its successors, endorsees, and assigns, that Guarantor now has no defense whatever to any action, suit, or proceeding at law, or otherwise, that may be instituted on this guaranty.

Each reference herein to Creditor shall be deemed to include its successors and assigns, in whose favor the provisions of this guaranty shall also run. The term "Guarantor", as used in this guaranty, shall, if this instrument is signed by more than one party, mean the "Guarantor and each of them" and each undertaking herein contained shall be their joint and several undertaking, provided, however, that in the next succeeding paragraph hereof, the term "Guarantor" shall mean the "Guarantor or any of them". If any party hereto shall be a partnership, the agreements and obligations on the part of Guarantor herein contained shall remain in force and applicable notwithstanding any changes in the individuals composing the partnership and the term "Guarantor" shall include any altered or successive partnerships but the predecessor partnerships and their partners shall not thereby be released from any obligation or liability. The release of any party to this guaranty shall not release any of the others from the obligation of this guaranty.

No exercise, delay in exercising, or omission to exercise any of the rights, powers, remedies, and discretions of Creditor shall be deemed a waiver thereof, and every such right, power, remedy, and discretion may be exercised repeatedly. No notice to or demand on Guarantor shall be deemed to be a waiver of the obligation of Guarantor or of the right of Creditor to take further action without notice or demand as provided herein; nor in any event shall any modification or waiver of the provisions of this guaranty be effective unless in writing nor shall any such waiver be applicable except in the specific instance of which given. Failure of Creditor to insist upon strict performance or observance of any of the terms, provisions, and covenants of any indebtedness of Obligor or to exercise any right therein contained shall not be construed as a waiver or relinquishment for the future of any term, provision, or covenant thereof, but as to Guarantor, the same shall continue to remain in full force and effect. Receipt by Creditor of payment or payments with knowledge of the breach of any provision or any indebtedness of Obligor shall not, as to Guarantor, be deemed a waiver of such breach. All rights, powers, and remedies of Creditor hereunder and under any other agreement now or at any time hereafter in force between Creditor and Guarantor shall be cumulative and not alternative and shall be in addition to all rights, powers, and remedies given to Creditor by law.

This guaranty may be terminated by Guarantor serving written notice upon Creditor, but as to all indebtedness purchased or acquired and all obligations of the Obligor, contingent or absolute, incurred up to the time of the receipt of such notice or such subsequent effective date as may be stated therein. This guaranty shall be continuing and unconditional until the same are fully paid, performed, or discharged. This guaranty shall not be discharged or affected by the death of any party, but shall bind the respective heirs, executors, administrators, successors, and assigns of each party.

Dated this ____ day of ____________, XXXX

________________________________, Guarantor

By: ________________________________

Address: ____________________________

____

____

WITNESS:

By: ______________________________

______________________________, Guarantor

(CORPORATE SEAL)

By: ______________________________

Address: ______________________________

____

____

WITNESS:

By: ______________________________

Acknowledgments

STATE OF ______________________________)

) ss:

COUNTY OF ____________________________)

On the ____ day of ______________________________ XXXX, before me personally came ____ to me known to be the individual described in and who executed the foregoing instrument, and acknowledged that he/she executed the same.

My Commission Expires: _________________ ______________________________ Notary Public

STATE OF ______________________________)

) ss:

COUNTY OF ____________________________)

On the ____ day of ______________________________ XXXX, before me personally came ____ to me known, who, being by me duly sworn, did depose and say that he resides at ______________ ____, that he is the ______________________________ of ______________________________, the corporation described in and which executed the foregoing instrument; that he knows the seal of said corporation; that the seal affixed to said instrument is such corporate seal; that it was so affixed by order of the board of directors of said corporation, and that he signed his name thereto by like order.

My Commission Expires: _________________ ______________________________ Notary Public

Form: g-05
Disk File Name: g-05.rtf

GUARANTY—VENDOR

Form Purpose

An equipment vendor continuing guaranty to a leasing company purchasing, from time to time, equipment from the vendor that the vendor has put on leases with various customer/lessees. The guaranty provides the leasing company with recourse against the vendor in the event that any of these lessees default in the performance of their lease obligations. This form is set up for use by an individual or corporate guarantor.

Executing Parties

The equipment vendor/guarantor.

Continuing Guaranty

This Guaranty Agreement, dated this ____ day of ______________________, XXXX, provided by (insert name of equipment vendor), a (insert jurisdiction of incorporation, if applicable) with a principal place of business at (insert address) to (insert name of beneficiary of this Guaranty Agreement).

1. In order to induce (insert name of leasing company purchasing equipment and leases from equipment vendor) (the "Creditor") to purchase leases and equipment subject to such leases (the "Equipment") from the undersigned and which the undersigned has entered into with various lessees (each a "Lessee" and collectively the "Lessees"), which shall be fair and sufficient consideration for the execution of this Guaranty, the undersigned, jointly and severally if more than one, hereby unconditionally, directly, and absolutely guarantees to Creditor, its successors and assigns, all present and future obligations (collectively the "Obligations") of Lessees to Creditor under any and all leases of the Equipment, as the same may from time to time be amended, modified, renewed, or replaced (each a "Lease" and collectively the "Leases"), including, without limitation (1) punctual payment (whether upon demand, at stated maturity, upon acceleration, or otherwise) of all sums of money, including renewals, extensions, and refinancings, matured and unmatured, now and hereafter owed to Creditor by each Lessee under each Lease, including, without limitation, rental installments, interest, fees, finance charges, late charges, attorney's fees, and costs and expenses of collection, irrespective of the manner in which such obligations shall arise, whether directly or indirectly, voluntarily or by operation of law; and (2) performance by each Lessee of all present and future covenants, conditions, agreements, and undertakings under each Lease. The undersigned hereby agrees to save harmless and indemnify Creditor from and against all obligations, demands, loss, or liability, by whomever asserted, suffered, incurred, or paid, arising out of or with respect to the Obligations.

2. This shall be a continuing guaranty, terminable only as hereinafter provided. No termination hereof shall be effected by the death, or dissolution, as the case may be, of any or all of the undersigned. No termination shall be effective except by notice sent by the undersigned by certified or registered mail naming a termination date effective not less than 90 days after the receipt of such notice by Creditor; or effective as to any of the undersigned who has not given such notice; or affect the guaranty of the undersigned with respect to the Obligations of any Lessee under any Lease executed prior to the effective date of termination.

3. The undersigned hereby waive(s) notice of acceptance of this Guaranty with regard to each of the Obligations that may now exist or may hereafter come into existence. The undersigned hereby waive(s) presentment, demand, diligence in the enforcement or collection of any of the Obligations, protest, and all notices of any kind whatsoever, including, without limitation, notice of default in the payment of any of the Obligations.

4. The undersigned hereby waive(s) notice of each and every one of the following acts, events, and/or conditions and agree(s) that the creation or existence of any such act, event, or condition or the performance thereof by Creditor (in any number of instances) shall in no way release or discharge any of the undersigned from liability hereunder, in whole or in part (a) the renewal, extension, modification, refinancing, or granting of any indulgence of any nature whatsoever with respect to any or all of the Obligations; (b) the addition of or partial or entire release of any guarantor, maker, surety, endorser, indemnitor, or other party or parties primarily or secondarily liable for the payment and/or performance of any of the Obligations; (c) the assumption of any of the

Obligations by any other person, whether by assignment, sale, sublease, conveyance, or otherwise; (d) the institution of any suit or the obtaining of any judgment against any Lessee, any guarantor, maker, surety, endorser, indemnitor, or other party primarily or secondarily liable for the payment and/or performance of any of the Obligations; (e) the sale, exchange, pledge, release, disposition, surrender, loss, destruction, damage to, or impairment of any collateral now or hereafter granted or received to secure any of the Obligations; (f) the obtention, perfection, continuation, amendment, release, waiver, or modification of any security interest or lien with respect to any of the Obligations or the settlement, subordination, compromise, or discharge of same; or (g) any other event, circumstance, or condition which might otherwise constitute a legal or equitable discharge of a surety or a guarantor. It is expressly agreed that Creditor shall have no obligation to obtain, perfect, or continue in effect any security interest or lien with respect to any of the Obligations and that the obligations of the undersigned hereunder shall in no way be diminished, impaired, affected, or released by Creditor's commission of or omission to do any of the above-described acts or by the invalidity, unenforceability, loss or change in priority of any security interest or lien with respect to any of the Obligations.

5. Any money or other property that Creditor may receive in respect of or as security for any of the Obligations of any Lessee from any source whatsoever may be applied to any of the Obligations of such Lessee, whether secured or unsecured, as Creditor shall determine in its sole discretion. Any property that Creditor may receive from a guarantor of any of the Obligations or with respect to which a guarantor of any of the Obligations has granted or shall grant to Creditor a lien or security interest shall secure the payment of the Obligations. In the event that Creditor shall be granted a security interest in or lien upon any real or personal property in respect of or as security for any of the Obligations, the same shall be for the sole and exclusive benefit of Creditor, and not for the benefit, whether direct or indirect, by subrogation or otherwise, of any of the undersigned, unless Creditor shall expressly and in writing grant subrogation or other rights to the undersigned. The undersigned shall not be subrogated to the rights of Creditor against any Lessee or against any property of any Lessee securing any of the Obligations, either in whole or in part, until such time as the Obligations of such Lessee have been paid in full and there is no amount owing to Creditor hereunder with respect to any of the Obligations.

6. If any of the Obligations of any Lessee are not duly paid or performed, as the case may be, all of the Obligations of such Lessee shall at Creditor's option be deemed to be forthwith due and payable for the purposes of this Guaranty and the liability of the undersigned hereunder. If the undersigned shall default in the payment or performance of any of its obligations to Creditor hereunder, all of the Obligations shall at Creditor's option be deemed to be forthwith due and payable for the purposes of this Guaranty and the liability of the undersigned hereunder.

7. The undersigned agree(s) that any suit, action, or proceeding instituted against it with respect to any of the Obligations of this Guaranty may be brought in any court of competent jurisdiction located in the State of (insert appropriate state). The undersigned, by the execution and delivery of this Guaranty, irrevocably waive(s) any objection and any right of immunity on the ground of venue, the convenience of the forum or the jurisdiction of such courts or from the execution of judgments resulting therefrom. The undersigned hereby irrevocably accept(s) and submit(s) to the jurisdiction of the aforesaid courts in any suit, action, or proceeding. The undersigned agree(s) to reimburse Creditor for all attorney fees and other expenses (including stamp taxes and other duties, taxes, filing and other fees and charges) paid or incurred in enforcing this Guaranty. The undersigned further agree(s) that any claim which any of the undersigned may now or

hereafter have against Creditor, any Lessee, or any other person for any reason whatsoever shall not affect the obligations of any of the undersigned under this Guaranty and shall not be used or asserted against Creditor as a defense to the performance of said obligations or as a setoff, counterclaim, or deduction against any sums due hereunder. The performance and construction of this Guaranty shall be governed by the laws of the State of ________________. The use of the singular in this Guaranty shall also include the plural, and vice versa, and the use of any gender or the neuter shall also refer to the other gender or the neuter.

8. In the event that Creditor shall suffer, pay, or be responsible for the payment of any losses, costs, court costs, or attorney fees with respect to any of the Obligations and/or the collection thereof, the undersigned agree(s) to pay and do(es) hereby guarantee payment to Creditor of such amounts in full. Such expenses shall include all attorney fees incurred by Creditor before the filing of any action to enforce this Guaranty, and, in the event of such an action, shall include all attorney fees incurred by Creditor in connection with such action. No delay in making any demand hereunder shall prejudice the right of Creditor to enforce this Guaranty.

9. All of Creditor's rights hereunder shall inure to the benefit of Creditor, its successors and assigns, and all obligations, covenants, and agreements of the undersigned shall be binding upon the undersigned, jointly and severally if more than one, and their heirs, executors, successors and assigns. Creditor may, without notice to, or consent of, any of the undersigned, sell, assign, or transfer to any person or persons all or any part of the Obligations, and each such person or persons shall have the right to enforce this Guaranty as fully as Creditor, provided that Creditor shall continue to have the unimpaired right to enforce this Guaranty as to so much of the Obligations that it has not sold, assigned, or transferred.

10. The liability of the undersigned shall not be conditioned upon or subject to a defense of reliance upon the guaranty of any other person. In any action to enforce any of the Obligations of this Guaranty, Creditor may, at its option, join the appropriate Lessee, any of the undersigned and any other guarantors in one action, or bring successive actions against any of them in such order as Creditor may elect, in its sole discretion.

11. No waiver by Creditor of any right or remedy shall be effective unless in writing nor, in any event, shall the same operate as a waiver of any other or future right or remedy that may accrue to Creditor. If any part of this Guaranty shall be adjudged invalid, then such partial invalidity shall not cause the remainder of this Guaranty to be or to become invalid, and if a provision hereof is held invalid in one or more of its applications, said provision shall remain in effect in valid applications that are severable from the invalid application or applications. Notwithstanding any partial or entire payment of all or any of the Obligations, this Guaranty shall remain in effect or be reinstated, as the case may be, as though such payment had never been made, with respect to any such payment which is rescinded or recovered from or restored or returned by Creditor under authority of any law, rule, regulation, order of court or governmental agency, whether arising out of any proceedings under the United States bankruptcy laws or otherwise.

12. The undersigned hereby authorize(s) any attorney at law to appear for (it, him/her) them (or any of them) before any court having jurisdiction and, after one or more declarations filed, confess judgment against (it, him/her) them (or any of them) as of any time after any of the Obligations are due (whether by demand, stated maturity, acceleration, or otherwise) for the unpaid balance of the Obligations declared due, together with interest, court costs, and reasonable attorney's fees.

13. The undersigned agree(s) to furnish to Creditor from time to time, upon Creditor's request, current written financial statements of the undersigned.

14. Any notice or other communication in connection with this Guaranty, if by registered or certified mail, shall be deemed to have been given when received by the party to whom directed, or, if by mail but not registered or certified, when deposited in the mail, postage prepaid, provided that any such notice or communication shall be addressed to a party as provided below (or as otherwise specified in writing by such party) (a) if to the undersigned, at the address(es) specified below and; (b) if to Creditor, at:

(insert address)

IN WITNESS WHEREOF, (each of) the undersigned, intending to be legally bound hereby and intending this to be a sealed instrument, has caused this Guaranty to be duly executed under seal the day and year first above written.

Individual Guarantors (*Author's Note:* Individual guarantors must sign without titles. Also, use street addresses, not P.O. Boxes)

____________________	____________________
Individually	Home Address
____________________	____________________
Individually	Home Address

Corporate Guarantors (*Author's Note:* Use street addresses, not P.O. Boxes)

(Insert name and address of corporation)

(CORPORATE SEAL)

By: ____________________ ____________________

Attest Secretary

Name: ____________________

Title: ____________________

(CORPORATE SEAL)

By: ____________________ ____________________

Attest Secretary

Name: ____________________

Title: ____________________

Incumbency Documents

[See Forms c-16 and I-02e.]

Insurance Documents

Form: i-01
Disk File Name: i-01.rtf

INSURANCE REQUEST LETTER TO LESSEE (FROM LESSOR)

Form Purpose

A leasing company form notification for advising lessees of lease insurance requirements.

Executing Parties

The equipment lessor.

[Letterhead of Leasing Company]

To: ______________________________, Lessee

Lease No.: ______________________________

Lease Agreement Date: __________________

Equipment Description: _________________

Important

In accordance with the terms of the above-referenced lease you have with our leasing company, the equipment must be insured. You are required to carry adequate fire, theft, and extended physical damage insurance coverage on the equipment in the amount of $ ________________, as well as third-party liability insurance coverage in the amount of $ _______________. Your insurance must also conform to any additional requirements set forth in Section _____________ of the above-referenced lease.

Please furnish us with a loss payable endorsement, originated by your agent, showing the above-named lessor as loss payee and additional insured. Be sure to include your customer lease number so that insurance can be applied to the proper account. Normally, your agent will be able to handle this request without any additional charge to your firm.

In the event you have any questions, please feel free to notify this office. Your attention to this matter will be greatly appreciated.

(Insert name of leasing company)

By: ______________________________

Title: ______________________________

Form: i-02
Disk File Name: i-02.rtf

Insurance Request to Insurance Company (From Lessee)

Form Purpose

An equipment lessee form for requesting that its insurance company provide a certificate of insurance verifying insurance coverage on the specified leased equipment.

Executing Parties

The equipment lessee.

Request for Certificate of Insurance

Lessor: ______________________ Telephone No.: (____) __________

Street Address: ______________________

City: ______________ State: ______________ Zip: __________

Lease No. ______________________

Insurance Agent: ______________________ Telephone No.: (____) __________

Street Address: ______________________

City: ______________ State: ______________ Zip: __________

Insurance Company: ______________________

Policy No.: ______________________

Gentlemen:

We wish to advise you that we have leased equipment from the above-referenced Lessor, and the conditions of the Lease require that we, as Lessee, carry insurance indemnifying Lessor against any loss, damage, or destruction of the equipment which is valued at $ ______________, as well as indemnifying Lessor from and against any claims or actions filed against Lessor as a result of personal injury, death, property damage, or commercial losses in any way claimed to have been sustained by or from the equipment.

A certificate certifying the following limits of liability are requested: $ ______________ Bodily Injury Liability, $ ______________ Property Damage Liability, and Physical Damage "All Risk" coverage.

The Lessor must be named as additional insured and loss payee under a Certificate of Insurance so indicating. The insurance policy must provide that it may not be canceled for a period of thirty (30) days following written notice by the insurance carrier to the Lessor, and this must be so acknowledged in the Certificate of Insurance.

(Insert name of Equipment Lessee)

By: ______________________

Title: ______________________

Date: ______________________

Form: i-03
Disk File Name: i-03.rtf

INSURANCE REQUIREMENT NOTICE—INTEGRATED (FROM LESSOR)

Form Purpose

Lessee insurance requirement letter. This form has been integrated with the short-form net finance master lease agreement, Lease Agreement Form l-03.

Executing Parties

The equipment lessor.
The equipment lessee.

See:

Lease Agreement, Form l-03

Lessee: ______________________________

Address: ______________________________

____

____

Attn.: ______________________________

Re: Insurance Requirements

Gentlemen:

Reference is made to the proposed lease of equipment ("Lease") between ____________ ____ ("Lessor") and you ("Lessee").

We have set forth below the insurance requirements of Lessor to be complied with by you, as Lessee, in accordance with the Lease. The terms used in this letter shall have the same meanings as in the Lease, unless otherwise defined herein.

You, as Lessee, will as to all Units, at all times commencing when any risk shall pass to Lessor until the return of such Units to Lessor in accordance with the terms of the Lease, at your expense, cause to be carried and maintained with insurers of recognized responsibility acceptable to Lessor (a) property and casualty insurance in respect of such Units and (b) public liability insurance against claims for personal injury, death, or property damage resulting from such Units, including without limitation the ownership, possession, maintenance, use, and operation of such Units, in both cases in at least such amounts and against such risks as are customarily insured against by companies of recognized standing engaged in a business similar to that of Lessee with respect to similar equipment; provided, however, that in no event shall (i) the amount of such property and casualty insurance be less than $ ____________ and (ii) the amount of such public liability insurance be less than $ __________________ in respect of any one person or $ __________ in respect of any one occurrence; and the benefits thereof shall be payable to Lessor and Lessee, as their respective interests may appear. Each such policy of insurance shall (i) require 30 days prior written notice to Lessor of a material change, cancellation, or nonrenewal, (ii) name Lessor as an additional named insured and loss payee, as its interest may appear, (iii) provide that all provisions of such policy, except the limits of liability, will operate in the same manner as if there were a separate policy governing such additional insured, (iv) include a waiver by the insurer of all claims for premiums, commissions, or similar costs or charges against Lessor, (v) provide that, in respect of the interests of Lessor, such insurance will not be invalidated by reason of any breach of representation or warranty made by Lessee to the insurer in connection with obtaining such policy of insurance or maintaining the same in full force and effect, and (vi) be primary without rights of contribution from any other insurance which Lessor or Lessee may have. Lessee shall deliver to Lessor a certificate of insurance or other evidence of insurance satisfactory to Lessor no later than the execution of the Lease.

Please acknowledge your receipt of the insurance requirements relating to the Units by executing and returning to the undersigned the extra copy of this letter enclosed.

______________________________, Lessor

By: ______________________________

Title: ______________________________

Received this ______ day of __________, XXXX

______________________________, Lessee

By: ______________________________

Title: ______________________________

Landlord Waiver Documents

Form: I-01
Disk File Name: I-01.rtf

LANDLORD WAIVER

Form Purpose

A real estate landlord's waiver to ensure that the landlord of the property on which leased equipment will be located will not exercise any claim against the equipment for obligations due from the lessee to the landlord.

Executing Parties

The real estate landlord.

Landlord's Waiver

The undersigned ("Landlord") is the owner and landlord of the premises at ____, which Landlord has leased to (insert name of equipment lessee) ("Tenant"). In order to induce (insert name of leasing company) ("Lessor") to extend credit to Tenant, and intending to be legally bound hereby, agrees as follows:

1. The following equipment ("Collateral") in which Lessor is, or will be, the legal owner, will remain personal property and will not be deemed to be fixtures:

2. Lessor may enter the leased premises to remove the Collateral, or any part thereof, at any time in the exercise of its rights as the owner of the Collateral.
3. Landlord waives any right of distraint or execution against the Collateral or any claim to it so long as Lessor owns it.
4. Landlord agrees that it will notify:

A. Lessor of the termination of the lease between Landlord and Tenant for any reason, and
B. Any purchaser of the leased premises and any subsequent mortgagee or other encumbrance holder of the lease's premises of the existence of this waiver.

5. This waiver shall be binding upon the successors and transferees of Landlord, and shall inure to the benefit of the successors and assigns of Lessor.

Dated: ______________________________

(Insert name of landlord), Landlord

By: ______________________________

Title: ______________________________

Lease Agreement Documents

[Also see Forms a-13, c-09, c-10, g-01, i-02, o-11 through o-16, and o-19.]

Form: l-02
Disk File Name: l-02.rtf

LEASE AGREEMENT—MASTER (HIGH TECH/GENERAL EQUIPMENT)

Form Purpose

Form of master net finance equipment lease, containing particular business and legal needs in large ticket lease transactions of computer equipment. This form is part of an integrated package, including all key closing documents. Although it contains certain specialized language for leasing computer equipment, it can be readily modified to cover any type of equipment. The master format allows future equipment to be easily added by means of a schedule.

Executing Parties

The equipment lessor.
The equipment lessee.

See:

Equipment Schedule, Form l-02a
Certificate of Acceptance, Form l-02b
Casualty Value Schedule, Form l-02c
Termination Value Schedule, Form l-02d
Incumbency Certificate, Form l-02e
Certified Resolutions, Form l-02f
Opinion of Counsel, Form l-02g
Prohibited Lender Assignees, Form l-02h

Master Lease of Computer Equipment

dated as of ________________, XXXX

between

[ ]

Lessor

and

[ ]

Lessee

Master Lease of Computer Equipment

Table of Contents

Master Lease of Computer Equipment, dated as of ______________________, XXXX, between ______________________, a ______________________ corporation, with a principal place of business located at ______________________ (the "Lessor", such term to include, to the extent permitted hereunder, its successors and assigns), and ______________________, a ______________________ corporation, with a principal place of business located at ______________________ (the "Lessee", such term to include, to the extent permitted hereunder, its successors and assigns).

Section 1. Definitions

The following terms shall have the respective meanings set forth below for all purposes of this Lease.

1.1 "Acceptance Date" as to each Item of Equipment shall mean the date on which Lessee determines that such Item of Equipment is acceptable for lease pursuant to the terms and conditions of this Lease, as specified by Lessee in the applicable Certificate of Acceptance.

1.2 "Appraiser" shall mean a qualified independent computer equipment appraiser selected in accordance with the provisions of Section 14 of this Lease.

1.3 "Basic Lease Commencement Date" as to each Unit shall mean the date on which the Primary Term shall begin, as specified in the applicable Equipment Schedule.

1.4 "Basic Lease Rate Factor" as to each Unit shall mean the percentage rental set forth in the applicable Equipment Schedule.

1.5 "Basic Rent" as to each Unit shall mean the rent due and payable on each Rent Date during the Primary Term, as specified in the applicable Equipment Schedule.

1.6 "Business Day" shall mean a calendar day, excluding Saturdays, Sundays, and all days on which banking institutions in [insert jurisdiction(s) of Lessee's and/or Lessor's principal place(s) of business] shall be closed.

1.7 "Casualty Occurrence" shall have the meaning set forth in Section 9 of this Lease.

1.8 "Casualty Value" as to each Unit shall be the amount calculated in accordance with the Casualty Value provisions of the applicable Equipment Schedule.

1.9 "Certificate of Acceptance" shall mean a certificate substantially in the form attached as Annex A to the form of Equipment Schedule attached hereto as Exhibit A.

1.10 "Code" shall mean the United States Internal Revenue Code of 1986, as amended and in effect from time to time [if appropriate, insert other relevant governing tax law].

1.11 "Cut-Off Date" as to each Item of Equipment shall mean the date specified in the applicable Equipment Schedule after which Lessor shall not be obligated to purchase and lease such Item of Equipment to Lessee in accordance with the terms and conditions of this Lease.

1.12 "Discount Rate" shall mean the per annum interest charge (calculated on the basis of a 360-day year and 30-day month) specified in the applicable Equipment Schedule.

1.13 "Equipment Schedule" shall mean each schedule, substantially in the form of Exhibit A attached hereto, which shall refer to this Lease and which shall become a part hereof as executed from time to time by the parties hereto, covering one or more Items of Equipment that may be leased by Lessee from Lessor hereunder.

1.14 "Event of Default" shall mean any of the events specified in Section 13.1 of this Lease.

1.15 "Fair Market Rental" shall mean the rental value of a Unit determined in accordance with the provisions of Section 14 of this Lease.

1.16 "Fair Market Value" shall mean the sale value of a Unit determined in accordance with the provisions of Section 14 of this Lease.

1.17 "Impositions" shall have the meaning set forth in Section 7.1 of this Lease.

1.18 "Interim Rent" as to each Unit shall mean the rent payable with respect to any Interim Term, as specified in the applicable Equipment Schedule.

1.19 "Interim Term" as to each Unit shall mean the period of time, if any, commencing on the Acceptance Date and ending on the day immediately preceding the Basic Lease Commencement Date.

1.20 "Item of Equipment" shall mean an item of electronic data processing equipment described in an Equipment Schedule. When an "Item of Equipment" becomes subject to this Lease it is thereafter for all purposes of this Lease referred to and defined as a "Unit".

1.21 "Invoice Purchase Price" as to each Unit shall mean the aggregate amount payable by the Lessor to Manufacturer for such Unit, as specified in one or more Manufacturer's invoices for such Unit.

1.22 "Lease" shall mean this Master Lease of Computer Equipment between Lessor and Lessee, including without limitation all Equipment Schedules and all exhibits to this Lease and to all Equipment Schedules. The words "herein," "hereof," "hereunder," and other words of similar import used in this Lease refer to this Lease as a whole and not to any particular Section, Subsection, or other portion of this Lease.

1.23 "Lessor's Cost" as to each Unit shall mean the Invoice Purchase Price plus additional costs and expenses that are assumed and subsequently paid by Lessor pursuant to the applicable Equipment Schedule.

1.24 "Lessor's Lien" shall have the meaning set forth in Section 15.3 of this Lease.

1.25 "Lien" shall have the meaning set forth in Section 15.3 of this Lease.

1.26 "Loss Payment Date" as to a Unit suffering a Casualty Occurrence shall mean the date on which Lessee shall be obligated to pay Lessor the Casualty Value in accordance with provisions of Section 9.1 of this Lease.

1.27 "Manufacturer" as to each Unit shall mean the manufacturer or vendor thereof specified by Lessee in the applicable Equipment Schedule.

1.28 "Overdue Rate" shall mean the per annum interest charge (calculated on the basis of a 360-day year and 30-day month) pursuant to Section 18 as specified in the applicable Equipment Schedule.

1.29 "Primary Term" as to each Unit shall mean that period of time commencing on, and including, the Basic Lease Commencement Date and ending that period of time thereafter, as designated in the applicable Equipment Schedule, unless earlier terminated pursuant to the provisions of this Lease.

1.30 "Purchase Documents" shall mean those documents relating to the purchase of a Unit or Units by Lessor from Manufacturer.

1.31 "Purchase Right" as to each Unit shall have the meaning specified in Section 16.1 of this Lease.

1.32 "Renewal Rent" as to each Unit shall mean the rent due and payable on each Rent Date during a Renewal Term, as specified in the applicable Equipment Schedule.

1.33 "Renewal Right" as to each Unit shall have the meaning specified in Section 16.2 of this Lease.

1.34 "Renewal Term" as to each Unit shall mean that aggregate period of time following the end of the Primary Term for which this Lease is extended.

1.35 "Rent" as to each Unit shall mean and include Basic Rent and any Interim Rent and Renewal Rent payable or to become payable, by Lessee to Lessor.

1.36 "Rent Date" as to each Unit shall mean each date during the Term on which Rent is due and payable, as specified in the applicable Equipment Schedule.

1.37 "Term" as to each Unit shall mean the Primary Term and any Interim Term and Renewal Term.

1.38 "Termination Right" as to each Unit shall have the meaning specified in Section 16.3 of this Lease.

1.39 "Termination Value" as to each Unit shall be the amount calculated in accordance with the Termination Value provisions of the applicable Equipment Schedule.

1.40 "Unit" shall mean an Item of Equipment, and any modifications thereof, or improvements or additions thereto, which is leased by Lessor to Lessee pursuant to the terms and provisions of this Lease.

1.41 "Upgrade Right" shall have all the meaning specified in Section 16.4 of this Lease.

Section 2. Equipment Acquisition and Acceptance

2.1 Lease Commitment. In consideration of the Rent to be paid by Lessee and the other covenants contained in this Lease to be kept and performed by Lessee, Lessor hereby agrees to lease to Lessee each Item of Equipment described in each Equipment Schedule in accordance with the terms and conditions of this Lease.

2.2 Lessor Payment. Lessor shall purchase each Unit from Manufacturer solely for its own investment and account as a principal and not as a broker and promptly pay to Manufacturer the full Invoice Purchase Price for each Unit. In no event shall Lessor make such payment later than the earlier of the due date specified by Manufacturer or thirty (30) days after the Acceptance Date. Lessor shall, immediately upon making such payment, deliver to Lessee reasonably satisfactory evidence of such payment. If the full Invoice Purchase Price for any such Unit is not so paid to Manufacturer as provided in this Section 2.2, Lessee shall have the absolute right, in its discretion, (a) to make such payment to Manufacturer, whereupon all of Lessor's rights in, and title to, such Unit shall automatically vest in Lessee and (b) to withhold any Rent and/or (c) terminate this Lease as to such Unit. In addition to paying the Invoice Purchase Price for each Unit, Lessor shall also pay, no later than the due date, such other costs and expenses as to a Unit as specified as part of the Lessor's Cost for such Unit in the applicable Equipment Schedule.

2.3 Cut-Off Date. Lessor shall have no obligation to purchase and lease any Item of Equipment hereunder which has not been accepted by Lessee in accordance with the provisions of Section 2.5 on or before the Cut-Off Date.

2.4 Installation Location. Each Unit shall be installed at the address set forth in the applicable Equipment Schedule. Lessee may, without Lessor's consent, move any such Unit from such address, or any relocated address, to any other address in the United States of America, provided Lessee has notified Lessor in writing at least thirty (30) days prior to effecting any change of location.

2.5 Lessee Acceptance. Lessee shall acknowledge its acceptance of each Item of Equipment for lease hereunder by executing and delivering to Lessor a Certificate of Acceptance as to each such Item of Equipment, whereupon each such Item of Equipment shall become subject to this Lease as of the Acceptance Date.

Section 3. Lease Term

3.1 Term of Lease. The Term of each Unit shall be as specified in the applicable Equipment Schedule.

3.2 Lease Termination. This Lease shall not be terminated by Lessor or Lessee with respect to any Unit for any reason whatsoever, except as expressly provided herein.

Section 4. Net Lease

This Lease is a net lease and Lessee, subject to the provisions of Section 2.2, shall not be entitled to any abatement or reduction of Rent, or setoff against Rent, including without limitation abatements, reductions, or setoffs due or alleged to be due by reason of any past, present, or future claims of Lessee against Lessor under this Lease. Notwithstanding the foregoing, however, nothing shall preclude Lessee from otherwise enforcing any and all other rights it may have against Lessor under this Lease or otherwise.

Section 5. Rent and Usage

5.1 Rent Payment. Lessee agrees to pay Lessor Rent for each Unit in accordance with the provisions of this Lease. The Rent for each Unit shall be paid on each Rent Date in the amount set forth in the applicable Equipment Schedule. In accordance with Section 23.1 hereof, if any date on which a Rent payment is due is not a Business Day, the Rent payment otherwise payable on such date shall be payable on the next succeeding Business Day.

5.2 Unlimited Usage. Lessor agrees that there shall be no limit on the number of hours for which any Unit may be used.

Section 6. Identification Marks

Lessee, at its own cost and expense, will cause each Unit to be legibly and permanently marked, in a reasonably prominent location, with the following legend evidencing the fact that such Unit is owned by Lessor and subject to this Lease:

"[Name and Address of Lessor], Owner, Lessor."

Lessee shall, upon at least thirty (30) Business Days prior written notice from Lessor, make such changes and/or additions in such markings specified by Lessor as may be required by law in order to protect Lessor's ownership of such Unit and the rights of Lessor under this Lease. Lessee will promptly replace or cause to be replaced any such markings that are removed, defaced, or destroyed.

Section 7. General Tax Indemnification

7.1 General Tax Indemnity. All Rent and other payments required to be made by Lessee hereunder shall be net of any deductions, charges, costs, expenses, and Impositions with respect to collection or otherwise. Lessee agrees to pay, on written demand by Lessor specifying such Impositions in reasonable detail, any and all Impositions and shall keep and save harmless and indemnify Lessor from and against all such Impositions. "Impositions" shall mean the amount of any local, state, federal, or foreign taxes of any nature whatsoever, assessments, license fees, governmental charges, duties, fines, interest charges, or penalties with respect to any Unit or any part thereof, or with respect to the purchase, ownership, delivery, leasing, possession, use, or operation thereof. The term "Impositions" shall not include (a) federal, state, local, and foreign tax on, or measured by, the net income of Lessor; (b) any tax based on, or measured by, gross income or gross receipts of Lessor as a substitute for and not in addition to taxes based on net income of Lessor; (c) any tax imposed by Section 531 [Accumulated Earnings Tax] or Section 541 [Personal Holding Company Tax] of the Code; (d) taxes, fees, or other charges included in Lessor's Cost; (e) the aggregate of all franchise taxes or other similar taxes up to the amount in the aggregate of any such taxes which would be payable to the states and cities in which Lessor maintains or has maintained places of, or otherwise does, business during the Term of this Lease, except any such tax which is in substitution for or relieves Lessee from the payment of taxes which it would otherwise be obligated to pay or reimburse Lessor for as herein provided; (f) any fines or penalties that are imposed as a result of (A) the misconduct or negligence of Lessor or (B) a failure by Lessor to take reasonable action or to furnish reasonable cooperation to Lessee as a result of which Lessee is unable to diligently fulfill its obligations under this Section 7; (g) any claim made against Lessor for any Imposition that Lessee is obligated to pay hereunder with respect to which Lessor has not notified Lessee in writing pursuant to Section 7.2; (h) any tax imposed on the purchase of a Unit or Units from Manufacturer; and (i) any sales or use tax imposed upon (A) the voluntary transfer or other disposition by Lessor, or any assignee of Lessor, of all or any of the Units, or (B) another obtaining any interest in a Unit by, through, or under Lessor. In this regard it is understood that any transfer or disposition (A) that occurs in the Lessor's exercise of the remedies provided in Section 13.2 after an Event of Default has occurred and while the same is continuing or (B) of a unit which has suffered a Casualty Occurrence, shall not be deemed to be a voluntary transfer or disposition.

7.2 Claim Notification. If a claim is made against Lessor for any Imposition that Lessee is obligated to pay hereunder, Lessor shall promptly notify Lessee in writing.

7.3 Right to Contest. Lessee shall be under no obligation to pay any imposition so long as Lessee is contesting such Imposition in good faith. Lessor hereby agrees to fully cooperate with Lessee, including providing any information Lessee shall request, in connection with any such contest. So long as Lessee is so contesting such Imposition and no final, unreviewable judgment adverse to Lessee has been entered by a court of competent jurisdiction, Lessee shall not be in default hereunder with respect to the nonpayment of any such Imposition.

7.4 Lessor Payment Reimbursement. If any Imposition shall have been charged or levied against Lessor directly and paid by Lessor, Lessee shall reimburse Lessor on presentation of reasonably satisfactory evidence of payment; provided, however, Lessor has obtained Lessee's prior written approval for the payment thereof, which approval shall not be unreasonably withheld.

7.5 Lessor Refund Reimbursement. If Lessee has reimbursed Lessor for any Imposition pursuant to this Section 7 (or if Lessee has made a payment to the appropriate taxing authority for an Imposition which it is required to pay hereunder), Lessee may take such steps (in the name of Lessee or in the name of Lessor) as are necessary or appropriate to seek a refund of such Imposition, and Lessor shall fully cooperate with Lessee in seeking such refund. In the event of a refund of any Imposition for which Lessor has received a payment from Lessee, the amount of such refund shall be immediately paid over to or retained by Lessee, as appropriate.

Section 8. General Indemnification

8.1 Conflict. The provisions of this Section 8 are in addition to, and not in limitation of, the provisions of Section 7 hereof; provided, however, that in the event of a conflict between the provisions of this Section 8 and the provisions of Section 7, the provisions of Section 7 shall be controlling.

8.2 General Indemnity. Lessee hereby agrees to assume liability for, and does hereby agreed to indemnify, protect, save, and keep Lessor harmless from and against any and all liabilities, obligations, losses, damages, penalties, claims, actions, suits, costs, expenses, or disbursements arising out of Lessee's actions that may be imposed on, incurred by, or asserted against Lessor relating to or arising out this Lease or the manufacture, purchase, acceptance, rejection, return, lease, ownership, possession, use, condition, operation, or sale of each Unit or any accident in connection therewith. Lessor hereby expressly authorizes Lessee to contest, and agrees to cooperate fully with Lessee in contesting, in the name of Lessee or Lessor as Lessee shall deem appropriate for the benefit of Lessee, any such liability, obligation, penalty, or claim asserted against either Lessee or Lessor. Lessee shall not be required to indemnify Lessor except as specifically set forth in the preceding sentence, including without limitation as to (a) loss or liability in respect of any Unit arising from any act or event which occurs after such Unit has been returned to Lessor pursuant to the provisions of this Lease; (b) loss or liability resulting from the breach of any covenant, representation, or warranty made by Lessor in this Lease or in any document relating to the transactions contemplated by this Lease; (c) loss or liability resulting from the negligence or misconduct of Lessor (including acts by employees, agents, or other representatives of Lessor); (d) any legal or accounting fees or other expense incurred by Lessor in connection with this Lease and the other documents referred to herein and any amendments or other modifications or additions to this Lease or such other documents; (e) any brokerage fees or similar fees or commissions incurred by Lessor in connection with any transactions contemplated hereby; or (f) any liability, obligation, penalty, or claim indemnified against herein so long as the validity or amount thereof is being contested by Lessee in good faith.

Section 9. Payment for Casualty Occurrence

9.1 Casualty Occurrence. In the event that any Unit becomes damaged or otherwise inoperable so as to preclude its use for the purpose intended by Lessee, as determined by Lessee in good faith, or in the event any Unit is lost or stolen or is permanently returned by Lessee to Manufacturer pursuant to the Purchase Documents [*Author's Note:* This relates to when a Unit is permitted to be returned to the manufacturer because it is defective or otherwise fails to meet requirements set forth in the Purchase Documents], or for ninety (90) consecutive days or more is taken or requisitioned by condemnation or otherwise in such a manner as to result in Lessee's loss of possession or use, excluding any permitted sublease (any such occurrence being hereinafter referred to as a "Casualty Occurrence") during the Term of this Lease, Lessee shall promptly so notify Lessor. On the Rent Date next succeeding a Casualty Occurrence (the "Loss Payment Date"), Lessee shall pay to Lessor an amount equal to the Casualty Value of such Unit applicable on the date of such Casualty Occurrence. [*Author's Note:* Casualty Value payments vary in arrangement—each situation must be looked at independently.] Upon, but not prior to, the time when such payment is made by Lessee as to any Unit, Lessee's obligation to pay Rent for such Unit, including without limitation any Rent that would be attributable to any Rent payment period subsequent to the Loss Payment Date, shall cease and the Term of this Lease as to such Unit shall automatically terminate. Lessor hereby appoints Lessee as its sole agent to dispose of any Unit or any part thereof suffering a Casualty Occurrence in the best manner and at the best price obtainable, as determined by Lessee in its sole discretion, on an "as is, where is" basis. If Lessee shall have so paid the Casualty Value to Lessor, unless an Event of Default shall have occurred and be continuing, Lessee shall be entitled to the proceeds of such sale up to an amount equal to the sum of the Casualty Value of such Unit plus all costs, expenses, and damages incurred by Lessee in connection with such Casualty Occurrence and the disposition of such Unit. Lessor shall be entitled to any excess. In the case of the taking or requisition of any Unit by any governmental authority, any payments received from such governmental authority as compensation for such taking or requisition shall, if Lessee has therefore paid the Casualty Value, be immediately paid over to or retained by Lessee, as appropriate, up to an amount equal to the sum of the Casualty Value of such Unit plus all costs, expenses, and damages incurred by Lessee in connection with such Casualty Occurrence, and Lessor shall be entitled to any excess. Lessor shall have no duty to Lessee to pursue any claim against any governmental authority but Lessee may at its own cost and expense pursue the same on its own behalf and on behalf of Lessor, and Lessor shall cooperate fully in Lessee's pursuit of such claim.

9.2 Manufacturer Returned Unit. As to each Unit returned to Manufacturer in the manner described in the first sentence of Section 9.1, Lessee shall be entitled to immediately receive and retain all amounts paid or payable to Lessor by Manufacturer with respect to the return of such Unit, up to the Casualty Value paid by Lessee hereunder plus all cost, expenses, and damages incurred by Lessee in connection therewith. Any excess shall immediately be paid over to or retained by Lessor, as appropriate.

9.3. Return After Requisition. In the event of the taking or requisition for use by any governmental authority of any Unit during the Term of this Lease as to such Unit, unless such taking or requisition shall constitute a Casualty Occurrence, all of Lessee's obligations under this Lease with respect to such Unit shall continue to the same extent as if such taking or requisition had not occurred, except that if such Unit is returned by such governmental authority to Lessee at any time after the end of the Term of this Lease as to such Unit, anything to the contrary contained in this Lease notwithstanding, Lessee shall only be required to promptly return such Unit to Lessor upon such return by such governmental authority, rather than at the end of the Term of this Lease as to such Unit. All payments received by Lessor or Lessee from any governmental authority for the use during the Term of this Lease of such Unit as provided in this Section 9.3 shall be immediately paid over to or retained by Lessee, as appropriate, unless an Event of Default shall have occurred and be continuing, in which case the amount otherwise payable to Lessee may be retained by Lessor and applied to discharge the liabilities of Lessee under Section 13.

Section 10. Insurance

10.1 Insurance Maintenance. Lessee will, at all times during the Term of this Lease as to each Unit prior to the return of such Unit to Lessor in accordance with Section 17 of this Lease, at its own expense, cause to be carried and maintained with insurers of recognized responsibility (a) property and casualty insurance for such Unit and (b) public liability insurance against claims for personal injury, death, or property damage resulting from the ownership, possession, maintenance, use, or operation of such Unit, in both cases in at least such amounts and against such risks as are customarily insured against by Lessee on similar equipment; provided, however, that in no event shall (a) the amount of such property and casualty insurance be less than the Casualty Value of such Unit from time to time (except that Lessee may self-insure in an amount up to ____) and (b) the amount of such public liability insurance be less than [$ ____] as to any one occurrence. The benefits under such insurance shall be payable to Lessor and Lessee, as their respective interests may appear. Any policy of insurance carried in accordance with this Section 10 shall (a) require thirty (30) days prior written notice to Lessor of a material change or cancellation or nonrenewal; (b) name Lessor as additional insured, as its interest may appear, and provide that all provisions of such policy, except the limits of liability, will operate in the same manner as if there were a separate policy governing such additional insured; and (c) provide that, as to Lessor's interest, such insurance shall not be invalidated by reason of any breach of representation or violation of warranty made by Lessee to the insurer in connection with obtaining such policy of insurance or maintaining the same in full force and effect. Lessee shall deliver to Lessor together with each Certificate of Acceptance a copy of each such policy (or a certificate of insurance relating thereto) with respect to each Unit covered by such Certificate of Acceptance.

10.2 Insurance Proceeds. Any insurance proceeds resulting from insurance carried by Lessee or condemnation payments received by Lessor for each Unit suffering a Casualty Occurrence shall be deducted from the amounts payable by Lessee for a Casualty Occurrence pursuant to Section 9. If Lessor shall receive any such insurance proceeds or condemnation payments after Lessee shall have made payment to Section 9 without deduction for such insurance proceeds or such condemnation payments, Lessee shall immediately pay such insurance proceeds or condemnation payments to Lessee, up to the sum of the Casualty Value amount paid by Lessee plus all costs, expenses, and damages incurred by Lessee in connection with the disposition of each Unit suffering a Casualty Occurrence, unless an Event of Default shall have occurred and be continuing, in which case the amount otherwise payable to Lessee may be retained by Lessor and applied to discharge the liabilities of Lessee under Section 13. The balance of such insurance proceeds or condemnation payments shall be retained by Lessor. All property damage insurance proceeds received by Lessor or Lessee with respect to a damaged Unit not suffering a Casualty Occurrence shall be applied toward the payment, when due, of the cost of repairing such Unit. Any condemnation payments received with respect to a Unit not suffering a Casualty Occurrence shall be the property of Lessee unless an Event of Default shall have occurred and be continuing, in which case the amount otherwise payable to Lessee shall be paid to or retained by Lessor, as appropriate, and applied to discharge the liabilities of Lessee under Section 13.

Section 11. Inspection

Lessor shall have the right during the Term of this Lease upon not less than ten (10) Business Days prior written notice to Lessee to inspect any Unit for the purpose of confirming its existence, condition, and proper maintenance, at mutually agreeable times during Lessee's regular business hours. Notwithstanding the foregoing, Lessor may not inspect any Units if it would unreasonably interfere with Lessee's business operations, violate any applicable governmental security laws, regulations rules, or violate the reasonable security regulations or procedures of Lessee.

Section 12. Disclaimer of Warranties; Compliance With Laws and Rules; Maintenance; Additions

12.1 Warranty Disclaimer. LESSOR MAKES NO WARRANTY OR REPRESENTATION, EITHER EXPRESS OR IMPLIED, AS TO THE DESIGN OR CONDITION, OR QUALITY OF THE MATERIAL, EQUIPMENT, OR WORKMANSHIP OF THE UNITS LEASED HEREUNDER, AND LESSOR MAKES NO WARRANTY OF MERCHANTABILITY OR FITNESS OF THE UNITS FOR ANY PARTICULAR PURPOSE [*Author's Note:* This warranty disclaimer should be given to a lessor only when the lessor is not also the vendor], it being agreed that all such risks, as between Lessor and Lessee, are to be borne by Lessee; but Lessor hereby assigns and transfers to Lessee, and hereby irrevocably appoints and constitutes Lessee as its agent and attorney-in-fact to assert and enforce from time to time as Lessee shall deem appropriate, in the name of and for the account of Lessor and/or Lessee, as their respective interest may appear, at Lessee's sole cost and expense, whatever claims and rights Lessor may have as owner of each Unit against Manufacturer (or any subcontractor or supplier of Manufacturer) under the Purchase Documents or otherwise. Lessor agrees to cooperate fully at Lessee's request in Lessee's pursuit of any such claims or rights. If for any reason Lessee is prevented from asserting such claims or rights in the name of and for the account of Lessor and/or Lessee, as their respective interests may appear, Lessor will, at Lessee's expense, promptly upon Lessee's request enforce such claims or rights as directed from time to time by Lessee.

12.2 Compliance With Laws. Lessee agrees to use its best efforts to comply in all material respects with all applicable laws (including without limitation laws with respect to Lessee's use, maintenance, and operation of each Unit) of each jurisdiction in which a Unit is located; provided, however, Lessee shall not be required to comply with any such law so long as Lessee is, in good faith, contesting the validity or application of any such law. Lessor agrees to cooperate fully at Lessee's request in Lessee's contest of any such law or its applicability.

12.3 Maintenance. Lessee shall pay all costs, expenses, fees, and charges (other than those included in Lessor's Cost) incurred in connection with Lessee's use and operation of the Units. Subject to the provisions of Section 9, Lessee, at its own cost and expense, shall maintain, repair, and service, or cause to be maintained, repaired, and serviced, each Unit so as to keep it in the same operating condition and repair as it was when it first became subject to this Lease, ordinary wear and tear for the use intended by Lessee excepted, and within a reasonable period of time shall replace all parts of any Unit that may have become worn out, stolen, confiscated, destroyed, or otherwise rendered permanently unfit for use with appropriate replacement parts, which shall be free and clear from all Liens, other than any Lessor's Lien. Upon replacement, title to the replacement parts shall automatically be vested in Lessee.

12.4 Maintenance Agreement. Lessee shall, upon expiration of the Manufacturer's warranty period applicable to each Unit, enter into and maintain in force for the longest possible period obtainable by Lessee during the Term of this Lease as to such Unit a maintenance agreement (the "Maintenance Agreement") with Manufacturer or with another qualified party covering at least the prime shift maintenance of such Unit; provided, however, if Lessee is unable to obtain Maintenance Agreement reasonably satisfactory to it as to any Unit, Lessee shall have the right to maintain such Unit itself. Charges under the Maintenance Agreement and all other maintenance and service charges, including installation and dismantling charges, shall be borne by Lessee.

12.5 Additions. Lessee may, at its option and at its own cost and expense, make additions, modifications, and improvements to any Unit provided such additions, modifications, and improvements are readily removable without causing material damage to such Unit. All such additions, modifications, and improvements shall remain the property of Lessee and shall be removed by Lessee before such Unit is returned to Lessor. Lessee shall repair all damage to any such Unit resulting from such installation and removal. Lessee shall not, without the prior written consent of Lessor, which consent shall not be unreasonably withheld, alter any Unit, or affix or install any accessories or devices on any Unit, if the same shall materially impair the function or use of such Unit. Except to the extent otherwise provided in the first sentence of this Section 12.5, any and all other additions or modifications and improvements to any Lien (except for any Lessor's Lien), shall immediately be vested in Lessor, any and all warranties of Manufacturer with respect thereto shall thereupon automatically be assigned to Lessee and Lessor shall cooperate fully with Lessee in their enforcement the same extent and on the same basis as provided in Section 12.1

Section 13. Events of Default and Remedies

13.1 Events of Default. During the Term of this Lease the occurrence of any of the following events shall constitute an "Event of Default":

(a) Nonpayment of all or any part of the Rent provided for in Section 5 (except as otherwise expressly provided in Section 2.2), if such nonpayment shall continue for ten (10) Business Days after Lessee's receipt from Lessor of written notice of such nonpayment;

(b) Lessee shall make or permit any unauthorized assignment or transfer of this Lease or any interest herein or any unauthorized transfer of the right to possession of any Unit;

(c) Lessee shall fail or refuse to comply with any other covenant, agreement, term, or provision of this Lease required to be kept or performed by Lessee or to make reasonable provision for such compliance with thirty (30) days after Lessee's receipt from Lessor of a written demand for the performance thereof, which demand shall specify in reasonable detail the nonperformance;

(d) Any proceedings shall be commenced by or against Lessee for any relief under any bankruptcy or insolvency law, or any law relating to the relief of debtors, readjustment of indebtedness, reorganization, arrangement, composition, or extension, and, unless such proceedings shall have been dismissed, nullified, stayed, or otherwise rendered ineffective (but then only so long as such stay shall continue in force or such ineffectiveness shall continue), all of the obligations of Lessee hereunder shall not have been and shall not continue to be duly assumed in writing, pursuant to a court order or decree, by a trustee or trustees or receiver or receivers appointed (whether or not subject to ratification) for Lessee or its property in connection with any such proceedings in such manner that such obligations shall have the same status as obligations incurred by such trustee or trustees or receiver or receivers, within thirty (30) days after such appointment, if any, or thirty (30) days after such proceedings shall have been commenced, whichever is earlier, or Lessee shall make a general assignment for the benefit of creditors or shall admit in writing its inability to pay its debts generally as they become due;

(e) any representation or warranty made by Lessee in this Lease, or in any certificate or other document delivered by Lessee pursuant hereto, shall be incorrect in any material respect as of the date made and shall remain uncorrected for a period of thirty (30) days after receipt by Lessee of written notice from Lessor specifying in reasonable detail the incorrect representation or warranty.

13.2 Remedies. Upon the occurrence of an Event of Default, and so long as such Event of Default shall be continuing, Lessor may, at its option, declare this Lease to be in default and may exercise in its sole discretion any one or more of the following remedies:

(a) proceed by appropriate court action or actions, either at law or in equity, to enforce performance by Lessee of the applicable covenants of this Lease or to recover damages for the breach thereof; or

(b) by notice in writing to Lessee terminate this Lease with respect to any or all of the Units, whereupon all rights of Lessee to the possession and use of such Unit or units shall absolutely cease and terminate as though this Lease had never been made, but Lessee shall remain liable as hereinafter provided; and thereupon Lessor may, by its agent or agents, enter upon the premises of Lessee or any other premises where any of such Units may be located and take possession of all or any of such Units and thenceforth hold, possess, operate, sell, lease, and enjoy such Unit or Units free from any right of Lessee to use such Unit or Units for any purpose whatsoever and without any duty to account to Lessee for any action or inaction or for any proceeds arising therefrom, but Lessor shall, nevertheless, have a right to recover from Lessee any and all amounts that under the provisions of this Lease and any applicable Equipment Schedule may then be due or which may have accrued to the date of such termination (computing the Rent for any number of days less than a full Rent payment period by multiplying the Rent for such full Rent payment period by a fraction the numerator of which is such number of days and the denominator of which is the total number of days in the full Rent payment period) and also to recover from Lessee as damages for loss of the bargain and not as a penalty, whichever of the following sums, with respect to each such Unit, Lessor, in its sole discretion, shall specify by written notice to Lessee: (a) an amount equal to the excess, if any, computed as of the Rent Date immediately succeeding the date of the Event of Default, of the Casualty Value for such Unit over the present value of the Fair Market Rental of such Unit for the remainder of the Term of this Lease following such Rent Date, such present value to be computed in each case using the Discount Rate specified in the applicable Equipment Schedule [*Author's Note:* This is for an "in advance" rental structure]; or (b) an amount equal to the excess, if any, computed as of the Rent Date immediately succeeding the date of the Event of Default, of the Casualty Value for such Unit over the

Fair Market Value of such Unit [*Author's Note:* This is for an "in advance" rental structure]; and any reasonable costs and expenses (including legal and accounting fees) incurred in connection with the recovery, repair, repainting, return, and remarketing of such Unit or other exercise of Lessor's remedies hereunder.

The remedies in this Lease provided in favor of Lessor shall not be deemed exclusive, but shall be cumulative and shall be in addition to all other remedies existing in its favor at law or in equity.

Lessor shall use its best efforts to mitigate any damages suffered by it. IN NO EVENT SHALL LESSEE BE LIABLE FOR ANY INDIRECT, SPECIAL, OR CONSEQUENTIAL DAMAGES OF ANY KIND UNDER THE LEASE.

Section 14. Fair Market Value and Fair Market Rental

"Fair Market Value" and "Fair Market Rental," as to each Unit for all purposes in connection with this Lease, shall have the respective meanings and shall be determined in accordance with the procedure set forth in this Section 14. Fair Market Value and Fair Market Rental shall be determined on the basis of, and be equal in amount to, the value which would obtain in an arm's-length transaction between an informed and willing buyer-user (or lessee, if determining Fair Market Rental), other than a lessee currently in possession or a used equipment dealer, under no compulsion to buy (or lease), and an informed and willing seller (or lessor, if determining Fair Market Rental) under no compulsion to sell (or lease), and, in such determination, costs of removal from the location of current use shall not be a deduction from such value.

In the event that a determination of Fair Market Value or Fair Market Rental of a Unit shall be made under any provision of this Lease, the party requesting the determination shall deliver a written notice to the other party so indicating and appointing an Appraiser selected by the requesting party to determine the Fair Market Value or Fair Market Rental. Within fifteen (15) days after the receipt of such written notice the party receiving such notice shall deliver to the requesting party a written notice appointing an Appraiser of its selection to make such determination. The two Appraisers appointed in such written notices shall meet promptly to determine the Fair Market Value or Fair Market Rental of such Unit as of the applicable date. If within thirty (30) days after the initial written notice the two Appraisers so appointed by Lessor and Lessee shall be unable to agree upon the Fair Market Value or the Fair Market Rental of such Unit, whichever is applicable, such Appraisers shall within five (5) days thereafter appoint a third Appraiser. The decision of the three Appraisers so appointed shall be given within a period of ten (10) days after the appointment of such third Appraiser. Any decision in which any two Appraisers so appointed and acting hereunder concur shall in all cases be binding and conclusive upon Lessor and Lessee. The fees and expenses of the Appraisers shall be borne equally by Lessee and Lessor, unless the Lease shall have been terminated pursuant to Section 13 hereof, in which case Lessee shall pay all such fees and expenses.

Section 15. Assignment, Possession, Liens, Sublease, and Merger

15.1 Lessor Assignment. Lessor agrees that it will not assign all or any portion of its rights under, or interests in, this Lease or any of the Units unless such assignment is made pursuant to a security agreement relating to any borrowing by Lessor from one or more institutional lenders. Notwithstanding the foregoing, Lessor agrees that it will not make any such assignment to any entities listed on an Annex to any Equipment Schedule. Lessor agrees that if such a security interest in any Unit is granted, the security agreement covering such Unit shall expressly provide that the rights and interests of Lessee in and to such Unit as provided in this Lease shall remain paramount so long as no Event of Default shall have occurred and be continuing. Lessor shall give Lessee prompt written notice of any such assignment by Lessor. All the rights of Lessor hereunder (including without limitation the right to receive Rent payable under this Lease) shall inure to the benefit of Lessor's permitted assigns to the extent of such assignment. Any payment of Rent or other payment by Lessee to such assignee shall be full satisfaction of Lessee's obligation to make such payment under this Lease and Lessor hereby indemnifies Lessee against any damages, claims, costs, or expenses incurred by Lessee in connection therewith, but Lessee shall be under no obligation to make any payment to any such assignee until Lessor shall give Lessee written notice to make such payment to such assignee. Notwithstanding anything to the contrary herein, any permitted assignee of Lessor can declare an Event of Default hereunder only with respect to one or more Units subject to such assignee's security interest.

15.2 Lessee Possession and Assignment. So long as an Event of Default under this Lease shall not have occurred and be continuing, Lessee shall be entitled to the quiet enjoyment and peaceful possession and use of the Units in accordance with and subject to all the terms and conditions of this Lease, but without the prior written consent of Lessor, which consent shall not be unreasonably withheld, Lessee shall not, except as otherwise permitted herein, lease, assign, or transfer its leasehold interest in any or all of the Units.

15.3 Liens. Except as otherwise provided herein, Lessee, at its own expense, shall promptly pay or discharge any and all sums claimed by, or liabilities in favor of, any person that, if unpaid, would become a mortgage, lien, charge, security interest, or other encumbrance (any of the foregoing being herein referred to as a "Lien"), other than a Lien by, through, or under Lessor on or with respect to any Unit, including any accession thereto, or the interest of Lessor or Lessee therein, which shall include without limitation any Lien resulting from a breach of Lessor's covenant in Section 2.2 or resulting from claims against Lessor not related to the ownership or leasing of any Unit (any of the foregoing being herein referred to as a "Lessor's Lien"), and shall promptly discharge any such Lien that arises. Lessee shall not be required to pay or discharge any such Lien so long as the validity thereof is being contested in good faith. The existence of any Lessor's Lien or any Lien for taxes, assessments, or governmental charges, or levies (in each case so long as not due and delinquent), or inchoate materialmen's, mechanics', workmen's, repairmen's, employees' or other like Liens arising in the ordinary course of business and in each case not delinquent shall not constitute a breach of this covenant.

15.4 Lessee Sublease. So long as no Event of Default under this Lease shall have occurred and be continuing, Lessee shall be entitled without Lessor's consent to sublease any or all of the Units, or any part thereof, to, or permit their use by, any person or entity, including without limitation any subsidiary, affiliate, or parent corporation of Lessee, incorporated in the United States of America or any state thereof, but in all cases only upon and subject to all the terms and conditions of this Lease. No such sublease or other assignment of use by Lessee shall relieve Lessee of its obligations hereunder.

15.5 Merger or Consolidation. Notwithstanding anything herein to the contrary, Lessee may assign or transfer this Lease and its leasehold interest in the Units to any corporation incorporated under the laws of any state of the United States of America into or with which Lessee shall have merged or consolidated or which shall have acquired all or substantially all of the property of Lessee, provided that such assignee or transferee will not, upon the effectiveness of such merger, consolidation, or acquisition and the assignment or transfer of this Lease to it, be in default under any provision of this Lease.

Section 16. Lessee Rights

16.1 Purchase Right. Lessee shall have the right to purchase any Units provided in the applicable Equipment Schedule.

16.2 Renewal Right. Lessee shall have the right to renew this Lease as to any Unit as provided in the applicable Equipment Schedule.

16.3 Termination Right. Lessee shall have the right to terminate this Lease as to any Unit as provided in the applicable Equipment Schedule.

16.4 Upgrade Right. Lessee shall have the right to upgrade any Unit as provided in the applicable Equipment Schedule.

Section 17. Return of Equipment

As soon as practicable on or after the expiration of the Term of this Lease as to each Unit, Lessee shall prepare the Unit for return to Lessor and deliver possession of such Unit to Lessor at the location of such Unit on the final day of the Term of this Lease. The Units shall be returned in the condition in which they are required to be maintained by Lessee under Section 12.3.

Section 18. Interest on Overdue Payments

Anything herein to the contrary notwithstanding, any nonpayment of Rent or any other payment obligation with respect to any Unit after the due date shall result in the obligation on the part of Lessee promptly to pay with respect to such Unit, to the extent legally enforceable, interest on such Rent or other payment obligation for the period of time during which it is overdue at the Overdue Rate as specified in the applicable Equipment Schedule, or such lesser amount as may be legally enforceable.

Section 19. Confidential Information

Lessor agrees that it will not, without first obtaining Lessee's written consent, disclose to any person, firm, or enterprise, or use for its benefit, any information not generally available to the public relating to Lessee's business, including without limitation any pricing methods, processes, financial data, lists, apparatus, statistics, program, research, development, or related information concerning past, present, or future business activities of Lessee.

Section 20. Advertising or Publicity

Neither Lessor nor Lessee shall use the name of the other in publicity releases or advertising without securing the prior written consent of the other.

Section 21. Representations and Warranties

Each of Lessor and Lessee represents and warrants to the other that:

(a) It is a corporation duly organized, validly existing, and in good standing under the laws of the jurisdiction of its incorporation. It has full power and authority to carry on its business presently conducted, to own or hold under lease its properties, and to enter into and perform its obligations under this Lease; and it is duly qualified to do business as a foreign corporation and is in good standing in each jurisdiction in which the location of any Unit requires such qualification.

(b) Its execution, delivery, and performance of this Lease have been duly authorized by all necessary corporate action on its part, do not contravene its corporate charter or by-laws or any law, governmental rule, or regulation, or any order, writ, injunction, decree, judgment, award, determination, direction, or demand (collectively "Order") of which it is aware binding on it or its properties and do not and will not contravene the provisions of, or constitute a default under, or result in the creation of any Lien upon any Unit under, any material indenture, mortgage, contract, or other instrument to which it is a party or by which it or its property is bound.

(c) No consent or approval of, giving notice to, registration with, or taking of any other action by, any [state/province—as appropriate], federal or other governmental commission, agency, or regulatory authority required for the performance by it of the transactions contemplated by this Lease, or if any such approval, registration, or giving of notice is required it has been obtained, so registered, or given, as the case may be.

(d) This Lease has been duly entered into and delivered by it and constitutes a legal, valid, and binding agreement of it enforceable against it in accordance with its terms, except as limited by (i) any bankruptcy, insolvency, reorganization, or other similar laws of general application affecting the enforcement of creditors' or lessors' rights generally, (ii) emergency powers lawfully conferred upon any governmental agency, and (iii) laws or judicial decisions limiting the right to specific performance or other equitable remedies.

(e) To the best of its knowledge there are no actions, suits, or proceedings pending or threatened against or affecting it or any of its property in any court or before any arbitrator or before or by any federal, state, municipal, or other governmental department, commission, board, bureau, agency, or instrumentality, domestic or foreign (collectively "Governmental Body"), except actions, suits, or proceedings of the character normally incident to the kind of business conducted by it as to which any adverse determination in excess of any accruals to reflect potential liability would not materially adversely affect its business, assets, operations, or condition, financial or otherwise, taken as a whole, or materially adversely affect its ability to perform its obligations under this Lease, and it is not in material default with respect to any material Order of any court, arbitrator, or Governmental Body.

(f) As to Lessee only, its consolidated balance sheet as of ____, and its related consolidated statements of income, retained earnings and changes in financial position for the two years then ended, heretofore delivered to Lessor, fairly present its consolidated financial position as of such date and its consolidated results of operations and consolidated changes in financial position for the two years then ended, all in conformity with general accepted accounting principles consistently applied during the periods. Since the date of such balance sheet there has not been any material adverse change in its business, assets, liabilities, results of operations, or condition, financial or otherwise.

(g) It is not a party to any agreement or instrument or subject to any charter or other corporate restriction that, so far as it is now aware, materially adversely affects or will, so far as it can now foresee, materially adversely affect, its business, operations, or properties or its ability to perform its obligations under this Lease.

(h) To the best of its knowledge it has filed all required tax returns in all jurisdictions in which such returns were required to be filed and has paid, or made provision for, all material taxes shown to be due and payable on such returns and all other material taxes and assessments that are payable by it, except for any taxes and assessments of which the amount, applicability, or validity is currently being contested in good faith and as to which any adverse determination in excess of any accruals to reflect potential liability would not materially adversely affect its ability to perform its obligations under this Lease.

Section 22. Financial Information

During the term of this Lease, Lessee agrees to provide Lessor with its consolidated quarterly and annual financial statements promptly as they become available and such other financial information as may be provided to Lessee's shareholders from time to time.

Section 23. Payments

23.1 Postponement of Payment Date. If any date on which a Rent or other payment is due and payable is not a Business Day, the payment otherwise payable on such date shall be due and payable on the next succeeding Business Day.

23.2 Payment Address. All Rent and other payments required to be made by Lessee to Lessor shall be made to Lessor at the address of Lessor set forth in Section 24 or at such other address as may be specified in writing by Lessor at least thirty (30) Business Days prior to the date such notice is intended to become effective.

23.3 Method of Payment. All Rent and other payments under this Lease shall be made in lawful money of the United States of America.

Section 24. Notices

Any notice or document or payment to be delivered hereunder to any of the persons designated below, except as otherwise expressly provided herein, shall be deemed to have been properly delivered if delivered personally or deposited with the United States Postal Service, registered or certified mail, return receipt requested, postage prepaid, to the following respective addresses:

If to Lessor: ____________________

____

Attn: ____________________

If to Lessee ______________________

____

Attn: ______________________

or such other address as may be furnished from time to time by any of the parties hereto upon at least thirty (30) days prior written notice.

Section 25. Statement of Lease

It is expressly understood and agreed by and between the parties hereto that this instrument constitutes a lease of the Units, and nothing herein shall be construed as conveying to Lessee any right, title, or interest in the Units except as a lessee only. Neither the execution nor the filing of any financing statement with respect to any of the Units or the execution or filing of any financing statement with respect to this Lease or the recording hereof shall in any manner imply that the relationship between Lessor and Lessee is anything other than that of lessor and lessee. Any such filing of financing statements or recordation of this Lease is solely to protect the interests of Lessor and Lessee in the event of any unwarranted assertions by any person not a party to this Lease transaction.

Section 26. Severability, Effect, and Interpretation of Lease

26.1 Severability. Any provision of this Lease that is prohibited or unenforceable by any applicable law of any jurisdiction shall as to such jurisdiction be ineffective to the extent of such prohibition or unenforceability without invalidating the remaining provisions hereof, and any such prohibition or unenforceability in any jurisdiction shall not invalidate or render unenforceable such provision in any other jurisdiction.

26.2 Complete Statement of Rights. This Lease exclusively and completely states the rights of Lessor and Lessee with respect to the leasing of the Units and supersedes all other agreements, oral or written, with respect thereto.

26.3 Section Headings. All Section headings are inserted for convenience only and shall not affect any construction or interpretation of this Lease.

Section 27. Law Governing

The terms and provisions of this Lease and all rights and obligations hereunder shall be governed in all respects by the laws of [______________________].

Section 28. Further Assurances

Each of Lessor and Lessee agrees that at any time and from time to time, after the execution and delivery of this Lease, it shall, upon request of the other party, promptly execute and deliver such further documents and do such further acts and things the requesting party may reasonably request in order fully to effectuate the purposes of this Lease.

Section 29. Modification, Waiver, and Consent

Any modification or waiver of any provision of this Lease, or any consent to any departure by Lessee or Lessor, as the case may be, therefrom, shall not be effective in any event unless the same is in writing and signed by the party to be charged, and then such modification, waiver, or consent shall be effective only in the specific instance and for the specific purpose given.

Section 30. Binding Effect

This Lease shall be binding upon and shall inure to the benefit of the respective successors and permitted assigns of Lessee and Lessor.

Section 31. Execution in Counterparts

This Lease may be executed in any number of counterparts, each of which shall constitute an original and which taken together shall constitute one and the same Lease.

IN WITNESS WHEREOF, the parties, pursuant to due authority, have caused this Lease to be signed in their respective names by duly authorized officers or representatives as of the date first above written.

____
as Lessor

By: ________________________________

Title: ______________________________

____
as Lessee

By: ________________________________

Title: ______________________________

Form: l-02a
Disk File Name: l-02a.rtf

Equipment Schedule

Form Purpose

Form of master net finance equipment lease schedule. This form is integrated with a master lease agreement, Lease Agreement Form l-02.

Executing Parties

The equipment lessor.
The equipment lessee.

See:

Lease Agreement, Form l-02

Exhibit A

Equipment Schedule No. ________ ("Schedule")

Dated of ______________, XXXX

to Master Lease of Computer Equipment ("Lease")

Dated as of ______________, XXXX

between

______________________________ ("Lessor")

and

______________________________ ("Lessee")

1. Equipment Description

Quantity	*Manufacturer*	*Model*	*New/Used*	*Description*	*Per Unit*	*Aggregate*	*Estimated Invoice Purchase Price*

****

[Insert Equipment Description]

Total Estimated Invoice Purchase Price $______________

2. Basic Lease Commencement Date
   The Basic Lease Commencement Date for each Unit shall commence on [insert relevant time, such as the first day of the month immediately following the Unit's Acceptance Date if the Acceptance Date does not fall on the first day of a month].
3. Cut-Off Date
   Lessor shall be obligated to purchase and lease each Item of Equipment specified in Section 1 of this Schedule to Lessee provided such Item of Equipment has been accepted by Lessee for lease in accordance with the provisions of Section 2.5 of the Lease on or before ____________, XXXX.
4. Discount Rate
   The Discount Rate applicable to each Unit shall be equal to an interest charge of ____ % per annum.
5. Lessor's Cost
   The Lessor's Cost for each Item of Equipment subject to this Schedule shall be an amount equal to the Invoice Purchase Price for such Item of Equipment plus all sales taxes in connection with the purchase from Manufacturer of such Item of Equipment, transportation charges in connection with the delivery of such Item of Equipment from the Manufacturer to Lessee and [insert other relevant charges which are to be included].
6. Overdue Rate
   The Overdue Rate for each Unit shall be equal to an interest charge of ____ % per annum.
7. Rent Date
   The Rent Date as to each Unit shall be the ________________ day of each ______________________ during the Primary Term and the

______ day of each ______________________ during any Renewal Term.

8. Unit Location
Each Unit shall be located at Lessee's place of business at ______________ ____.
9. Lessor Commitment
Lessor shall be obligated to purchase and lease Items of Equipment pursuant to the terms of the Lease and this Schedule with an aggregate Lessor's Cost of not less than $ ______________.
10. Lease Term

    (a) The Primary Term for each Unit shall commence on the Basic Lease Commencement Date of such Unit and shall end on the anniversary date thereof that number of years indicated below opposite the relevant Unit thereafter.

Unit Description	*Primary Term in Years*

    (b) The Renewal Term for each Unit shall be as specified in Section 13 of this Schedule.
11. Unit Rent

    (a) The Interim Rent for each Unit as to any Interim Term shall be payable on the Basic Lease Commencement Date of such Unit and shall be an amount equal to the Basic Rent multiplied by a fraction, the numerator of which is that number of days in the Interim Term and the denominator of which is that number of days in a Primary Term Rent payment period.
    (b) The Basic Rent shall be an amount equal to the product of the Basic Lease Rate Factor indicated below for the relevant Unit times the Lessor's Cost of such Unit.

Unit Description	*Basic Lease Rate Factor as a % of Lessor's Cost*

    (c) The Renewal Rent for each Unit shall be payable on each Rent Date during the Renewal Term in the amounts specified in Section 13 of this Schedule.
12. Casualty Value
The Casualty Value of each Unit shall be that percentage of the Lessor's Cost for such Unit as specified on Annex B attached hereto opposite the Rent Date through which Lessee has paid Rent.
13. Purchase and Renewal Right
Provided that the Lease has not been terminated earlier and no Event of Default has occurred and is continuing not earlier than one hundred eight (180) days and not later than ninety (90) days before the end of the Primary Term or each year of any Renewal Term of each Unit, Lessee may deliver to Lessor a written notice (a) tentatively electing either to purchase such Unit at the end of the Primary Term or each year of any Renewal Term for an amount equal to the Fair Market Value of such Unit at the end of such Term, or to extend the Term of this Lease at the end of the Primary Term or each year of any Renewal Term as to such Unit on a year-to-year basis (but such aggregate Renewal Term shall not exceed ____ years) at the Fair Market Rental at the end of such Term; and (b) appointing an Appraiser selected by Lessee to determine the Fair Market Value

or the Fair Market Rental thereof, whichever is applicable, in accordance with the provisions of Section 14 of the Lease. If no such written notice is delivered by Lessee to Lessor within such period, Lessee shall be deemed to have waived any right to purchase or extend the Term with respect to such Unit. At any time within the fifteen (15) day period following the determination of Fair Market Value or Fair Market Rental, as appropriate, of such Unit, Lessee may deliver to Lessor a further written notice finally electing to purchase or extend the Term with respect to such Unit. If no such further notice is delivered by Lessee to Lessor within such fifteen (15) day period, Lessee shall be deemed to have waived any right to purchase or extend the Term with respect to such Unit. At the end of the Term, if Lessee has finally elected to purchase such Unit, Lessee shall purchase from Lessor, and Lessor shall sell to Lessee, such Unit for a cash consideration equal to the Fair Market Value of such Unit, and Lessor shall transfer title to such Unit to Lessee without recourse or warranty, except that Lessor shall represent and warrant that it owns such Unit free and clear of any Lessor's Lien.

14. Early Termination Right

(a) Provided an Event of Default shall not have occurred and be continuing, Lessee shall have the right at its option at any time with not less than ninety (90) days prior written notice to Lessor to terminate the Lease with respect to any or all of the Units on the ______ Primary Term Rent Date or any Primary Term Rent Date thereafter for any one or more such Units (hereinafter called the "Termination Date"), provided that Lessee shall have made a good faith determination that such Unit or Units are obsolete or surplus to Lessee's requirements. During the period from the giving of such notice until the Termination Date Lessee, as agent for Lessor, shall use its best efforts to obtain bids for the purchase of such Unit or Units by a person other than Lessee or an affiliate of Lessee. Lessee shall promptly certify in writing to Lessor the amount and terms of each bid received by Lessee and the name and address of the party submitting such bid. Subject to Lessor's right to retain such Unit or Units as provided in Subsection (b) below, on the Termination Date Lessor shall sell such Unit or Units for cash to the bidder or bidders who shall have submitted the highest bid for each such Unit prior to such date and shall transfer title to such Unit or Units to such purchaser or purchasers without recourse or warranty, except that Lessor shall represent and warrant that it owns such Unit or Units free and clear of any Lessor's Lien. The total sale price realized upon such sale shall be retained by Lessor and, in addition, on the Termination Date, Lessee shall pay to Lessor the amount, if any, by which the Termination Value of such Unit or Units as provided in Subsection (d) below, computed as of the Termination Date, exceeds the proceeds of such sale, whereupon the Lease shall terminate as to such Unit or Units except as herein otherwise expressly provided. Subject to the provisions of Subsection (c) below, in the event no bids are received by Lessee, Lessee shall pay to Lessor the Termination Value of such Unit or Units, computed as of the Termination Date, and deliver such Unit or Units to the Lessor in accordance with the provisions of Section 17 of the Lease, whereupon the Lease shall terminate as to such Unit or Units, except as herein otherwise expressly provided.

(b) Notwithstanding the provisions of Subsection (a) above but subject to the provisions of Subsection (c) below, Lessor shall have the right at any time up to and including thirty (30) days prior to the Termination Date, within its sole discretion, to elect not to sell such Unit or Units to any prospective purchaser obtained by Lessee ("Third Party Purchaser"). In the event Lessor elects not to sell such Unit or Units to the Third Party Purchaser, Lessee shall return such Unit or Units to Lessor in accordance with the provisions of Section 17 of the Lease, and Lessor thereupon may retain such Unit or Units for its own account without further obligation under the Lease. If no sale shall have occurred on or as of the Termination Date because the Third Party Purchaser fails to consummate a proposed sale and Lessor shall not have requested the return of such Unit or Units pursuant hereto, the Lease shall continue in full force and effect as to such Unit or Units. In the event of any such sale or the return of such Unit or Units to Lessor pursuant hereto, and provided no Event of Default has occurred and is continuing, all obligations of Lessee to pay Rent and otherwise with respect to such Unit or Units for any period subsequent to the Termination Date shall cease.

(c) If the Termination Value exceeds the highest bidder in the event no bids are received by Lessee, or if Lessor should exercise its election under Subsection (b) above, Lessee may, at its option, upon written notice given to Lessor not less than fifteen (15) days prior to the Termination Date, elect to (i) rescind and cancel Lessee's notice of termination with respect to any one or more of such Units, whereupon the Lease shall not terminate with respect to such Unit or Units pursuant to this Section 14 but shall continue in full force and effect as though no notice of termination had been given by Lessee with respect to such Unit or Units, or (ii) pay Lessor the applicable Termination Value with respect to any one or more of such Units, whereupon Lessor shall transfer title to such Unit or Units to Lessee without recourse or warranty, except that Lessor shall represent and warrant that it owns such Unit or Units free and clear of any Lessor's Lien. In the event Lessee fails to pay Lessor an amount of money equal to the applicable Termination Value on the Termination Date, the Lease as to such Unit or Units shall continue in full force and effect.

(d) The Termination Value of any Unit shall be that percentage described on Annex C attached hereto of Lessor's Cost set forth opposite the Rent Date through which the Lessee has paid Rent.

15. Upgrade Right

[*Author's note:* This must be negotiated on a case-by-case basis. There is no one standard form.]

16. Representations and Warranties

Each of Lessor and Lessee represents and warrants to the other that:

(a) Its representations and warranties contained in Section 21 of the Lease are true and accurate on and as of the date of this Schedule as though made on and as of such date.

(b) It is not in default under any of the terms, covenants, agreements, or other provisions of the Lease.

(c) Simultaneously with the execution and delivery hereof it has delivered to the other its Incumbency Certificate, Certified Resolutions, and Opinion of Counsel substantially in the respective forms of Annexes D, E, and F attached hereto, with such changes as the receiving party shall reasonably request.

17. Term Definitions
    The terms used in this Schedule, where not defined in this Schedule to the contrary, shall have the same meanings as defined in the Lease.

______________________________, as Lessor

By: ______________________________

Title: ______________________________

______________________________, as Lessee

By: ______________________________

Title: ______________________________

Form: l-02b
Disk File Name: l-02b.rtf

CERTIFICATE OF ACCEPTANCE

Form Purpose

Form of master net finance equipment lease equipment lessee certificate of acceptance. This form is integrated with a master lease agreement, Lease Agreement Form l-02.

Executing Parties

The equipment lessee.

See:

Lease Agreement, Form l-02

Annex A

Certificate of Acceptance

Date ______________________________

Certificate of Acceptance No. ______________

to Equipment Schedule No. _____ ("Schedule")

dated as of, ______________________ XXXX

to Master Lease of Computer Equipment ("Lease")

dated as of ______________________, XXXX

between

_____________________________ ("Lessor")

and

_____________________________ ("Lessee")

Lessee hereby confirms that the Acceptance Date of the Unit or Units described in Exhibit A attached hereto shall be the date of this Certificate.

Lessee confirms that (a) such Unit or Units have been examined by duly appointed and authorized representatives of Lessee, (b) such Unit or Units have been duly accepted by Lessee as Units for Leasing under the Lease, (c) such Unit or Units have become subject to and governed by the terms of the Lease, and (d) Lessee has become obligated to pay to Lessor the Rent provided for in the Lease and the Schedule with respect to such Unit or Units.

The terms used herein shall have the respective meanings given to such terms in the Lease.

_____________________________, as Lessee

By: _____________________________

Title: ___________________________

Form: I-02c
Disk File Name: I-02c.rtf

Casualty Value Schedule

Form Purpose

Form of master net finance equipment lease casualty value schedule. This form is integrated with a master lease agreement, Lease Agreement Form I-02.

See:

Lease Agreement, Form I-02

Annex B

Casualty Value Schedule

After Rent Date No.	*Percentage of per Unit Cost*

Form: I-02d
Disk File Name: I-02d.rtf

Termination Value Schedule

Form Purpose

Form of master net finance equipment lease termination value schedule. This form is integrated with a master lease agreement, Lease Agreement Form I-02.

See:

Lease Agreement, Form I-02

Annex C

Termination Value Schedule

After Rent Date No.	*Percentage of Lessor's Cost*

Form: I-02e
Disk File Name: I-02e.rtf

INCUMBENCY CERTIFICATE

Form Purpose

Form of master net finance equipment lease incumbency certificate. This form is integrated with a master lease agreement, Lease Agreement Form I-02.

Executing Parties

The equipment lessee's secretary or assistant secretary.

See:

Lease Agreement, Form I-02

Annex D

Incumbency Certificate

This Certificate is delivered by the undersigned pursuant to the Master Lease of Computer Equipment (the "Lease") dated as of ______________________________ between ______________________________ (the "Lessor"), and ______________________________ (the "Lessee"):

The undersigned hereby certifies that the following persons are on the date hereof, and have been at all times since __________________________, duly elected or appointed, qualified, and acting officers of the undersigned holding the offices set forth opposite their respective names below and that the signatures set forth opposite their respective names and offices below are their genuine signatures:

Name	*Title*	*Signature*
____________________	____________________	____________________
____________________	____________________	____________________
____________________	____________________	____________________
____________________	____________________	____________________

____

Secretary

Form: l-02f
Disk File Name: l-02f.rtf

Certified Resolutions

Form Purpose

Form of lessee's certified corporate resolutions authorizing the entering into of an equipment lease transaction. This form is integrated with a master lease agreement, Lease Agreement Form l-02.

Executing Parties

The equipment lessee's secretary or assistant secretary.

See:

Lease Agreement, Form l-02

Annex E

Certified Resolutions

The undersigned, being the ______________________ of ______________________ a ______________________ corporation ("______________________"), does hereby certify that the following is a true and correct copy of certain resolutions duly adopted by the ______________________ of ______________________ on ______________________, XXXX, and that such resolutions have not been modified or rescinded and remain in full force and effect on the date hereof:

"RESOLVED, that the proposed Master Lease of Computer Equipment (the "Lease"), including the proposed Equipment Schedule attached as Annex A thereto (the "Schedule"), between ______________________ as ______________________ and this Corporation as ______________________, in the form of the draft of ______________________, XXXX filed with the records of this Corporation, be, and it hereby is, approved in all respects; and further

RESOLVED, that the officers of this Corporation be, and each and any of them hereby is, authorized and empowered, in the name and on behalf of this Corporation, to execute and deliver the Lease and any Schedule substantially in the form approved in the preceding resolution, together with such changes therein as such officers or any of them, in conjunction with counsel to this Corporation, shall from time to time in their discretion deem necessary or desirable and shall approve, such approval to be conclusively evidenced by their execution and delivery thereof, and to enforce all rights and perform all obligations of this Corporation thereunder; provided, however, that without further action by this Board of Directors the aggregate cost of equipment to become subject to the Lease and all Schedules shall not exceed $ ______________________; and further

RESOLVED, that the officers of this Corporation be, and each and any of them hereby is, authorized and empowered, in the name and on behalf of this Corporation, to execute, deliver, file, and record any and all such further agreements, undertakings, instruments, certificates, letters, and documents, and to perform any and all such further actions, as such officers or any of them, in conjunction with counsel to this Corporation, shall from time to time in their discretion deem necessary or desirable to fully effectuate the Lease and the purposes of the foregoing resolutions."

IN WITNESS WHEREOF, the undersigned has made and executed this Certificate as of this ____ day of ______________________, XXXX.

____

Secretary

Form: I-02g
Disk File Name: I-02g.rtf

Opinion of Counsel

Form Purpose

Form of master net finance lease lessee's counsel opinion. This form is integrated with a master lease agreement, Lease Agreement Form I-02.

Executing Parties

The equipment lessee's counsel.

See:

Lease Agreement, Form I-02

Annex F

Opinion of Counsel

______________________________, XXXX

Gentlemen:

As counsel to ____________________ ("____________________") I have examined the Master Lease of Computer Equipment dated as of ________ XXXX (the "Lease"), between ______________ and ______________ and Equipment Schedule No. ________ to the Lease dated of even date herewith, such other documents and corporate records, and such questions of law as I have deemed relevant for purposes of the opinions expressed below. The terms used herein have the same meanings as defined in the Lease. Based on such examination, I am of the opinion that:

1. ____________________________ is a corporation duly organized, validly existing, and in good standing under the laws of the ____________; has full power and authority to carry on its business as presently conducted, to own or hold under lease its properties and to enter into and perform its obligations under the Lease; and is duly qualified to do business as a foreign corporation and is in good standing in each jurisdiction in which the location of any Unit requires such qualification.

2. The execution, delivery, and performance by ____________________ of the Lease have been duly authorized by all necessary corporate action on the part of ____________________________, do not materially contravene any law, governmental rule, regulation, or Order binding on ____________________ or its properties or the corporate charter or By-Laws of ____________________, and to the best of my knowledge do not contravene the provisions of, or constitute a material default under, or result in the creation of any Lien upon the Units under, any material indenture, mortgage, contract, or other instrument to which ________________ is a party or by which ____________________________ or its property is bound.

3. No consent or approval of, giving of notice to, registration with, or taking of any other action by, any state, federal, or other governmental commission, agency, or regulatory authority is required for the performance by ____________________ of the transactions contemplated by the Lease; or, if any such action is required, it has been obtained, performed, or registered.

4. The Lease has been duly entered into and delivered by ____________________, and constitutes a legal, valid, and binding agreement of ____________________ enforceable against ____________________________ in accordance with its terms, except as limited by (a) bankruptcy, insolvency, reorganization, or other similar laws of general application affecting the enforcement of creditors' or lessors' rights (b) emergency powers lawfully conferred upon any governmental agency, and (c) laws or judicial decisions limiting the right to specific performance or other equitable remedies, and the Lease creates a valid leasehold interest in the Units.

5. To the best of my knowledge there are no actions, suits, or proceedings pending or threatened before any court, administrative agency, arbitrator, or Governmental Body which would, if determined adversely to ____________________________,

have a material adverse effect on the business, assets, operations, or condition, financial or otherwise, of ______________________, or materially adversely affect the ability of ______________________ to perform its obligations under the Lease; and to the best of my knowledge ______________________ is not in material default with respect to any material Order of any court, arbitrator, or Governmental Body.

6. No recorded Lien other than the Lease of any nature whatsoever which now covers or affects, or which will hereafter cover or affect, any property (or interests therein) of ______________________ now attaches or hereafter will attach to any of the Units, or materially adversely affects or will affect ______________________ right, title and interest in or to any of the Units.

Very truly yours,

Form: l-02h
Disk File Name: l-02h.rtf

PROHIBITED LENDER ASSIGNEE SCHEDULE

Form Purpose

Form of master net finance lease prohibited lender assignees. This form is integrated with a master lease agreement, Lease Agreement Form l-02.

See:

Lease Agreement, Form l-02

Annex G

Prohibited Lender Assignees

Form: l-03
Disk File Name: l-03.rtf

LEASE AGREEMENT—SHORT FORM (GENERAL)

Form Purpose

Short-form, net finance master equipment lease agreement. The master format allows future equipment to be easily added by means of a schedule. This form is set up so that each schedule is a lease, making it easy to enter into loan arrangements with various lenders that provide equipment purchase funds, and is part of an integrated package, including all key closing documents.

Executing Parties

The equipment lessor.
The equipment lessee.

See:

Schedule, Form l-03a
Acceptance Certificate, Form l-03b
Casualty Value Table, Form l-03c
Amendment, Form a-13
Automatic Transfer of Title, Form o-16
Insurance Notification, Form i-02
Representation and Warranties, Form l-03d
Opinion of Counsel–Lessee, Form l-03e
Opinion of Counsel–Guarantor, Form l-03f
Purchase–Fair Market Value, Form o-11
Purchase–Fixed Price, Form o-12
Put, Form o–17
Renewal–Fair Market Value, Form o-13
Renewal–Fixed Price, Form o-14
Sublease Right, Form o-15
Secretary's Certificate-Lessee Resolutions, Form c-15
Secretary's Certificate-Guarantor's Resolutions, Form c-09

Master Agreement No. ________________

Master Agreement to Lease Equipment

(Insert name of leasing company), Lessor

Home Office: Address: ____

Phone: ( ) ________________

and ____, Lessee, a ____________________________________ corporation, hereby agree as of this ________ day of __________________, XXXX as follows:

1. Agreement to Lease. This Agreement sets forth the basic terms and conditions upon which Lessor shall lease to Lessee and Lessee shall lease from Lessor items of equipment ("Units") specified in Schedules to be entered into from time to time. Each Schedule shall incorporate the terms and conditions of this Agreement and shall constitute a lease as to the Units specified in such Schedule. The term "Lease" as to each Unit as used in this Agreement shall mean the applicable Schedule which incorporates the terms and conditions of this Agreement.

2. Acceptance. Lessee shall accept each Unit for lease by delivering to Lessor an executed Acceptance Certificate in the form provided by Lessor whereupon such Unit shall be deemed accepted by Lessee and become subject to the Lease on the Acceptance Certificate Execution Date.

3. Rent and Lease Term. Lessee shall pay Lessor Rent for each Unit in the amounts and at the times specified in the Lease. The Lease Term for each Unit shall commence on the Acceptance Certificate Execution Date and shall continue for the period specified in the Lease. The Lease Term as to any Unit may not be terminated by Lessee unless otherwise expressly provided in the Lease.

4. Payment Obligation. All Rent and other payments under each Lease shall be made to Lessor at its address shown above, or at such other address as Lessor may designate, in immediately available funds in such coin or currency of the United States of America which at the time of payment shall be legal tender for the payment of public and private debts. EACH LEASE SHALL BE A NET LEASE, AND LESSEE'S OBLIGATION TO PAY ALL RENT AND OTHER SUMS THEREUNDER SHALL BE ABSOLUTE AND UNCONDITIONAL, AND SHALL NOT BE SUBJECT TO ANY ABATEMENT, REDUCTION, SETOFF, DEFENSE, COUNTERCLAIM, INTERRUPTION, DEFERMENT, OR RECOUPMENT, FOR ANY REASON WHATSOEVER.

5. Statement of Lease. Each Lease shall constitute a lease of personal property and Lessee agrees to take all actions necessary or reasonably requested by Lessor to ensure that each Unit shall be and remain personal property, and nothing in any Lease shall be constituted as conveying to Lessee any interest in any Unit other than its interest as a lessee. Lessee shall, at its expense, protect and defined the interests of Lessor in each Unit against all third party claims; keep each Unit free and clear of any mortgage, security interest, pledge, lien, charge, claim, or other encumbrance (collectively, "Lien"), except any Lien arising solely through acts of Lessor ("Lessor's Lien"); give Lessor immediate notice of the existence of any such Lien; and indemnify and defend Lessor

against any claim, liability, loss, damage, or expense arising in connection with any of the foregoing.

6. Use. Each Unit shall be used and operated by Lessee only in the ordinary conduct of its business by qualified employees of Lessee and in accordance with all applicable manufacturer and vendor instructions as well as with all applicable legal and regulatory requirements. Lessee shall not change the location of any Unit from that specified in the Lease without obtaining Lessor's prior consent.

7. Maintenance and Alterations. Lessee shall, at its expense, repair and maintain each Unit so that it will remain in the same condition as when delivered to Lessee, ordinary wear and tear from proper use excepted. Such repair and maintenance shall be performed in compliance with all requirements necessary to enforce all product warranty rights and with all applicable legal and regulatory requirements. Lessee shall enter into and keep in effect during the Lease Term those maintenance agreements with respect to each Unit required by the Lease. Lessee shall, at its expense, make such alterations ("Required Alterations") to each Unit during the Unit's Lease Term as may be required by applicable legal and regulatory requirements. In addition, Lessee may at its expense, without Lessor's consent, so long as no Event of Default, or event which with the passage of time or giving of notice, or both, would constitute an Event of Default ("Incipient Default"), has occurred and is continuing, make alterations ("Permitted Alterations") to any Unit which do not impair the commercial value or originally intended function or use of such Unit and which are readily removable without causing material damage to such Unit. Any Permitted Alterations not removed by Lessee prior to the return of such Unit to Lessor, and all Required Alterations, shall immediately without further action become the property of Lessor and part of such Unit for all purposes of the Lease. Other than as provided in this Section 7, Lessee may make no alterations to any Unit. Any prohibited alterations to a Unit shall, at Lessor's election, immediately become the property of Lessor without further action and without Lessor thereby waiving any Incipient Default or Event of Default.

8. Return. At the expiration or earlier termination of the Lease Term as to each Unit, Lessee shall, at its expense, return such Unit to Lessor at the location in the continental United States specified by Lessor.

9. Identification. Lessee shall, at its expense, place and maintain permanent markings on each Unit evidencing Ownership, security and other interests therein, as specified from time to time by Lessor. Lessee shall not place or permit to be placed any other markings on any Unit which might indicate any ownership or security interest in such Unit. Any markings, on any Unit not made at Lessor's request shall be removed by Lessee, at its expense, prior to the return of such Unit in accordance with Section 8.

10. Inspection. Upon reasonable prior notice, Lessee shall make each Unit and all related records available to Lessor or its agents for inspection during regular business hours, at the location of such Unit.

11. No Lessee Sublease or Assignment. Lessee shall not, unless, expressly permitted in the Lease, sublease or otherwise, relinquish possession or control of, or assign, pledge, hypothecate, or otherwise transfer, dispose of, or encumber, any Unit, this Agreement or any Lease or any part thereof or interest therein, or any right or obligation with respect thereto.

12. Lessor Assignment. Lessor may from time to time without notice to Lessee sell, grant a security interest in, assign, or otherwise transfer (collectively "Transfer"), in whole or in part, this Agreement, one or more Leases, any or all Units, or any of its

interests, rights, or obligations with respect thereto, including without limitation all Rent and other sums due or to become due under any Lease, to one or more persons or entities ("Assignee"). Each Assignee shall have, to the extent provided in any Transfer document, Lessor's rights, powers, privileges, and remedies with respect thereto, but shall not be obligated to Lessee, except to the extent expressly provided in any Transfer document, to observe or perform any duty, covenant, or condition required to be observed or performed by Lessor. Except to the extent expressly assumed by an Assignee in any Transfer document, no Transfer shall relieve Lessor from any of its obligations to Lessee. Lessee shall, upon receipt of notice of a Transfer from Lessor, be bound by such Transfer. Lessee shall not assert against any Assignee any claim, defense, counterclaim, or setoff that Lessee may at any time have against Lessor.

13. Liens. Lessee shall not directly or indirectly create, incur, assume, or suffer to exist any Lien on or with respect to any Unit or Lease, Lessor's title to any such Unit, or other interest or right of Lessor with respect thereto, except Lessor's, Liens. Lessee, at its expense, shall promptly pay, satisfy, and take such other action as may be necessary or reasonably requested by Lessor to keep each Unit and Lease free and clear of, and to duly and promptly discharge, any such Lien.

14. Risk of Loss, Lessee shall bear all risk of loss, damage, theft, taking, destruction, confiscation, or requisition with respect to each Unit, however caused or occasioned, which shall occur prior to the return of such Unit in accordance with Section 8. In addition, Lessee hereby assumes all other risks and liabilities, including without limitation personal injury or death and property damage, arising with respect to each Unit (unless arising solely through Lessor's willful misconduct), including without limitation those arising with respect to the manufacture, purchase, ownership, shipment, transportation, delivery, installation, leasing, possession, use, storage, and return of such Unit, howsoever arising, in connection with any event occurring prior to such Unit's return in accordance with Section 8.

15. Casualty. If any Unit shall become lost, stolen, destroyed, or irreparably damaged from any cause whatsoever, or shall be taken, confiscated, or requisitioned (any such event herein called an "Event of Loss"), Lessee shall promptly notify Lessor of the occurrence of such Event of Loss, and shall pay Lessor, within 15 days after the date of such Event of Loss (but in no event later than the Rent payment date next following such Event of Loss), an amount equal to the applicable Casualty Value of such Unit as specified in the Lease. Upon Lessor's receipt of such payment in full, the Lease shall automatically terminate as to such Unit, and Lessor's right, title, and interest in such Unit shall immediately without further action pass to Lessee, on an as-is, where-is basis, without recourse or warranty.

16. Insurance. Lessee shall, at its expense, cause to be carried and maintained for each Unit, commencing at the time any risk shall pass to Lessor as to such Unit and continuing until the return of such Unit in accordance with Section 8, insurance against such risks, in such amounts, in such form, and with such insurers, all as may be satisfactory to Lessor. If any insurance proceeds are received with respect to an occurrence which does not constitute an Event of Loss, and no Incipient Default or Event of Default has occurred and is continuing, such proceeds shall be applied to payment for repairs. If any insurance proceeds are received by Lessor with respect to an occurrence which constitutes an Event of Loss, and no Incipient Default or Event of Default has occurred and is continuing, such proceeds shall be applied toward Lessee's obligation to pay the applicable Casualty Value for such Unit. If an Incipient Default or Event of Default has occurred and is continuing, any insurance proceeds received shall be applied as Lessor in its sole

discretion may determine. At the time each Schedule is executed and thereafter on a date not less than 30 days prior to each insurance policy expiration date, Lessee shall deliver to Lessor certificates of insurance or other evidence satisfactory to Lessor showing that such insurance coverage is and will remain in effect in accordance with Lessee's obligations under this Section 16. Lessor shall be under no duty to ascertain the existence of any insurance coverage or to examine any certificate of insurance or other evidence of insurance coverage or to advise Lessee in the event the insurance coverage does not comply with the requirements hereof. Lessee shall give Lessor prompt notice of any damage, loss, or other occurrence required to be insured against with respect to any Unit.

17. Taxes and Fees. Lessee hereby assumes liability for, and shall pay when due, and on a net after-tax basis shall indemnify and defend Lessor against, all fees, taxes, and governmental charges (including without limitation interest and penalties) of any nature imposed upon or in any way relating to Lessor, Lessee, any Unit (including without limitation the manufacture, purchase, ownership, shipment, transportation, delivery, installation. leasing, possession, use, operation, storage, and return of such Unit) or any Lease, except state and local taxes on or measured by Lessor's net income payable to each state and locality in which Lessor maintains one or more places of business immediately prior to the date of the applicable Lease (other than any such tax which is in substitution for or relieves Lessee from the payment of taxes it would otherwise be obligated to pay or reimburse Lessor as provided), and federal taxes on Lessor's net income. Lessee shall at its expense file when due with the appropriate authorities any and all tax and similar returns and reports required to be filed with respect thereto (with copies to Lessor) or, if requested by Lessor, notify Lessor of all such requirements and furnish Lessor with all information required for Lessor to effect such filings, which filings shall also be at Lessee's expense.

18. Indemnification. Lessee hereby assumes liability for, and shall pay when due, and shall indemnity and defend Lessor against, any and all liabilities, losses, damages, claims, and expenses in any way relating to or arising out of any Lease or any Unit, including without limitation the manufacture, purchase, ownership, shipment, transportation, delivery, installation, leasing, possession, use, operation, storage, and return of such Unit. Lessee shall give Lessor prompt notice of any occurrence, event, or condition in connection with which Lessor may be entitled to indemnification hereunder. The provisions of this Section 18 are in addition to, and not in limitation of, the provisions of Section 17.

19. Limited Warranty. Lessor warrants to Lessee that, so long as no Incipient Default or Event of Default has occurred and is continuing, Lessor will not interfere with Lessee's use and possession of the Units. LESSOR, NOT BEING THE MANUFACTURER OR VENDOR OF THE UNITS, MAKES NO OTHER REPRESENTATION OR WARRANTY, EXPRESS OR IMPLIED, AS TO ANY MATTER WHATSOEVER, INCLUDING WITHOUT LIMITATION THE DESIGN OR CONDITION OF THE UNITS, THEIR MERCHANTABILITY, DURABILITY, SUITABILITY OR FITNESS FOR ANY PARTICULAR PURPOSE, THE QUALITY OF THE MATERIAL OR WORKMANSHIP OF THE UNITS, OR THE CONFORMITY OF THE UNITS TO THE PROVISIONS OR SPECIFICATIONS OF ANY PURCHASE ORDER RELATING THERETO, AND LESSOR HEREBY DISCLAIMS ANY AND ALL SUCH REPRESENTATIONS AND WARRANTIES, LESSEE ACKNOWLEDGES THAT IT HAS MADE THE SELECTION OF EACH UNIT BASED UPON ITS OWN JUDGMENT AND EXPRESSLY DISCLAIMS ANY RELIANCE ON STATEMENTS MADE BY LESSOR. Lessor hereby appoints Lessee as Lessor's agent, so long as no Incipient Default or Event of Default has occurred and is continuing, to assert

at Lessee's expense any right Lessor may have against any manufacturer or vendor to enforce any product warranties with respect to each Unit during such Unit's Lease Term; provided, however, Lessee shall indemnify and defend Lessor against all claims, expenses, damages, losses and liabilities incurred or suffered by Lessor in connection with any such action taken by Lessee.

20. Events of Default. An "Event of Default" shall occur if (a) Lessee fails to make any Rent or other payment under any Lease when due and such failure continues for a period of 5 days thereafter; (b) Lessee violates any covenant set forth in Section 8, 11, or 16 or the last sentence of this Section 20; (c) Lessee violates any other provision of this Agreement, any Lease or any document furnished Lessor in connection herewith or therewith and such violation shall continue unremedied for a period of 20 days after notice from Lessor; (d) Lessee or any guarantor of Lessee's obligations under any Lease ("Guarantor") or any material subsidiary of Lessee or Guarantor ("Subsidiary") shall be in default with respect to any other agreement with Lessor or any other obligation for the payment of borrowed money or rent; (e) Lessee, any Guarantor or any Subsidiary shall commit an act of bankruptcy or become or be adjudicated insolvent or bankrupt or make an assignment for the benefit of creditors or become unable or admit in writing its inability to pay its debts as they become due, or a trustee receiver or liquidator shall be appointed for Lessee, any Guarantor or any Subsidiary, or for a substantial part of its property, with or without its consent, or bankruptcy, arrangement, reorganization, composition, readjustment, liquidation, insolvency, dissolution, or similar proceedings under any present or future statute, law, or regulation shall be instituted by or against Lessee, any Guarantor, or any Subsidiary, or Lessee, any Guarantor, or any Subsidiary shall file an answer admitting the material allegations of a petition filed against it in any such proceeding, or any execution or writ or process shall be issued under any proceeding whereby any Unit may be taken or restrained, or Lessee, any Guarantor, or any Subsidiary shall cease doing business as a going concern; or Lessee, any Guarantor, or any Subsidiary shall, without Lessor's prior consent, sell, transfer, pledge, or otherwise dispose of all or any substantial part of its assets, or consolidate or merge with any other entity; or (f) any representation or warranty made by Lessee, any Guarantor, or any Subsidiary in any document furnished Lessor under or pursuant to this Agreement or any Lease shall be incorrect or incomplete at any time in any material respect. Lessee shall promptly notify Lessor of the occurrence of any Incipient Default or Event of Default.

21. Remedies. If one or more Events of Default shall have occurred and be continuing, Lessor, at its option, may (a) proceed by appropriate court action or actions, either at law or in equity, to enforce performance by Lessee of the applicable covenants of each Lease or to recover damages for the breach thereof, including without limitation net after-tax losses of federal, state, and local income tax benefits to which Lessor would otherwise be entitled as a result of owning any Unit or leasing such Unit to Lessee, or (b) by notice to Lessee terminate any or all Leases with respect to any one or more of the Units covered thereby, whereupon all rights of Lessee to the possession and use of such Units shall absolutely cease and terminate as though each such Lease as to such Units had never been entered into; provided, however, Lessee shall nevertheless remain liable under each such Lease; and thereupon Lessor may, by its agent or agents, enter upon the premises of Lessee or any other premises where any of such Units maybe located and take possession of all or any of such Units and from that point hold, possess, operate, sell, lease, and enjoy such Units free from any right of Lessee, its successors and assigns, to use such Units for any purposes whatsoever without any duty to account to Lessee for any action or inaction or for any proceeds arising therefrom; provided, however, Les-

sor shall nevertheless have a right to recover from Lessee any and all amounts which under the terms of each such Lease may be then due or which may have accrued to the date of such termination and also to recover immediately from Lessee (x) as damages for loss of the bargain and not as a penalty, whichever of the following sums, with respect to each such Unit, Lessor in its sole discretion shall specify by notice to Lessee: (i) an amount equal to the excess, if any, of the Casualty Value for such Unit, in effect for the Rent payment period during which the specified Event of Default occurred, over the present value (computed as of the Rent payment date next following the date of such notice) of the rent which Lessor reasonably estimates will be realized for such Unit for the remainder of the initially specified Lease Term of such Unit following the termination of the Lease, such present value to be computed by discounting such estimated rent payments at a 5% per annum rate of interest (based on a 360-day year and 30-day month), or (ii) an amount equal to the excess, if any, of the Casualty Value for such Unit in effect for the Rent payment period during which the specified Event of Default has occurred over the amount Lessor reasonably estimates to be the sales value of such Unit as of the date of the estimate specified in such notice and (y) all damages, losses, liabilities, claims, and expenses (including without limitation expenses incurred in connection with the recovery, repair, repainting, return, and remarking of any Unit or other exercise of Lessor's remedies hereunder and reasonable attorneys' fees) which Lessor shall sustain in connection with any Event of Default. No remedy referred to in this Section 21 shall be deemed exclusive, but all such remedies shall be cumulative and shall be in addition to all other remedies in Lessor's favor existing under this Agreement, any Lease or otherwise at law or in equity.

22. Financial Information. Lessee agrees to furnish Lessor (a) as soon as available, and in any event within 120 days after the last day of' each fiscal year of Lessee, a copy of the financial statements of Lessee as of the end of such fiscal year, certified by an independent certified public accounting firm of recognized standing reasonably satisfactory to Lessor, (b) within 45 days after the last day of each fiscal quarter of Lessee a copy of its financial statements as of the end of such quarter certified by the principal financial officer of Lessee, and (c) such additional information concerning Lessee, any Guarantor, and any Subsidiary as Lessor may reasonably request.

23. Lessor's Qualified Obligation. Lessor shall not be obligated to lease any Unit specified in a Lease to Lessee if (i) such Unit is not accepted by Lessee on or before the Acquisition Expiration Date specified in such Lease or (ii) the Acquisition Cost of such Unit, when added to the Acquisition Cost of the Units specified in such Lease previously accepted for lease, is in excess of the Aggregate Acquisition Cost set forth in such Lease. In addition, anything in this Agreement or any Lease to the contrary notwithstanding, Lessor shall not be obligated to acquire or lease to Lessee any Units not already subject to a Lease if Lessor determines Lessee's financial or business condition (or that of any Guarantor or any Subsidiary) has suffered any material adverse change from the condition existing or represented to Lessor as at the date of such Lease. In such event, Lessee shall promptly pay Lessor and indemnify and defend Lessor against all amounts which Lessor has expended or may be or become obligated to expend with respect to each such Unit and the transactions contemplated under the Lease and shall assume, undertake, and relieve Lessor of, and indemnify and defend Lessor against, all damages, losses, claims, liabilities, obligations, and duties under any related requisition, purchase order, purchase contract, or otherwise with respect thereto.

24. Late Charges. Any nonpayment of Rent or other amounts payable under any Lease shall result in Lessee's obligation to promptly pay Lessor as additional Rent on

such overdue payment, for the period of time during which it is overdue (without regard to any grace period), interest at a rate equal to the lesser of (a) the Late Charge set forth in the Lease, or (b) the maximum rate of interest permitted by law.

25. Lessor's Right to Perform for Lessee. If Lessee fails to duly and promptly pay, perform, or comply with any of its obligations, covenants, or agreements under any Lease, Lessor may itself pay, perform, or comply with any of such obligations, covenants, or agreements for the account of Lessee without thereby waiving any Incipient Default or Event of Default. In such event, any amount paid or expense incurred by Lessor in connection therewith shall immediately on demand, together with interest as provided in Section 24, be paid to Lessor as additional Rent, and Lessee shall indemnify and defend Lessor against any damage, loss, claim, liability, or expense suffered or incurred by Lessor in connection therewith.

26. Notices. Any consent, instruction, or notice required or permitted to be given under any Lease shall be in writing and shall become effective when delivered, or if mailed when deposited in the United States mail with proper postage prepaid for registered or certified mail, return receipt requested, addressed to Lessor or Lessee, as the case may be, at their respective addresses set forth herein or at such other address as Lessor or Lessee shall from time to time designate to the other party by notice similarly given.

27. Miscellaneous. Lessee shall, at its expense and upon Lessor's demand, promptly execute, acknowledge, deliver, file, register, and record any and all further documents and take any and all other action reasonably requested by Lessor from time to time, for the purpose of fully effectuating the intent and purposes of each Lease, and to protect the interests of Lessor, its successors and assigns. Any provision of any Lease which is prohibited or not fully enforceable in any jurisdiction shall, as to such jurisdiction, be ineffective only to the extent of such prohibition or unenforceability without otherwise invalidating or diminishing Lessor's rights thereunder or under the remaining provisions thereof in such jurisdiction, and any such prohibition or unenforceability in any jurisdiction shall not invalidate or render unenforceable such provision in any other jurisdiction. To the extent permitted by applicable law, Lessee hereby waives its rights under any provision of law now or hereafter in effect which might limit or modify or otherwise render unenforceable in any respect any remedy or other provision of any Lease. No term or provision of any Lease may be amended, altered, waived, discharged, or terminated except by an instrument in writing signed by a duly authorized officer of the party against which the enforcement of the amendment, alteration, waiver, discharge, or termination is sought. No delay by Lessor in exercising any right, power, or remedy under any Lease shall constitute a waiver, and any waiver by Lessor on any one occasion or for any one purpose shall not be construed as a waiver on any future occasion or for any other purpose. Except as otherwise specifically provided in any Lease, each Lease shall be governed in all respects by, and construed in accordance with, the laws of the State of ________. All of the covenants and agreements of Lessee contained in each Lease shall survive the expiration or earlier termination of such Lease and the Lease Term of the Units leased thereunder. Subject to all of the terms and provisions of each Lease, all of the covenants, conditions, and obligations contained in such Lease shall be binding upon and inure to the benefit of the respective successors and assigns of Lessor and Lessee. Each Lease, and any documents executed and delivered in connection therewith, shall constitute the entire agreement of Lessor and Lessee with respect to the Units leased thereby, and shall automatically cancel and supersede any and all prior oral or written understandings with respect thereto. This Agreement and each Lease may be

executed in any number of counterparts, each of which, when so executed and delivered, shall be an original (except that to the extent, if any, this Agreement or any Lease constitutes chattel paper, no security interest therein may be created except through the transfer or possession of the original counterpart, which shall be identified by Lessor), but all such counterparts taken together shall constitute one and the same instrument. The headings in this Agreement and each Lease shall be for convenience of reference only and shall form no part of this Agreement or such Lease.

IN WITNESS WHEREOF, the parties hereto have caused this Agreement to be duly executed by their authorized representatives as of the date first above written.

(Insert name of leasing company), Lessor

By: ______________________________

Title: ______________________________

______________________________, Lessee

By: ______________________________

Title: ______________________________

Address: ______________________________

____

____

Phone: (   ) ______________________________

Form: l-03a
Disk File Name: l-03a.rtf

SCHEDULE

Form Purpose

Schedule to short-form, net finance master equipment lease agreement. This form is integrated with Lease Agreement Form l-03. The Schedule sets forth those terms and conditions that will vary from time to time with respect to equipment identified in the Schedule.

Executing Parties

The equipment lessor.
The equipment lessee.

See:

Lease Agreement, Form l-03

Master Agreement No. ________________

Schedule No. ________ ("Lease"),

Dated as of ________________________________, to Master Agreement to Lease

Equipment, Dated as of ________________________________, between

________________________, Lessor

Home Office: Address: ________________________

Phone: ( ) ________________________

and ________________________, Lessee

Address: ________________________

____

____

Phone: ( ) ________________

1. Equipment Description:

Manufacturer or Vendor	*Unit Description*	*New/ Model Used*	*Acquisition Cost Per Unit*	*Total*	*Qty.*

Aggregate Acquisition Cost $ ________________

2. Equipment Location:

Unit Description	*Street Address*	*City*	*County*	*State*	*Zip*

3. Acquisition Cost:

The "Acquisition Cost" of each Unit shall mean the sum of the actual purchase price of such Unit plus the additional expenses listed below (not to exceed in the aggregate ____ % of the actual purchase price of such Unit):

4. Acquisition Expiration Date: ________________

5. Lease Term:

The "Lease Term" of each Unit shall be that period specified below:

Unit Description *Primary Term*

plus a period of time ("Interim Term"), if any, from the Acceptance Certificate Execution Date to, but not including, ____________________

6. Rent:

The daily Rent for each Unit for the Interim Term, if any, shall be equal to the daily equivalent (based on a 30-day month and a 360-day year) of the Rent specified below.

The Rent for each Unit during the Primary Term shall be payable in that number of consecutive, level payments indicated below, in ______________________________ on the ____________ day of each ____________________ and each Rent payment shall be in an amount equal to the indicated percentage of Acquisition Cost of such Unit.

Unit Description	*Number of Rent Payments*	*Percentage of Acquisition Cost*

7. Late Charge:

_________ % per annum.

8. Casualty Value:

The Casualty Value from time to time of each Unit shall be as specified on Annex A to this Lease.

9. Maintenance Agreement Requirements:

(If none, so state.)

10. Identification:

Lessee shall place the following identification marking prominently on each Unit:

(Insert name of leasing company), Lessor/Owner, (Insert City of Lessor) (Insert State of Lessor)

11. Special Terms:

The following Riders attached hereto shall constitute a part of this Lease:

12. Definitions:

The terms used in this Lease which are not otherwise defined herein shall have the meanings set forth in the Master Agreement to Lease Equipment identified above.

13. Terms of Schedule:

Lessor and Lessee agree that this Lease shall constitute a lease of each Unit described in Section 1 of this Lease, upon the execution and delivery to Lessor by Lessee of an Acceptance Certificate with respect to such Unit in the form of Annex B to this Lease, and of which each such Unit shall be subject to the terms and conditions of this Lease and of the Master Agreement to Lease Equipment, the terms and conditions of which are hereby incorporated by reference in full in this Lease and made a part of this Lease to the same extent as if such terms and conditions were set forth herein.

IN WITNESS WHEREOF, Lessor and Lessee have caused this Lease to be duly executed by their authorized representatives as of the date first above written.

________________________________, Lessor

By: ________________________________

Title: ______________________________

________________________________, Lessee

By: ________________________________

Title: ______________________________

Annex A
to Schedule No. __________

[See Casualty Value Table, Form 1-03c]

Annex B
to Schedule No. ___________

[See Acceptance Certificate, Form l-03b]

Form: l-03b
Disk File Name: l-03b.rtf

ACCEPTANCE CERTIFICATE

Form Purpose

Lessee equipment certificate of acceptance. This form is integrated with a master equipment lease agreement, Lease Agreement Form l-03.

Executing Parties

The equipment lessee.

See:

Lease Agreement, Form l-03

Annex B
to Schedule No. ____________

Acceptance Certificate No. __________ under Schedule No. ________, dated as of ______________________________ to Master Agreement to Lease Equipment dated as of ________________ between

__________________________, Lessor, and __________________________, Lessee

Acceptance Certificate Execution Date: ______________________________

This Acceptance Certificate is issued pursuant to the Master Agreement to Lease Equipment and Schedule designated above.

Lessee acknowledges that each Unit specified on Exhibit A (i) has been delivered to, inspected by, and accepted as of this date for lease by Lessee, (ii) is of a size, design, capacity, and manufacture acceptable to Lessee and suitable for Lessee's purposes, (iii) is in good working order, repair, and condition, and (iv) has been installed to Lessee's satisfaction or located, as the case may be, at the location specified on Exhibit A.

Lessee confirms and agrees that (i) no Incipient Default or Event of Default under any Lease entered into pursuant to the Master Agreement to Lease Equipment has occurred and is continuing and (ii) the representations and warranties in the Officer's Certificate dated ______________ executed and delivered in connection with the Lease are correct and complete as though made on and as of the date hereof and shall continue to be correct and complete throughout the Lease Term of each Unit accepted hereby.

The person signing this Acceptance Certificate on behalf of Lessee hereby certifies that such person has read and acknowledges all terms and conditions of the Lease, and is duly authorized to execute this Acceptance Certificate on behalf of Lessee.

The terms used in this Acceptance Certificate shall have the same meanings defined in the Master Agreement to Lease Equipment and the Schedule designated above.

__________________________, Lessee

By: __________________________

Title: __________________________

Exhibit A
to

Acceptance Certificate No. ________, dated ________________________, to Schedule No. ______, dated ______________________________________, to Master Agreement to Lease Equipment, dated ____________________________________, between

______________________________, Lessor

and

______________________________, Lessee

Qty.	Mfr. or Vendor	Descrip.	Unit Model	Term	Periodic Primary Rent (In Dollars)	New/ Used	Location	I.D. or Ser. No.	Acquisition Cost Per Unit	Total

Aggregate Acquisition Cost of Units subject to this Acceptance Certificate $ __________

Form: I-03c
Disk File Name: I-03c.rtf

Casualty Value Table

Form Purpose

Equipment casualty value table. This form is integrated with a master equipment lease agreement, Lease Agreement, Form I-03.

Executing Parties

The equipment lessee.

See:

Lease Agreement, Form I-3

Annex A

to Schedule No. ___________

Casualty Value Table

The Casualty Value of any Unit shall be an amount equal to the product of the Acquisition Cost of such Unit times the percentage below corresponding to the number of the last Rent payment received by Lessor, plus any unpaid Rent with respect to the Rent payment period during which the applicable Event of Loss occurred.

After Rent Payment No.	*Percentage*	*After Rent Payment No.*	*Percentage*	*After Rent Payment No.*	*Percentage*
0	________				
1	________	25	________	49	________
2	________	26	________	50	________
3	________	27	________	51	________
4	________	28	________	52	________
5	________	29	________	53	________
6	________	30	________	54	________
7	________	31	________	55	________
8	________	32	________	56	________
9	________	33	________	57	________
10	________	34	________	58	________
11	________	35	________	59	________
12	________	36	________	60	________
13	________	37	________	61	________
14	________	38	________	62	________
15	________	39	________	63	________
16	________	40	________	64	________
17	________	41	________	65	________
18	________	42	________	66	________
19	________	43	________	67	________
20	________	44	________	68	________
21	________	45	________	69	________
22	________	46	________	70	________
23	________	47	________	71	________
24	________	48	________	72	________

After Rent Payment No.	Percentage	After Rent Payment No.	Percentage	After Rent Payment No.	Percentage
73	______	89	______	105	______
74	______	90	______	106	______
75	______	91	______	107	______
76	______	92	______	108	______
77	______	93	______	109	______
78	______	94	______	110	______
79	______	95	______	111	______
80	______	96	______	112	______
81	______	97	______	113	______
82	______	98	______	114	______
83	______	99	______	115	______
84	______	100	______	116	______
85	______	101	______	117	______
86	______	102	______	118	______
87	______	103	______	119	______
88	______	104	______	120	______

Acknowledged by Lessee this ______________ day of ______________, XXXX.

________________________, Lessee

By: ________________________

Title: ________________________

Form: l-03d
Disk File Name: l-03d.rtf

REPRESENTATION AND WARRANTIES

Form Purpose

Lessee representation and warranty Rider integrated with a master equipment lease agreement, Lease Agreement, Form l-03.

Executing Parties

The equipment lessee.

See:

Lease Agreement, Form l-03

RIDER ______ to Schedule No. ______ dated as of ____________,
to Master Agreement to Lease Equipment, dated as of ________________,
between ________________, Lessor, and ______________, Lessee.

Lessee's Representations and Warranties

The undersigned ("Lessee"), in connection with the execution and delivery of the Equipment Leasing Agreement ("Lessee") dated as of the date hereof, entered into between ________________ ("Lessor") and Lessee, hereby represents and warrants to you, and agrees with you, as follows:

(a) Lessee is a corporation duly organized, validly existing, and in good standing under the laws of the State of ____________; Lessee has full power and authority and all necessary licenses and permits to carry on its business as presently conducted, to own or hold under lease its properties and to enter into the Lease and to perform its obligations under the Lease; and Lessee is duly qualified to do business as a foreign corporation and is in good standing in each jurisdiction in which the character of its properties or the nature of its business or the performance of its obligations under the Lease requires such qualifications.

(b) The execution and delivery by Lessee of the Lease and the performance by Lessee of its obligations under the Lease have been duly authorized by all necessary corporate action on the part of Lessee; do not contravene any law, governmental rule or regulation, or any order, writ, injunction, decree, judgment, award, determination, direction, or demand (collectively "Order") binding on Lessee or its properties or the corporate charter or by-laws of Lessee, and do not and will not contravene the provisions of, or constitute a default (either with or without notice or lapse of time, or both) under, or result in the creation of any security interests in or lien, charge, claim, or encumbrance upon, the Equipment or any property of Lessee under any indenture, mortgage, contract, or other instrument to which Lessee is a party or by which Lessee or its properties is bound.

(c) No consent or approval of, giving of notice to, registration with, or taking of any action by, any state, federal or other governmental commission, agency, or regulatory authority or any other person or entity is required for the consummation or performance by Lessee of the transactions contemplated under the Lease.

(d) The Lease has been duly entered into and delivered by Lessee, and constitutes a legal, valid, and binding agreement of Lessee enforceable against Lessee in accordance with its terms, except as limited by any bankruptcy, insolvency, reorganization, or other similar laws of general application affecting the enforcement of creditor or lessor rights.

(e) There are no actions, suits, or proceedings pending or threatened against or affecting Lessee or any property of Lessee in any court, before any arbitrator of any kind or before or by any federal, state, municipal, or other governmental department, commission, board, bureau agency, or instrumentality (collectively "Governmental Body"), which if adversely determined, would materially adversely affect the business, assets, operations, or conditions, financial or otherwise, of Lessee, or adversely affect the ability of Lessee to perform its obligations under the Lease; and Lessee is not in default with respect to any Order of any court, arbitrator, or Governmental Body.

(f) Each financial statement of Lessee furnished to Lessor by Lessee fairly presents the financial information set forth therein with respect to Lessee as of and for the period ended on each date specified therein in conformity with generally accepted accounting principles and practices consistently applied, and since the latest such date of each type of financial statement furnished to Lessor by Lessee, there has not been any material adverse change in the information set forth therein, in the business or condition, financial or otherwise, of Lessee.

(g) Lessee is not a party to any agreement or instrument or subject to any charter or other corporate restriction which materially adversely affects or, so far as Lessee can now foresee, will materially adversely affect the business, operations or properties of Lessee or the ability of Lessee to perform its obligations under the Lease.

(h) Lessee has filed all required tax returns in all jurisdictions in which such returns were required to be filed and has paid, or made provision for, all taxes shown to be due and payable on such returns and all other taxes and assessments which are payable by it, except for any taxes and assessments of which the amount applicability or validity is currently being contested in good faith by appropriate proceedings and which in the aggregate do not involve material amounts.

(i) Lessee is not in default in the payment of the principal or interest on any indebtedness for borrowed money or in default under any instrument or agreement under or subject to which any indebtedness for borrowed money has been issued; no event has occurred and is continuing under the provisions of any such instrument or agreement which with the lapse of time or the giving of notice, or both, would constitute a default or an event of default thereunder; Lessee is not in violation of any provision of its corporate charter or by-laws or of any term of any material agreement, lease of real or personal property, including any term providing for the payment of rent, or other instrument; and no Event of Default has occurred and is continuing with respect to the Lease as of the date hereof.

(j) Lessee has not taken and will not take any action or maintain any position inconsistent with treating the Lease as a valid leasehold interest in the Equipment.

The terms used herein which are defined in the Lease shall have the respective meanings set forth in the Lease, unless otherwise defined herein.

Dated: , XXXX

_______________________________, Lessee

By: ___________________________

Title: __________________________

Attest:

____

Clerk/Secretary, if corporate Lessee

Form: l-03e
Disk File Name: l-03e.rtf

OPINION OF COUNSEL—LESSEE

Form Purpose

A Lessee's counsel form of legal opinion. The form opinion is integrated with master lease agreement, Lease Agreement, Form l-03.

Executing Parties

Counsel for the equipment lessee.

See:

Lease Agreement, Form l-03

[Form of Opinion to be Delivered by Counsel for Lessee]

Dated ______________________

[Insert name and address of leasing company.]

Re: Equipment Lease dated ______________, XXXX, by and between (insert name of lessor), and (insert name of lessee)

Dear Sirs:

We have acted as counsel for ______________________ a ______________________ corporation ("Lessee"), in connection with the execution and delivery of a lease between you, as Lessor, and Lessee, in the form of a Schedule, dated ______________, XXXX. ("Lease"), relating to the lease of certain equipment described therein, entered into pursuant to a Master Agreement to Lease Equipment, dated ______________, XXXX, between you, as Lessor, and Lessee ("Agreement"). The Lease incorporates the terms and provisions of the Agreement.

This opinion is furnished to you in connection with Lessee's execution and delivery to you of the Lease. The terms used herein which are defined in the Lease shall have the meanings set forth in the Lease, unless otherwise defined herein.

In connection with this opinion, we have examined executed counterparts of the Agreement and the Lease and such corporate documents and records of Lessee, certificates of public officials and of officers of Lessee, and such other documents and questions of fact and law as we have deemed necessary or appropriate for the purposes of this opinion.

Based upon the foregoing, we are of the opinion that:

(1) Lessee is a corporation duly organized and validly existing in good standing under the laws of the State of ______________________ and is duly qualified and authorized to do business and is in good standing in every other jurisdiction where the nature of Lessee's business or activities and the transactions contemplated by the Agreement and the Lease require such qualification;

(2) Lessee is duly authorized to lease the Units, execute and deliver the Agreement and the Lease, and to perform its obligations under the Lease;

(3) The execution and delivery of the Agreement and the Lease by Lessee, and the performance by Lessee of its obligations under the Lease, do not and will not conflict with any provision of law or any provision of the charter or by-laws of Lessee or of any indenture, mortgage, deed of trust, or other agreement or instrument binding upon Lessee or its properties or to which Lessee is a party;

(4) The execution and delivery of the Agreement and the Lease by Lessee, and the performance and consummation by Lessee of the transactions contemplated thereunder, do not require the consent, approval, or authorization of, or giving of notice to, or registration or filing with, any federal, state, or local governmental authority or public regulatory body or any other person or entity;

(5) The Lease is a legal, valid, and binding obligation of Lessee enforceable against Lessee in accordance with its terms, except as limited by any bankruptcy, insolvency, reorganization, or other similar laws of general application affecting the enforcement of creditor or lessor rights;

(6) There are no pending or threatened actions or proceedings before any arbitrator, court, or administrative agency which will, if adversely determined, adversely affect to a material extent the financial condition or operations of Lessee or its ability to perform its obligations under the Lease; and

(7) There exists no person, partnership, corporation, or other entity which is or will as a result of Lessee's execution, delivery, and performance of the Lease be entitled to a Lien (except Lessor's Liens) with respect to any Unit,

Very truly yours,

Form: l-03f
Disk File Name: l-03f.rtf

Opinion of Counsel—Guarantor Form

Form Purpose

A lessee guarantor's counsel form of legal opinion. The form opinion is integrated with the master lease agreement, Lease Agreement, Form l-03.

Executing Parties

Counsel for the equipment lessee's guarantor.

See:

Lease Agreement, Form l-03

[Form of Opinion to be Delivered by Counsel for Guarantor of Lessee's Obligations

Dated ____________________

[Insert name and address of leasing company.]

Re: Equipment Lease dated __________, XXXX,
by and between (insert name of lessor), and
(insert name of lessee).

Dear Sirs,

We have acted as counsel for ____________________, a ____________________ corporation ("Guarantor"), in connection with the execution and delivery of the Guaranty, dated ____________________, XXXX ("Guaranty"), made by the Guarantor in your favor. The Guaranty relates to the performance by ____________________, a ____________________ corporation ("Lessee"), of its obligations under a lease in the form of a Schedule, dated ____________________ XXXX, between you, as Lessor, and Lessee ("Lease"), relating to the lease of certain equipment described therein, entered into pursuant to a Master Agreement to Lease Equipment, dated ____________________, XXXX, (the "Agreement").

This opinion is furnished to you in connection with Guarantor's execution and delivery of the Guaranty.

In connection with this opinion, we have examined executed counterparts of the Agreement, the Lease and the Guaranty, and such corporate documents and records of Guarantor, certificates of public officials and of officers of Guarantor, and such other documents and questions of fact and law as we have deemed necessary or appropriate for the purposes of this opinion.

Based upon the foregoing, we are of the opinion that:

(1) Guarantor is a corporation duly organized and validly existing in good standing under the laws of the State of __________ and is duly qualified and authorized to do business and is in good standing in every other jurisdiction where the nature of Guarantor's business or activities and the performance of its obligations under the Guaranty require such qualification;

(2) Guarantor is duly authorized to execute and deliver the Guaranty and to perform its obligations thereunder;

(3) The execution and delivery of the Guaranty by Guarantor, and the performance by Guarantor of its obligations thereunder, do not conflict with any provision of law or any provision of the charter or by-laws of Guarantor or of any indenture, mortgage, deed of trust, or agreement or instrument binding upon Guarantor or its properties or to which Guarantor is a party;

(4) The execution, delivery, and performance of the Guaranty by Guarantor do not require the consent, approval, or authorization of, or giving of notice to, or regis-

tration or filing with, any federal, state, or local governmental authority or public regulatory body or any other person or entity;

(5) The Guaranty is a legal, valid, and binding obligation of the Guarantor enforceable against Guarantor in accordance with its terms, except as limited by any bankruptcy, insolvency, reorganization, or other similar laws of general application affecting the enforcement of creditor or lessor rights; and

(6) There are no pending or threatened actions or proceedings before any arbitrator, court, or administrative agency which will if adversely determined, adversely affect to a material extent the financial condition or operations of Guarantor or its ability to perform its obligations under the Guaranty.

Very truly yours,

Leveraged Lease Documents

Form: l-04
Disk File Name: l-04.rtf

Leveraged Lease (Aircraft/General)

Form Purpose

A comprehensive equipment lease agreement, part of a leveraged lease financing transaction. The transaction contemplates the sale of an aircraft by the manufacturer to an airline, and then the entering into of a sale/leaseback between the airline (lessee) and the aircraft lessor. Although the form contemplates the lease of an aircraft, modifications can be made for any type of equipment. This form is integrated with typical documents found in a leveraged lease transaction. (*Author's note:* The capitalized terms, which are not defined in the lease agreement, or the other transaction documents [see below], are defined in the Participation Agreement, Form l-04b, as is customary; specifically in Appendix A to the agreement. This form, although it covers the lease of an aircraft, is an excellent reference for a wide variety of leasing concepts and provisions.)

Executing Parties

The equipment lessor.
The equipment lessee.

See:

Assignment of Rights under Purchase Agreement, Form l-04a
Participation Agreement, Form l-04b
Trust and Indenture Agreement and Security Agreement, Form l-04c
Trust Agreement, Form l-04d
Tax Indemnity Agreement, Form l-04e

Lease Agreement

dated as of September 15, XXXX

between

MARTIN TRUST COMPANY,
not in its individual capacity, but solely
as Owner Trustee under the Trust Agreement,
except as otherwise expressly provided herein,

Lessor,

and

PLANET AVIATION, INC.,

Lessee.

Covering One New Blackhawk
Model 555-300 Aircraft
Registration Number N777P

All right, title and interest in and to this Lease Agreement and the Aircraft covered hereby on the part of Martin Trust Company, as Lessor, has been assigned to and is subject to a security interest in favor of The Rhode Island Bank and Trust Company, National Association, as Indenture Trustee, under the Trust Indenture and Security Agreement dated as of September 15, XXXX (as such Trust Indenture and Security Agreement may be amended or supplemented as permitted thereby), for the benefit of the holders of Loan Certificates referred to in such Trust Indenture and Security Agreement. This Lease Agreement has been executed in several counterparts. To the extent, if any, that this Lease Agreement constitutes chattel paper (as such term is defined in the Uniform Commercial Code as in effect in any applicable jurisdiction), no security interest in this Lease Agreement may be created through the transfer or possession of any counterpart other than the original counterpart that contains the receipt therefor executed by The Rhode Island Bank and Trust Company, National Association, as Indenture Trustee, on the signature page thereof.

Table of Contents

Sections

Lease Agreement

This Lease Agreement dated as of September 15, XXXX between MARTIN TRUST COMPANY, a New York trust company having its principal place of business at ______________________________________, not in its individual capacity but solely as Owner Trustee under the Trust Agreement, except as otherwise expressly provided herein, Lessor, and PLANET AVIATION, INC., a New Jersey corporation having its principal place of business at ______________________________________, Lessee;

WITNESSETH:

WHEREAS, Lessor intends to purchase the Aircraft described herein, pursuant to the terms of that certain Participation Agreement; and

WHEREAS, Lessee desires to lease from Lessor and Lessor is willing to lease to Lessee the said Aircraft described herein upon and subject to the terms and conditions of this Lease;

NOW, THEREFORE, in consideration of the mutual covenants and agreements contained herein, Lessor and Lessee agree as follows:

Section 1. Definitions

Unless the context otherwise requires, all Capitalized terms used herein shall have the meanings set forth in Appendix A to the Participation Agreement entered into between the parties hereto and dated ________________, for all purposes of this Lease.

Section 2. Acceptance Under Lease

(a) Acceptance and Leasing of Aircraft. Lessor hereby agrees (subject to satisfaction of the conditions set forth in the Participation Agreement) to purchase and accept delivery of the Aircraft pursuant to the Participation Agreement on the Delivery Date therefor from Lessee and simultaneously lease to Lessee hereunder, and Lessee hereby agrees to deliver to and simultaneously lease from Lessor hereunder, the Aircraft, such leasing to be evidenced by the execution by Lessor and Lessee of a separate Lease Supplement leasing the Aircraft hereunder.

(b) Title in Lessor. At all times during the term of this Lease, full legal title to the Aircraft shall remain vested in Lessor to the exclusion of Lessee, notwithstanding the possession and use thereof by Lessee.

(c) Designation of Lessor's Representative for Acceptance of Delivery. Lessor hereby authorizes each of the persons designated by Lessee on Schedule I hereto as the representative or representatives of Lessor, to accept delivery of the Aircraft. Lessee hereby agrees that such acceptance of delivery of the Aircraft by such authorized representative or representatives on behalf of Lessor shall, without further act, irrevocably constitute acceptance by Lessee of the Aircraft for all purposes of this Lease.

Section 3. Term and Rent

(a) Term. Except as otherwise provided herein, the Aircraft shall be leased for a Term which shall comprise the Interim Term and the Basic Term. The Interim Term for the Aircraft leased hereunder shall commence on the Delivery Date and continue through January 2, XXXX; the Basic Term for the Aircraft leased hereunder shall commence on January 3, XXXX and continue through January 2, XXXX, except that the Term (and the Interim Term or the Basic Term, as the case may be), with respect to the Aircraft shall end upon any earlier termination of this Lease according to its terms.

(b) Interim Rent. Lessee agrees to pay Interim Rent for the Aircraft on January 2, XXXX in an amount equal to 2.0000% of Lessor's Cost.

(c) Basic Rent. Lessee agrees to pay Basic Rent for the Aircraft in consecutive annual installments on each Basic Rent Payment Date during the Basic Term in an amount equal to the product of the percentage shown in the column labeled "Percentage of Lessor's Cost" set forth opposite such date in Exhibit C hereto times Lessor' s Cost, which amount will accrue in equal daily portions.

(d) Supplemental Rent. Lessee also agrees to pay to Lessor, or to whomsoever shall be entitled thereto, any and all Supplemental Rent when the same shall become due and owing, and in the event of any failure on the part of Lessee to pay any Supplemental Rent, Lessor shall have all rights, powers, and remedies provided for herein or by law or equity in the case of nonpayment of Basic Rent. Lessee will also pay, on demand, as Supplemental Rent interest at the Overdue Rate on any part of any installment of Basic Rent or Interim Rent not paid when due for any period for which the same shall be overdue and, to the extent permitted by Applicable Law, on any payment of Supplemental Rent not paid when due or rightfully demanded for the period until the same shall be paid. The expiration or termination of Lessee's obligation to pay Basic Rent hereunder shall not limit or modify Lessee's obligation to pay Supplemental Rent as provided hereunder.

(e) Adjustments to Basic Rent, Stipulated Loss Value, and Termination Value.

(i) (A) If the Aircraft is not delivered on September 17, XXXX or (B) if a Tax Law Change has occurred, or (C) if the Percentage Commitment of Owner Participant shall not be 41.000000% for the Aircraft, or (D) if the interest rate payable is not 8.XX% per annum on the Series A Loan Certificates or 9.XX% per annum on the Series B Loan Certificates (other than any Additional Loan Certificates) during both the Interim Term and Basic Term, or (E) if the Transaction Costs paid by the Owner Participant pursuant to Section 14 of the Participation Agreement exceed 1.5% of Lessor's Cost, then all installments of Basic Rent and Stipulated Loss Values and Termination Values with respect to the Term will be recalculated (upward or downward, as the case may be) to preserve the Net Economic Return of Owner Participant, and, if appropriate, the Assumed Tax Benefits shall be modified to reflect the change in the Basic Tax Assumptions which give rise to such adjustment; provided, however, any such adjustment shall be made only to the extent that the same (i) does not violate the uneven rent guidelines set forth in Revenue Procedure 75–21 (as then interpreted) and (ii) does not increase the likelihood that the Lease will be treated as a "disqualified leaseback or long term agreement" [within the meaning of Section 467(b)(4) of the Code, as then interpreted].

(ii) The adjustments to the percentages for Basic Rent set forth in Exhibit C and for Stipulated Loss Value and Termination Value set forth in Exhibit B, shall be determined by Owner Participant, which shall deliver to Lessee schedules setting forth the revised percentages and to Lessee and each holder of a Loan Certificate a statement showing the revisions to such schedules and to Lessee a statement indicating which provisions of this Lease or the Tax Indemnity Agreement are involved in such adjustments. Within 15 days following Lessee's receipt of such schedules, Lessee may request that the accounting firm that regularly prepares Owner Participant's certified financial statements determine whether the computation of such schedules is mathematically accurate, based on the Basic Tax Assumptions and in conformity with the provisions of this Lease. Such accounting firm shall be requested to make its determination within 30 days. Owner Participant shall provide to such accounting firm such information as they may reasonably require, including a description of the methodology of the calculation used in computing such adjustment and such other information as is necessary to determine whether the computation is mathematically accurate. The accounting firm shall hold in strict confidence such methodology and information. If such accounting firm shall determine that such computations are inaccurate or not based on the Basic Tax Assumptions, then such firm shall determine what it believes to be the appropriate computations. If Owner Participant does not agree with such firm's determination, then another accounting firm, to be selected jointly by Owner Participant and Lessee, or if they cannot agree, by the American Arbitration Association, from among the ten largest accounting firms, shall determine the appropriate computations. Such accounting firm shall be requested to make its determination within 30 days. Owner Participant shall provide to such accounting firm such information as they may reasonably require, including a description of the methodology of the calculation used in computing such adjustment and such other information as is necessary to determine whether the computation is mathematically accurate. The accounting firm shall hold in strict confidence such methodology and information. The computations of Owner Participant, its accounting firm, or the accounting firm selected as provided above, whichever is applicable, shall be final, binding, and conclusive upon Lessee and Lessee shall have no right to inspect the books, records, tax returns, or other documents of or relating to Owner Participant to verify such computations or for any other purpose. All fees and expenses payable under this paragraph shall be borne equally by Lessee and Owner Participant. Owner Participant and Lessee shall execute and deliver, and Lessee shall cause to be duly filed with the FAA, an amendment to this Lease to reflect each such adjustment, provided that such adjustment shall be effective for all purposes of this Lease regardless of whether such amendment is actually executed and delivered.

(f) Minimum Rent, etc. Anything contained herein or in any other Operative Document to the contrary notwithstanding, (including the percentages set forth from time to time in Exhibits B and C hereto) each installment of Interim Rent and Basic Rent and each Stipulated Loss Value and Termination Value for the Aircraft [whether or not the same are adjusted pursuant to Section 3(e) hereof] shall be [after giving effect to any prepayment or offset as provided in Section 3(h) hereof] in an amount which is at least sufficient for Lessor to pay in full as of the date of such installment or date of payment of Stipulated Loss Value or Termination Value any unpaid principal amount and interest on the Loan Certificates required to be paid by Lessor on the due date of such installment of Interim Rent or Basic Rent or on such Loss Payment Date, as the case may be.

(g) Manner of Payment. All Rent (other than Excepted Property) shall be paid by Lessee to Lessor at its principal office in Reading, New York (or such other office of Lessor or such account as Lessor shall direct in a written notice to Lessee at least 10 days prior to the date such payment is due), in immediately available funds consisting of lawful currency of the United States of America, so that Lessor receives the full amount of such payment no later than 11:00 A. M. New York City time on the due dates thereof, provided that so long as the Indenture shall not have been discharged pursuant to Section 10(a) thereof, Lessor hereby irrevocably directs, and Lessee agrees, that all Rent payable to Lessor (other than Excepted Property) shall be paid directly to the Indenture Trustee, in the manner provided above and in Section 4 hereof, at its principal corporate trust office in Providence, Rhode Island or as the Indenture Trustee may otherwise direct prior to the date of payment. If any Rent is due on a day which is not a Business Day, such Rent shall be paid on the next succeeding Business Day. Payments constituting Excepted Property shall be made to the Person entitled thereto.

(h) Lessee's Debt Service Payment Covenant. If and to the extent that the Indenture Trustee on any July 2 (the "Payment Date") shall not have received funds for the payment in full of the amounts then due on the Loan Certificates from the Owner Participant pursuant to and on the day required by Section 7(1) of the Participation Agreement, Lessee shall prepay on such Payment Date a portion of Basic Rent equal to such amounts (such Rent to be prepaid being herein called the "Payment Amount"); provided, that Lessee shall also pay to the Indenture Trustee, on demand, as Supplemental Rent to the extent permitted by applicable law, interest, at the Overdue Rate on any part of the Payment Amount not paid when due for any period for which the same shall be overdue. Any Rent prepaid pursuant to this Section 3(h) shall be prepaid in the order in which the installments of Rent become due. Lessor agrees to reimburse Lessee, in the manner provided in the next sentence, for (x) the Payment Amount so paid by Lessee, plus (y) accrued interest on the unreimbursed portion thereof at the Overdue Rate from the date such amount is prepaid to but not including the date such reimbursement is complete (such amount to be reimbursed being herein called the "Reimbursement Amount"). Lessee shall be entitled to offsets, without limitation of any other rights Lessee may have against any person, without duplication, against any payments (other than as limited by the proviso to this sentence) due from Lessee to Lessor or Owner Participant (including, without limitation, Basic Rent and payments due to Lessor under Section 16 of the Participation Agreement or to Owner Participant under the Tax Indemnity Agreement), until Lessee has been fully reimbursed for the Reimbursement Amount; provided, however, that in the case of any payment due from Lessee which is distributable under the terms of the Indenture, Lessee's right of offset shall be limited to the amount distributable to Lessor thereunder (and shall not include any amounts distributable to the Indenture Trustee in its individual capacity or to the holders of the Loan Certificates). No such prepayment, offset, or aggregate combined effect of separate prepayments or offsets shall reduce the amount of any installment of Basic Rent to below the minimum rent required to be paid pursuant to Section 3(f) hereof. Lessee shall have, and shall be entitled to file and perfect but shall not enforce during the Term, a Lien on the Aircraft, which shall be junior and subordinated to the Lien of the Indenture, for any Reimbursement Amount for which it has not been reimbursed.

Section 4. Net Lease, etc.

This Lease is a net lease. Lessee acknowledges and agrees that its obligations to pay all Rent due and owing under the terms hereof shall be absolute and unconditional and shall not be affected by any circumstance whatsoever [except as provided in Section 3(h) hereof but subject always to the provisions of Section 3(f) hereof], including, without limitation (a) any setoff, counterclaim, recoupment, defense, or other right which Lessee may have against Lessor, the Indenture Trustee, any Participant, or anyone else for any reason whatsoever, (b) any defect in the title, airworthiness, eligibility for registration under the Federal Aviation Act, condition, design, operation, merchantability, or fitness for use of, or any damage to or loss or destruction of, the Aircraft, any Engine or any Part or any interference, interruption, or cessation in or prohibition of the use or possession thereof by Lessee for any reason whatsoever, including, without limitation, any such interference, interruption, cessation, or prohibition resulting from the act of any governmental authority or any violation by Lessor of Section 5(b) hereof, (c) any liens, with respect to the Aircraft, any Engine or any Part, (d) the invalidity or unenforceability or lack of due authorization or other infirmity of this Lease or any lack of right, power, or authority of Lessor or Lessee to enter into this Lease, (e) any insolvency, bankruptcy, reorganization, or similar proceedings by or against Lessee, or any other Person, (f) any furnishing or acceptance of any additional security, or any failure or inability to perfect any security, (g) any failure on the part of Owner Trustee, the Indenture Trustee, or any Participant or any other person whomsoever to perform or comply with any terms of any such instrument or agreement, (h) any waiver, consent, change, extension, indulgence, or any action or inaction under or in respect of any such instrument or agreement or any exercise or nonexercise of any right, remedy, power, or privilege in respect of any such instrument or agreement of this Lease, (i) except as otherwise expressly provided herein or in any other Operative Document, any assignment or other transfer of this Lease by Lessee or Lessor or any lien on or affecting Lessee's estate in the Airframe, an Engine, or Part, (j) any act, omission, or breach on the part of Lessor and Lessee or any other law, governmental regulation, or other agreement applicable to Lessor and Lessee or any other law, governmental regulation, or other agreement applicable to Lessor or the Airframe, an Engine, or Part, (k) any claim as a result of any other dealing between Lessor and Lessee, (1) any ineligibility of the Airframe, an Engine, or Part for documentation under the laws of the United States or any other jurisdiction, and (m) any other cause whether similar or dissimilar to the foregoing, any present or future law notwithstanding, it being the intention of the parties hereto that all Rent being payable by Lessee hereunder shall continue to be payable in all events in the manner and at the times provided herein. Except as set forth in Section 3(h) hereof [but subject always to the provisions of Section 3(f) hereof], such Rent shall not be subject to any abatement, suspension, deferral, or diminution and the payments thereof shall not be subject to any setoff or reduction for any reason whatsoever, including any present or future claims of Lessee against the Lessor under this Lease or otherwise. Each Rent payment made pursuant to this Lease by Lessee shall be final and Lessee will not seek to recover all or any part of such payment from Lessor or the Indenture Trustee for any reason except manifest error. If for any reason whatsoever this Lease shall be terminated in whole or in part by operation of law or otherwise except as specifically provided herein or as otherwise agreed, Lessee nonetheless agrees to pay to Lessor an amount equal to each Rent payment at the time such payment would have become due and payable in accordance with the terms hereof had this Lease not been terminated in whole or in part. The obligation of Lessee in the immediately preceding sentence shall survive the expiration or the termination of this Lease other than in accordance with its terms. To the extent permitted by Applicable Law, Lessee hereby waives any rights which it may now have or which may be conferred upon it, by statute or otherwise, to terminate, cancel, quit, or surrender this Lease except in accordance with the terms hereof. Nothing contained in this Section 4 shall be construed to waive any claim which Lessee might have under any of the Operative Documents (including, without limitation, claims that Rent payments demanded from or paid by Lessee are or were erroneous) or otherwise or to limit the right of Lessee to make any claim it might have against Lessor or any other Person or to pursue such claim in such manner as Lessee shall deem appropriate other than by setoff, counterclaim, recoupment, or defense prohibited by clause (a) of this Section 4.

Section 5. Lessor's Representations and Warranties

(a) LESSOR LEASES THE AIRCRAFT HEREUNDER "AS IS" AND NEITHER LESSOR IN ITS INDIVIDUAL CAPACITY OR OTHERWISE NOR THE OWNER PARTICIPANT SHALL BE DEEMED TO HAVE MADE ANY REPRESENTATION OR WARRANTY, EXPRESS OR IMPLIED, AS TO THE TITLE, AIRWORTHINESS, CONDITION, VALUE, DESIGN, OPERATION, MERCHANTABILITY, OR FITNESS FOR USE OF THE AIRCRAFT OR ANY PART THEREOF, AS TO THE ABSENCE OF LATENT OR OTHER DEFECTS, WHETHER OR NOT DISCOVERABLE, AS TO THE ABSENCE OF ANY INFRINGEMENT OF ANY PATENT, TRADEMARK, OR COPYRIGHT, AS TO THE ABSENCE OF OBLIGATIONS BASED ON STRICT LIABILITY IN TORT, OR AS TO THE QUALITY OF THE MATERIAL OR WORKMANSHIP OF THE AIRCRAFT OR ANY OTHER REPRESENTATION OR WARRANTY WHATSOEVER, EXPRESS OR IMPLIED, WITH RESPECT TO THE AIRCRAFT OR ANY PART THEREOF, except that Lessor warrants that on the Delivery Date Lessor shall have received whatever title was conveyed to it by Lessee and Lessor warrants in its individual capacity that the Aircraft shall during the Term be free of Lessor's Liens attributable to Lessor in its individual capacity. Lessor otherwise warrants that the Aircraft shall, during the Term, be free of Lessor's Liens. Lessor in its individual capacity also represents and warrants that it is a "citizen of the United States" as defined in Section 101(16) of the Federal Aviation Act.

(b) Lessor warrants and agrees that during the Term, as long as no Event of Default has occurred and is continuing, Lessee's use of the Aircraft leased hereunder shall not be interrupted by Lessor or anyone claiming solely through or under Lessor.

Section 6. Possession, Operation and Use, Maintenance, Registration and Insignia

(a) Possession. Lessee shall not sell, assign, sublease, or otherwise in any manner deliver, relinquish, or transfer possession of the Airframe or any Engine leased hereunder to any Person or install any Engine, or permit any Engine to be installed, on any airframe other than the Airframe during the Term without the prior written consent of Lessor, which consent shall not be unreasonably withheld, provided, however, that so long as Lessee shall comply with the provisions of Section 10 hereof, so long as no Event of Default shall have occurred and be continuing and so long as such action will not affect the first mortgage Lien of the Indenture Trustee on the Airframe, Lessee may, without the prior written consent of Lessor:

(i) enter into a lease under which Lessee has operational control of the Aircraft in the ordinary course of Lessee's business (which shall not be considered a transfer of possession hereunder), provided that Lessee's obligations under this Lease shall continue in full force and effect notwithstanding any such lease;

(ii) deliver possession of the Airframe or any Engine to the manufacturer thereof for testing or other similar purposes or to any organization for service, repair, maintenance, or overhaul work on the Airframe or such Engine or for alterations or modifications in or additions to the Airframe or such Engine, to the extent required or permitted by the terms of this Lease;

(iii) subject the Aircraft or Airframe to normal interchange agreements or any Engine to normal interchange or pooling agreements or arrangements, in each case customary in the airline industry applicable to other similar aircraft and engines operated by Lessee and entered into by Lessee in the ordinary course of its business with any Certificated Air Carrier or Permitted Foreign Air Carrier, provided, that no transfer of the registration of the Aircraft shall be effected in connection therewith, provided, further, that (A) no such agreement or arrangement contemplates or requires the transfer of title to the Aircraft and (B) if, notwithstanding the provisions of clause (A) above, Lessor's title to any Engine shall be divested under any such agreement or arrangement, such divestiture shall be deemed to be an Event of Loss with respect to such Engine and Lessee shall comply with Section 9 hereof in respect thereof, Lessor not intending hereby to waive any right or interest it may have in or to the Aircraft or Airframe under Applicable Law until compliance by Lessee with such Section 9.

(iv) install an Engine on an airframe Owned by Lessee free and clear of all Liens, except (A) Permitted Liens, (B) those which apply only to the engines (other than Engines), appliances, parts, instruments, appurtenances, accessories, furnishings, and other equipment (other than Parts) installed on such airframe (but not to the airframe as an entirety), and (C) those created by the rights of other Certificated Air Carriers and Permitted Foreign Air Carriers under normal interchange agreements customary in the airline industry which do not contemplate, permit, or require the transfer of title to the airframe or engines installed thereon;

(v) install an Engine on an airframe leased to Lessee or purchased by Lessee subject to a conditional sale or other security agreement, provided that (A) such airframe is free and clear of all Liens except (x) the rights of the parties to the lease, conditional sale, or other security agreement and (y) Liens of the type permitted by clause (iv) above, and (B) such lease, conditional sale, or other security agreement effectively provides that such Engine shall not become subject to the lien of such lease, conditional sale, or other security agreement, notwithstanding the installation thereof on such airframe;

(vi) install an Engine on an airframe owned by Lessee, leased by Lessee, or purchased by Lessee subject to a conditional sale or other security agreement under circumstances where neither clause (iv) nor clause (v) above is applicable, provided that such installation shall be deemed an Event of Loss with respect to such Engine and Lessee shall comply with Section 9 hereof, Lessor not intending hereby to waive any right or interest it may have in or to such Engine under Applicable Law until compliance by Lessee with such Section 9;

(vii) transfer possession of the Airframe or any Engine to the United States of America or any instrumentality thereof pursuant to the Civil Reserve Air Fleet Program (as established pursuant to the Executive Order 10219 dated February 28, 1951), provided such transfer of possession does not exceed the Term for such Aircraft;

(viii) transfer possession of the Airframe or any Engine to the United States of America for a period not in excess of one year or to a foreign government for a period not in excess of 90 days when required by Applicable Law, provided that such transfer of possession shall not extend beyond the end of the Term; and

(ix) so long as no Default shall have occurred and be continuing, and subject to the provisions of the immediately following paragraph, enter into, renew, or extend a sublease of the Aircraft or the Airframe and any Engine or Engines attached thereto to any Certificated Air Carrier or Permitted Foreign Air Carrier which is not the subject of a petition filed under any bankruptcy laws or other insolvency laws in effect at the time such sublease is entered into; and provided, that the rights of any transferee who receives possession by reason of a transfer permitted by this Section 6(a) (other than by a transfer of Engine which is deemed an Event of Loss) shall be subject and subordinate to all the terms of this Lease and of the Indenture, and Lessee shall remain primarily liable hereunder for the performance of all of the terms of this Lease to the same extent as if such sublease or transfer had not occurred.

In the case of any sublease permitted under this Section 6(a), Lessee will provide to Lessor and the Indenture Trustee prior written notice of such sublease and insurance certificates evidencing that insurance complying with Section 10 hereof will be in force with respect to the subject Airframe and Engines during such sublease. In addition, Lessee will include in such sublease appropriate provisions which (t) make such sublease expressly subject and subordinate to all of the terms of this Lease and the Indenture, including the rights of Lessor and the Indenture Trustee to avoid such sublease in the exercise of their rights to repossession of the Airframe and Engines hereunder and thereunder; (u) expressly prohibit any further subleasing of the subject Airframe and Engines; (v) require that the subject Airframe and Engines be maintained in accordance with an FAA-approved maintenance program applicable thereto; (w) require the sublessee to comply with the terms of Section 10 hereof; (x) limit the term of such sublease (including renewal rights) to a period not beyond the end of the Term; and (y) require that the subject Airframe and Engines not be operated, used, or located, or suffered to be operated, used, or located, (I) in any recognized or, in Lessee's reasonable judgment, threatened area of hostilities unless fully covered by war risk insurance, or unless such Airframe or Engine is operated or used under contract with the government of the United States under which contract said government assumes liability for any damages, loss, destruction, or failure to return possession of such Airframe or Engine at the end of the term of such contract or for injury to persons or damage to property of others arising out of such use and (II) at any time to any country with which the United States government does not maintain at such time diplomatic relations. Lessee's right to sublease to Permitted Foreign Air Carriers shall also be subject to the limitations that such Permitted Foreign Air Carrier shall be based in a country with which the United States government maintains diplomatic relations at the time of such sublease and throughout the term thereof.

As security for the due and punctual payment of all Rent by Lessee and the performance and observance by Lessee of all of the covenants made by it in the Operative Documents Lessee hereby grants to Lessor a security interest in all of Lessee's right, title, and interest in and to each sublease having a stated term in excess of 5 years and in and to all payments of rent and all other amounts due and to become due under each Sublease of the Airframe and any renewal or extension thereof. It is understood and agreed that the payment of rent and all other amounts due and to become due under each such sublease shall be made to Lessee unless and until Lessor or the Indenture Trustee shall have given written notice to the sublessee (with a copy of such notice to Lessee) that an Event of Default has occurred and is continuing hereunder, from the time of which notice payment of such rent and other amounts shall be made to the Indenture Trustee so long as the Indenture shall be in effect and to Lessor after the Indenture shall have been discharged pursuant to the terms thereof, in each case, until the sublessee shall have received written notice from the Indenture Trustee or Lessor, as the case may be, that such Event of Default has been cured.

In the event Lessor shall have received from the lessor or secured party of any airframe leased to Lessee or purchased by Lessee subject to a conditional sale or other security agreement a written agreement which provides that the lessor or secured party under such agreement shall not acquire or claim any right, title, or interest in any Engine, and the lease or conditional sale or other security agreement covering such airframe also covers an engine or engines owned by the lessor under such lease or subject to a security interest in favor of the secured party under such conditional sale or other security agreement, Lessor hereby agrees for the benefit of such lessor or secured party that Lessor will not acquire or claim, as against such lessor or secured party, any right, title, or interest in any such engine as the result of such engine being installed on the Airframe at any time while such engine is owned by such lessor or is subject to such conditional sale or other security agreement or security interest in favor of such secured party. The existence of a clause substantially similar to the foregoing in such lease, conditional sale, or other security agreement whereby the lessor or secured party, as the case may be, is substituted for the Lessor, shall suffice as the required written agreement.

(b) Operation and Use. Lessee agrees not to (i) operate the Airframe or any Engine or permit the Airframe or any Engine to be operated during the Term except in a passenger configuration, in commercial or other operations related to Lessee's business for which Lessee (or any sublessee or other person permitted by the provisions of Section 6(a) above to operate the Airframe or any Engine) is duly authorized by the FAA or the appropriate foreign authority; (ii) use or permit the Aircraft to be used for a purpose for which the Aircraft is not designed or reasonably suitable; (iii) operate, use, or locate the Airframe or any Engine, or suffer such Airframe or Engine to be operated, used, or located (A) in any area excluded from coverage by any insurance required by the terms of Section 10 hereof, except in the case of a requisition by the United States of America where Lessee obtains indemnity in lieu of such insurance from the United States of America against the risks and in the amounts required by Section 10 hereof covering such area, or (B) to or within any country with which the United States does not maintain diplomatic relations other than on routes on which Lessee is authorized to operate scheduled service under a certificate issued under Section 401 of the Federal Aviation Act or (C) outside the United States or Canada in any area or recognized or, in Lessee's reasonable judgment, threatened hostilities or any area in which Lessee is required to carry war risk insurance pursuant to Section 10(b) hereof, unless such insurance shall be in full force and effect, or unless such Airframe or Engine is operated or used under contract with the government of the United States under which contract said government assumes liability for any damages, loss, destruction, or failure to return possession of such Airframe or Engine at the end of the term of such contract or for injury to persons or damage to property of others arising out of such use. Lessee will not permit the Aircraft or any Engine to be maintained, used, or operated during the Term in violation of any Applicable Law (including any airworthiness certificate, license, or registration) or contrary to any manufacturer's operating manuals or instructions, relating to the Aircraft or such Engines issued by any such authority, unless the validity thereof in the case of an Applicable Law (including any airworthiness certificate, license, or registration) is being contested in good faith and by appropriate proceedings but only so long as such proceedings do not involve any danger of criminal liability of Owner Trustee or any Participant or a danger (other than an immaterial danger) of a loss of title to, or first mortgage security interest in the Aircraft. Lessee agrees not to operate the Aircraft, or suffer the Aircraft to be operated during the Term (i) unless the Aircraft is covered by insurance as required by the provisions of Section 10 hereof, or (ii) contrary to the terms of such insurance as required by the provision of Section 10 hereof.

(c) Maintenance. Lessee, at its own cost and expense, shall service, repair, maintain, and overhaul, test or cause the same to be done to the Airframe and each Engine during the Term (i) so as to keep the Airframe and each Engine in as good operating condition and appearance as when delivered to Lessee by Manufacturer, ordinary wear and tear excepted, (ii) so as to keep the Airframe and each Engine in such operating condition as may be necessary to enable the airworthiness certification of the Aircraft to be maintained in good standing at all times under the applicable rules and regulations of the FAA, (iii) to the extent necessary to maintain the effectiveness of any warranties from Manufacturer, and (iv) in accordance with Lessee's FAA-approved maintenance program for Blackhawk 555-300 series aircraft and in the same manner and with the same care used by Lessee with respect to similar aircraft and engines operated by Lessee and utilized in similar circumstances. Lessee shall maintain all records, logs, and other materials required by the Department of Transportation or the FAA to be maintained in respect of the Aircraft and shall promptly furnish to Lessor upon Lessor's request such information as may be required to enable Lessor to file any reports required to be filed with any governmental authority because of Lessor's interest in the Aircraft.

(d) Registration and Insignia. Lessor, at the expense of Lessee, upon the Delivery Date shall cause the Aircraft to be duly registered in the name of Lessor under the Federal Aviation Act and at all times thereafter during the Term to remain so registered. On the Delivery Date, Lessee shall place in the cockpit of the Airframe in a location reasonably adjacent to the airworthiness certificate of the Aircraft, and on each Engine, a metal nameplate identifying the ownership interest of Lessor in the Aircraft, as follows:

"MERIDAN TRUST COMPANY,
Owner Trustee, Owner and Lessor"

and, for so long as the Aircraft shall be subject to any security interest as provided in the Indenture bearing the following additional inscription:

"THE RHODE ISLAND BANK AND TRUST COMPANY, NATIONAL ASSOCIATION,
Indenture Trustee, Mortgagee"

Lessee will affix comparable nameplates to the Airframe and each Engine covering any successors to the foregoing. Lessee will not allow the name of any Person other than Lessor, or its successors or assigns, to be placed on the Aircraft or any Engine as a designation that might be interpreted as a claim of ownership or of any interest therein, provided, however, that Lessee or any permitted sublessee may operate the Aircraft in its livery, including its name and logo.

Section 7. Inspection; Financial Information

(a) Information and Inspection Upon Request. During the Term, Lessee shall, with reasonable promptness, furnish to Lessor, the Indenture Trustee and each Participant such additional information concerning the location, condition, use, and operation of, or other matters relating to, the Aircraft as Lessor, the Indenture Trustee or any Participant may reasonably request, and Lessee, at such reasonable times as Lessor, the Indenture Trustee or such Participant may reasonably request, shall permit any person or persons designated by Lessor, the Indenture Trustee or such Participant in writing to visit the property of Lessee to inspect the Aircraft, its condition, use, and operation, and the inspection, modification, overhaul, and other records maintained in connection therewith, and to obtain copies of such records, at such person's or persons' expense, provided that such visits do not interfere with the operations of Lessee and provided further that nothing contained in this Section 7(a) shall be deemed to require Lessor, the Indenture Trustee or any Participant to inspect the Aircraft or create any liability for the failure of Lessor, the Indenture Trustee or any Participant to conduct any such inspection.

(b) Financial and Other Information to Be Supplied. Lessee also agrees to furnish to the Lessor, the Indenture Trustee and each Participant during the Term:

(i) as soon as possible and in any event within 10 days after the occurrence of any Default or Event of Default which is continuing, an Officer's Certificate setting forth in detail the nature of such Default or Event of Default and the action which Lessee proposes to take with respect thereto;

(ii) as soon as available, and in any event within 60 days after the end of each of the first three fiscal quarters in each fiscal year of Lessee, consolidated balance sheets of Lessee as of the end of such quarter and related statements of income, shareholders' equity, and changes in financial condition of Lessee for the period commencing at the end of the previous fiscal year and ending with the end of such quarter, setting forth in each case in comparative form the corresponding figures for the corresponding period in such other preceding fiscal year, all in reasonable detail and duly certified (subject to year-end audit adjustments) by a financial officer of Lessee as having been prepared in accordance with generally accepted accounting principles and practices;

(iii) as soon as available, and in any event within 120 days after the end of each fiscal year of Lessee, a copy of the annual report for such year for Lessee on a consolidated basis, including therein consolidated balance sheets of Lessee as of the end of such fiscal year and related statements of income, shareholders' equity, and changes in financial condition of Lessee for such fiscal year, in comparative form with the preceding fiscal year, in each case certified by independent certified public accountants of national standing as having been prepared in accordance with generally accepted accounting principles and practices consistently applied (except as noted therein; provided that any changes in accounting principles or practices must be approved by such accountants), provided that so long as Lessee is subject to the reporting provisions of the Securities Exchange Act of 1934 a copy of Lessee 's annual report on Form 10-K will satisfy this requirement;

(iv) promptly upon the sending or filing thereof, copies of all such proxy statements, financial statements, and reports which Lessee sends to its stockholders, and copies of all regular, periodic, and special reports and all registration statements under the Securities Act of 1933, as amended, which Lessee files with the Securities and Exchange Commission or any governmental authority which may be substituted therefor, or with any national securities exchange;

(v) within 120 days after the end of each fiscal year of Lessee commencing in XXXX, an Officer's Certificate of Lessee, to the effect that the signer is familiar with or has reviewed the relevant terms of this Lease and has made, or caused to be made under his supervision, a review of the transactions and conditions of Lessee during the preceding fiscal year, and that such review has not disclosed the existence during such fiscal year, nor does the signer have knowledge of the existence as at the date of such certificate, of any condition or event which constituted or constitutes a Default or Event of Default, or, if any such condition or event existed or exists, specifying the nature and period of existence thereof and what action Lessee has taken or is taking or proposes to take with respect thereto; and

(vi) from time to time, such other information relating to its financial, operational, or business affairs or conditions as Lessor, the Indenture Trustee or any Participant may reasonably request which information in addition to other information supplied hereunder may be discussed with officers of Lessee at reasonable times.

Section 8. Replacement and Pooling of Parts; Alterations, Modifications, and Additions

(a) Replacement of Parts. Except as otherwise provided in Section 8(d) hereof, Lessee, at its own cost and expense, will during the Term promptly replace all Parts that may from time to time become worn out, lost, stolen, destroyed, seized, confiscated, damaged beyond repair, or permanently rendered unfit for use for any reason whatsoever. In addition, in the ordinary course of maintenance, service, repair, overhaul, or testing, Lessee may remove any Parts, whether or not worn out, lost, stolen, destroyed, seized, confiscated, damaged beyond repair, or permanently rendered unfit for use, provided that Lessee shall replace such Parts as promptly as practicable with replacement Parts or temporary replacement parts as provided in Section 8(c) hereof. All replacement Parts shall be free and clear of all Liens except Permitted Liens and shall be in as good operating condition as, and shall have a value and utility at least equal to, the Parts replaced assuming such replaced Parts were in the condition and repair required to be maintained by the terms hereof.

(b) Title to Parts. All Parts at any time removed from the Airframe or any Engine shall remain the property of Lessor and subject to this Lease, no matter where located, until such time as such Parts shall be replaced by Parts that have been incorporated or installed in or attached to the Airframe or any Engine and that meet the requirements for replacement Parts specified above. Immediately upon any replacement Part becoming incorporated or installed in or attached to the Airframe or an Engine as above provided, without further act, (i) title to the replaced Part shall thereupon vest in Lessee, free and clear of all rights of Lessor and shall no longer be deemed a Part hereunder; (ii) title to such replacement Part shall thereupon vest in Lessor; and (iii) such replacement Part shall become subject to this Lease and be deemed part of such Airframe or Engine, as the case may be, for all purposes hereof to the same extent as the Parts originally incorporated or installed in or attached to such Airframe or Engine.

(c) Pooling or Parts Leasing. Any Part removed from the Airframe or from any Engine as provided in Section 8(a) hereof may be subjected by Lessee to a normal pooling arrangement customary in the airline industry entered into in the ordinary course of Lessee's business with any Certificated Air Carrier or Permitted Foreign Air Carrier, provided the part replacing such removed Part shall be incorporated or installed in or attached to such Airframe or Engine in accordance with Sections 8(a) and 8(b) as promptly as possible after the removal of such removed Part. In addition, any temporary replacement part when incorporated or installed in or attached to the Airframe or any Engine in accordance with Section 8(a) hereof may be owned by another airline or vendor as customary in the airline industry, subject to such a normal pooling or leasing arrangement, provided Lessee, at its expense, as promptly thereafter as possible, either (i) causes title to such temporary replacement part to vest in Lessor in accordance with Section 8(b) hereof by Lessee acquiring title thereto for the benefit of Lessor free and clear of all Liens except Permitted Liens, at which time such temporary replacement part shall become a Part and become subject to this Lease; or (ii) replaces such temporary replacement part by incorporating or installing in or attaching to such Airframe or Engine a further replacement Part owned by Lessee free and clear of all Liens except Permitted

Liens, and by causing title to such further replacement Part to vest in Lessor in accordance with Section 8(b) hereof.

(d) Alterations, Modifications, and Additions. Lessee, at its own expense, shall make alterations and modifications in and additions to the Airframe and any Engine as may be required to be made from time to time during the Term by Applicable Law regardless upon whom such requirements are, by their terms, nominally imposed. In addition, Lessee, at its own expense, may from time to time make such alterations and modifications in and additions to the Airframe and any Engine as Lessee may deem desirable in the proper conduct of its business (including, without limitation, removal of Parts), provided that no such alteration, modification or addition diminishes the value, utility, condition, and airworthiness of such Airframe or Engine below the value, utility, condition, and airworthiness thereof immediately prior to such alteration, modification, or addition, assuming such Airframe or Engine was then in the condition required to be maintained by the terms of this Lease.

(e) Removal of Parts by Lessee. Title to all Parts incorporated or installed in or attached or added to the Airframe or an Engine as the result of any alteration, modification, or addition effected by Lessee shall, without further act, vest in the Lessor and become subject to this Lease; provided, however, that so long as no Event of Default has occurred and is continuing Lessee may remove any such Part from the Airframe or an Engine if (i) such Part is in addition to, and not in replacement of or in substitution for, any Part originally incorporated or installed in or attached to such Airframe or Engine at the time of delivery thereof hereunder or any Part in replacement of, or in substitution for, any such original Part, (ii) such Part is not required to be incorporated or installed in or attached or added to such Airframe or Engine pursuant to the terms of Section 6(c) or 6(d) hereof or the first sentence of Section 8(d), and (iii) such Part is readily removable without causing damage which is not readily repairable to such Airframe or Engine and such Part can be removed from such Airframe or Engine without diminishing or impairing the value, condition, utility, or airworthiness which such Airframe or Engine would have had at the time of removal had such alteration, modification, or addition not been effected by Lessee. Upon the removal by Lessee of any such Part as above provided, title thereto shall, without further act, vest in Lessee and such Part shall no longer be deemed a Part hereunder. Any Part not removed by Lessee as above provided prior to the return of the Airframe or Engine to Lessor hereunder shall remain the property of Lessor and subject to this Lease.

Section 9. Loss, Destruction, or Requisition

(a) Event of Loss with Respect to the Airframe. Upon the occurrence of an Event of Loss with respect to the Airframe during the Term, Lessee shall forthwith (and in any event within 10 days after such occurrence) give Lessor, the Indenture Trustee, and each holder of a Loan Certificate written notice of such Event of Loss. Lessee shall, within 60 days after such occurrence, give Lessor, the Indenture Trustee, and each holder of a Loan Certificate written notice of its election to perform one of the following options (it being agreed that if Lessee shall not have given Lessor and the Indenture Trustee such notice of such election, Lessee shall be deemed to have elected to perform the option identified in the following clause (ii)):

(i) subject to the satisfaction of the conditions contained in Section 9(b) hereof, convey or cause to be conveyed to Lessor on the Replacement Closing Date, and to be leased by Lessee hereunder in replacement thereof, a Replacement Airframe (together with the same number of Replacement Engines as the number of Engines, if any, installed on the Airframe at the time such Event of Loss occurred), such Replacement Airframe and Replacement Engines to be free and clear of all Liens except Permitted Liens, to have a value and utility at least equal to, and to be in as good operating condition and repair, and as airworthy as the Airframe and Engines, if any, so replaced (assuming such Airframe and Engines were in the condition and repair required by the terms hereof); or

(ii) pay or cause to be paid to Lessor in immediately available funds on the next Loss Payment Date following the Event of Loss (or if the Event of Loss occurs on a Loss Payment Date or within 59 days prior to a Loss Payment Date, on the 60th day following the occurrence of the Event of Loss) an amount equal to (A) the Interim Rent or Basic Rent, if any, due and payable on or before such payment date or, if such Loss Payment Date is not a Rent Payment Date, the Basic Rent accrued to such Loss Payment Date, plus (B) all unpaid Supplemental Rent due on or before such payment date, plus (C) the Stipulated Loss Value for the Aircraft determined as of the date of such Event of Loss; provided that if Lessee shall have elected pursuant to clause (i) above and shall fail to make the replacement required thereunder in accordance with Section 9(b) hereof, Lessee shall lose its right to make such replacement and shall make the payments required by this clause; (ii) provided, further, that in the case of an Event of Loss described in clause (g) of the definition thereof, the Lessee shall, promptly upon determination of the Fair Market Value (but not before the payment date otherwise provided herein) pay to Lessor, as Supplemental Rent, an amount equal to the excess, if any, of Fair Market Value over Stipulated Loss Value.

Should Lessee have provided a Replacement Aircraft as provided for in this Section 9(a)(i) above, (w) this Lease shall continue with respect to such Replacement Aircraft as though no Event of Loss had occurred; (x) Lessor shall convey to Lessee all of Lessor's right, title, and interest, as-is, where-is, without recourse or warranty, express or implied, except for a warranty against Lessor's Liens, in and to the Airframe and the Engine or Engines, if any, attached to the Airframe upon the occurrence of the Event of Loss, and shall exercise such rights as it has to cause such Airframe and Engines to be released from the Lien of the Indenture; (y) Lessor shall assign to Lessee all property damage claims it may have against any other Person arising from the Event of Loss (to the extent an insurer under a policy of insurance required by Section 10 hereof is not subrogated to such claims); and (z) Lessee shall receive all hull insurance proceeds and proceeds from any award in respect of condemnation, certification, seizure, or requisition, including any investment interest thereon, to the extent not previously applied to the purchase price of the Replacement Aircraft as provided in Sections l0(e)(ii) and 9(d)(i)(A) hereof.

In the event of a payment in full of the Stipulated Loss Value for the Aircraft and other Rent payable as provided in Section 9(a)(ii) above, (xx) this Lease and the obligations of Lessee to pay Interim Rent, Basic Rent, and Supplemental Rent (except for Supplemental Rent obligations surviving pursuant to Sections 16 and 17 of the Participation Agreement or which have otherwise accrued but not been paid as of the date of such payment) shall terminate; (yy) any remaining hull insurance proceeds (other than proceeds of policies maintained by Lessor for its own account), including any investment interest thereon, shall be promptly paid over to Lessee; and (zz) Lessor shall convey to Lessee all of Lessor's right, title, and interest, as-is, where-is without recourse or warranty, express or implied except for a warranty against Lessor's Liens, in and to, the Airframe and Engines and shall exercise such rights as it has to cause to be released from the Lien of the

Indenture (i) the Airframe and Engines subject to such Event of Loss and (ii) all claims for damage to such Airframe and Engines, if any, against third persons arising from the Event of Loss (unless any insurance carrier requires that such claims be assigned to it).

(b) Conditions to Airframe Replacement. Lessee's right to make a replacement under Section 9(a) hereof shall be subject to the fulfillment, in addition to the conditions contained in such Section 9(a), of the following conditions precedent at Lessee's sole cost and expense:

(i) No Event of Default shall, on the Replacement Closing Date referred to below, have occurred and be continuing;

(ii) On the date that the Replacement Aircraft is delivered, which date shall be not later than 120 days after the Event of Loss leading to such replacement, (hereinafter referred to in this Section 9(b) as the "Replacement Closing Date") the following documents shall have been duly authorized, executed, and delivered by the respective party or parties thereto and shall be in full force and effect, and an executed counterpart of each thereof (or, in the case of the Bills of Sale referred to below, a photocopy thereof) shall have been delivered to Lessor and the Indenture Trustee:

(A) a Lease Supplement covering the Replacement Aircraft;

(B) a Trust Agreement and Indenture Supplement covering the Replacement Aircraft;

(C) an FAA Bill of Sale covering the Replacement Aircraft, executed by the owner thereof in favor of Lessor, and dated the Replacement Closing Date;

(D) an additional full warranty bill of sale (as to title), in form and substance satisfactory to the Indenture Trustee and Lessor, covering the Replacement Aircraft (together with the Bill of Sale referred to in clause (C) of this Section 9(b) collectively called "Replacement Bills of Sale"), executed by the owner thereof in favor of Lessor, dated the Replacement Closing Date; and

(E) an Officer's Certificate of Lessee certifying that the Replacement Aircraft is a 555-300 series aircraft of at least equal value and utility, is in as good operating condition and has at least the same useful life remaining as the Aircraft it replaces immediately prior to the Event of Loss;

(iii) On or before the Replacement Closing Date, Lessor, the Indenture Trustee, and each Participant (acting directly or by authorization to their respective special counsel) shall have received such documents and evidence with respect to Lessee, Lessor, the owner of such Aircraft or the Indenture Trustee, as Lessor, the Indenture Trustee, or any Participant or their respective special counsel may reasonably request in order to establish the consummation of the transactions contemplated by this Section 9(b), the taking of all necessary corporate action in connection therewith and compliance with the conditions set forth in this Section 9(b), in each case in form and substance reasonably satisfactory to Lessor, the Indenture Trustee, the Owner Participant, and a Majority in Interest of Holders.

(iv) Lessor, the Indenture Trustee, and each Participant (acting directly or by authorization to their respective special counsel) shall each have received evidence satisfactory to Lessor and the Indenture Trustee as to the due compliance with Section 10 hereof with respect to the Replacement Aircraft.

(v) (A) On the Replacement Closing Date, Lessor shall receive good title to the Replacement Aircraft, free and clear of Liens (other than the Lien of the Indenture); (B) the Indenture Trustee shall have a first mortgage lien and security interest in the Replacement Aircraft; (C) the Replacement Aircraft shall have been duly certified by the FAA as to type and airworthiness in accordance with the terms of the relevant purchase agreement and of this Lease, and application for registration of the Replacement Aircraft in the name of Lessor shall have been duly made with the FAA, and Lessee shall have authority to operate the Replacement Aircraft; and (D) Lessor and the Indenture Trustee (acting directly or by authorization to their respective special counsel) shall have received evidence satisfactory to it with respect to the matters covered by this subparagraph (v).

(vi) On the Replacement Closing Date, the following statements shall be true and Lessor and the Indenture Trustee and their respective special counsel shall have received an Officer's Certificate of Lessee, dated the Replacement Closing Date, stating that (A) the representations and warranties contained in Section 6 of the Participation Agreement are true and accurate on and as of the Replacement Closing Date as though made on and as of the Replacement Closing Date except to the extent that such representations and warranties relate solely to an earlier date, (B) the matters set forth in clause (i) above are confirmed and (C) no Default or Event of Default will result from the purchase or lease of the Replacement Aircraft.

(vii) Each Participant, Lessor and the Indenture Trustee shall, at the expense of Lessee, have received (acting directly or by authorization to its special counsel) (A) an opinion, satisfactory in form and substance to Lessor and each Participant, of Thompson & Achetson or other counsel selected by Lessee and reasonably satisfactory to Lessor and each Participant (i) to the effect that good and marketable title to the Replacement Airframe and Replacement Engines, if any, has been vested in Lessor free and clear of all Liens other than the rights of Lessee hereunder and the rights of the Indenture Trustee under the Indenture and (ii) with respect to the effectiveness, priority, recordation, and filing of the interests in the Estate which the Indenture purports to create, and (iii) to effect that Owner Trustee, as Lessor under the Lease, and the Indenture Trustee as assignee of Owner Trustee's rights under the Lease pursuant to the Indenture, are entitled to the benefits of 11 U.S.C. Section 1110 (or any successor or replacement statute) with respect to the Replacement Airframe and Replacement Engine, if any, to the same extent as they were so entitled with respect to the replaced airframe and replaced engines, if any (B) an opinion of qualified FAA counsel satisfactory to the Lessor, the Owner Participant, and a Majority in Interest of Holders to the effect of the form of opinion of counsel attached as Exhibit VI-6 to the Participation Agreement and (C) such other opinions of such counsel as Lessor or the Indenture Trustee may reasonably request.

(viii) On or before the Replacement Closing Date, Lessee shall have made all payments and/or effected all Rent adjustments required in connection with such Event of Loss and replacement pursuant to the Tax Indemnity Agreement (such Event of Loss and replacement being hereby deemed to be an "act" of Lessee giving rise to an indemnity obligation of Lessee).

(ix) On or before the Replacement Closing Date, Lessee shall have furnished Lessor and Indenture Trustee with such other evidence as Lessor or Indenture Trustee has reasonably requested of the value, useful life, and utility of, and good title to, and mortgage upon, such Replacement Airframe and Replacement Engines and of the airworthiness of such Replacement Airframe and Replacement Engines.

(c) With Respect to an Engine. Upon the occurrence during the Term of an Event of Loss with respect to an Engine not then installed on the Airframe, or an Event of Loss with respect to an Engine installed on the Airframe not involving an Event of Loss with respect to such Airframe, Lessee shall give Lessor prompt written notice thereof and Lessee shall replace such Engine as soon as reasonably practicable under the circumstances but in no event later than 60 days after the occurrence of such Event of Loss by duly conveying to Lessor as a replacement for said Engine, title to another engine of the type specified in the applicable Lease Supplement (or an engine of the same manufacturer and of the same or an improved model and suitable for installation and use on such Airframe), which engine shall be free and clear of all Liens except Permitted Liens and shall have a value and utility at least equal to, and be in as good operating condition as, the Engine with respect to which such Event of Loss occurred, assuming such Engine was of the value and utility and in the condition and repair required by the terms hereof immediately prior to the occurrence of such Event of Loss. Lessee agrees to take such action with respect to such Replacement Engine as Lessee is required to take with respect to a Replacement Airframe under Section 9(b)(ii) (except under clauses [C] and [E] thereunder) and to deliver an Officer's Certificate of Lessee certifying that such Replacement Engine complies with this Section 9(c). Lessee agrees to take such further action as Lessor or the Indenture Trustee may reasonably request with respect to such Replacement Engine including, without limitation, the actions required to be taken by it under Section 5(f) of the Indenture. Such Replacement Engine, upon being titled in the name of Lessor free of all Liens except Permitted Liens, shall be deemed an "Engine" as defined herein for all purposes hereof. Upon full compliance with this Section 9(c), Lessor shall transfer to Lessee all Lessor's right, title, and interest, as-is, where-is, without recourse or warranty, express or implied, except for a warranty against Lessor's Liens, in and to the Engine with respect to which such Event of Loss occurred, including claims for damage to the Engine, if any, against third persons arising from the Event of Loss (to the extent an insurer under a policy of insurance required by Section 10 hereof is not subrogated to such claims). No Event of Loss with respect to an Engine under the circumstances contemplated by the terms of this Section 9(c) shall result in any reduction in Rent or Lessee's obligation to pay Basic Rent hereunder. Lessee agrees that it shall at all times during the term of this Lease maintain two Engines or other aircraft engines suitable for use on the Airframe.

(d) Payments from Governmental Authorities for Requisition of Title or Use.

(i) Any payments on account of an Event of Loss (other than insurance proceeds or other payments the application of which is provided for in this Section 9, or elsewhere in this Lease, as the case may be) received at any time by Lessor or by Lessee from any governmental authority or other Person will be applied as follows:

(A) if such payments are received with respect to the Airframe or the Airframe and the Engines or engines installed on such Airframe that has been or is being replaced by Lessee pursuant to Section 9(a) hereof, such payments shall be paid over to, or retained by, Lessor, and upon completion of (or, if requested by Lessee, simultaneously with) such replacement be paid over to, or retained by, Lessee, and

(B) if such payments are received with respect to the Airframe or the Airframe and the Engines or engines installed on such Airframe that has not been and will not be replaced as contemplated by Section 9(a) hereof, so much of such payments as shall not exceed the Stipulated Loss Value required to be paid by Lessee pursuant to Section 9(a) hereof, shall be applied in reduction of Lessee's obligation to pay such Stipulated Loss Value, to the extent not already paid by Lessee, and, to the extent already paid by Lessee, shall be applied to reimburse Lessee for its payment of such Stipulated Loss Value, and the balance, if any, of such payment remaining thereafter shall be divided between Lessee and Lessor, as provided in the next to last proviso of this Section 9(d)(i) hereof; and

(C) if such payments are received with respect to an Engine under circumstances contemplated by Section 9(c) or 9(d)(iii) hereof, such payments shall be paid over to, or retained by, Lessee, provided that Lessee shall have fully performed the terms of Section 9(c) hereof with respect to the Event of Loss for which such payments are made; provided, however, that any remaining proceeds from any award in respect of any condemnation, confiscation, seizure, or requisition constituting an Event of Loss shall be distributed between Lessor and Lessee pro rata in the respective ratios that the amount computed pursuant to clause (I) below, said amount being the assumed value of the Lessor's interest, and the amount computed pursuant to clause (II) below, said amount being the assumed value of Lessee's interest, bear to the sum of the amounts computed pursuant to clauses (I) and (II) below:

(I) the sum of (1) the present value (as discounted annually as of each January 2 at the rate of 10% per annum, hereinafter in this Section 9[d] called the "Present Value") of the remaining Basic Rent payments as set forth in Exhibit C for the Aircraft during the Term and (2) the Present Value of the Fair Market Sales Value (not to exceed 50% of Lessor's Cost) for the Aircraft at the end of the Term, less (3) the Stipulated Loss Value paid hereunder, and

(II) (1) the Present Value of the Fair Market Rental Value of the Aircraft for the remainder of the Term less (2) the amount referred to in clause (I)(1) above. Provided further that if the amount computed under either clause (I) or (II) above shall be a negative number such amount shall be deemed to be zero.

(ii) In the event of a requisition for use by any government, so long as it does not constitute an Event of Loss, of the Aircraft, the Airframe, and the Engines or engines installed on the Airframe during the Term, Lessee shall promptly notify Lessor of such requisition and all the Lessee's obligations under this Lease shall continue to the same extent as if such requisition had not occurred except to the extent that any failure or delay in the performance or observance of each obligation by Lessee shall have been prevented or delayed by such requisition, provided that Lessee's obligations for the payment of money and under Section 10 hereof shall in no way be affected, reduced, or delayed by such requisition. Any payments received by Lessor or Lessee from such government with respect to such requisition shall be paid over to or retained by, Lessee.

(iii) In the event of the requisition for use by a government of any Engine (but not the Airframe), Lessee will replace such Engine hereunder by complying with the terms of Section 9(c) hereof to the same extent as if an Event of Loss had occurred with respect to such Engine, and any payments received by Lessor or Lessee from such government with respect to such requisition shall be paid over to, or retained by, Lessee.

(e) Application of Payments During Existence of Event of Default. Any amount referred to in this Section 9 or Section 10 hereof which is payable to Lessee shall not be paid to Lessee, or, if it has been previously paid directly to Lessee, shall not be retained by Lessee, if at the time of such payment either a Default under Sections 17(a), (e), (f) or (g) hereof or an Event of Default, shall have occurred and be continuing, but shall be paid to and held by Lessor (or, so long as the Indenture shall not have been discharged, the Indenture Trustee) as security for the obligations of Lessee under this Lease, and at such time as there shall not be continuing any such Default or Event of Default such amount shall be paid over to Lessee.

Section 10. Insurance

(a) Public Liability and Property Damage Insurance. Subject to the rights of Lessee under Section 10(d) hereof, Lessee will, without expense to Lessor, the Indenture Trustee, or any Participant, maintain or cause to be maintained in effect, at all times during the Term (and if the Aircraft is returned thereafter pursuant to Section 13 hereof, until such return), with insurers of recognized responsibility, comprehensive aircraft and general liability insurance (including, without limitation, passenger and baggage liability, property damage, and product liability coverage but excluding manufacturer's product liability coverage) with respect to the Aircraft in an amount not less than a $300,000,000 combined single limit, or such greater amounts as Lessee may carry from time to time on other similar aircraft in its fleet. Such insurance shall be of the type usually carried by corporations engaged in the same or a similar business, similarly situated with Lessee and owning and operating similar aircraft and engines, and covering such other risks as are customarily insured against by such corporations.

(b) Insurance Against Loss or Damage to the Aircraft and Engines. Subject to the rights of Lessee under Section 10(d) hereof, Lessee will, without expense to Lessor, the Indenture Trustee, or any Participant, maintain or cause to be maintained in effect, at all times during the Term (and if the Aircraft is returned thereafter pursuant to Section 13 hereof, until such return), with insurers of recognized responsibility, all-risk, agreed value ground and flight hull insurance, excluding war risks and allied perils (but including nonpolitical hijacking), covering the Aircraft for an amount not less than the amount referred to in clause (x) of the definition of "Stipulated Loss Value" from time to time. Such hull insurance shall cover Engines or engines and Parts temporarily removed from the Airframe pending replacement by installation of the same or similar Engines, engines or Parts on the Airframe. Such insurance shall be of the type usually carried by corporations engaged in the same or a similar business, similarly situated with Lessee and owning and operating similar aircraft and engines, and covering such other risks as are customarily insured against by such corporations. If and to the extent that Lessee or a sublessee (A) maintains war risk insurance (including political hijacking and governmental confiscation insurance) in effect with respect to other similar owned or leased aircraft in its fleet and used in similar operations, or (B) operates the Aircraft on routes other than routes within or between the United States, Canada, Bermuda, and the Bahama Islands, where the custom in the industry is to carry such insurance, Lessee shall maintain or cause to be maintained such insurance in effect with respect to the Aircraft in an amount not less than the amount referred to in clause (x) of the definition of "Stipulated Loss Value" of the Aircraft from time to time and with such notice of cancellation provisions as may be customary with respect to such insurance.

(c) Additional Insureds; Loss Payment. Lessee shall cause all policies of insurance carried in accordance with this Section 10 to name the Lessor in its individual capacity and as Owner Trustee, the Owner Participant, the Indenture Trustee, and the Loan Participants as additional insureds as their respective interests may appear. Such policies shall provide with respect to such additional insureds that (i) none of their respective interests in such policies shall be invalidated by any act or omission or breach of warranty of Lessee or any other named insured or by any act or omission of any other additional insured; (ii) no cancellation or lapse of coverage for nonpayment of premium or otherwise, and no material change of coverage which adversely affects the interests of such additional insured, shall be effective as to such additional insured until 30 days (or such lesser period as may be applicable in the case of any war risk coverage) after receipt by such additional insured of written notice from the insurers of such cancellation, lapse, or change; (iii) they shall have no liability for premiums, commissions, calls, assessments, or advances with respect to such policies; (iv) such policies will be primary without any right of contribution from any other insurance carried by such additional insureds; and (v) the insurers waive any rights of setoff, counterclaim, deduction, or subrogation against such additional insureds. Each liability policy shall provide that all the provisions thereof, except the limits of liability, shall operate in the same manner as if there were a separate policy covering each insured. Each hull policy shall provide that, so long as the insurers shall not have received written notice that an Event of Default has occurred and is continuing, any proceeds of less than $750,000 shall be payable to Lessee; and any proceeds in excess of $750,000, and any proceeds in respect of a total loss, or if the insurers shall have received written notice that an Event of Default has occurred and is continuing, any single loss regardless of the amount, shall be payable to the Indenture Trustee as long as the Indenture is in effect, and to Lessor after the Indenture shall have been discharged.

(d) Deductibles and Self-Insurance. Lessee may from time to time self-insure, by way of deductible or premium adjustment provisions in insurance policies, the risks required to be insured against pursuant to this Section 10 in such reasonable amounts as are then applicable to similar owned or leased aircraft in Lessee's fleet but in no case shall such self-insurance exceed an aggregate hull and liability self-insurance retention of (i) for the period from the date hereof until April 30, XXXX, $1,000,000 for the Aircraft per occurrence and (ii) for the period thereafter, $2,500,000 for the Aircraft per occurrence (or such higher amount as may be approved by Lessor, which approval will not be unreasonably withheld).

(e) Application of Hull Insurance Proceeds. As between Lessor and Lessee, any payments received under policies of hull insurance required to be maintained by Lessee pursuant to this Section 10, shall be applied as follows:

(i) if such payments are received with respect to loss or damage (including an Event of Loss with respect to an Engine) not constituting an Event of Loss with respect to the Airframe, such payments shall be paid over to or retained by Lessee upon completion of, or at Lessee's option, and upon presentation of satisfactory invoices, in conjunction with, Lessee's performance of its repair or replacement obligations under this Lease;

(ii) if such payments are received with respect to an Event of Loss with respect to the Airframe, so much of such payments as shall not exceed the amount required to be paid by Lessee pursuant to Section 9 hereof shall be applied in reduction of Lessee's obligation to pay such amount to the extent not already paid by Lessee, and thereafter to reimburse Lessee if it shall have paid all or part of such amount, and the balance, if any, of such payments shall be promptly paid over to, or retained by, Lessee; and

(iii) if such payments are received with respect to the Airframe or the Airframe and Engines or engines installed on such Airframe that has been or is being replaced by Lessee pursuant to Section 9(a) hereof, such payments shall be paid over to, or retained by, Lessor, and upon completion of (or, if requested by Lessee, simultaneously with the transfer of title to) such replacement be paid over to, or retained by Lessee.

(f) Insurance for Own Account. Nothing in this Section 10 shall prohibit Lessor or Lessee from obtaining insurance for its own account and any proceeds payable thereunder shall be payable as provided in the insurance policy relating thereto, provided that no such insurance may be obtained which would limit or otherwise adversely affect the coverage or payment of any insurance required to be obtained or maintained pursuant to this Section 10.

(g) Reports, etc. Lessee will during the Term furnish to Lessor, the Indenture Trustee, and each Loan Participant, evidence of renewal of the insurance policies required pursuant to this Section 10 prior to the cancellation, lapse, or expiration of such insurance policies and, on the renewal dates of the insurance policies carried by Lessee pursuant to this Section 10, a report signed by a firm of independent aircraft insurance brokers, appointed by Lessee and reasonably satisfactory to Lessor, stating the opinion of such firm that the insurance then carried and maintained on the Aircraft complies with the terms hereof (including, without limitation, with respect to war risk insurance), provided that all information contained in such report shall be held confidential by Lessor, the Indenture Trustee, and such Loan Participant and shall not be furnished or disclosed by them to anyone except that (A) they may disclose any such information (v) as has become generally available to the public, (w) as may be required or appropriate in any report, statement, or testimony submitted to any municipal, state, or federal regulatory body having or claiming to have jurisdiction or to the National Association of Insurance Commissioners or similar organizations or their successors, (x) as may be required or appropriate in response to any summons or subpoena or in connection with any litigation, (y) to the extent that they believe it appropriate in order to protect their investment in the Trust Estate or the Loan Certificates, as the case may be, or in order to comply with any law, order, regulation, or ruling applicable to them and (z) to the prospective transferee in connection with any contemplated transfer of its interest in the Trust Estate by Lessor or any contemplated transfer of any of the Loan Certificates, and (B) Lessee agrees that neither Lessor, the Indenture Trustee, nor any Loan Participant will be liable to Lessee in the event that any such information is disclosed. Lessee will cause such firm to advise Lessor, the Indenture Trustee, and each Loan Participant in writing promptly of any default in the payment of any premium and of any other act or omission on the part of Lessee of which they have knowledge and which would in such firm's opinion invalidate or render unenforceable, in whole or in any material part, any insurance on the Aircraft. Lessee will also cause such firm to advise Lessor, the Indenture Trustee, and each Loan Participant in writing at least 30 days prior to the termination or cancellation of, or material adverse change in, such insurance carried and maintained on the Aircraft pursuant to this Section 10.

Section 11. Liens

Lessee shall not during the Term, directly or indirectly create, incur, assume, or suffer to exist any Lien on or with respect to the Airframe or any Engine or title thereto or any interest therein, or in this Lease except (a) the respective rights of Lessor and Lessee as provided herein, the Lien of the Indenture and the rights of the parties to the other Operative Documents; (b) the rights of others under agreements or arrangements to the extent expressly permitted in Sections 6(a) and 8(c) hereof; (c) Liens for Taxes either not yet due or being contested in good faith by appropriate proceedings so long as such proceedings do not involve any material danger of the sale, forfeiture, or loss of the Airframe or an Engine; (d) material suppliers', mechanics', workers', repairers', employees' or other like liens arising in the ordinary course of business and for amounts the payment of which is either not yet delinquent or is being contested in good faith (and for the payment of which adequate reserves have been provided) by appropriate proceedings, and so long as such proceedings do not involve a material danger of the sale, forfeiture, or loss of the Airframe or an Engine; (e) Liens arising out of judgments or awards against Lessee with respect to which at the time an appeal or proceeding for review is being prosecuted in good faith by appropriate proceedings and there shall have been secured a stay of execution pending such appeal or proceeding for review; and (f) Lessor's Liens (Liens described in clauses [a] through [f] above are referred to herein as "Permitted Liens"). Lessee shall promptly, at its own expense, take such action as may be necessary to duly discharge any such Lien not excepted above if the same shall arise at any time.

Section 12. Recordation and Further Assurances

(a) Recordation of Lease. Lessee, at its expense, shall cause this Lease, all Exhibits hereto, any Lease Supplements, and any and all additional instruments which shall be executed pursuant to the terms hereof so far as permitted by Applicable Law or regulations, to be kept, filed, and recorded and to be reexecuted, refiled, and rerecorded at all times during the Term in the office of the FAA, pursuant to the Federal Aviation Act and in such other places or with such other governmental authority as Lessor may reasonably request to perfect and preserve Lessor 's rights hereunder.

(b) Further Assurances. Lessee will promptly and duly execute and deliver to Lessor such further documents and assurances and take such further action as Lessor may from time to time during the Term reasonably request in order to more effectively carry out the intent and purpose of this Lease and to establish and protect the rights and remedies created or intended to be created in favor of Lessor hereunder, including, without limitation, if requested by Lessor, at the expense of Lessee, the execution and delivery of supplements or amendments hereto, in recordable form, subjecting any replacement or substituted aircraft or engine to this Lease and the recording or filing of counterparts hereof, or of financing statements with respect hereto, in accordance with the laws of such jurisdictions as Lessor may reasonably deem advisable.

Section 13. Return of Aircraft and Records

(a) Return of Aircraft. With respect to the Aircraft, unless purchased by Lessee as provided in Section 14(b) hereof or as may be required by Section 15(a) or (b) hereof, at the expiration of the Term with respect to the Aircraft (subject to reimbursement of any Reimbursement Amount which may be due to Lessee under Section 3[h] hereof), or upon the termination of this Lease pursuant to Section 18 hereof, Lessee, at its own expense, shall, except as otherwise provided in Section 18(a) hereof, return the Aircraft by delivering the same to Lessor in the continental United States of America at a mutually agreeable location but if no location is agreed, at a location on Lessee's domestic route system chosen by Lessee at which Lessee customarily has maintenance personnel and available ramp storage space with the Aircraft fully equipped with two Engines or other CFM International 56–3-BI engines (or engines of the same or another manufacturer of the same or an improved model and suitable for installation and use on the Aircraft, owned by Lessee) duly installed thereon.

(b) Return of Other Engines. In the event any engine not owned by Lessor shall be returned with the Airframe, such engine shall have a value and utility at least equal to, and shall be in as good operating condition as, an Engine assuming such Engine was in the condition and repair required by the terms hereof for an Engine immediately prior to such return, and Lessee will, at its own expense and concurrently with such return, furnish Lessor with a full warranty bill of sale, in form and substance satisfactory to Lessor, with respect to each such engine and shall take such other action as Lessor may reasonably request in order that such engine shall be duly and properly titled in Lessor's name. Upon passage of title such engine shall be deemed to be an Engine for all purposes hereof and thereupon Lessor will transfer to Lessee, without recourse or warranty except a warranty against Lessor's Liens, all of Lessor's right, title, and interest in and to an Engine not installed on the Airframe at the time of the return thereof and, if the Indenture has not been discharged, will request in writing that the Indenture Trustee execute and deliver to Lessee an appropriate instrument releasing the Engine being transferred to Lessee from the Lien of the Indenture and from the pledge or assignment of any agreement under the Indenture.

(c) Fuel; Records. Upon the return of the Aircraft, (i) Lessor shall reimburse Lessee for all fuel contained in the Aircraft's fuel tanks at Lessee's then current cost of fuel at the place of redelivery, and (ii) Lessee shall deliver to Lessor all logs, manuals, certificates, data, and inspection, modification and overhaul records which are required to be maintained with respect thereto under applicable rules and regulations of the FAA and Department of Transportation.

(d) Condition of Aircraft. The Aircraft when returned to Lessor shall be in good operating condition and appearance, ordinary wear and tear excepted, the Aircraft shall have a valid FAA Certificate of Airworthiness, a valid certification for operations under Part 121 of the Federal Aviation Regulations, be in compliance with Lessee's FAA approved maintenance program (including the supplemental structural inspection document) and be in compliance with all applicable airworthiness directives and manufacturer's mandatory service bulletins (except for bulletins that permit compliance at a later time without waiver or exemption that would delay such compliance) on or prior to return of the Aircraft (before any storage by Lessee pursuant to Section 13[e] hereof), and the Aircraft shall have been treated in a nondiscriminatory manner with other similar Blackhawk 555-300 series aircraft in Lessee's fleet, and the Aircraft shall be free and clear of all Liens and rights of others other than Lessor's Liens. The Aircraft shall be in a suitable configuration for commercial passenger service. Lessee shall remove all Lessee identification (i.e. name and logo) from the Aircraft, which removal shall be completed in a workman-like manner. The Engines shall have remaining until the next scheduled engine removal an average of at least 3,000 hours or cycles in the aggregate for the Aircraft and each Engine shall have no less than 1,500 hours or cycles for any engine until its next scheduled engine removal. The Aircraft will have at least 50% of the time remaining to the next applicable "C" check (it being understood that Lessee performs the equivalent of 1/6 of a "D" check with each "C" check) if such standard continues to constitute a part of Lessee's maintenance program or an equivalent standard if Lessee elects to change its maintenance program (for example, if Lessee changes to a block maintenance program, the Aircraft will have 50% of the time remaining to the next "D" check). If, however, the Aircraft has between 35% and 50% of the time remaining to the next "C" check (or an equivalent standard), Lessor may elect either to have Lessee perform a "C" check or to make a financial adjustment at the rate then charged by Lessee to third parties for performing such work, or if Lessee does not perform such work, at the rate then charged by a reputable outside FAA approved maintenance facility mutually agreed upon by Lessor and Lessee; provided, however, if Lessor elects to have Lessee perform such "C" check, Lessee shall bear a percentage of the cost of such "C" check equal to the difference between the percentage of time remaining to the next "C" check for such Aircraft (if lower than 50%) and 50% and Lessor shall bear the balance of such cost. If the Aircraft has less than 35% of the time remaining to the next "C" check (or equivalent standard) Lessor may elect either to have Lessee perform a "C" check prior to return of the Aircraft, at Lessee's expense, or to make a financial adjustment at the rate then charged by Lessee to third parties for performing such work or if Lessee does not perform such work, at the rate then charged by a reputable outside FAA approved maintenance facility mutually agreed upon by Lessor and Lessee. Lessee will notify the Lessor of the last "C" check to be performed prior to return of the Aircraft and Lessor's inspectors may, provided that it does not result in increasing the downtime of the Aircraft, observe such "C" check. Prior to the return of the Aircraft, if requested by Lessor, and at Lessor's expense, a test flight will be conducted by Lessee at a time convenient to Lessee, with Lessor's observers on board the Aircraft, in accordance with procedures of the Manufacturer designated for such purpose for used Aircraft.

(e) Storage. Upon any expiration or termination of this Lease with respect to the Aircraft, at the written request of Lessor received by Lessee 60 days in advance of the date provided for redelivery to Lessor hereunder, Lessee will arrange, or will cause to be arranged, storage of the Aircraft beyond the Term for a period not exceeding 30 days at Lessor's risk and at Lessee's expense, except for expenses relating to insurance and any required preventative maintenance. If prior to the end of such 30 day period Lessor shall request Lessee to maintain insurance on the Aircraft for an additional 90 days, Lessee shall at Lessor's expense, maintain such insurance.

(f) Overhaul. After the end of the Term but prior to the return of the Aircraft, Lessee, without disruption of its operations or preexisting commitments, upon the written request of Lessor, will perform such work on the Airframe and Engines or engines constituting a part of the Aircraft as Lessor may request, subject to Lessee's capabilities. Lessor shall reimburse Lessee for such work at the rates which Lessee then charges unaffiliated third parties generally for similar work on similar aircraft and Lessee shall have the same but no greater responsibility with respect to such work as it would have under its then current warranty policy with respect to similar work performed for such parties.

Section 14. Renewal Option and Purchase Options

(a) Renewal Terms. Lessee shall have the right, subject to the provisions set forth herein, to extend this Lease for the Aircraft for one or more successive periods (each such period being hereafter referred to as a "Renewal Term"), the first Renewal Term commencing at the end of the Basic Term and each of the following Renewal Terms commencing at the end of the immediately proceeding Renewal Term. Such right to extend this Lease shall be exercised upon written notice to Lessor not less than 270 days before the expiration of the Basic Term or immediately preceding Renewal Term, as the case may be. Such notice shall be irrevocable except that Lessee may revoke its election to extend this Lease 15 days following the determination of the Fair Market Rental Value of the Aircraft but in no event later than 180 days prior to the end of the Basic Term or preceding Renewal Term, if any. If no Event of Default shall have occurred and be continuing on the date of such notice or on the date of the commencement of any Renewal Term, then this Lease shall be extended for the additional period of such Renewal Term as specified in such notice on substantially the same conditions as provided for herein, and upon such extension, the word "Term" whenever used herein shall be deemed to include, without limitation, such Renewal Term. The rental payable during each Renewal Term shall be the Fair Market Rental Value for the Aircraft. The Stipulated Loss Value of the Aircraft during a Renewal Term shall be the Fair Market Sales Value (but not to exceed 50% of Lessor's Cost) as of the commencement date of such Renewal Term and shall decline evenly in annual steps to 20% of Lessor's Cost on the rent payment dates for such Renewal Term over the remaining useful life of the Aircraft.

(b) Purchase Options. Lessee shall have the right to purchase the Aircraft (i) upon the expiration of the Basic Term for a price (which shall not exceed 50% of Lessor's Cost for the Aircraft) equal to the Fair Market Sales Value for the Aircraft and (ii) upon the expiration of a Renewal Term for a price equal to the Fair Market Sales Value for the Aircraft, in each case less any Reimbursement Amount due to Lessee under Section 3(h) hereof. Such right to purchase shall be exercised upon written notice to Lessor not less than 270 days before the expiration of the Basic Term or Renewal Term, as the case may be. Such notice shall be irrevocable, except if Lessee exercises its option to purchase pursuant to clause (ii) above, Lessee may revoke its option to purchase the Aircraft 15 days following the determination of Fair Market Sales Value of the Aircraft, but in no event later than 180 days prior to the end of the Renewal convey to Lessee at the end of the Basic Term or Renewal Term, as the case may be, all of Lessor's right, title, and interest in and to the Aircraft concerned on an "as-is, where-is" basis, without recourse or warranty, except a warranty against Lessor's Liens.

Section 15. Voluntary Termination

(a) Termination for Obsolescence.

(i) So long as no Event of Default shall have occurred and be continuing, Lessee shall have the right at its option at any time after the tenth anniversary of the Delivery Date, and before the end of the Term with at least 270 days prior written notice (which notice shall be irrevocable, except as provided below) to Lessor, the Loan Participants and the Indenture Trustee specifying a proposed date of termination (which shall be a Basic Rent Payment Date) (the "Termination Date"), to terminate this Lease for the Aircraft, if, the Board of Directors of Lessee shall have determined in good faith that the Aircraft shall have become obsolete or shall be surplus to its equipment requirements, such termination to be effective on the date of sale, if any, referred to below in this Section 15(a). During the period following the giving of such notice of termination until the Termination Date, Lessee, as agent for Lessor, shall use its best efforts to obtain cash bids from Persons other than Lessee or affiliates thereof for the said purchase on or prior to the Termination Date of the Aircraft and, in the event that it receives any such bid, Lessee shall, within 5 Business Days after receipt thereof and at least 15 days prior to the proposed date of sale, certify in writing to Lessor, the amount and terms of each such bid, the proposed date of such sale and the name and address of the party submitting such bid. Lessee may, not less than 60 days prior to the Termination Date by notice in writing to Lessor, the Indenture Trustee, and each Participant, withdraw its notice of termination, and thereupon this Lease shall continue in full force and effect; provided that Lessee shall be entitled to withdraw a notice of termination only two times during the Lease Term. If Lessee shall so withdraw any notice of termination, Lessee shall reimburse Lessor, the Indenture Trustee, and each Participant for its out-of-pocket expenses incurred as a result of Lessee's having previously given such notice of termination. Unless Lessee shall withdraw its notice of termination as stated above or Lessor shall have submitted a bid in accordance with this Section 15(a), on the Termination Date, or such earlier date of sale as shall be consented to in writing by Lessor and Lessee, which date shall thereafter be deemed the Termination Date, if no Event of Default has occurred and is continuing (A) Lessee shall, subject to receipt (x) by Lessor of an amount equal to the Termination Value for the Aircraft as of the Termination Date, (y) by the Persons entitled thereto of all unpaid Supplemental Rent due on or before the Termination Date and (z) by Lessor of all Basic Rent due and payable on such date, deliver the Aircraft to the bidder or bidders, as the case may be, if any, which shall have prior to such date submitted the highest cash bid and of which notice shall have been given in the same manner as if delivery were made to Lessor at the end of the Term pursuant to Section 13, and shall duly transfer to Lessor title to any engines installed on the Aircraft, all in accordance with the terms of Section 13, and (B) Lessor shall, without recourse or warranty (except as to Lessor's Liens), simultaneously therewith sell the Aircraft for cash to such bidder or bidders, as the case may be.

(ii) The total selling price realized at such sale shall be retained by Lessor and, in addition, on the Termination Date, Lessee shall pay to Lessor or, in the case of Supplemental Rent, to the Persons entitled thereto, in immediately available funds, an amount equal to the sum of (A) the excess, if any, of (x) the Termination Value for the Aircraft as of the Termination Date, over (y) the proceeds of the sale of the Aircraft after deducting the reasonable expenses incurred by Lessor, the Indenture Trustee, and each Participant plus (B) all unpaid Supplemental Rent due on or before the Termination Date plus (C) all Basic Rent due on or before the Termination Date with respect to the Aircraft.

(iii) Upon the sale of the Aircraft pursuant to Section 15(a)(i) Lessor will transfer to Lessee, without recourse or warranty (except as to Lessor's Liens), all of Lessor's right, title, and interest in and to any Engines constituting part of the Aircraft but which were not then installed on the Aircraft. Lessor may, but shall be under no duty, to solicit bids, to inquire into the efforts of Lessee to obtain bids or, subject to the last sentence of this Section 15(a)(iii), otherwise take any action in connection with the sale of the Aircraft under Section 15(a)(i) other than to transfer to the purchaser of the Aircraft (or to such purchaser and to Lessee, as the case may be), without recourse or warranty (except as to Lessor's Liens), all of Lessor's right, title, and interest in and to the Aircraft against receipt of the payments provided for herein. Lessor agrees promptly to notify Lessee of the appointment by Lessor of any broker or finder in connection with the sale of the Aircraft pursuant to Section 15(a)(i) and to pay the fees or commissions of any broker or finder employed by Lessor in connection with the sale of the Aircraft pursuant to Section 15(a)(i).

Notwithstanding the foregoing provisions of this Section 15(a), Lessor may, within 30 days after Lessee's certification under Section 15(a)(i) of a bid at or above Termination Value or, if Lessee does not certify any such bids, at any time up to 90 days prior to the Termination Date, notify Lessee in writing of its preemptive election to take possession of the Aircraft, which notice shall be accompanied by an irrevocable undertaking by Lessor to pay to the Indenture Trustee the amount required to pay in full (after giving effect to any installment of Basic Rent due on such date) the aggregate unpaid principal amount of the outstanding Loan Certificates, together with all accrued interest thereon and all other amounts, if any, payable under the Indenture. Upon receipt of such notice, Lessee and Lessor shall cease efforts to obtain bids as provided above and shall reject all other bids theretofore or thereafter received. On the Termination Date, provided that Lessee has not withdrawn its notice of termination as provided in the preceding paragraph and Lessor has made the payments required by the terms of this paragraph, Lessee shall deliver the Aircraft to Lessor in accordance with Section 13 hereof and shall pay all Rent accrued and unpaid on or before the Termination Date, and Lessor shall transfer to the Lessee any Engines constituting part of the Aircraft but which were not then installed on the Aircraft as provided in Section 13 hereof, whereupon the obligation of Lessee to pay Basic Rent due and payable after the Termination Date shall cease and from and after the Termination Date the Aircraft shall no longer be subject to this Lease and the Lease Term with respect to the Aircraft shall end on such Date.

If on the Termination Date no sale of the Aircraft shall have occurred and Lessee has not delivered the Aircraft to Lessor pursuant to the immediately preceding paragraph, Lessee's notice given pursuant to Section 15(a)(i) shall be deemed to be withdrawn as of such date and this Lease shall continue in full force and effect in respect to the Aircraft. Lessee shall reimburse Lessor, the Indenture Trustee, and the Loan Participants for their out-of-pocket expenses incurred as a result of Lessee's having given such notice of termination.

(b) Termination for Burdensome Expenses. Upon the occurrence of a Tax Law Change which would require an upward adjustment to Basic Rent under Section 3(e) hereof in an aggregate amount over the then remaining period of the Basic Term the present value of which discounted at the Fixed Rate shall be 400 basis points or more greater than the present value of the aggregate rental payments otherwise payable over the remaining period of the Basic Term discounted at the Fixed Rate Lessee may, upon not less than 45 days nor more than 90 days prior written notice to Lessor, the Indenture Trustee, and each Loan Participant, which notice shall be given within 90 days after the amount of any such adjustment is finally determined under the provisions hereof, terminate this Lease (but in no event later than September 1, XXXX). Such written notice shall be irrevocable and shall designate the date on which Lessee will purchase the Aircraft, which shall be a date not earlier than 45 days nor more than 90 days after the date of such notice (the "Proposed Purchase Date") and shall be accompanied by an Officer's Certificate of Lessee setting forth in reasonable detail the basis for such termination, and if such notice is not given within such 90 day period, Lessee's rights under this Section 15(b) shall lapse. On the Proposed Purchase Date, Lessee will pay to Lessor an amount equal to the sum of (A) the greater of (x) (1) Lessor's Cost for the Aircraft plus interest at the rate of ________%, compounded monthly, from the Delivery Date for the Aircraft through the date of purchase under this Section 15(b); plus (2) all costs and expenses incurred by Lessor and the Owner Participant in connection with Lessor's purchase, financing, and leasing of such Aircraft; plus (3) the excess of any debt service payment made by Lessor over the rents paid by the Lessee; plus (4) all costs and expenses incurred by Lessor and the Owner Participant due to the exercise by Lessee of its purchase option under this Section 15(b); plus (5) interest on the amounts payable under clauses (2), (3), and (4) hereof at the annual rate of ________% compounded monthly from the date of payment by Lessor and the Owner Participant of such costs and expenses through the date of purchase under this Section 15(b); plus (6) an amount which, after deduction of all federal, state, and local income taxes required to be paid by the Owner Participant in respect of the receipt of such amount (and after giving credit for any saving in respect of such taxes by reason of deductions, credits, or allowances related to the payment of such amount) shall be equal to the amount of estimated tax penalties actually incurred by the Owner Participant as a result of Lessee's purchase of the Aircraft under this Section 15 (b) or (y) the then Fair Market Sales Value of the Aircraft plus (B) all amounts accrued and unpaid under Section 16 or 17 of the Participation Agreement or under the Tax Indemnity Agreement. Upon receipt by Lessor and the Owner Participant of such payments and all other sums then due and payable by Lessee under this Lease and the other Operative Documents, this Lease shall, except as aforesaid and as provided in Sections 16 and 17 of the Participation Agreement, terminate and Lessor will transfer to Lessee without recourse, representation, or warranty except as to the absence of Lessor's Liens attributable to Lessor, all Lessor's right, title, and interest in and to the Aircraft.

Section 16. Investment of Security Funds

Any monies required to be paid to or retained by Lessor which are not required to be paid to Lessee solely because a Default or an Event of Default shall have occurred, or which are required to be paid to Lessee pursuant to Section 9 or 10 hereof shall, until paid to Lessee or applied as provided herein or in the Indenture, be invested by the Indenture Trustee as provided in Section 6(d)(ii) of the Indenture or by Lessor (if the Indenture shall have been discharged) from time to time at the expense of Lessee in Permitted Investments. There shall be promptly remitted to Lessee any gain (including interest received) realized as the result of any such investment (net of any fees, commissions, and other expenses, if any, incurred in connection with such investment) unless a Default or an Event of Default shall have occurred and be continuing. Lessee will promptly pay to Lessor or the Indenture Trustee, as the case may be, on demand, the amount of any loss realized as the result of any such investment (together with any fees, commissions, and other expenses, if any, incurred in connection with such investment).

Section 17. Events of Default

The following events shall constitute Events of Default:

(a) Lessee shall fail to make any payment of Rent when due (which in the case of Basic Rent prepaid pursuant to Section 3(h) hereof, shall be the Payment Date, as defined therein, with respect thereto), and such failure shall continue for a period of five Business Days; or

(b) There shall occur any failure of Lessee to procure any of the insurance coverage required by Section 10 hereof or such insurance shall cease to be in effect; or

(c) Lessee shall fail to perform or observe any other covenant or condition to be performed or observed by it hereunder or under any other Operative Document, and such failure shall continue for a period of 30 days after delivery of written notice specifying the same from Lessor, the Indenture Trustee, or any Participant to Lessee and Lessor unless Lessee shall be diligently proceeding to take appropriate actions reasonably calculated to correct such failure; or

(d) A responsible officer of Lessee shall have actual knowledge that Lessee has violated (i) Section 12(a) of the Participation Agreement by failing to make a filing required thereby or (ii) Section 6(a)(ix) of this Agreement by entering into a sublease with a foreign air carrier that is not a Permitted Foreign Air Carrier, and such violation shall continue for a period of 30 days after such officer has learned of it; or

(e) Any representation or warranty made by Lessee herein or in any Operative Document or any document (other than in the Tax Indemnity Agreement) or certificate furnished Lessor pursuant hereto or thereto shall prove to have been incorrect in any material respect when made and shall remain material; or

(f) Lessee shall consent to the appointment of or taking possession by a receiver, assignee, custodian, sequestrator, trustee, or liquidator (or other similar official) of itself or of a substantial part of its property, or Lessee shall fail to pay its debts generally as they come due [as provided in 11 U.S.C. S 303(h)(l)], or shall make a general assignment for the benefit of its creditors, or Lessee shall commence a voluntary case or other proceeding seeking liquidation, reorganization, or other relief with respect to itself or its debts under the federal bankruptcy laws, as now or hereafter constituted or any other applicable federal or state bankruptcy, insolvency, or other similar law or shall consent to the entry of an order for relief in an involuntary case under any such law or Lessee shall file an answer admitting the material allegations of a petition filed against Lessee in any such proceeding, or otherwise seek relief under the provisions of any now existing or future federal or state bankruptcy, insolvency, or other similar law providing for the reorganization or winding-up of corporations, or providing for an agreement, composition, extension, or adjustment with its creditors; or

(g) An order, judgment, or decree shall be entered in any proceedings by any court of competent jurisdiction appointing, without the consent of Lessee, a receiver, trustee, or liquidator of Lessee or of any substantial part of its property, or any substantial part of the property of Lessee shall be sequestered, and any such order, judgment, or decree or appointment or sequestration shall remain in force undismissed, unstayed, or unvacated for a period of 60 days after the date of entry thereof; or

(h) A petition against Lessee in a proceeding or case under the bankruptcy laws or other insolvency laws (as now or hereafter in effect) shall be filed and shall not be withdrawn or dismissed within 60 days thereafter, or, in case the approval of such petition by a court of competent jurisdiction is required, the petition as filed or amended shall be approved by such a court as properly filed and such approval shall not be withdrawn or the proceeding dismissed within 60 days thereafter, or a decree or order for relief in respect of Lessee shall be entered by a court of competent jurisdiction in an involuntary case under the federal bankruptcy laws, as now or hereafter constituted, or any other applicable federal or state bankruptcy, insolvency, or other similar law, as now or hereafter constituted, and such decree or order shall remain unstayed in effect for a period of 60 days, or if, under the provisions of any law providing for reorganization or winding-up of corporations which may apply to Lessee, any court of competent jurisdiction shall assume jurisdiction, custody, or control of Lessee or of any substantial part of its property and such jurisdiction, custody, or control shall remain in force unrelinquished, unstayed, or unterminated for a period of 60 days;

(i) A final judgment or judgments by a court or courts of competent jurisdiction for the payment of money in excess of $5,000,000 individually or $10,000,000 in the aggregate shall be rendered against Lessee and the same shall remain undischarged for a period of 60 days during which execution of such judgment shall not be effectively stayed; or

(j) Any Event of Default (as defined therein) under the Leases between Martin Trust Company, not in its individual capacity but solely as Owner Trustee, except as otherwise expressly provided therein, and Planet Aviation, Inc. dated as of ________________.

Section 18. Remedies

Upon the occurrence of any Event of Default and at any time thereafter so long as the same shall be continuing, Lessor may, at its option, declare this Lease to be in default (provided that no such declaration shall be necessary with respect to the events listed in Sections 17(e), (f) and (g) hereof); and at any time thereafter so long as Lessee shall not have remedied all outstanding Events of Default, Lessor may do, and Lessee shall comply with, one or more of the following with respect to all or any part of the Airframe and the Engines, as Lessor in its sole discretion shall elect, to the extent permitted by, and subject to compliance with any mandatory requirements of, Applicable Law then in effect:

(a) Cause Lessee, upon the written demand of Lessor and at Lessee's expense, to, and Lessee shall, promptly return all or such part of the Airframe or the Engines as Lessor may demand to Lessor at such location in the continental United States of America on Lessee 's route system as selected by Lessor in the manner and condition required by, and otherwise in accordance with all of the provisions of, Section 13 hereof as if such Airframe or such Engines were being returned at the end of the Term; or Lessor, at its option, may enter upon the premises where the Airframe or any or all Engines are located or believed to be located and take immediate possession of and remove such Airframe or Engines without the necessity for first instituting proceedings, or by summary proceedings or otherwise, and Lessee shall comply therewith, all without liability to Lessor for or by reason of such entry or taking possession, whether for the restoration of damage to property caused by such taking or otherwise;

(b) Sell or otherwise dispose of the Aircraft, at public or private sale and with or without notice to Lessee or advertisement, as Lessor may determine or hold, use, operate, lease to others, or keep idle all or any part of the Airframe or any Engine as Lessor, in its sole discretion, may determine, in any such case free and clear of any rights of Lessee except as hereinafter set forth in this Section 18 and without any duty to account to Lessee with respect to such action or inaction or for any proceeds with respect thereto except to the extent required by paragraph (d) below in the event Lessor elects to exercise its rights under said paragraph in lieu of its rights under paragraph (c) below;

(c) Whether or not Lessor shall have exercised, or shall thereafter at any time exercise, any of its rights under paragraph (a) or paragraph (b) above with respect to the Aircraft, Lessor, by written notice to Lessee specifying a payment date not earlier than 10 days from the date of such notice, may cause Lessee to pay to Lessor, and Lessee shall pay to Lessor, on the payment date specified in such notice, as liquidated damages for loss of a bargain and not as a penalty, any installment of Basic Rent with respect to the Aircraft due on or before such payment date and a sum equal to Basic Rent accrued from the last Rent Payment Date to such payment date plus an amount equal to the excess, if any, of (i) the Stipulated Loss Value for the Aircraft, determined as of such payment date over (ii) the Fair Market Sale Value for the Aircraft, computed as of the payment date specified pursuant to this paragraph (c), together with interest, to the extent permitted by Applicable Law, at the Overdue Rate on the amount of such excess, if any, from such payment date specified pursuant to this paragraph (c), to the date of actual payment of such amount;

(d) In the event Lessor, pursuant to paragraph (b) above, shall have sold the Aircraft, Lessor in lieu of exercising its rights under paragraph (c) above with respect to the Aircraft, may, if it shall so elect, cause Lessee to pay Lessor, and Lessee shall pay to Lessor, on the date of such sale, as liquidated damages for loss of a bargain and not as a penalty (in lieu of the Basic Rent for the Aircraft due after the date on which such sale occurs but in addition to any installment of Basic Rent for the Aircraft due on or up to the date on which such sale occurs and a sum equal to Basic Rent accrued from the last Rent Payment Date to such payment date), the amount of any deficiency of the net proceeds of such sale below the Stipulated Loss Value of the Aircraft, determined as of the date of such sale, together with interest, to the extent permitted by Applicable Law, at the Overdue Rate on the amount of such deficiency from the date as of which such Stipulated Loss Value is determined to the date of actual payment; or

(e) Rescind this Lease as to the Aircraft, Airframe, or any or all of the Engines, or exercise any other right or remedy which may be available under Applicable Law or proceed by appropriate court action to enforce the terms hereof or to recover damages for the breach hereof.

In addition, Lessee shall be liable for any and all Supplemental Rent due hereunder before or after any termination hereof, including all costs and expenses (including reasonable attorneys' fees and disbursements) incurred by reason of the occurrence of any

Event of Default or the exercise of Lessor 's remedies with respect thereto including all costs and expenses incurred in connection with the return of the Airframe or any Engine in accordance with the terms of Section 13 hereof or any appraisal of the Aircraft. At any sale of the Aircraft, the Airframe, or any Engine, or portion thereof pursuant to this Section 18, Lessor may bid for and purchase such property. Except as otherwise expressly provided above, no remedy referred to in this Section 18 is intended to be exclusive, but each shall be cumulative and in addition to any other remedy referred to above or otherwise available to Lessor at law or in equity; and the exercise or beginning of exercise by Lessor of any one or more of such remedies shall not preclude the simultaneous or later exercise by Lessor of any or all such other remedies. No express or implied waiver by Lessor of any Event of Default hereunder shall in any way be, or be construed to be, a waiver of any future or subsequent Event of Default. To the extent permitted by Applicable Law, Lessee hereby waives any rights of redemption and any rights now or hereafter conferred by statute or otherwise which may require Lessor, otherwise than in accordance with the provisions of this Section 18, to sell, lease, or otherwise use the Airframe or any Engine in mitigation of Lessor's damages or which may otherwise limit or modify any of Lessor's rights or remedies under this Section 18.

Section 19. Lessor's Right to Perform for Lessee

If Lessee fails to make any payment of Rent required to be made by it hereunder or fails to perform or comply with any of its agreements contained herein, Lessor may itself make such payment or perform or comply with such agreement, and the amount of such payment and the amount of the reasonable expenses of Lessor incurred in connection with such payment or the performance of or compliance with such agreement, as the case may be, together with interest thereon at the Overdue Rate, shall be deemed Supplemental Rent, payable by Lessee upon demand.

Section 20. Bankruptcy

To the extent consistent with the provisions of 11 U.S.C. Section 1110, or any analogous section of the federal bankruptcy laws, as amended from time to time, it is hereby expressly agreed and provided that, notwithstanding any other provisions of the federal bankruptcy laws, as amended from time to time, the title of Lessor to the Aircraft and any right of Lessor to take possession of the Aircraft in compliance with the provisions of this Lease shall not be affected by the provisions of 11 U.S.C. Section 362 or 363, as amended from time to time, or any analogous provisions of any superseding statute.

Section 21. Assignment

Lessee will not, without the prior written consent of Lessor, assign any of its rights hereunder except as permitted by Section 6(a) hereof or Section 12 of the Participation Agreement. Lessor will not, without the prior written consent of Lessee, assign any of its rights hereunder except to the Indenture Trustee as security for the Loan Certificates or to a successor trustee pursuant to the terms of the Trust Agreement or to a transferee permitted by Section 15 of the Participation Agreement. The terms and provisions of this Lease shall inure to the benefit of and be binding on Lessor and Lessee and their respective successors and permitted assigns.

Section 22. Limitation of Owner Trustee's Liability

Lessor is entering into this Lease solely as Owner Trustee under the Trust Agreement and not in its individual capacity, except as otherwise expressly provided in Section 5(a) hereof, and Lessor shall not be personally liable for, or for any loss in respect of, any of the statements, representations, warranties, agreements, or obligations of Lessor hereunder or in any other Operative Document, as to which all parties shall look solely to the Trust Estate, except to the extent that such statements, representations, warranties, agreements, or obligations expressly are made or incurred by Lessor in its individual capacity, or except for any loss caused by the willful misconduct or gross negligence of Lessor.

Section 23. Permitted Foreign Air Carriers

(a) Notice of Proposed Deletions or Additions of Airlines. Within 30 days after each of the fifth, tenth, and fifteenth anniversaries of the date hereof, Lessor may, by written notice to Lessee and the Indenture Trustee, propose the deletion of particular airlines from the list of Permitted Foreign Air Carriers annexed hereto as Schedule II based upon Lessor's reasonable judgment that (i) there has been a change of law or political circumstances in the country of which such airline is a national which makes it doubtful whether Lessor's title or the first mortgage security interest of the Indenture would be enforceable in such country, and/or (ii) there has been a material adverse change in the creditworthiness of such airline. Within 30 days after each of the fifth, tenth and fifteenth anniversaries of the date hereof, (or, in the event Lessor has delivered a notice pursuant to the preceding sentence, within 15 days after receipt thereof) Lessee may, by written notice to Lessor, propose the addition of particular airlines to such list of Permitted Foreign Air Carriers based upon Lessee's reasonable judgment that (i) each such airline is a national of a politically stable country under the laws of which Lessor's title and the first mortgage security interest of the Indenture would be enforceable and (ii) each such airline is a creditworthy operator of jet aircraft.

(b) Objections to Proposed Deletions or Additions. If neither the Indenture Trustee, Lessor, nor Lessee, as the case may be, has objected in writing to the deletion or addition of a particular airline proposed by the other, as provided in Section 23(a), within 30 days after receipt of notice of such proposal, the list of Permitted Foreign Air Carriers annexed hereto as Schedule I shall be deemed amended without further act to delete or add such airline. If any such party delivers a timely objection in writing to a proposal made by another pursuant to Section 23(a), the parties agree to consult promptly at the request of either in a good faith effort to resolve the disagreement through negotiation. Should such a disagreement not be resolved within 30 days after delivery of such objection, no airline shall be added to the list of Permitted Foreign Air Carriers over the objection of Lessor or the Indenture Trustee, and no airline shall be deleted from such list over the objection of Lessee, provided, however, that an airline which Lessor has proposed to delete shall be deleted from such list if there will be at least 50 other airlines remaining on such list after giving effect to such deletion and any other deletions then proposed by Lessor.

(c) Deletions Not to Affect Existing Subleases. Notwithstanding any other provision hereof, no deletion of an airline from the list of Permitted Foreign Air Carriers pursuant to this Section 23 shall affect any existing sublease or other agreement providing for transfer of possession of the Aircraft, Airframe, any Engine or Part which was permitted hereunder at the time entered into or preclude any subsequent renewal or extension of such sublease or other agreement.

Section 24. Miscellaneous

(a) Applicable Law. This Lease shall in all respects be governed by, and construed in accordance with, the laws of the State of ________________, including all matters of construction, validity and performance. This Lease shall be effective for all purposes as of the date first above written.

(b) Notices. Unless otherwise specifically provided herein, all notices required or permitted by the terms hereof shall, unless otherwise specified, be in writing. Any written notice shall become effective when received and shall be transmitted and directed as required by Section 22(a) of the Participation Agreement. Copies of all notices required by the terms hereof to be given to the Lessor shall, in addition, be delivered to the Indenture Trustee in accordance with this Section 24.

(c) Assignment Under Indenture. Lessee hereby acknowledges receipt of due notice that Lessor 's interest in this Lease (including the Lease Supplements and any amendments hereto) has been assigned to the Indenture Trustee pursuant to the Indenture for the benefit and security of the holders of the Loan Certificates issued thereunder, to the extent provided in the Indenture. Unless and until Lessee shall have received written notice from the Indenture Trustee that the Indenture has been discharged, except as otherwise provided in the Indenture, the Indenture Trustee shall have the right to receive all amounts payable hereunder Other than Excepted Property, to exercise the rights of Lessor under the Lease to give consents, approvals, waivers, notices, or the like, to make elections, demands, or the like and to take any other discretionary action under this Lease as though named as Lessor herein and no amendment or modification of, or waiver by or consent of Lessor in respect of, any of the provisions of this Lease shall be effective unless the Indenture Trustee shall have joined in such amendment, modification, waiver, or consent or shall have given its prior written consent thereto.

(d) Waivers, Headings. No term or provision of this Lease may be changed, waived, discharged, or terminated orally, but only by an instrument in writing signed by the party against which the enforcement of the change, waiver, discharge, or termination is sought. This Lease shall constitute an agreement of lease, and nothing contained herein shall be construed as conveying to Lessee any right, title, or interest in the Aircraft except as a lessee only. The section and paragraph headings in this Lease and the table of contents are for convenience of reference only and shall not modify, define, expand, or limit any of the terms or provisions hereof and all references herein to numbered sections, unless otherwise indicated, are to sections of this Lease.

(e) Counterparts. This Lease may be executed by the parties hereto in separate counterparts, each of which when so executed and delivered shall, subject to the next sentence and the legends appearing on the cover and signature page hereof, be an original, but all such counterparts shall together constitute but one and the same instrument. To the extent, if any, that this Lease constitutes chattel paper (as the term is defined in the Uniform Commercial Code as in effect in any applicable jurisdiction), no security interest in this Lease may be created through the transfer or possession of any counterpart other than the "original" counterpart which shall be identified as the counterpart containing the receipt therefor executed by the Indenture Trustee on the signature page thereof.

IN WITNESS WHEREOF, Lessor and Lessee have each caused this Lease to be duly executed by their authorized officers as of the day and year first above written.

Lessor:

Martin Trust Company, not in its individual capacity but solely as Owner Trustee

By: ______________________________

Title: ____________________________

Lessee:

Planet Aviation, Inc.

By: ______________________________

Title: ____________________________

Receipt of the original counterpart of the foregoing Lease Agreement is hereby acknowledged on this ________ day of ______________________________, XXXX.

The Rhode Island Bank and Trust Company, National Association,

Indenture Trustee

By: ______________________________

Title: ____________________________

Schedule I

List of Authorized Representatives

Schedule II

List of Permitted Foreign Air Carriers

Exhibit A
to Lease

Lease Supplement No. 1

THIS LEASE SUPPLEMENT No. 1 dated ______________, XXXX, between MARTIN TRUST COMPANY, a New York trust company, having its principal place of business at ______________________________ (not in its individual capacity but solely as Owner Trustee under the Trust Agreement dated as of September 15, XXXX), ("Lessor") and PLANET AVIATION, INC., a New Jersey corporation having its principal place of business at ______________________________ ("Lessee");

WITNESSETH:

WHEREAS, Lessor and Lessee have heretofore entered into that certain Lease Agreement, dated as of September 15, XXXX (the "Lease", the terms defined therein being herein used with the same meaning), which Lease provides for the execution and delivery of Lease Supplements in substantially the form hereof for the purpose of leasing specific Aircraft under the Lease when delivered by Lessor to Lessee in accordance with the terms thereof;

WHEREAS, the Lease, a counterpart of which is attached hereto and made a part hereof, relates to the Aircraft and Engines described below, and this Lease Supplement, together with such attachment, and together with Lease Supplement No. 1 dated the date hereof is being filed for recordation on the date hereof with the Federal Aviation Administration as one document;

NOW, THEREFORE, in consideration of the premises and other good and sufficient consideration, and pursuant to Section 2 of the Lease, Lessor and Lessee hereby agree as follows:

1. Lessor hereby delivers and leases to Lessee, and Lessee hereby accepts and leases from Lessor, under the Lease as herein supplemented, the following Blackhawk 555–300 Aircraft, which Aircraft as of the date hereof consists of the following:

(i) Airframe: U.S. Registration Number N777P manufacturer's serial number 45541; and

(ii) Engines: Two (2) CFM International 56-3-BI Engines, bearing manufacturer's serial numbers 848-990 and 848-995.

2. The Delivery Date of the Aircraft is the date of this Lease Supplement set forth in the opening paragraph hereof.

3. The Interim Term shall run from the Delivery Date through January 2, XXXX, and the Basic Term shall run from January 3, XXXX through January 2, XXXX, unless terminated earlier as provided in the Lease.

4. The Lessor's Cost for the Aircraft is $28,000,000.

5. All of the terms and provisions of the Lease are hereby incorporated by reference in this Lease Supplement to the same extent as if fully set forth herein.

6. To the extent, if any, that this Lease Supplement constitutes chattel paper (as such term is defined in the Uniform Commercial Code as in effect in any applicable jurisdiction), no security interest in this Lease may be created through the transfer or possession of any counterpart other than the "original" counterpart containing the receipt therefor executed by the Indenture Trustee on the signature page thereof.

7. This Lease Supplement shall in all respects be governed by, and construed in accordance with, the laws of the State of ______, including all matters of construction, validity, and performance.

IN WITNESS WHEREOF, Lessor and Lessee have each caused this Lease Supplement to be duly executed by their authorized officers as of the day and year first above written.

MARTIN TRUST COMPANY, not in its individual capacity but solely as Owner Trustee

By: ______________________________

Title: ______________________________

LESSOR

PLANET AVIATION, INC.

By: ______________________________

Title: ______________________________

LESSEE

AS SET FORTH IN SECTION 22(c) OF THE LEASE, LESSOR HAS ASSIGNED TO THE INDENTURE TRUSTEE THIS LEASE SUPPLEMENT. TO THE EXTENT, IF ANY, THAT THIS LEASE SUPPLEMENT CONSTITUTES CHATTEL PAPER (AS SUCH TERM IS DEFINED IN THE UNIFORM COMMERCIAL CODE AS IN EFFECT IN ANY APPLICABLE JURISDICTION), NO SECURITY INTEREST IN THIS LEASE SUPPLEMENT MAY BE CREATED BY THE TRANSFER OR POSSESSION OF ANY COUNTERPART HEREOF OTHER THAN THE COUNTERPART CONTAINING THE PRINTED RECEIPT THERE FOR EXECUTED BY THE INDENTURE TRUSTEE IMMEDIATELY FOLLOWING THIS LEGEND.

Receipt of this original counterpart of the foregoing Lease Supplement is hereby acknowledged on this ____ day of September, XXXX.

THE RHODE ISLAND BANK AND TRUST
COMPANY, NATIONAL ASSOCIATION,

Indenture Trustee

By: ______________________________

Title: ______________________________

Exhibit B
to Lease

Stipulated Loss and Termination Values
(as a percentage of lessor's cost)

Exhibit C
to Lease

Basic Rent Payment Schedule

Basic Rent Payment Date	*Basic Rent Payment as a Percentage of Lessor's Cost*

Form: I-04a
Disk File Name: I-04a.rtf

ASSIGNMENT OF RIGHTS UNDER PURCHASE AGREEMENT

Form Purpose

An assignment of rights under an equipment purchase agreement in which the parties set forth the terms and conditions of the equipment purchase. This form is part of a leveraged lease transaction and is integrated with a Participation Agreement, a Trust Indenture and Security Agreement, a Trust Agreement, and a Lease Agreement.

Executing Parties

The equipment lessee.
The owner participant.

See:

Participation Agreement, Form I-04b
Trust Indenture and Security Agreement, Form I-04c
Trust Agreement, Form I-04d
Leveraged Lease Agreement, Form I-04
Tax Indemnity Agreement, Form I-04e

Assignment of Rights Under Purchase Agreement

Dated as of September 15, XXXX

between

PLANET AVIATION, INC.

and

MARTIN TRUST COMPANY, as Owner Trustee

and

Consent and Agreement

Dated as of September 15, XXXX

by

THE BLACKHAWK COMPANY

One New Blackhawk Model 555-300 Aircraft

Registration Number N777P

ASSIGNMENT OF RIGHTS UNDER PURCHASE AGREEMENT dated as of ________, XXXX, between PLANET AVIATION, INC., a New Jersey corporation (herein called the "Assignor") and MARTIN TRUST COMPANY, a New York trust company not in its individual capacity but solely as Owner Trustee under the Trust Agreement (herein called the "Assignee").

WHEREAS, Assignor and Manufacturer are parties to the Purchase Agreement, providing, among other things, for the manufacture and sale by Manufacturer to Assignor of certain aircraft, engines, and related equipment, including the Aircraft, and the Aircraft is covered by the Participation Agreement;

WHEREAS, the Aircraft has been, or will be, delivered to Assignor pursuant to the terms of the Purchase Agreement;

WHEREAS, Assignee wishes to acquire title to the Aircraft and Assignor, on the terms and conditions hereinafter set forth, is willing to assign to Assignee certain of Assignor's rights and interests under the Purchase Agreement with respect to the Aircraft, and Assignee is willing to accept such assignment, as hereinafter set forth.

NOW, THEREFORE, in consideration of the mutual covenants and agreements herein contained and for other valuable consideration, receipt of which is hereby acknowledged by Assignor, the parties hereto agree as follows:

1. For all purposes of this Assignment, except as otherwise expressly provided or unless the context otherwise requires:

"Aircraft" means the Blackhawk 555-300 aircraft specifically described in the Lease and Lease Supplement, bearing number N777P, and including the two CFM International 56-3-B1 aircraft engines installed on the aircraft on the delivery date thereof bearing manufacturer's serial numbers (a) 848-990 and (b) 848-995, respectively, delivered under the Purchase Agreement.

"Purchase Agreement" means Purchase Agreement No. ____, dated as of ____, between Manufacturer and Lessee (as heretofore amended, modified, and supplemented), providing, among other things, for the manufacture and sale by Manufacturer to Lessee of a number of Blackhawk Model 555-300 aircraft, as such Purchase Agreement may hereafter be amended, modified, or supplemented to the extent permitted by the terms of the Assignment and the Indenture, and including, without limitation, as part of such Purchase Agreement, any and all change orders from time to time entered into with respect thereof, but solely as such Purchase Agreement, as amended, modified, and supplemented, relates to the Aircraft.

All other terms used herein in capitalized form shall have meanings set forth in Appendix A to the Participation Agreement entered into between the parties hereto and dated ________________, for all purposes hereof.

2. Subject to the terms and conditions of this Assignment, Assignor does hereby sell, assign, and convey to Assignee all of Assignor's rights in and to the Purchase Agreement as and to the extent that the same relate to the Aircraft and survive or will

survive the delivery thereof to Assignor, including in such assignment all claims for damages in respect to the Aircraft arising as a result of any default by Manufacturer under the Purchase Agreement including all warranty and indemnity provisions thereof and all claims arising thereunder with respect to the Aircraft, reserving to Assignor, however, (i) all of Assignor's rights and interests in and to the Purchase Agreement as and to the extent that the Purchase Agreement relates to aircraft other than the Aircraft, (ii) with respect to the Aircraft, all of Assignor's rights with respect to payments made by Assignor pursuant to the Purchase Agreement (including without limitation any post-delivery adjustments to the purchase price or amounts credited or to be credited by Manufacturer to Assignor); (iii) with respect to the Aircraft, so long as the Aircraft shall be subject to the Lease, all rights to obtain services, credit, training, product support, promotional support, data, publications, or demonstration and test flights pursuant to the Purchase Agreement. The foregoing assignment is subject to the conditions that (i) concurrently with its effectiveness with respect to the Aircraft Assignee shall lease such Aircraft to Assignor under the Lease and, unless an Event of Default shall have occurred and be continuing, Assignee shall and it does hereby authorize Assignor as Lessee, to the exclusion of Assignee, to exercise in Assignor's name, all rights and powers of the "Buyer" under the Purchase Agreement and any warranty with respect to such Aircraft made by Manufacturer, subcontractor, or supplier, and any other claims against such Manufacturer, subcontractor, or supplier with respect to such Aircraft and to retain any recovery or benefit resulting from enforcement of any warranty, indemnity, or claim, and (ii) the written consent of Manufacturer to such assignment be provided in form and substance satisfactory to Assignor. Assignee hereby accepts the foregoing assignment subject to the terms hereof.

3. It is expressly agreed that, anything herein contained to the contrary notwithstanding: (a) Assignor shall at all times remain liable to "Blackhawk" under the Purchase Agreement to perform all the duties and obligations of the "Buyer" thereunder to the same extent as if this Assignment had not been executed; (b) the exercise by Assignee of any of the rights assigned hereunder shall not release Assignor from any of its duties or obligations to Manufacturer under the Purchase Agreement except to the extent that such exercise by Assignee shall constitute performance of such duties and obligations; and (c) Assignee shall not have any obligation or liability under the Purchase Agreement by reason of, or arising out of, this assignment or be obligated to perform any of the obligations or duties of Assignor under the Purchase Agreement or to make any payment or to make any inquiry as to the sufficiency of any payment received by it or to present or file any claim or to take any other action to collect or enforce any claim for any payment assigned hereunder.

Without in any way releasing Assignor from any of its duties or obligations under the Purchase Agreement, Assignee confirms for the benefit of Manufacturer that, insofar as the provisions of the Purchase Agreement relate to the Aircraft accepted by Assignor under the Purchase Agreement, sold to Assignee under the Participation Agreement, and leased to Assignor under the Lease, in exercising any rights under the Purchase Agreement, or in making any claim with respect to such Aircraft, the terms and conditions of the Purchase Agreement shall apply to, and be binding upon, Assignee to the same extent as Assignor; provided, however, that nothing contained in this Assignment shall in any way diminish or limit the provisions of Assignor's indemnity in Section 17 of the Participation Agreement with respect to any liability of Assignee to Manufacturer in any way relating to or arising out of the Purchase Agreement.

Nothing contained herein shall subject Manufacturer to any liability to which it would not otherwise be subject under the Purchase Agreement or modify in any respect the contract rights of Manufacturer under the Purchase Agreement.

Assignor does hereby constitute, effective at any time after the occurrence and continuance of an Event of Default under the Lease and thereafter so long as Assignor has not remedied all Events of Default thereunder, Assignee, its successors and assigns, Assignor's true and lawful attorney, irrevocably, with full power (in the name of Assignor or otherwise) to ask, require, demand, receive, compound, and give acquittance for any and all monies and claims for monies due and to become due under, or arising out of, the Purchase Agreement in respect to the Aircraft, to the extent that the same have been assigned by this Assignment and for such period as Assignee may exercise rights with respect thereto under this Assignment, to endorse any checks or other instruments or orders in connection therewith and to file any claims or take any action or institute (or, if previously commenced, assume control of) any proceedings and to obtain any recovery in connection therewith that Assignee may deem to be necessary or advisable.

For all purposes of this Assignment, Manufacturer shall not be deemed to have knowledge of and need not recognize nor take any action with respect to the declaration of a default under the Lease, the discontinuance of an Event of Default or the Aircraft's becoming no longer subject to the Lease unless and until Manufacturer shall have received from Assignee or the Indenture Trustee written notice (including by telex or telecopy) thereof addressed to ______________________________, and, if by telex, to ______________________________, and in acting in accordance with the terms and conditions of the Purchase Agreement and this Assignment, Manufacturer may act with acquittance and conclusively rely upon any such notice.

4. Assignor agrees that at any time and from time to time, upon the written request of Assignee, Assignor will promptly and duly execute and deliver any and all such further instruments and documents and take such further action as Assignee may reasonably request in order to obtain the full benefits of this Assignment and of the rights and powers herein granted.

5. Assignor does hereby represent and warrant that the Purchase Agreement is in full force and effect to the extent that, by its terms, the provisions thereof survive or will survive the delivery of the Aircraft, and is enforceable in accordance with its terms and Assignor is not in default thereunder. Assignor does hereby further represent and warrant that Assignor has not assigned or pledged, and hereby covenants that it will not assign or pledge, so long as this Assignment shall remain in effect, the whole or any part of the rights hereby assigned or any of its rights with respect to the Aircraft under the Purchase Agreement not assigned hereby, to anyone other than Assignee.

6. Pursuant to the Indenture, Assignee has assigned to and pledged with the Indenture Trustee, as security for the Loan Certificates to be issued thereunder, all of Assignee's rights and interests in and to the Purchase Agreement and this Assignment. The Indenture Trustee pursuant to such assignment may exercise all the rights of Assignee hereunder, subject to the terms and conditions hereof to which the Indenture Trustee agrees by its endorsement hereof.

7. This Assignment is executed by Assignor and Assignee concurrently with the execution and delivery of the Lease Agreement.

8. This Assignment may be executed by the parties hereto in separate counterparts, each of which when so executed and delivered shall be an original, but all such counterparts shall together constitute one and the same instrument.

9. Neither this Assignment nor any of the terms hereof may be terminated, amended, supplemented, waived, or modified orally, but only by an instrument in writing signed by the party against which the enforcement of the termination, amendment, supplement, waiver, or modification is sought.

10. This Assignment shall in all respects be governed by, and construed in accordance with, the laws of the State of ________, including all matters of construction, validity, and performance. This Assignment is being delivered in the State of ________.

IN WITNESS WHEREOF, the parties hereto have caused this Assignment to be duly executed as of the day and year first above written.

PLANET AVIATION, INC.
Assignor

By: ______________________________

Title: ______________________________

MARTIN TRUST COMPANY, not in its individual capacity but solely as Owner Trustee, Assignee

By: ______________________________

Title: ______________________________

The Indenture Trustee hereby agrees and consents to the foregoing:

THE RHODE ISLAND BANK
AND TRUST COMPANY, NATIONAL
ASSOCIATION, as Indenture Trustee

By: ______________________________

Title: ______________________________

Consent and Agreement

The undersigned, THE BLACKHAWK COMPANY ("Manufacturer"), hereby acknowledges notice of and consents to the terms of the foregoing Assignment of Rights under Purchase Agreement (the "Assignment") dated as of September 15, XXXX, between Planet Aviation, Inc. ("Assignor") and Martin Trust Company (the "Assignee"), the capitalized terms used hereinafter being defined as such terms are defined in the Assignment. Manufacturer hereby confirms to Assignor and Assignee that (i) all representations, warranties, indemnities, and agreements of Manufacturer under the Purchase Agreement which survived or will survive the delivery of the Aircraft to Assignor, shall, subject to the terms and conditions of the Purchase Agreement, inure to the benefit of Assignee to the same extent as if originally named the "Buyer" therein with respect to the Aircraft except as provided in Section 2 of the Assignment; (ii) Assignee shall not be liable for any of the obligations or duties of Assignor under the Purchase Agreement, nor shall the Assignment give rise to any duties or obligations whatsoever on the part of Assignee owing to Manufacturer except for Assignee's agreement in the Assignment to the effect that in exercising any right under the Purchase Agreement with respect to the Aircraft, or in making any claim with respect to the Aircraft or the goods and services delivered or to be delivered pursuant to the Purchase Agreement, the terms and conditions of such Purchase Agreement relating to the Aircraft shall apply to and be binding upon Assignee to the same extent as Assignor, and with respect to such agreement Manufacturer agrees that, anything contained in the Purchase Agreement or the Assignment to the contrary notwithstanding, so long as Manufacturer shall not have received notice that an Event of Default under the Lease has occurred and is continuing, Assignee shall not have any liability to Manufacturer for failure to comply with any of the terms of the Purchase Agreement with respect to the Aircraft while under lease to Assignor so long as the Assignee acts upon the written instructions of the Assignor (to which instructions the undersigned understands that it shall have access on request), provided, however, that no person other than Manufacturer shall have any rights against Assignee with respect to the undertaking and agreement set forth in clause (ii); (iii) notwithstanding any provisions of the Purchase Agreement, Manufacturer consents to the assignment of Assignor's interest in the Purchase Agreement as it relates to the Aircraft to Assignee pursuant to the Assignment; and (iv) Manufacturer will continue to pay all amounts and provide all goods and services to Assignor which it may be required to pay or provide in respect to the Aircraft under the Purchase Agreement unless and until Manufacturer shall have received written notice from Assignee that the Lease has been declared to be in default, whereupon Manufacturer will pay such amounts or provide such goods and services directly to Assignee unless and until Manufacturer shall have received written notice from Assignee that no Event of Default is continuing, whereupon the Manufacturer will pay such amounts or provide such goods and services to Assignor.

Manufacturer hereby represents and warrants that: (A) Manufacturer is a corporation duly organized and existing in good standing under the laws of Delaware; (B) the making and performance of this Consent and Agreement in accordance with its terms have been duly authorized by all necessary corporate action on the part of Manufacturer, do not require any stockholder approval, and do not contravene Manufacturer's certificate of incorporation or by-laws or any indenture, credit agreement, or other contractual agreement to which Manufacturer is a party or by which it is bound or any law binding on Manufacturer; (C) the making and performance of the Purchase Agreement in accordance with its terms have been duly authorized by all necessary corporate action on the part of Manufacturer, do not require any stockholder approval, do not contravene Manufacturer's certificate of incorporation or by-laws or any indenture, credit agreement, or other contractual agreement to which Manufacturer is a party or by which it is bound, and do not, as to the making thereof, contravene any law binding on Manufacturer and, to the best knowledge of Manufacturer do not, as to the performance thereof, contravene any law binding on Manufacturer; and (D) the Purchase Agreement constituted as of the date thereof and at all times thereafter, to and including the date of this Consent and Agreement, a binding obligation of Manufacturer enforceable against the Manufacturer in accordance with its terms, and this Consent and Agreement is a binding obligation of Manufacturer enforceable against Manufacturer in accordance with its terms. It is understood that the execution by Manufacturer of this Consent and Agreement is subject to the condition that, concurrently with the delivery of the Aircraft to Assignee, Assignee shall lease such Aircraft to Assignor under the Lease Agreement.

THE BLACKHAWK COMPANY

By: ______________________________

Title: _____________________________

Dated as of _________________________.

Form: l-04b
Disk File Name: l-04b.rtf

Participation Agreement

Form Purpose

A leveraged lease participation agreement in which all parties to the leveraged lease transaction set forth the terms and conditions of their participation in the financing transaction. This form is integrated with a Leveraged Lease Agreement, an Assignment of Rights Under Purchase Agreement, a Trust Indenture and Security Agreement, a Trust Agreement, and a Tax Indemnity Agreement.

Executing Parties

The equipment lessee.
The equipment lessor.
The equipment lenders.
The lender trustee.

See:

Leveraged Lease Arrangement, Form l-04
Assignment of Rights Under Purchase Agreement, Form l-04a
Trust Indenture and Security Agreement, Form l-04c
Trust Agreement, Form l-04d
Tax Indemnity Agreement, Form l-04e

Participation Agreement

dated as of September 15, XXXX

among

PLANET AVIATION, INC.,
Lessee,

AATX LIFE INSURANCE COMPANY,

ABLE RE-INSURANCE COMPANY,

COOPER LIFE INSURANCE COMPANY,

PEACHTREE SECURITY LIFE INSURANCE COMPANY,

SYNX LIFE ASSURANCE COMPANY OF CANADA (U.S.),

SYNX LIFE ASSURANCE COMPANY OF CANADA,

and

STATE OF NEW YORK INVESTMENT BOARD,
Loan Participants,

MARTIN TRUST COMPANY,
Owner Trustee, not in its individual
capacity, but solely as Owner Trustee
except as otherwise expressly
provided herein,

THE RHODE ISLAND BANK AND TRUST COMPANY,
NATIONAL ASSOCIATION,
Indenture Trustee

and

PBC LEASING CORPORATION,

Owner Participant
Covering One New Blackhawk
Model 555-300 Aircraft
Registration Number
N777P

Table of Contents

THIS PARTICIPATION AGREEMENT dated as of September 15, XXXX, among PLANET AVIATION, INC., a New Jersey corporation, Lessee; MARTIN TRUST COMPANY, a New York trust company, not in its individual capacity but solely as Owner Trustee, except as otherwise expressly provided herein; PBC LEASING CORPORATION, a Florida corporation, Owner Participant; AATX LIFE INSURANCE COMPANY, a Rhode Island corporation, ABLE RE-INSURANCE COMPANY, a Delaware corporation, COOPER LIFE INSURANCE COMPANY, a Delaware corporation, PEACHTREE SECURITY LIFE INSURANCE COMPANY, a New Jersey corporation, SYNX LIFE ASSURANCE COMPANY OF CANADA (U.S.), a Delaware corporation, SYNX LIFE ASSURANCE COMPANY OF CANADA, a Canadian corporation, and STATE OF NEW YORK INVESTMENT BOARD, an independent agency of the State of NEW YORK, Loan Participants; and THE RHODE ISLAND BANK AND TRUST COMPANY, NATIONAL ASSOCIATION, a national banking association, Indenture Trustee.

WITNESSETH:

WHEREAS, pursuant to the Purchase Agreement, Lessee has purchased the Aircraft from the Manufacturer;

WHEREAS, the Owner Participant is entering into a Trust Agreement with the Owner Trustee whereby the Owner Trustee agrees to acquire and hold the Trust Estate to the benefit of the Owner Participant;

WHEREAS, subject to the terms and conditions of this Agreement and the Assignment the Owner Trustee will purchase the Aircraft from Lessee;

WHEREAS, subject to the terms and conditions of this Agreement and the Indenture, the Loan Participants will participate in such purchase by lending funds to the Owner Trustee in exchange for the issuance by the Owner Trustee of Loan Certificates; and

WHEREAS, the Owner Trustee is entering into a Lease with Lessee whereby, subject to the terms and conditions set forth therein, the Owner Trustee agrees to lease to Lessee, and Lessee agrees to lease from the Owner Trustee, the Aircraft;

NOW, THEREFORE, in consideration of the mutual agreements herein contained, and other good and valuable consideration, receipt of which is acknowledged, the parties hereto agree as follows:

Section 1. Definitions and Terms

Unless the context requires otherwise, all capitalized terms used herein shall have the meanings set forth in Appendix A hereto for all purposes of this Agreement.

Section 2. Participations in Lessor's Cost

(a) Agreements to Participate. Subject to the terms and conditions of this Agreement, and in reliance on the agreements, representations, and warranties herein contained and made pursuant hereto, on the Delivery Date for the Aircraft, but in no event later than October 6, XXXX (and time shall be of the essence),

(i) Each Loan Participant agrees to participate in payment of Lessor's Cost for the Aircraft by making a secured loan to the Owner Trustee in an amount equal to its Percentage Commitment times Lessor's Cost for such Aircraft (such Loan Participant's "Commitment"), paid to the Owner Trustee, in immediately available funds, at its account no. 123456789 at Walden Trust Company, to be held in trust by the Owner Trustee for the benefit of such Loan Participant until used to purchase the Aircraft or returned to such Loan Participant, as provided herein, and

(ii) The Owner Participant agrees to participate in Lessor's Cost for the Aircraft by making an investment in the Trust Estate, in an amount equal to its Percentage Commitment times Lessor's Cost for such Aircraft (the Owner Participant's "Commitment"), to be paid to the Owner Trustee, in immediately available funds, at its account no. 123456789 at Walden Trust Company, to be held in trust by the Owner Trustee for the benefit of the Owner Participant until used to purchase the Aircraft or returned to the Owner Participant, as provided herein.

(b) Notice of Delivery Date. Lessee agrees to give the Participants, the Owner Trustee, and the Indenture Trustee at least five Business Days' notice by telex or telecopy of the Delivery Date of the Aircraft, which notice shall specify the amounts of the Participants' Commitments with respect to such Aircraft. The making by any Participant of its Commitment available in the manner required by Section 2(a) shall constitute a waiver of such notice by such Participant. The making by the Loan Participants of their Commitments as required by Section 2(a) shall be deemed a waiver of such notice by the Indenture Trustee.

(c) Closing. The closing shall take place at 11:00 a.m. local time on the Delivery Date at the offices of Thompson & Achetson, 120 Broadway, New York, New York.

(d) Postponement of Delivery Date.

(i) Notice. The scheduled Delivery Date may be postponed by Lessee from time to time for any reason to a date not later than October 10, XXXX, if Lessee gives each Participant, the Owner Trustee, and the Indenture Trustee telex or telecopy notice (or telephonic notice followed by written confirmation thereof) of such postponement and notice of the date to which such Delivery Date has been postponed, such notice of postponement to be received by each party not later than the then scheduled Delivery Date; provided that in the event of any such postponement, Lessee will have no liability to any Participant for interest under Section 2(d)(ii) hereof if such notice of postponement is received by such Participant not later than 11:00 a.m., New York City time in the city named in the address of such Participant set forth in the signature pages to this Agreement, on the Business Day immediately prior to the originally scheduled Delivery Date.

(ii) Reimbursement. In the event of any postponement of the Delivery Date pursuant to Section 2(d)(i) hereof, or if the Aircraft is not delivered, or is not accepted by the Owner Trustee under this Agreement or by Lessee under the Lease for any reason (any such originally scheduled Delivery Date being referred to herein as the "Postponed Delivery Date"): (A) Lessee will reimburse each Participant [other than a Participant receiving at least one Business Day's notice of a postponement by the time set forth in the proviso to Section 2(d)(i) hereof] for the loss of the use of its funds occasioned by such postponement or failure to deliver or accept (unless such failure to accept is caused by a default by such Participant hereunder), by paying to such Participant interest at the Fixed Rate (or, with respect to each Loan Participant, at the rate applicable with respect to its Loan Certificates) on the amount of such funds for each calendar day from and including the Postponed Delivery Date to but excluding the earlier of the Business Day on which such Participant's funds are returned to it in accordance with clause (B) of this Section 2(d)(ii) (but including such Business Day in the event such funds are not received by 11:00 a.m. New York City time on such Business Day) or the actual date of delivery and acceptance of such Aircraft and (B) the Owner Trustee shall, subject to the following proviso, return any funds which it shall have received from any Participant to such Participant on the next Business Day by 11:00 a.m. New York City time unless the Aircraft shall have been delivered and accepted under the Lease on or prior to such time on such next Business Day; provided that Lessee may give telex or telecopy instructions (or telephonic instructions followed by written confirmation thereof) to the Owner Trustee prior to its return of such funds to retain such funds in trust for the benefit of each other Participant until the third Business Day after the Postponed Delivery Date, on which day (or at such earlier times as may have been directed in the same manner by the Lessee) such funds shall be returned to such Participant together with interest thereon as above provided [by the time on such Business Day set forth in clause (B) of this sentence] unless the Aircraft shall have been delivered and accepted under the Lease prior to such return of funds. In any case in which the Owner Trustee holds the funds of Participants pursuant to this Section 2(d)(ii) and receives such funds in time to permit overnight investment thereof, the Owner Trustee shall, at the request of Lessee, invest such funds overnight at the risk of loss of Lessee in Permitted Investments. The Owner Trustee shall apply the proceeds of such investment (less the cost, if any, of making such investment) in reduction of Lessee's obligation under clause (A) of the preceding sentence to reimburse the Participants. Any excess of such proceeds over said reimbursement obligation shall be for the account of Lessee. The Owner Trustee shall exercise reasonable efforts to invest funds when requested to do so by Lessee, provided that Lessee shall hold harmless the Owner Trustee for making such investment (except for any loss or damage caused by gross negligence or willful misconduct of the Owner Trustee) and shall compensate each Participant for any loss as a result of such investment.

Section 3. Sale, Purchase, and Lease of Aircraft.

(a) Each Loan Participant agrees that its making of the amount of its Commitment available to the Owner Trustee in accordance with the terms of Section 2(a) hereof together with an oral instruction from such Loan Participant or its special counsel on the Delivery Date shall constitute, without further act, authorization and direction by such Loan Participant to the Owner Trustee to transfer into the Trust Estate the funds transferred to it by such Loan Participant, to the extent received by the Owner Trustee as set forth in Section 2 hereof.

(b) The Owner Participant confirms that the making available of the amount of its Commitment to the Owner Trustee in accordance with the terms of Section 2(a) hereof together with an oral instruction from the Owner Participant or its special counsel on the Delivery Date shall constitute, without further act, authorization and direction by the Owner Participant to the Owner Trustee, and the Owner Trustee hereby agrees that it shall, upon receipt of the Participants' Commitments and instructions as provided in this Section 3, purchase the Aircraft from Lessee and lease the Aircraft to Lessee and, to accomplish such purchase and lease, shall (to the extent that it has not already done so) take the following action with respect to the Aircraft:

(i) authorize its representative or representatives (who shall be a person or persons designated by Lessee and acceptable to the Owner Trustee) to accept delivery of the Aircraft on the Delivery Date of the Aircraft pursuant to this Agreement;

(ii) accept from Lessee the Bills of Sale for the Aircraft;

(iii) take such action as may be appropriate or requested by Owner Participant or Lessee in connection with the application to the FAA for registration of the Aircraft in the name of the Owner Trustee;

(iv) execute and deliver the Lease Supplement and the Trust Agreement and Indenture Supplement covering the Aircraft;

(v) pay Lessee the Lessor's Cost for the Aircraft on the Delivery Date by transferring such amount, in immediately available funds, into Lessee's account no. 1222-989898 at Western Bank & Trust Company, N.A.

(vi) execute, cause to be authenticated, and deliver to each Loan Participant a Loan Certificate or Loan Certificates in a principal amount equal to its Commitment for the Aircraft; and

(vii) execute and deliver all other documents or certificates and take such other actions as are required to be executed and delivered or taken by the Owner Trustee on or before the Delivery Date for the Aircraft pursuant to any Operative Document.

(c) Subject to the terms and conditions of this Agreement and any other Operative Document, and upon oral notice from the Owner Trustee on each Delivery Date that it has received the Commitments for the Aircraft and is prepared to pay Lessee Lessor 's Cost for the Aircraft as provided herein, Lessee shall sell the Aircraft to the Owner Trustee and lease the Aircraft from the Owner Trustee and, to accomplish such sale and lease, shall (to the extent that it has not already done so) take the following action with respect to the Aircraft:

(i) execute and deliver the Lessee's Bill of Sale for the Aircraft to the Owner Trustee;

(ii) execute and release for filing the FAA Bill of Sale for the Aircraft;

(iii) accept delivery of the Aircraft for purposes of the Lease, and in accordance with the terms thereof [such acceptance to be made by the employee or employees of Lessee who are accepting delivery of such Aircraft for the Owner Trustee pursuant to Section 3(b)(i) hereof];

(iv) execute and deliver the Lease Supplement covering the Aircraft; and

(v) execute and deliver all other documents and certificates, and take all other actions as are required to be executed and delivered or taken by Lessee on or before the Delivery Date for the Aircraft pursuant to any Operative Document.

Section 4. Conditions Precedent to Obligations of the Participants

The obligation of each Participant to participate in the payment of Lessor's Cost for the Aircraft is subject to the fulfillment to the satisfaction of such Participant on or before the Delivery Date for the Aircraft, of the following conditions precedent:

(a) Such Participant shall have received due notice pursuant to Section 2(b) hereof or such notice shall have been waived.

(b) No change shall have occurred after the date of this Agreement in Applicable Law that (i) in the opinion of any Loan Participant, would make it illegal for such Loan

Participant to acquire a Loan Certificate or (ii) in the opinion of the Owner Participant, would make it illegal for the Owner Participant to acquire its interest in the Trust Estate. No action or proceeding shall have been instituted, nor shall governmental action be threatened before any governmental authority, nor shall any order, judgment, or decree have been issued, or proposed to be issued, by any governmental authority at the time of the Delivery Date to set aside, restrain, enjoin, or prevent the consummation of this Agreement or to set aside, restrain, enjoin, or prevent the consummation of the transactions contemplated hereby.

(c) In the case of the Owner Participant, since the date hereof there shall not have been any change in the Code or the Regulations, or in the interpretation of the Code or the Regulations in a decision by the United States Supreme Court, the United States Tax Court, the United States Court of Claims or any one of the United States Courts of Appeals or any issuance of a revenue ruling, revenue procedure, or other pronouncement by the Internal Revenue Service or the Department of the Treasury which, in the opinion of the Owner Participant, renders doubtful or invalid the Assumed Tax Benefits.

(d) Each other Participant shall have made available its Commitment for the Aircraft in accordance with Section 2(a) hereof.

(e) Each of the Operative Documents, and such other documents as have been reasonably requested by such Participant or its special counsel, shall have been duly authorized, executed, and delivered by the respective party or parties thereto and shall be satisfactory in form and substance to such Participant, and an executed original or conformed copy, as appropriate, of the Operative Documents and such other documents shall have been delivered to such Participant.

(f) Such Participant shall have received the following, in each case in form and substance satisfactory to it:

(i) incumbency certificates of Lessee, Owner Participant, and Owner Trustee regarding the officers of each authorized to execute and deliver the Operative Documents to which each is a party and other documents and agreements delivered in connection therewith;

(ii) a report from Air Valuation, Inc. in form and substance satisfactory to the Owner Participant, as to the Aircraft;

(iii) an insurance report of an independent insurance broker and certificates of insurance, as to Lessee's due compliance with the terms of Section 10 of the Lease;

(iv) certified copies of all documents evidencing the corporate actions of Lessee, the Owner Participant and the Owner Trustee, the Boards of Directors, or the executive committees of such Boards of Directors of the foregoing, duly authorizing the sale and the lease by Lessee of the Aircraft, with respect to Lessee, and the execution, delivery, and performance by each such party of each of the Operative Documents to which each is a party;

(v) a copy of the full warranty bill of sale for the Aircraft from the Manufacturer to Lessee;

(vi) such other documents. and evidence with respect to Lessee as each Participant may reasonably request in order to establish consummation of the transactions contemplated by the Operative Documents, the taking of all corporate proceedings in connection therewith and compliance with the conditions herein set forth.

(g) On the Delivery Date for the Aircraft, the following statements shall be true and such Participant shall have received evidence in form and substance satisfactory to it to the effect that:

(i) Upon consummation of the transactions contemplated by the Operative Documents, the Owner Trustee will have good title (subject to the filing and recording with the FAA of the FAA Bill of Sale) to the Aircraft, including the Engines, free and clear of Liens, except Permitted Liens;

(ii) the Aircraft is duly certified by the FAA as to type and airworthiness in accordance with the terms of the Lease;

(iii) the Lease and the Lease Supplement for the Aircraft, the Trust Agreement, the Indenture and the Trust Agreement, and Indenture Supplement for the Aircraft and the FAA Bill of Sale for the Aircraft have been duly filed for recordation with the FAA pursuant to the Federal Aviation Act; and

(iv) application for registration of the Aircraft in the name of the Owner Trustee, has been duly made with the FAA and Lessee has authority to operate the Aircraft.

(h) On the Delivery Date for the Aircraft (i) the representations and warranties of Lessee, the Owner Trustee, the Indenture Trustee, and each other Participant contained herein shall be true and accurate on and as of such date as though made on and as of such date except to the extent that such representations and warranties relate solely to an earlier date (in which case such representations and warranties shall be true and accurate on and as of such earlier date), (ii) nothing shall have occurred which materially and adversely has affected or will affect the ability of Lessee to carry on its business and to perform its obligations under the Operative Documents and (iii) no event shall have occurred and be continuing, or would result from the sale or lease of the Aircraft, which constitutes a Default, an Event of Default, or an Event of Acceleration.

(i) Lessee shall have delivered an Officer's Certificate certifying as to each of the matters set forth in Section 4 (h) hereof (except with respect to the representations and warranties of the Participants, the Owner Trustee, and the Indenture Trustee referred to in clause [i] thereof).

(j) Such Participant, the Owner Trustee, and the Indenture Trustee shall have received such other documents and evidence with respect to the Owner Participants, the Owner Trustee, and the Indenture Trustee as such Participant may reasonably request in order to establish the consummation of the transactions contemplated by this Agreement, the taking of all required corporate and governmental actions in connection therewith and compliance with the conditions set forth herein.

(k) Such Participant, the Owner Trustee and the Indenture Trustee shall have received a favorable opinion from Richard R. Stone, Esq., Corporate Counsel of Lessee, in substantially the covering such matters incident to the transactions hereto as such Participant may reasonably request.

(l) Such Participant, the Owner Trustee, and the Indenture Trustee shall have received a favorable opinion from Sarrett Smith Schapiro Simon & Armstrong, special counsel for Lessee covering such matters incident to the transactions hereto as such Participant may reasonably request.

(m) Such Participant, the Owner Trustee, and the Indenture Trustee shall have received a favorable opinion from Merriweather & Sailing, special counsel for the Owner Participant, and from a legal officer of the Owner Participant covering such matters incident to the transactions hereto as such Participant may reasonably request.

(n) Such Participant, the Owner Trustee, and the Indenture Trustee shall have received a favorable opinion from Nightingale & Flyer, special counsel for the Indenture

Trustee covering such matters incident to the transactions hereto as such Participant may reasonably request.

(o) Such Participant, the Owner Trustee, the Indenture Trustee and Lessee shall have received a favorable opinion from Wingnet & Flash, counsel, covering such matters incident to the transactions hereto as such Participant or Lessee may reasonably request.

(p) Such Participant, Lessee, the Indenture Trustee, and the Owner Trustee shall have received a favorable opinion addressed to them, from Nickel & Dime, special counsel for the Owner Trustee, covering such matters incident to the transactions hereto as they may reasonably request.

(q) Each Loan Participant shall have received a favorable opinion from Nickel & Dime, special counsel for the Loan Participants, in form and substance satisfactory to it.

(r) The Owner Participant shall have received an opinion from Merriweather & Sailing covering such tax matters related to the transactions contemplated hereby as the Owner Participant may reasonably request.

(s) Uniform Commercial Code financing statements covering all of the security or other interests created by or pursuant to the Indenture shall have been executed and delivered by the Owner Trustee as debtor for the benefit of the Indenture Trustee as secured party, and such "precautionary" financing or similar statements describing the Aircraft as are deemed necessary or desirable by counsel for any Participant to protect the ownership interests of the Owner Trustee, and the security interests therein of the Indenture Trustee, in the Lease (including the Lease Supplement) shall have been duly executed and delivered by the Lessee, as debtor-lessee, for the benefit of the Owner Trustee, as the secured party-lessor, and the Indenture Trustee, as the assignee of such secured party-lessor and duly filed in all places as, in the reasonable opinion of counsel for any Participant, are necessary or desirable to perfect said ownership, security, or other interests. The Indenture Trustee shall have received the "original" counterpart of the Lease, with the receipt therefor executed by the Indenture Trustee, and the "original" counterpart of the Lease Supplement related to the Aircraft, with the receipt therefor executed by the Indenture Trustee, and there shall have been taken all other action reasonably requested by any Participant or the Indenture Trustee to perfect such security or other interests.

(t) Each Loan Participant shall have received the Loan Certificate or Loan Certificates to be issued to it pursuant to the Indenture.

Promptly upon the recordation with the FAA of the documents filed with respect to the Aircraft referred to in Section 4(g) hereof, Lessee will cause Wingnet & Flash, counsel, to deliver to each Participant, the Owner Trustee, the Indenture Trustee, and Lessee an opinion addressed to such party as to the due registration of the Aircraft, the due recordation of the FAA Bill of Sale for the Aircraft, the due recordation of such documents filed with respect to the Aircraft referred to in the Section 4(g) hereof and the lack of the filing of any intervening documents with respect to the Aircraft.

Section 5. Conditions Precedent to Obligations of Lessee

Lessee's obligations to sell the Aircraft to the Owner Trustee and to lease the Aircraft from the Owner Trustee are subject to fulfillment to the satisfaction of Lessee, on or before the Delivery Date, of the following conditions precedent with respect to the Aircraft:

(a) Lessee shall have been paid Lessor's Cost for the Aircraft.

(b) Since the date hereof there shall not have been any change in tax law, or any reasonably anticipated change in tax law other than as contained in (H.R. ____________ as passed by the House of Representatives or the Senate), which, discounted at the Fixed Rate, would result in an increase in Rent pursuant to Section 3 (e) (i) (B) of the Lease of 50 basis points or more over the Term on a present value basis.

(c) Each of the Operative Documents shall have been duly authorized, executed, and delivered by the parties thereto in form and substance satisfactory to Lessee.

(d) Application for registration of the Aircraft in the name of the Owner Trustee shall have been duly made with the FAA and the Lease, the Lease Supplement, the Trust Agreement, the Indenture, the Trust Agreement and Indenture Supplement and the FAA Bill of Sale for the Aircraft shall be in due form for recording and shall have been duly filed for recordation with the FAA.

Section 6. Representations and Warranties of Lessee

The Lessee represents and warrants that:

(a) Organization; Good Standing. Lessee is a corporation duly organized, validly existing, and in good standing under the laws of New Jersey; it is an "air carrier" within the meaning of the Federal Aviation Act operating under a certificate issued under Section 401 thereof and has the corporate power and authority to own or hold under lease its properties and to enter into and perform its obligations under each of the Operative Documents to which it is a party; and it is duly qualified to do business as a foreign corporation in good standing in each state of the United States from or to which Lessee provides scheduled air service or in which failure to so qualify would have a material and adverse effect on its financial condition, business, or operations or on its ability to perform its obligations under each of the Operative Documents to which it is a party. Lessee's chief executive office (as such term is used in Sections 9-103 and 9-401 of the Uniform Commercial Code) is located at Fort Lee, New Jersey.

(b) Authority; Consent. The execution, delivery, and performance of each of the Operative Documents to which Lessee is a party have been duly authorized by all necessary corporate action on the part of Lessee and do not require any stockholder approval or approval or consent of, or notice to, any trustee or holders of any indebtedness or obligations of Lessee.

(c) Compliance with Other Instruments. Neither the execution, delivery, or performance by Lessee of the Operative Documents to which Lessee is a party nor the consummation or performance by Lessee of the transactions contemplated thereby will conflict with or result in any violation of, or constitute a default under, any term of the certificate of incorporation or by-laws of Lessee or any agreement, mortgage, indenture, lease or other instrument, or any Applicable Law by which Lessee or its properties or assets are bound.

(d) Governmental Consents. Neither the execution, delivery, or performance of any of the Operative Documents nor the consummation or performance of any of the transactions contemplated thereby by Lessee nor, to the knowledge of Lessee, any other party thereto, requires the consent or approval of, the giving of notice to, or the registration with, or the taking of any other action in respect of (i) the FAA or the Department of Transportation, except for the filings for recording and registration referred to in Section

4(g) hereof, or (ii) with respect to Lessee only, any other federal, state, or foreign governmental authority or agency, including any judicial body.

(e) No Adverse Agreements. Lessee is not a party to any agreement or instrument (other than as reflected in Lessee's Annual Report on Form 10-K for the fiscal year ended December 31, XXXX, including the financial statements contained therein, or as disclosed in writing to each Participant), or subject to any charter or any corporate restriction, which if performed in accordance with its terms, would materially and adversely affect Lessee's financial condition, business, or operations or the ability of Lessee to perform its obligations under any of the Operative Documents to which it is a party.

(f) Legal and Binding. This Agreement has been duly executed and delivered by Lessee and constitutes, and the other Operative Documents to which the Lessee is a party when executed and delivered, will (assuming due authorization, execution, and delivery by each other party thereto) each constitute, legal, valid, and binding obligations of Lessee enforceable against Lessee (subject to any qualifications as to remedies noted in the legal opinions of Lessee's counsel delivered at the closing) in accordance with their respective terms.

(g) No Defaults or Violations. No event exists which, upon the consummation of the transactions contemplated hereby would be a Default or Event of Default, and Lessee is not in default under any mortgage, deed of trust, indenture, or other instrument or agreement to which Lessee is a party or by which it or any of its properties or assets may be bound, or in violation of any Applicable Law, which default or violation would have a material adverse effect on the financial condition, business, or operations of Lessee or its ability to perform any of its obligations under the Operative Documents.

(h) Litigation. There are no pending or, to the knowledge of Lessee, threatened actions or proceedings by or before any court or administrative agency or arbitrator that would either individually or in the aggregate materially and adversely affect the financial condition, business, or operations of Lessee or the ability of Lessee to perform its obligations under any of the Operative Documents.

(i) Financial Statements. The audited consolidated balance sheet of Lessee and its subsidiaries as of the end of each of its last five fiscal years (up to December 31, XXXX), the related consolidated statements of income and changes in financial position, the unaudited consolidated balance sheet of Lessee for the fiscal quarter ending on June 30, XXXX, and the related unaudited consolidated statements of income and changes in financial position (copies of each of which have been furnished to the Participants), each prepared in accordance with generally accepted accounting principles and practices, fairly present the financial position of Lessee and its subsidiaries as of the dates thereof and changes in its financial position for the periods covered thereby. Since December 31, XXXX there has been no material adverse change in the financial condition, business, or operations of Lessee.

(j) Perfection of Title and Security Interest. The Indenture, as supplemented by the Indenture Supplement, creates the security interest in the Estate it purports to create. Except for (i) the registration of the Aircraft in the name of the Owner Trustee pursuant to the Federal Aviation Act, (ii) the filing and recordation of the Lease with the executed Lease Supplement covering the Aircraft, the Indenture, the Trust Agreement, and the Trust Agreement and Indenture Supplement covering the Aircraft, and the FAA Bill of Sale covering the Aircraft pursuant to the Federal Aviation Act, (iii) the filing of the Uniform Commercial Code financing statements as required by Section 4(s) hereof and (iv) the taking of possession by the Indenture Trustee of the "original" counterpart of the

Lease and the Lease Supplement referred to in Section 24 (e) of the Lease, no further action, including any filing or recording of any document, is necessary or advisable in order to establish and perfect the Owner Trustee's title to and interest in, or the first mortgage lien and security interest of the Indenture Trustee in, the Aircraft, and the assignment of the Lease to the Indenture Trustee, as against Lessee and any third parties.

(k) Taxes, Returns. Lessee has filed or caused to be filed all federal, state, local, and foreign tax returns which it is required to file and has paid or caused to be paid all taxes shown to be due and payable on such returns or [except to the extent being contested in good faith and for the payment of which adequate reserves have been provided as shown in the balance sheets referred to in Section 6 (i) hereof] on any assessment received by Lessee, to the extent that such taxes have become due and payable; the federal income tax liability of the Lessee has been determined by the Internal Revenue Service or the statute of limitations has expired with respect to the redetermination of such liability and (except to the extent being contested in good faith and for the payment of which adequate reserves have been provided) paid for all years prior to and including the fiscal year ended December 31, XXXX; the federal income tax returns of Lessee for the fiscal years ended December 31, XXXX, December 31, XXXX and December 31, XXXX are subject to examination by the Internal Revenue Service.

(l) Securities Representation. Neither Lessee nor anyone acting on behalf of Lessee (including Pertson, Inc.) has directly or indirectly offered any interest in the Aircraft for sale to, or solicited any offer to acquire the same from anyone other than the Owner Participant and not more than 25 other financial institutions. Neither Lessee nor anyone acting on its behalf (including New York Investment Corporation) has directly or indirectly offered any Loan Certificate or any similar security for sale to, or solicited any offer to acquire any of the same from, anyone other than the Loan Participants and not more than 30 other financial institutions.

(m) Warranty of Title. On the Delivery Date; the Owner Trustee will have received good and marketable title to the Aircraft free and clear of all Liens (other than Permitted Liens) and Lessee will defend such title forever against all claims and demands whatsoever.

(n) Condition of Aircraft. On the Delivery Date, the Aircraft shall be in such condition as when delivered new by the Manufacturer to Lessee, normal wear and tear excepted, and so as to enable the airworthiness certificate of the Aircraft to be in good standing under the Federal Aviation Act. The Aircraft has been duly certified by the FAA as to type and airworthiness; there is, or will be on the Delivery Date for the Aircraft, a current and valid airworthiness certificate issued by the FAA pursuant to the Federal Aviation Act in effect with respect to the Aircraft; and there is no fact known to Lessee which materially adversely affects or, so far as Lessee can now reasonably foresee, will materially adversely affect the value, utility, or condition of the Aircraft.

(o) Engines. The Engines delivered pursuant to the Lease each have a rated takeoff horsepower greater than 750 horsepower, or the equivalent of such horsepower.

(p) Margin. Lessee will not, directly or indirectly, use any of the proceeds of the sale of the Loan Certificates for the purpose of purchasing or carrying any "margin stock" within the meaning of Regulation G and Regulation U, respectively, or for the purpose of reducing or retiring any indebtedness which was originally incurred to purchase or carry a margin security or margin stock or for any other purpose which might cause the transactions contemplated by this Agreement to constitute a "purpose credit" within the meaning of Regulation G or Regulation U, or for the purpose of purchasing or carrying any security other than a security the extension or maintenance of credit for the purchase or carrying of which is permitted by Section 220.70(a) of Regulation T, and Lessee has not taken and will not otherwise take or permit any action in connection with any of the transactions contemplated by any of the Operative Documents which would involve a violation of Regulation G, T, U, or X, or any other regulation of the Board of Governors of the Federal Reserve System.

(q) Statements, Omissions, etc. The financial statements referred to in Section 6 (i) hereof and statements made by Lessee in other documents furnished by or on behalf of Lessee, to the Participants in connection with the transactions contemplated hereby, taken as a whole, do not contain any untrue statement of a material fact or omit to state a material fact necessary to make the statements contained therein not misleading; and there is no fact which Lessee has not disclosed to the Participants in writing which materially and adversely affects or, so far as Lessee can now reasonably foresee, will materially and adversely affect the financial condition, business, or operations of Lessee or will adversely affect the ability of Lessee to perform its obligations under any of the Operative Documents to which it is a party.

(r) ERISA. Each Plan is in substantial compliance with ERISA, no Plan is insolvent or in reorganization, no Plan has an accumulated or waived funding deficiency within the meaning of Section 412 of the Code, neither the Lessee or a subsidiary nor an affiliate has incurred any material liability (including any material contingent liability) to or on account of a Plan pursuant to Section 515, 4062, 4063, 4064, 4201 or 4204 of ERISA, no proceedings have been instituted to terminate any Plan, and no condition exists which presents a material risk to the Lessee or any subsidiary of incurring a liability to or on account of a Plan pursuant to ERISA or the Code. For purposes of the foregoing, "Plan" shall mean any employee benefit plan as defined in Section 3 (3) of ERISA, which has been established by, or which is maintained or sponsored, or to which contributions are or have been made by Lessee or by any subsidiary or affiliate of Lessee; and "affiliate" shall mean any trade or business (whether or not incorporated) which together with Lessee or any subsidiary of Lessee, would be deemed a single employer within the meaning of Sections 414 (b), 414 (c), and 414 (m) of the Code.

(s) No ERISA Conflict. Lessee is neither a party in interest as defined in Section 3 (14) of ERISA nor a disqualified person as defined in Section 4975 (e) of the Code with respect to the employee benefit plan or its underlying trust disclosed in writing by SYNX LIFE Assurance Company of Canada in the letter referred to in Section 8 (c) of the Participation Agreement.

(t) Representations and Warranties. EXCEPT TO THE EXTENT THAT LESSEE HAS MADE SPECIFIC REPRESENTATIONS OR WARRANTIES HEREIN OR IN THE OTHER OPERATIVE DOCUMENTS, LESSEE HAS NOT MADE AND SHALL NOT BE DEEMED TO HAVE MADE ANY REPRESENTATION OR WARRANTY, EXPRESS OR IMPLIED, AS TO AIRWORTHINESS, VALUE, CONDITION, DESIGN, OPERATION, MERCHANTABILITY, OR FITNESS FOR USE OF THE AIRCRAFT, AS TO THE ABSENCE OF LATENT OR OTHER DEFECTS, WHETHER OR NOT DISCOVERABLE, AS TO THE ABSENCE OF ANY INFRINGEMENT OF ANY PATENT, TRADEMARK, OR COPYRIGHT, AS TO THE ABSENCE OF OBLIGATIONS BASED ON STRICT LIABILITY IN TORT, OR ANY OTHER REPRESENTATION OR WARRANTY WHATSOEVER, EXPRESS OR IMPLIED, WITH RESPECT TO THE AIRCRAFT OR ANY PART THEREOF.

Section 7. Representations, Warranties, and Agreements of Owner Participant

The Owner Participant represents, warrants and agrees that:

(a) Organization; Authority; Legal and Binding. The Owner Participant is a corporation duly organized, validly existing and in good standing under the laws of the State of Florida and has the full power and authority and legal right to execute, deliver, and perform each of the Operative Documents to which it is a party, that such Operative Documents have been duly authorized by all necessary corporate action by it, do not required any stockholder approval, or approval or consent of, or notice to, any trustee or holders of indebtedness or obligations of the Owner Participant, that such Operative Documents have been duly executed and delivered by it and, assuming due authorization, execution, and delivery by each other party thereto, constitute its legal, valid, and binding obligations, enforceable in accordance with their terms (subject to any qualifications as to remedies noted in the legal opinion of Owner Participant's counsel delivered at the closing), and that the execution, delivery, and performance by the Owner Participant of each of the Operative Documents to which the Owner Participant is a party do not violate its certificate of incorporation or by-laws or any indenture, mortgage, contract, or other agreement to which the Owner Participant is a party or by which it is bound or any order or judgment applicable to such Owner Participant or any law, government rule, or regulation of the United States or any stated thereof applicable to its business generally.

(b) Securities Representation. The Owner Participant is acquiring its interest in the Aircraft for investment and not with a view to any resale or distribution thereof, but subject, nevertheless, to any requirement of law that the disposition of its property remain within its control at all times, and that neither it nor anyone acting on its behalf has directly or indirectly offered any Loan Certificate or interest in the Aircraft or any similar security for sale to, or solicited any offer to acquire any of the same from, anyone.

(c) U.S. Citizenship; Registration. The Owner Participant is a "citizen of the United States" within the meaning of Section 101 (16) of the Federal Aviation Act. The Owner Participant agrees that if it ceases to be a "citizen of the United States" within the meaning of Section 101 (16) of the Federal Aviation Act then the Owner Participant shall promptly, at its own expense, transfer, pursuant to Section 15 hereof, its right, title, and interest in and to the Trust Estate, the Trust Agreement, and this Agreement, or take such other action as may be necessary to maintain the United States registration of such Aircraft.

(d) Title to the Aircraft. On the Delivery Date for each Aircraft the Owner Trustee will have received whatever title to such Aircraft was conveyed to it by Lessee, and such Aircraft shall be free of Lessor's Liens.

(e) Liens; Indemnity. The Owner Participant hereby agrees that it will not directly or indirectly create, incur, assume, or suffer to exist any Lessor's Lien on the Aircraft, any interest therein or on the Trust Estate or the Estate, and that if it shall do so it will promptly at its own expense cause the same to be duly discharged and removed; provided, however, the Owner Participant shall not be required to so discharge such Lessor's Lien while it is contesting such Lien in good faith by appropriate proceedings as long as: (i) in the reasonable opinion of a Majority in Interest of Holders such contest does not involve any danger of the sale, forfeiture, or loss of title to any part of the Estate or adversely affect the Lien on the Estate created by the Indenture, or interferes with the payment of Rent or the performance of any other terms under the Lease or the Indenture; and (ii) in the reasonable opinion of Lessee, such contest does not or will not interfere with Lessee's right of quiet enjoyment under the Lease as provided in Section 20 of this Agreement and in Section 5 (b) of the Lease. The Owner Participant agrees to indemnify, protect, save, and keep harmless Lessee, the Owner Trustee, the Indenture Trustee, and each holder of a Loan Certificate from and against any reduction in the amount payable out of the Estate to such holders in respect of Loan Certificates, or any other loss, cost, or expense (including legal fees and expenses) incurred by such holders, the Indenture Trustee or Lessee, as a result of the imposition or enforcement of any Lessor's Lien against any Aircraft, any interest therein or on the Trust Estate or the Estate.

(f) ERISA. The Owner Participant represents and warrants that its Commitment has not been made available directly or indirectly with the assets of any employee benefit plan. "Employee benefit plan" as used in the preceding sentence shall have the meaning assigned in Section 3 of ERISA. Based on the representations of the Loan Participants in Section 8 (c) hereof, the performance by the Owner Participant of the transactions contemplated hereby and by the Operative Documents do not constitute "prohibited transactions" within the meaning of Section 406 of ERISA or Section 4975 of the Code.

(g) No ERISA Conflict. The Owner Participant is neither a party in interest as defined in Section 3 (14) of ERISA nor a disqualified person as defined in Section 4975 (e) of the Code with respect to the employee benefit plan or its underlying trust disclosed in writing by SYNX LIFE Assurance Company of Canada in the letter referred to in Section 8 (c) of the Participation Agreement.

(h) Governmental Consents. Neither the execution, delivery of or performance under any of the Operative Documents nor the consummation of or performance under any of the transactions contemplated thereby, by the Owner Participant, requires the consent or approval of, the giving of notice to, or the registration with, or the taking of any other action under any Applicable Law.

(i) Notice. In the event an officer of the Owner Participant shall have actual knowledge of an Event of Default, an Event of Acceleration, or an Event of Loss, the Owner Participant will give prompt written notice of such Event of Default, Event of Acceleration, or Event of Loss to the Indenture Trustee, the Owner Trustee, Lessee, and each holder of a Loan Certificate.

(j) Prepayment of Loan Certificates. If, as permitted by Section 15 (a) of the Lease, the Owner Trustee shall submit a "Preemptive Bid" as provided therein, the Owner Participant will deposit with the Indenture Trustee, in immediately available funds, on the termination date of the Lease with respect to the Aircraft, concurrently with the acceptance of delivery of possession of the Aircraft to the Owner Trustee pursuant to Section 15 (a) of the Lease, the amount prepayable on the Loan Certificates pursuant to Section 2 (k) of the Indenture.

(k) Trust Agreement. The Owner Participant and the Owner Trustee shall not amend or supplement the Trust Agreement except to the extent permitted by, and in accordance with, the terms thereof, and unless a signed copy of such amendment or supplement has been delivered to the Indenture Trustee, provided, however, that without the consent of the Indenture Trustee, no amendment or supplement shall be effective which could adversely affect the interests of the Indenture Trustee or the holders of the Loan Certificates. The Owner Participant confirms for the benefit of the holders of the Loan Certificates that it will not elect to revoke or otherwise terminate the trusts created by the Trust Agreement until full payment of the principal of and interest on the Loan Certificates has been made and the Lien of the Indenture on the Estate has been released.

(l) Debt Service Payments. The Owner Participant hereby agrees to pay or cause to be paid to the Indenture Trustee sufficient funds in immediately available funds, to effect the payment of any amounts due on the Loan Certificates on each July 2, such payment by the Owner Participant to be initiated by wire transfer, subject to the next sentence, on or before 11:00 a.m. New York City time on each such date and to be applied by the Indenture Trustee to the payment of the amounts due and payable on the Loan Certificates on each such date pursuant to the provisions of the Indenture. The Owner Participant shall provide the Indenture Trustee with such wire transfer information as the Indenture Trustee may reasonably request, including, without limitation, such wire transfer number and time of initiation. The agreement of the Owner Participant to make the payments provided for in the preceding sentence shall, except in the case of an Event of Default, be absolute and unconditional under any and all circumstances and shall not be affected by any circumstance of any character. Upon making such payment, or, in the event that such payment will not be made, at least one day prior to the date such payment is due, the Owner Participant shall inform Lessee by telephone that such payment has been made or (as the case may be) not made with immediate written confirmation to Lessee by telex or telecopy.

Section 7a. Representations, Warranties, and Agreements of Owner Trustee

(a) Securities Representation. The Owner Trustee represents and warrants, both in its individual capacity and as trustee, that it has not directly or indirectly offered any Loan Certificate or any interest in and to the Trust Estate and the Trust Agreement or any similar interest for sale to, or solicited any offer to acquire any of the same from, anyone. The Owner Trustee further represents and warrants that it has not authorized anyone to act on its behalf to directly or indirectly offer any Loan Certificate or any interest in and to the Trust Estate and the Trust Agreement or any similar interest for sale to, or solicited any offer to acquire any of the same from, anyone.

(b) Organization; Authority; Legal and Binding, etc. The Owner Trustee, in its individual capacity (except as otherwise expressly stated below), represents and warrants that:

(i) it is a trust company duly organized and validly existing in good standing under the laws of the State of New York and has full corporate power and authority to enter into and perform its obligations under the agreements referred to in clauses (ii) and (iii) of this Section 7 a (b);

(ii) the Trust Agreement has been duly authorized, executed, and delivered by the Owner Trustee, in its individual capacity, and constitutes the legal, valid, and binding obligation of the Owner Trustee, in its individual capacity, enforceable against it in accordance with the terms thereof (subject to any qualifications as to remedies noted in the legal opinion of Owner Trustee's counsel delivered at the closing);

(iii) it has the full corporate power, authority, and legal right to execute, deliver, and perform the Trust Agreement and, assuming due authorization, execution and delivery of the Trust Agreement by the Owner Participant, as Owner Trustee (except as otherwise expressly provided therein), each of the other Operative Documents to which the Owner Trustee is a party; that such Operative Documents have been duly authorized by all necessary corporate action by it, do not require any stockholder approval, or approval or consent of, or notice to, any trustee or holders of indebtedness or obligations of it; that such Operative Documents have been duly executed and delivered by it or one of its officers authorized to execute and deliver such Operative Documents on behalf of the Owner Trustee; and that the execution, delivery, and performance by the Owner Trustee of the Operative Documents to which the Owner Trustee is a party, do not violate the Articles of Incorporation or by-laws of Martin Trust Company or any indenture, mortgage, contract, or other agreement to which Martin Trust Company is a party or by which it is bound or any order or judgment applicable to it or any law, government rule, or regulation of the United States, Florida or New York applicable to its banking or trust powers;

(iv) the execution, delivery, and performance by the Owner Trustee in its individual capacity of the Trust Agreement and this Agreement does not (A) require the consent or approval of, the giving of notice to, or the registration with, or the taking of any other action with respect to, any governmental authority or agency in respect of or under federal, Florida or New York law (except such as shall have been duly obtained or given), or (B) violate nor will violate the Articles of Incorporation or by-laws of Martin Trust Company, or contravene nor will contravene any provision of, nor constitute nor will constitute a default under, nor result nor will result in the creation of any Lien (other than as permitted under the Lease) upon its property under, any indenture, mortgage, credit agreement or other agreement or instrument to which Martin Trust Company is a party or by which it is bound, nor contravene nor will contravene any New York or federal banking or trust law or any New York law applicable to it in the ordinary course of its business, or any judgment or order binding on it;

(v) there are no pending or, to the knowledge of the Owner Trustee, in its individual capacity, threatened actions or proceedings against the Owner Trustee, in its individual capacity, before any court or administrative agency which, if determined adversely to the Owner Trustee, in its individual capacity would materially adversely affect the ability of the Owner Trustee, in its individual capacity or as Owner Trustee, to perform its obligations under each of the Operative Documents to which it is a party;

(vi) it is a "citizen of the United States" as defined in Section 101 (16) of the Federal Aviation Act;

(vii) on the Delivery Date assuming a valid trust has been created under the Trust Agreement for the Aircraft, the Owner Trustee, as trustee, will have whatever title to the Aircraft as was conveyed to it and the Aircraft shall be free of Lessor's Liens attributable to the Owner Trustee in its individual capacity;

(viii) the chief executive office of the Owner Trustee is located at New York, New York and the place where its records concerning the Aircraft and all its interests in, to and under all documents relating to the Trust Estate to which it is a party are kept, is located at 21 Second Avenue, New York, New York, and the Owner Trustee, in its individual capacity, agrees to give each Participant written notice of any relocation of said chief executive office or said place from its respective present locations; and

(ix) the Owner Trustee, as trustee, has not by affirmative act conveyed title to the Aircraft to any Person or subjected the Aircraft to any Lien other than as contemplated hereby.

The representations and warranties of the Owner Trustee in its individual capacity in this Section 7a(b) notwithstanding, the representations and warranties of the Owner Trustee in the other Operative Documents (other than the Trust Agreement) are made in its capacity as Owner Trustee and not (except where expressly so provided therein) in its individual capacity.

(c) Valid and Binding, as Trustee. Assuming due authorization, execution, and delivery by each other party thereto, the Operative Documents to which the Owner Trustee is a party constitute the legal, valid, and binding obligations of the Owner Trustee enforceable against it as trustee in accordance with the terms of such Operative Documents (subject to any qualifications as to remedies noted in the legal opinion of Owner Trustee's counsel delivered at the closing).

(d) Valid and Binding, in Individual Capacity. Assuming due authorization, execution, and delivery by each other party thereto, the Operative Documents to which the Owner Trustee, in its individual capacity, is a party according to the express terms thereof, constitute the legal, valid, and binding obligations of the Owner Trustee, in its individual capacity, in accordance with the express terms thereof (subject to any qualifications as to remedies noted in the legal opinion of Owner Trustee's counsel delivered at the closing).

(e) Liens; Indemnity. The Owner Trustee agrees, in its individual capacity, that it will not directly or indirectly create, incur, assume, or suffer to exist any Lessor's Lien attributable to it in its individual capacity on any of the Trust Estate or the Estate. The Owner Trustee agrees, in its individual capacity, that it will, at its own cost and expense, promptly take such action as may be necessary duly to discharge any such Lessor's Lien attributable to the Owner Trustee in its individual capacity and will hold harmless and indemnify each holder of a Loan Certificate, Lessee, the Owner Participant, Indenture Trustee, the Trust Estate, the Estate and their respective successors, assigns, servants, and agents against any and all liabilities, obligations, losses, damages, penalties, claims, actions, suits, costs, expenses, and disbursements, including legal fees and expenses, of whatsoever kind and nature and any reduction in the amount payable out of the Trust Estate, the Estate or in respect of the Loan Certificates imposed on, incurred by or asserted against any of the foregoing as a consequence of any such Lessor's Liens attributable to the Owner Trustee in its individual capacity.

(f) U.S. Citizenship. The Owner Trustee, in its individual capacity, agrees that if at any time any of its corporate trust officers shall obtain actual knowledge that it has ceased to be a "citizen of the United States" within the meaning of Section 101 (16) of the Federal Aviation Act, the Owner Trustee will promptly resign as Owner Trustee if such citizenship is then necessary under the Federal Aviation Act, in order for the Owner Trustee to perform its obligations under the Operative Documents or for the United States registration of the Aircraft to be maintained.

(g) FAA Reporting. The Owner Trustee agrees, in its individual capacity, to comply with the FAA reporting requirements set forth in 14 C.F.R. Section 47.45 and 14 C.F.R. Section 47.51. The Owner Trustee also agrees, in its individual capacity, to promptly notify each Participant if it changes its corporate name.

(h) No ERISA Conflict. The Owner Trustee represents and warrants that it is neither a party in interest as defined in Section 3(14) of ERISA nor a disqualified person as defined in Section 4975(e) of the Code with respect to the employee benefit plan or its underlying trust disclosed in writing by Synx Life Assurance Company of Canada in the letter referred to in Section 8(c) of the Participation Agreement.

Section 8. Representations and Warranties of Loan Participants

(a) Securities Representation; Authorization; Legal and Binding. Each Loan Participant represents and warrants that each Loan Certificate to be issued to it will be acquired for its own account, and not with a view to any resale or distribution thereof, subject, however, to any requirement of law that the disposition of its property remains within its control at all times. Each Loan Participant represents that each of the Operative Documents executed and delivered by it has been duly authorized, executed, and delivered by it and, assuming due authorization, execution, and delivery by each other party thereto, constitutes its legal, valid, and binding obligation, enforceable in accordance with its terms (except as may be limited by applicable bankruptcy, insolvency, reorganization, moratorium, or other similar laws affecting the enforcement of creditors' rights generally and application of general principles of equity regardless of whether considered in a proceeding in equity or at law).

(b) Securities Act Acknowledgment. Each Loan Participant acknowledges that the Loan Certificates have not been registered under the Securities Act of 1933, as amended, and that the Loan Certificates must be held indefinitely unless in connection with a subsequent disposition thereof they are registered under said Act or disposed of in a transaction exempt from registration.

(c) ERISA. Each Loan Participant, except Synx Life Assurance Company of Canada and State of New York Investment Board, represents and warrants that no part of the funds to be used by it to acquire the interest to be acquired by it under this Agreement constitutes assets of an employee benefit plan within the meaning of Section 3(3) of ERISA or of any trust created pursuant to such employee benefit plan. State of New York Investment Board represents and warrants that it is a governmental plan, as defined in Section 3(32) of ERISA or Section 414(d) of the Code and as such is excepted by the provisions of Section 406 of ERISA and Section 4975 of the Code. Synx Life Assurance Company of Canada represents and warrants that the funds to be used by it to acquire the interest to be acquired by it under this Agreement do not constitute assets of an employee benefit plan within the meaning of Section 3(3) of ERISA or of any trust created under such employee benefit plan except as disclosed in the letter dated August 15, XXXX from Synx Life Assurance Company of Canada to Robert Roundtree, Esq., a copy of which has been delivered to each of the parties

(d) United States Person. Except for Synx Life Assurance Company of Canada, each Loan Participant represents and warrants that it is a "United States person" within the meaning of Section 770(a)(30) of the Code. Synx Life Assurance Company of Canada represents and warrants that interest payments made on any loan certificate held by it are exempt from U.S. withholding tax pursuant to an exemption, a copy of which has been provided to the parties hereto.

Section 9. Representations, Warranties, and Agreements of Indenture Trustee

(a) Organization: Authority; Legal and Binding. The Indenture Trustee represents and warrants that it is a national banking association duly organized, validly existing, and in good standing under the laws of the United States and has the full power and authority and legal right to execute, deliver, and perform each of the Operative Documents to which it is a party, that such Operative Documents have been duly authorized, executed, and delivered by it and, assuming due authorization, execution, and delivery by each other party thereto, constitute its legal, valid, and binding obligations, enforceable against it in accordance with their terms (subject to any qualifications as to remedies noted in the legal opinion of the Indenture Trustee's counsel delivered at the closing) and that the execution, delivery, and performance by the Indenture Trustee of each of the Operative Documents to which the Indenture Trustee is a party is not in violation of its articles of association or by-laws or of any indenture, mortgage, contract, or other agreement to which the Indenture Trustee is a party or by which it is bound or of any order or judgment applicable to such Indenture Trustee or any law, government rule, or regulation of the United States or the State of Rhode Island.

(b) Lien; Indemnity. The Indenture Trustee agrees that it shall not cause or permit to exist any Lien with respect to the Aircraft, any interest therein, or any other portion of the Estate, which Lien results from claims against or affecting it or from acts or omissions of the Indenture Trustee, in each case not related to its interest in the Aircraft or its administration of the Estate, and that it will promptly cause any such Lien to be discharged at its own expense. The Indenture Trustee agrees to indemnify, protect, save, and keep harmless the Owner Participant, the Owner Trustee, Lessee, and each holder of a Loan Certificate from and against any reduction in the amount payable out of the Estate to such holders in respect of Loan Certificates, or any other loss, cost, or expense (including legal fees and expenses) incurred by such holders, the Owner Participant, the Owner Trustee, or Lessee as a result of the imposition or enforcement of such Lien.

(c) Agreement to Release Lien of Indenture. The Indenture Trustee agrees that upon compliance with all the conditions in Section 9 of the Lease and Section 5(f) of the Indenture for replacement of the Aircraft, Airframe, or an Engine, or upon any prepayment under Section 2(k) of the Indenture of the amounts required to be paid thereunder, the Indenture Trustee will release promptly the Lien of the Indenture on the Aircraft, Airframe, or Engine being replaced, as the case may be, as provided in Section 5(h) of the Indenture, or the Aircraft with respect to which such prepayment has been made.

Section 10. Compliance with Other Operative Documents; Lessee's Consent to Indenture

The Owner Trustee and the Indenture Trustee hereby agree to comply with all the terms of the Indenture (as the same may hereafter be amended from time to time in accordance with the terms thereof) applicable to them. the Owner Trustee and the Owner Participant hereby agree to comply with all terms of the Trust Agreement applicable to them. Lessee hereby consents in all respects to the execution and delivery of the Trust Agreement and the Indenture and to all the terms thereof, including the assignment of the Lease thereunder, it being agreed that such consent shall not be construed to require Lessee's consent to any future supplement to or amendment, waiver, or modification of the terms of the Trust Agreement, the Indenture, or the Loan Certificates; provided that the last proviso of Section 9(a) of the Indenture, the clause describing the fifth priority in Section 3(b)(i) of the Indenture and Section 9(a)(iii) of the Trust Agreement shall not be amended without the prior written consent of Lessee. Lessee agrees to perform its obligations under the Lease. The Owner Participant agrees to comply with the terms of the Lease expressly applicable to the Owner Participant.

Section 11. Extent of Interest of Holders of Loan Certificates

A holder of a Loan Certificate shall have no further interest in, or other right with respect to, the Aircraft or this Agreement when the principal of, and interest on all Loan Certificates held by such holder and all other sums payable to such holder hereunder, under the Indenture, the Lease, and such Loan Certificates shall have been paid in full.

Section 12. Certain Agreements of Lessee

Lessee agrees as follows:

(a) Filings. Lessee will take, or cause to be taken, at Lessee's cost and expense, such action with respect to the recording, filing, re-recording and re-filing of the Lease, each Lease Supplement, the Trust Agreement, the Indenture, each Trust Agreement and Indenture Supplement, and any financing statements or other instruments as are necessary to maintain, so long as the Indenture or the Lease is in effect, the perfection of the first security interest and the continuance of the first mortgage lien created by the Indenture and any security interest that may be claimed to have been created by the Lease and the ownership interest of the Owner Trustee in the Aircraft, and each of the Owner Trustee, the Indenture Trustee, and the Participants agree to cooperate with Lessee in order to allow Lessee to effect such filings, including executing any necessary instruments prepared by Lessee and furnishing such other information as may be required to enable Lessee to take such action.

(b) Annual Opinion. Lessee will, at its own expense, furnish to the Indenture Trustee, the Owner Trustee, and each Participant annually after the execution hereof (but not later than February 15 of each year) commencing with the year XXXX, an opinion, reasonably satisfactory to each of them, of Lessee's corporate counsel or other counsel reasonably satisfactory to each of them, either stating:

(i) that in the opinion of such counsel such action has been taken with respect to the recording, filing, re-recording, and re-filing of the Lease, each Lease Supplement, Trust Agreement, the Indenture, each Trust Agreement and Indenture Supplement, and any financing statement, continuation statement, or other instruments, and all other action has been taken, as is necessary to maintain for the 15-month period following the date of such opinion the perfection of the rights and ownership, security and other interests created thereby and reciting the details of such recording or other action, except as noted in such opinion; or

(ii) that in the opinion of such counsel no action is necessary to maintain for the 15-month period following the date of such opinion the perfection of such rights and ownership, security and other interests.

(c) Corporate Existence. Lessee shall at all times maintain its corporate existence except as permitted by Section 12(d) hereof; and it will do or cause to be done all things necessary to preserve and keep in full force and effect its corporate rights, powers, privileges, and franchises, except for any corporate right, power, privilege, or franchise (i) that it determines, in its reasonable, good faith business judgment, is no longer necessary or desirable in the conduct of its business and (ii) the loss of which will not materially adversely affect or diminish the rights of any holder of a Loan Certificate or the Owner Participant. Lessee will maintain its status as a Certificated Air Carrier.

(d) Merger, Consolidation. Lessee shall not consolidate with or merge into any other corporation or convey, transfer, or lease substantially all its assets as an entirety to any Person unless:

(i) the corporation formed by such consolidation or into which it is merged or the Person which acquires by conveyance, transfer, or lease substantially all its assets as an entirety shall be a corporation organized and existing under the laws of the United States of America or any state thereof, shall be a "citizen of the United States" as defined in Section 101(16) of the Federal Aviation Act, shall be a Certificated Air Carrier, and shall have executed and delivered to each Participant, the Owner Trustee, and the Indenture Trustee an agreement in form and substance satisfactory to each of them containing an assumption by such successor corporation of the due and punctual performance and observance of each agreement and condition of this Agreement and the Lease;

(ii) it shall have delivered to each Participant, the Owner Trustee, and the Indenture Trustee an Officer's Certificate of Lessee and an opinion of counsel satisfactory to each such party, each stating that such consolidation, merger, conveyance, transfer, or lease and the assumption agreement mentioned in clause (i) above comply with this Section 12(d); and

(iii) such consolidation, merger, conveyance, transfer, or lease shall not result in a Default or an Event of Default.

Upon any consolidation or merger, or any conveyance, transfer, or lease of substantially all the assets of Lessee as an entirety in accordance with this Section 12(d), the successor corporation formed by such consolidation or into which Lessee is merged or to which such conveyance, transfer, or lease is made shall succeed to, and be substituted for, and may exercise every right and power of, Lessee, under this Agreement and the Lease with the same effect as if such successor corporation had been named as Lessee herein and therein. No such conveyance, transfer, or lease of substantially all the assets of Lessee as an entirety shall have the effect of releasing Lessee or any successor corporation which shall theretofore have become such in the manner prescribed in this paragraph from its liability hereunder.

(e) Notice of Change. Lessee agrees to give prompt notice to each Participant, the Owner Trustee, and the Indenture Trustee of any change in the address of its chief executive office and any change in its name.

Section 13. Owner for Tax Purposes

It is hereby agreed between Lessee and the Owner Participant that for federal and state income tax purposes the Owner Participant will be the owner of the Aircraft to be delivered under the Lease and Lessee will be the lessee thereof.

Section 14. Transaction Costs; Continuing Expenses

(a) Transaction Costs. The Owner Participant agrees to pay promptly all Transaction Costs (up to 2.000% of Lessor's cost) with respect to the Aircraft if the Participants make their Commitments and the Aircraft is delivered and accepted as provided herein. Lessee will pay the Transaction Costs if the Aircraft is not delivered and accepted as provided herein, provided, however, that Lessee shall have no obligation to pay Transaction Costs incurred solely by any Participant or Participants whose default caused the transaction not to be consummated.

(b) Continuing Expenses. Except as otherwise provided herein or in another Operative Document or as may be otherwise agreed, Lessee will pay upon written demand all reasonable costs and expenses, including outside legal fees and expenses:

(i) of the Indenture Trustee in the performance of its ongoing responsibilities under the Indenture to the extent not covered by its initial fee;

(ii) of the Owner Trustee in the performance of its ongoing responsibilities under the Trust Agreement to the extent not covered by its initial fee; and

(iii) of each Participant in connection with any supplements, amendments, modifications, or alterations to or waivers or consents relating to this Agreement, the Lease, the Trust Agreement, or the Indenture which are either (A) requested by Lessee, (B) required by Applicable Law or by the terms of the Operative Documents, (C) requested by another Participant (to the extent such other Participant shall not have paid such costs and expenses), or (D) requested by such Participant and agreed to by Lessee, provided, however, that Lessee shall have no liability for any costs or expenses arising out of or relating to the transfer of a Participant's interest in this Agreement, the Trust Agreement or the Estate (including without limitation any transfer of a Loan Certificate) other than transfers pursuant to Section 9, 15, or 18 of the Lease or during an Event of Acceleration.

Section 15. Transfer of Owner Participant's Interest

The Owner Participant shall not assign, convey, or otherwise transfer any of its right, title, or interest in the Trust Agreement or the Trust Estate, except upon compliance with the conditions set forth in this Section 15. The Owner Participant may transfer to another person or entity (hereinafter in this Section 15 referred to as the "Transferee"), after the Delivery Date for the Aircraft, all, but not less than all, of such right, title, and interest, subject to the conditions that:

(i) the Transferee shall have the requisite power and authority to enter into and carry out the transactions contemplated hereby and shall be, and shall have furnished evidence reasonably satisfactory to the Indenture Trustee and Lessee to the effect that it is, a "citizen of the United States" within the meaning of Section 101 (16) of the Federal Aviation Act, or any successor provision;

(ii) the Transferee will enter into an agreement or agreements, in form and substance reasonably satisfactory to Lessee, the Owner Trustee, the Indenture Trustee, and each holder of a Loan Certificate, whereby the Transferee confirms that it shall be deemed a party to this Agreement, the Trust Agreement, and the Tax Indemnity Agreement, and agrees to provide all of the representations, warranties, and agreements of the Owner Participant under Section 7 hereof and to be bound by all the terms of, and to undertake all the obligations of the Owner Participant contained in the Operative Documents to which it is a party;

(iii) such transfer shall not violate any provision of the Federal Aviation Act, or any Applicable Law or create a relationship which would be in violation thereof or prevent the continued United States registration of the Aircraft; and

(iv) the Transferee shall be either (A) a bank, trust company or insurance company, pension trust, credit or finance corporation, or other financial institution organized under the laws of the United States or any State thereof with capital and surplus of at least $100,000,000, or (B) a business corporation or leasing corporation or any other entity experienced in transactions of the type contemplated by this Agreement, organized and operating under the laws of any state of the United States with a net worth of at least $100,000,000, or (C) a subsidiary of any person described in clause (A) or (B) above, or (D) a corporation (other than a single purpose corporation substantially all of whose assets consist of aircraft under lease to Lessee) which is a member of the same consolidated group for Federal income tax purposes as the Owner Participant, or other Person owned and controlled by, or under common control with, the Owner Participant, provided that if the Transferee is a person described in (x) clause (C) above, a person described in clauses (A) or (B) above shall have executed and delivered to the Owner Trustee, the Indenture Trustee and Lessee a guaranty, reasonably satisfactory to them, with respect to the obligations of such Transferee as an Owner Participant, or (y) clause (D) above, the Owner Participant shall have executed and delivered a guaranty or a comparable credit support reasonably satisfactory to each of the Owner Trustee, the Indenture Trustee, Lessee, and the Owner Participant, unless such person meets the requirements of clause (A) or (B) above, and provided, further, that if the Transferee is an airline (or other commercial operator of aircraft) or a corporation or other entity controlling, controlled by, or under common control with an airline or other commercial operator of aircraft, the consent of Lessee shall have been obtained. Upon any transfer permitted by this Section 15, except as otherwise expressly provided herein, each reference herein to the Owner Participant shall thereafter be deemed to be a reference to the Transferee, except that, without affecting the primary liability of the Transferee assumed pursuant to the agreements entered into in accordance with Section 15(a)(ii) hereof, the Owner Participant shall continue to be secondarily liable when it has provided a guaranty under the terms of this provision.

(v) If the Owner Participant proposes to transfer its interest hereunder pursuant to this Section 15, the Owner Participant shall give written notice to Lessee, Owner Trustee, the Indenture Trustee, and each Loan Participant specifying the name and address of the proposed Transferee and specifying the facts necessary to determine compliance with this Section 15. The Owner Participant shall pay all costs and expenses incurred by any of the parties hereto in effectuating such transfer.

(vi) The parties hereto agree that, upon any transfer of the Owner Participant's interest pursuant to this Section 15 in which the Owner Participant need not provide a guaranty, the Owner Participant shall be thereby released from all of its future obligations under the Operative Documents except for accrued obligations and those attributable to periods prior to such transfer.

(vii) The Loan Participants and Lessee shall have received such legal opinions as they may reasonably request with respect to the requirements of this Section 15.

Section 16. General Tax Indemnity

(a) Indemnitee Defined. For purposes of this Section 16, "Indemnitee" means the Owner Participant, the Indenture Trustee, the Estate, the Trust Estate, the Owner Trustee in its individual capacity and as Trustee, the Loan Participants, any holder of a Loan Certificate, and each of their respective successors, transferees, or assigns permitted under the terms of the Operative Documents, provided that such persons, shall to the extent they are not signatories to this Agreement, have expressly agreed in writing to be bound by the terms of this Section 16.

(b) Taxes Indemnified. Subject to the exclusions stated in subsection (c) below, Lessee agrees to indemnify, defend, and hold harmless each Indemnitee against all Taxes, howsoever imposed [whether imposed upon any Indemnitee, Lessee, all or any part of the Aircraft (or any interest in the Aircraft or part) or otherwise], by any federal, state, or local government or taxing authority in the United States, by any government or taxing authority of or in a foreign country or of or in a territory or possession of the United States, or by any international authority, that relate, in whole or in part to:

(i) the Aircraft, the Airframe, the Engines, the Parts (or any part of any of the foregoing or interest therein), any data, or any other thing delivered or to be delivered under the Operative Documents;

(ii) the manufacture, purchase, financing, refinancing, ownership, delivery, nondelivery, leasing, subleasing, assignment, possession, presence, use, operation, condition, maintenance, modification, alteration, repair, release, return, storage, transfer of title, sale, acceptance, rejection, or other disposition of or action or event with respect to the Aircraft, the Airframe, the Engines, the Parts, or any part of any of the foregoing or interest therein;

(iii) the rentals, interest, fees, proceeds, receipts, earnings, or any other income or other amounts paid (whether actual or deemed) arising from, in connection with or in respect of the purchase, financing, ownership, delivery, nondelivery, leasing, subleasing, assignment, possession, presence, use, operation, condition, maintenance, modification, alteration, repair, release, return, storage, transfer of title, sale, acceptance, rejection or other disposition of, or action or event with respect to, the Aircraft, the Airframe, the Engines, the Parts, or any part of any of the foregoing or interest therein;

(iv) the Loan Certificates, their issuance or acquisition, their modification or reissuance, or the payment of any amounts thereon;

(v) the property, or the income or other proceeds received with respect to the property, held by the Indenture Trustee under the Indenture; or

(vi) the Operative Documents or amendments or supplements thereto, their execution or the transactions and activities contemplated thereby or any actions taken pursuant thereto.

(c) Taxes Excluded. The indemnity provided for in Section 16(b) above shall not extend to any of the following:

(i) Taxes which have been included in Lessor's Cost;

(ii) in the case of the Owner Participant, taxes on, based on, or measured by, the gross income, gross receipts or net income, capital, franchises, excess profits, or conduct of business (other than taxes which are in the nature of sales or use taxes, license taxes, or property taxes) of such Indemnitee that are imposed by the United States of America or any state or local government or other domestic or foreign taxing authority (collectively, "Income Taxes"), other than "Covered Income Taxes" (as such term is defined below) provided that if as of the close of a calendar year, the cumulative Income Taxes (other than federal Income Taxes, Income Taxes imposed by state or local authorities in Florida or such other state where the Owner Participant's principal place of business is located and Covered Income Taxes) payable by the Owner Participant as a result of the transactions contemplated by the Operative Documents exceed the cumulative reductions in Income Taxes (other than reductions in Federal Income Taxes, Covered Income Taxes, and Income Taxes imposed by state or local authorities in Florida or such other state where the Owner

Participant's principal place of business is located) realized as a result of the transactions contemplated by the Operative Documents, Lessee shall pay such excess (as reduced by the payments previously made to the Owner Participant pursuant to this proviso) to the Owner Participant. All amounts calculated under the immediately preceding proviso shall include interest at the Overdue Rate from the date payment was made by either Lessee or the Owner Participant (or would have been made in the case of the Owner Participant, if not offset against a refund) and from the date a reduction in net Income Taxes was realized. In the event (a) Lessee shall indemnify Owner Participant for net cumulative Income Taxes pursuant to the immediately preceding proviso and (b) in a subsequent year Owner Participant shall realize a net cumulative reduction in Income Taxes (other than reductions in federal Income Taxes and Income Taxes imposed by state or local authorities in Florida or such other state where the Owner Participant's principal place of business is located and Covered Income Taxes) as a result of the transactions contemplated by the Operative Documents, then Owner Participant shall promptly pay Lessee an amount equal to the sum of (a) the amount of such net cumulative reduction in Income Taxes plus (b) the amount of any additional tax savings realized by the Owner Participant in respect to such payment, provided, however, that Owner Participant shall not be obligated to make any payment pursuant to this sentence if, and to the extent that, the amount of such payment would exceed (x) the aggregate amount of all prior payments by Lessee to the Owner Participant pursuant to the immediately preceding proviso less (y) the aggregate amount of all prior payments by Owner Participant to Lessee pursuant to this sentence. The Owner Participant shall in good faith make the computations provided for herein and shall provide Lessee with a written statement describing in reasonable detail the manner in which such computations were made. The provisions for payment and verification contained in paragraph (e) of this Section 16 shall apply to the computation in the immediately preceding proviso except that if Lessee requests verification, the accounting firm shall be selected by Lessee from the eight largest (in revenues) accounting firms in the United States (but not an accounting firm that regularly audits the financial statements of the Owner Participant (or the affiliated group of which it is a member) or Lessee (or the affiliated group of which it is a member) and the costs and expenses of verification by such accounting firm shall be borne equally by Lessee and the Owner Participant.

(iii) in the case of the Loan Participants and any holders of a Loan Certificate, but not the Indenture Trustee, and each of their respective successors, transferees, or assigns permitted under the terms of the Operative Documents, Taxes on, based on, or measured by income, receipts, capital, franchises, or conduct of business, other than such Taxes imposed by any taxing authority of any jurisdiction to the extent such Taxes exceed the amount that would have been imposed had the Aircraft never been operated to or used in such jurisdiction;

(iv) Taxes imposed against a transferee of a Loan Participant to the extent of the excess of such Taxes over the amount of such Taxes which would have been imposed had there not been a transfer by such original Loan Participant of any interest of such Loan Participant in the Loan Certificates;

(v) Taxes relating to the Aircraft for any period after the expiration or early termination of the Term of the Lease and return of the Aircraft by Lessee (for purposes of this clause [v] the Aircraft shall be considered to have been returned to Lessor if the Aircraft is being stored by Lessee for Lessor pursuant to Section 13[e] of the Lease), unless such Taxes are the result of events or conditions that occurred prior to such expiration or early termination (and return), and except that Taxes incurred in connection with the exercise of any remedies pursuant to Section 18 of the Lease following the occurrence of an Event of Default shall not be excluded from the indemnity provided for in Section 16(b) hereof;

(vi) as to the Indenture Trustee, Taxes payable by the Indenture Trustee on or measured by any compensation received or accrued by the Indenture Trustee for its services under the Indenture and Taxes imposed on the Owner Trustee with respect to fees or compensation for services rendered in its capacity as Trustee under the Trust Agreement;

(vii) Taxes which arise out of or are caused by the Indemnitee to which Lessee would otherwise be required to make an indemnity payment pursuant to this Section 16 engaging in actions other than those contemplated or permitted by or resulting from the Operative Documents;

(viii) Taxes which become payable by reason of any transfer by the Indemnitee to which Lessee would otherwise be required to make an indemnity payment pursuant to this Section 16 of all or any portion of its interest in the Aircraft, the Estate or the Loan Certificates or shares of stock in an Indemnitee (other than transfers which occur or result from the exercise of any rights under Sections 8, 9, 15 or 18 of the Lease, or any remedies under Section 11 of the Indenture);

(ix) Taxes for which Lessee is obligated to and in fact does, indemnify the Owner Participant under the Tax Indemnity Agreement; and

(x) Taxes arising out of a misrepresentation by any Loan Participant in Sections 8(c) and (d) hereof.

A "Covered Income Tax" shall mean an Income Tax (other than an Income Tax imposed by the U.S. Federal Government) imposed on an Indemnitee by any government or taxing authority (A) in whose jurisdiction the Indemnitee (including for this purpose all entities with which it is combined, integrated, or consolidated under the rules of such government or taxing authority for purposes of the Income Tax in question) did not engage in business, did not maintain an office or other place of business, and was not otherwise located, but the term "Covered Income Tax" shall include any Income Tax imposed by a jurisdiction in which the Indemnitee is deemed to engage in business, maintain an office, or be otherwise located, solely as a result of the operation of the Aircraft in such jurisdiction or the transactions contemplated by the Operative Documents or (B) in whose jurisdiction the Indemnitee did engage in business, or maintain an office or other place of business, or was otherwise located, if such circumstance was no factor in the imposition of such Tax.

(d) Computations. The amount Lessee shall be required to pay with respect to any Tax indemnified against under Section 16(b) shall be an amount sufficient to make the Indemnitee whole after deducting all taxes actually required to be paid by such Indemnitee with respect to such indemnity payment under the laws of any federal, state, or local government or taxing authority in the United States, or under the laws of any foreign government or any taxing authority or governmental subdivision of a foreign country. If an Indemnitee realizes a tax benefit by reason of any Taxes indemnified against by Lessee under this Section 16, or receives a refund (or would have received a refund if not offset against other Tax liabilities of such Indemnitee not indemnified by the Lessee hereunder) of such Taxes, such Indemnitee shall pay to Lessee an amount which is equal to the amount of such tax benefit or refund plus the actual amount of any further tax savings such Indemnitee realizes under the laws of any Federal, state or local government or taxing authority in the United States, or under the laws of any foreign government or any taxing authority or governmental Subdivision of a foreign country as a result of any payment pursuant to this sentence, and provided that such Indemnitee shall not be obligated to make any payment pursuant to this Section 16(d) to the extent that the amount of such payment would exceed (x) the aggregate amount of all prior payments by the Lessee to such Indemnitee pursuant to this Section 16 (in the case of the Owner Participant, other than payments with respect to "net cumulative reduction in Income Taxes" pursuant to clause (ii) of paragraph (b) of this Section 16) less (y) the aggregate amount of all prior payments by such Indemnitee to Lessee under this Section 16 (in the case of the Owner Participant, other than with respect to "net cumulative reductions in Income Taxes" pursuant to clause (ii) of paragraph (b) of this Section 16), provided further that any Taxes that are imposed on such Indemnitee as a result of the subsequent disallowance of such benefit, reduction, or refund shall be indemnifiable under this Section 16 and without regard to any exclusion. The verification procedures contained in paragraph (e) of this Section 16 shall apply to such computations. An Indemnitee shall not be required to pay an amount to Lessee pursuant to the preceding sentence if an Event of Default exists and is continuing, but this restriction shall cease to apply if, and when, the Event of Default ceases to continue.

(e) Procedures. Any amount payable to an Indemnitee pursuant to this Section 16 shall be paid within 30 days after receipt of a written demand therefor from such Indemnitee accompanied by a written statement describing in reasonable detail the basis for such indemnity and the computation of the amount so payable, provided that such amount need not be paid prior to the earlier of (i) the time such Taxes have been paid by the Indemnitee (or would have been paid by the Indemnitee if not offset against a refund) or (ii) in the case of amounts which are being contested pursuant to Section 16(f) hereof, the time such contest is finally resolved. Within 15 days following Lessee's receipt of the computation of the amount of the indemnity, Lessee may request that an independent public accounting firm of recognized national standing selected by the Indemnitee and reasonably acceptable to Lessee (provided that the independent public firm that regularly audits the financial statements of the Indemnitee (or the affiliated group of which it is a member) shall be deemed to be reasonably acceptable to the Lessee) (the "Independent Accountants") verify that such computations of the Indemnitee are mathematically accurate and based on reasonable assumptions and in conformity with the provisions of this Agreement. Any information provided to the Independent Accountants shall be provided for their confidential use. The Independent Accountants shall be requested to make its determination within 30 days. If the Independent Accountants shall determine that such computations are inaccurate or not based on reasonable assumptions, then such firm shall determine what it believes to be the appropriate computations. The computations of the Indemnitee or the Independent Accountants, whichever is applicable, shall be final, binding, and conclusive upon Lessee and the Indemnitee and Lessee shall have no right to inspect the books, records, tax returns, or other documents of or relating to the Indemnitee to verify such computations or for any other purpose. All fees and expenses payable under this Section 16(e) shall be borne by Lessee except that such fees shall be borne by the Indemnitee if the computations provided by the Independent Accountants are different from those provided by the Indemnitee (and the difference is in favor of the Lessee) and the difference is greater than the lesser of (i) 8% of the amount computed by the Indemnitee and (ii) $50,000. In case of any late payment of an amount due hereunder, the relevant party shall promptly pay interest in respect thereof at the Overdue Rate (computed on the basis of a 360-day year of twelve 30-day months) for the period from the date such amount was due to the date on which payment thereof is made.

(f) Contest. If a claim is made against an Indemnitee for Taxes with respect to which Lessee is liable for payment or indemnity hereunder, such Indemnitee shall within 30 days of receiving notice of such claim give Lessee notice in writing of such claim and shall furnish Lessee with copies of any requests for information it has received from taxing authorities relating to such Taxes with respect to which Lessee may be required to indemnify hereunder (but the failure to so notify or provide copies to Lessee shall not impair the Indemnitee 's right to indemnification pursuant to this Section 16, unless Lessee's right to effect a contest with respect to such claim for Taxes has been adversely affected by such failure). The Indemnitee shall in good faith, with due diligence and at Lessee's expense, if requested in writing by Lessee within (i) 30 days of Lessee's receipt of written notice of such claim from such Indemnitee or (ii) five days prior to the final date a filing or notice to the applicable taxing authority is required to effect a contest (whichever is earlier), contest (or in the reasonable discretion of such Indernnitee, permit Lessee to contest in the name of Lessee and in the sole discretion of such Indemnitee) permit Lessee to contest in the name of such Indemnitee, the validity, applicability, or amount of such Taxes by,

(i) resisting payment thereof if practical;

(ii) paying the same under protest if protest is necessary and proper;

(iii) if the payment be made, using reasonable efforts to obtain a refund thereof in appropriate administrative and judicial proceedings; or

(iv) taking such other action as is reasonably requested by Lessee from time to time.

Notwithstanding the foregoing provisions of this Section 16(f), such Indemnitee shall not be required to take any judicial action unless (I) the amount of the claim due shall be at least $10,000, (II) such Indemnitee determines in its good faith discretion that such proceedings (including, if applicable, resisting payment of a claim) do not involve any risk or danger of the sale, forfeiture, or loss of the Aircraft, the Airframe, or any Engine or of the perfection or priority of the Lien of the Indenture, or if there is such a risk, Lessee has provided to the Indemnitee a bond in amount, form, and substance, reasonably satisfactory to such Indemnitee and (III) Lessee shall have (A) agreed to pay such Indemnitee on demand all reasonable out-of-pocket costs and expenses which such Indemnitee may incur in connection with contesting such Taxes, including without limitation, (y) reasonable fees and expenses of attorneys and accountants and (z) the amount of any Tax, interest, penalty, or addition to tax which may ultimately be payable as the result of contesting such Taxes, (B) delivered to the Indemnitee a written acknowledgement of Lessee's obligation to indemnify fully such Indemnitee for such Taxes pursuant to this Agreement to the extent that the contest is not successful, (C) at its cost furnished the Indemnitee with a written opinion of independent counsel selected by Lessee and reasonably satisfactory to the Indemnitee, to the effect that a meritorious defense exists to such claim, (D) Lessee has paid all indemnities and other amounts due to such Indemnitee under any Operative Document, and (E) in the event the Indemnitee decides in its reasonable discretion after consultation with Lessee to pay the Tax prior to the contest, Lessee shall provide to the Indemnitee an interest-free loan in an amount equal to the Tax which the Indemnitee is required to pay. Notwithstanding the foregoing, (a) if any

Indemnitee shall, without the express written permission of Lessee, release, waive, or settle any claim which may be indemnifiable by Lessee pursuant to this Section 16, and which such Indemnitee is obligated to contest pursuant to this paragraph (f), Lessee's obligation to indemnify such Indemnitee with respect to such claim shall terminate, and (b) an Indemnitee may at any time decline to take further action with respect to the contest of any claim for a Tax, provided, however, that if Lessee has properly requested such contest pursuant to this Section 16(f), such Indemnitee shall waive its rights to any indemnity payment by Lessee which would otherwise be payable by Lessee pursuant to this Section 16(f) in respect to such claim.

(g) Refund. Upon receipt by an Indemnitee of a refund or credit of all or part of any Taxes which Lessee shall have paid for such Indemnitee or for which Lessee shall have reimbursed or indemnified such Indemnitee, such Indemnitee shall pay to Lessee an amount which, after subtraction of the amount of any further net tax savings, if any, realized by such Indemnitee as a result of the receipt thereof and payment under this paragraph, is equal to the amount of such refund and any interest received or credited by such Indemnitee on such refund; provided, however, that such amount shall not be payable (i) before such time as Lessee shall have made all payments or indemnities then due and payable to such Indemnitee under this Section 16 and under any other provision of the Operative Documents or (ii) to the extent that such amount would exceed (A) the amount of all prior payments (other than amounts attributable to interest) by Lessee to such Indemnitee with respect to such Taxes pursuant to this Section 16 less (B) the amounts of all prior payments (other than amounts attributable to interest) by such Indemnitee to Lessee with respect to such Taxes pursuant to this Section 16. Anything to the contrary notwithstanding, an Indemnitee shall not be obligated to make any payments to the Lessee hereunder if, and so long as, an Event of Default shall have occurred and be continuing, but this restriction shall cease to apply, if and when, the Event of Default ceases to continue.

(h) Reports and Returns. In case any report or return is required to be made with respect to any obligation of the Lessee under this Section 16, Lessee will either make such report or return in such manner as will show the ownership of the Aircraft in the Owner Participant and shall send a copy of the applicable portion of such report or return to the Indemnitee and the Owner Participant or will notify the Indemnitee of such requirement and make such report or return in such manner as shall be satisfactory to such Indemnitee and the Owner Participant, but the Owner Participant may (but shall be under no duty to) assume responsibility for the filing of such reports or return if such action is reasonable and in good faith.

(i) Withholding Taxes. All payments of Rent and of amounts payable on the Loan Certificates will be free and clear of all withholding taxes, and if any withholding taxes are required with respect to any such payments, Lessee shall pay an additional amount such that the net amount actually received by the appropriate Indemnitee will be equal to the amount that would be due absent such withholding. Any withholding tax paid by Lessee under the preceding sentence that is for the payment of any Tax not subject to indemnification under Section 16(b) hereof as a result of the exclusions in Section 16(c) hereof shall be promptly repaid to Lessee by the appropriate Indemnitee. Notwithstanding the foregoing, under no circumstances will Lessee be obligated to make any additional payments to the Owner Participant or Indenture Trustee for the account of any Loan Participant pursuant to this paragraph as a result of any United States withholding taxes imposed on interest payments with respect to any Loan Certificate that is held by a person that is not a "United States person" as defined in Section 7701(a)(30) of the Code.

(j) As to the Indenture Trustee. Notwithstanding any other provision hereof, Lessee agrees to indemnify the Indenture Trustee (and its successors, assigns, agents, and servants) to the full extent the Indenture Trustee and its successors, assigns, agents, and servants shall be entitled to indemnification from the Estate or any other person pursuant to Section 7 of the Indenture.

Section 17. General Indemnification and Waiver of Certain Claims

(a) Claims Defined. For the purposes of this Section 17, "Claims" shall mean any and all liabilities (including strict or absolute liability without fault in tort or otherwise), losses, damages, penalties, costs, actions, or suits and all legal proceedings whether civil or criminal, fines and other sanctions, which may be imposed on, incurred by, suffered by, or asserted against an Indemnified Person, as defined herein, and, except as otherwise expressly provided in this Section 17, shall include all reasonable costs, disbursements, and expenses (including legal fees and expenses) of an Indemnified Person in connection therewith or related.

(b) Indemnified Person Defined. For the purposes of this Section 17, "Indemnified Person" means the Owner Participant, the Owner Trustee in its individual capacity and as trustee, the Indenture Trustee, each Loan Participant, any holder of a Loan Certificate, the Estate, the Trust Estate, each of their directors, officers, employees, servants, and agents, and each of the successors, transferees, or assigns of any of them permitted under the terms of the Operative Documents, provided that such persons, shall to the extent they are not signatories to this Agreement, have expressly agreed in writing to be bound by the terms of this Section 17.

(c) Claims Indemnified. Subject to the exclusions stated in subsection (d) below, Lessee agrees to indemnify, defend, and hold harmless each Indemnified Person [except as noted in clause (iv) of this paragraph (c)] against Claims resulting from, arising out of, or related to:

(i) the operation, possession, use, non-use, maintenance, storage, overhaul, testing, or disposition of the Aircraft, Airframe, or any Engine, or any engine used in connection with the Airframe, or any part thereof by Lessee, any sublessee, or any other Person whatsoever, whether or not such operation, possession, use, non-use, maintenance, storage, overhaul, or testing is in compliance with the terms of the Lease, including, without limitation, Claims for death, personal injury or property damage, or other loss or harm to any Person whatsoever, including, without limitation, any passengers, shippers, or other persons wherever located, and Claims relating to any laws, rules, or regulations, including, without limitation, environmental control, noise and pollution laws, rules, or regulations;

(ii) the manufacture, design, sale, purchase, acceptance, rejection, delivery, condition, repair, modification, servicing, rebuilding, airworthiness, performance, nondelivery, sublease, merchantability, fitness for use, substitution, or replacement of the Airframe, any Engine or Part under the Lease, or other transfer of use or possession of the Aircraft, Airframe, Engine or Part, and registration of the Aircraft, Airframe or any Engine, including, without limitation, latent and other defects, whether or not discoverable, and patent, trademark, or copyright infringement;

(iii) any breach of or failure to perform or observe, or any other noncompliance with, any covenant or agreement to be performed, or other obligation of Lessee under any of the Operative Documents, or the falsity or inaccuracy of any representation or warranty of Lessee in any of the Operative Documents other than representations and warranties in the Tax Indemnity Agreement; and

(iv) as to claims of the Loan Participants only, any failure of the Owner Trustee to make a filing which it is required to make pursuant to Section 6(d) of the Lease or to assist Lessee in making a filing as required by Section 12(a) hereof that results in loss of perfection of the first security interest and continuance of the first mortgage lien created by the Indenture on all or any part of the Estate or of any security interest that may be claimed to have been created by the Lease.

(d) Claims Excluded. The following are excluded from Lessee s agreement to indemnify under this Section 17:

(i) Claims attributable to acts or events occurring after the Term (except during the exercise of remedies pursuant to Section 18 of the Lease), or, if the Aircraft is returned at a later date pursuant to Section 13 of the Lease, acts or events occurring after such return, or if Aircraft is stored pursuant to Section 13(e) of the Lease or overhauled pursuant to Section 13(f) of the Lease, acts or events occurring during such period of storage or overhaul;

(ii) Claims which are Taxes, whether or not Lessee is required to Indemnify therefor under Section 16 hereof;

(iii) With respect to any particular Indemnified Person, Claims attributable to the gross negligence or willful misconduct of, or to the breach of any contractual undertaking by, such Indemnified Person;

(iv) Claims attributable to any transfer by an Indemnified Person of all or any portion of its interest in the Aircraft, the Estate, the Trust Estate, or the Loan Certificates or shares of stock in an Indemnified Person (other than transfers which occur in connection with the exercise of any rights under Sections 8, 9, 15, or 18 of the Lease, or any remedies under Section 11 of the Indenture or exercise of rights under Section 4 of the Indenture).

(e) Insured Claims. In the case of any Claim indemnified by Lessee hereunder which is covered by a policy of insurance maintained by Lessee pursuant to Section 10 of the Lease, each Indemnified Person agrees to cooperate with the insurers in the exercise of their rights to investigate, defend, or compromise such Claim as may be required to retain the benefits of such insurance with respect to such Claim.

(f) Claims Procedure. An Indemnified Person shall promptly notify Lessee of any Claim as to which indemnification is sought. Subject to the rights of insurers under policies of insurance maintained pursuant to Section 10 of the Lease, Lessee shall have the right to investigate, and the right in its sole discretion to defend or compromise any Claim for which indemnification is sought under this Section 17, and the Indemnified Person shall cooperate with all reasonable requests of Lessee in connection therewith; provided that at such time no Event of Default shall have occurred and be continuing. Where Lessee or the insurers under a policy of insurance maintained by Lessee undertake the defense of an Indemnified Person with respect to a Claim, no additional legal fees or expenses of such Indemnified Person in connection with the defense of such Claim shall be indemnified hereunder unless such fees or expenses were incurred at the request of Lessee or such insurers. Subject to the requirements of any policy of insurance, an Indemnified Person may participate at its own expense in any judicial proceeding controlled by Lessee pursuant to the preceding provisions, provided that such party's participation does not, in the opinion of the independent counsel appointed by Lessee or its insurers to conduct such proceedings, interfere with such control; and such participation shall not constitute a waiver of the indemnification provided in this Section 17. Nothing contained in this Section 17(f) shall be deemed to require an Indemnified Person to contest any Claim or to assume responsibility for or control of any judicial proceeding with respect thereto.

(g) Subrogation. To the extent that a Claim indemnified by Lessee under this Section 17 is in fact paid in full by Lessee and/or an insurer under a policy of insurance maintained by Lessee pursuant to Section 10 of the Lease, Lessee and/or such insurer as the case may be shall be subrogated to the rights and remedies of the Indemnified Person on whose behalf such Claim was paid with respect to the transaction or event giving rise to such Claim. Should an Indemnified Person receive any refund, in whole or in part, with respect to any Claim paid by Lessee hereunder, it shall promptly pay the amount refunded (but not an amount in excess of the amount Lessee has paid in respect of such claim) over to Lessee.

(h) Indemnification on After-Tax Basis. In the event Lessee is required to indemnify any Indemnified Person under this Section 17, Lessee shall pay to such Indemnified Person an amount which, after deduction of all taxes actually required to be paid by such Indemnified Person in respect of the receipt of such amount under the applicable laws of any government or taxing jurisdiction (after giving credit for any saving in respect of any such taxes by reason of deductions, credits, or allowances related to the payment of the Claim indemnified against and the payment of related taxes), shall be equal to the amount of the indemnification required.

(i) Waiver of Certain Claims. Lessee hereby waives and releases any Claim now or hereafter existing against any Indemnified Person arising out of death or personal injury to personnel of the Lessee, loss or damage to property of Lessee, or the loss of use of any property of Lessee, which may result from or arise out of the condition, use, or operation of the Aircraft during the Term, including without limitation any latent or patent defect whether or not discoverable.

(j) As to the Indenture Trustee. Notwithstanding any other provision hereof, Lessee agrees to indemnify the Indenture Trustee against all matters covered by Section 7 of the Indenture.

(k) Conflicting Provisions. The general indemnification provisions of this Section 17 are not intended to waive or supersede any specific provisions of the Lease, this Agreement, or any Other Operative Document to the extent such provisions apply to any Claim.

Section 18. Reoptimization and Adjustment of Debt-Equity Ratio

(a) Terms. In the event of a Tax Law Change requiring an adjustment to Basic Rent pursuant to Section 3(e) of the Lease, the Owner Participant may or, at the request of Lessee, shall (x) reoptimize the rent and debt payment structures and (y) increase but not decrease the ratio of the debt evidenced by the Loan Certificates to the Owner Participant's investment in the Trust Estate. Lessee and the Owner Participant shall consult promptly after the occurrence of a Tax Law Change requiring a Rent adjustment. If the Owner Participant elects, or if Lessee requests the Owner Participant to elect, to make such adjustments to the debt and equity structure, the Owner Participant shall include notice of such election in the schedule revisions it provides to the other parties pursuant to Section 3(e) of the Lease, and shall provide such notice not later than June 1, XXXX. The notice shall include the proposed decrease in the Owner Participant's Percentage Commitment and Commitment, the proposed increase in each Loan Participant's Percentage Commitment and Commitment (the "Additional Participation" of each Loan Participant), the revised debt amortization schedule [which shall be in compliance with the requirements set forth in last sentence of this Section 18(a)], and a statement summarizing, for the benefit of the Loan Participants, why such adjustments as provided for in this Section 18(a) reduce the Basic Rent otherwise required to be paid as a result of such Tax Law Change. The parties shall agree, subject to the procedures provided in Section 3(e)(ii) of the Lease, upon the adjustments to the Commitments and revised schedules by July 1, XXXX. The restructuring contemplated hereby shall occur on or before September 1, XXXX or such earlier date as agreed upon by the parties, (the "Reoptimization Closing Date"). Each Loan Participant shall pay its Additional Participation to the Owner Trustee on the Reoptimization Closing Date, as an increased participation in Lessor's Cost, which payment shall be retained by the Owner Trustee and shall not be part of the Estate or subject to the Lien of the Indenture. In exchange therefore the Owner Trustee shall issue Additional Loan Certificates in respect to the Aircraft to each Loan Participant in accordance with Section 2(b)(ii) of the Indenture and at the Additional Fixed Rate, as provided therein. The Basic Rent, Termination Value, and Stipulated Loss Values shall be adjusted in accordance with Section 3(e) of the Lease, and so as to provide for the timely amortization of the Loan Certificates in accordance with the revised amortization schedule. Each Loan Participant signing this Agreement expressly agrees, for the benefit of Lessee, to provide its Additional Participation in accordance with this Section 18, regardless of whether it has transferred any Loan Certificates under the Indenture prior to the Reoptimization Closing Date, provided that: (i) the aggregate Commitments of the Loan Participants, including their Additional Participations shall not exceed the lesser of (A) 65% of Lessor's Cost of the Aircraft and (B) $20,000,000.00 and the Additional Commitment of each Loan Participant shall be in the same proportion as the original principal amount of such Loan Participant's initial Loan Certificates bear to the aggregate original principal amount of Loan Certificates issued on the Delivery Date; (ii) the average life of the debt evidenced by the Series A Loan Certificates, including the Additional Loan Certificates related to such series, shall not be less than 7.5 years or greater than 8.5 years; (iii) the average life of the debt evidenced by the Series B Loan Certificates, including the Additional Loan Certificates related to such series, shall not be less than 17.5 years or greater than 18.5 years; (iv) the maturity of the Series A and Series B Loan Certificates shall not be extended by such Additional Participations; and (v) the Commitments of the Loan Participants shall not be adjusted pursuant to this Section 18(a) more than once.

(b) Conditions. The reoptimization and adjustment of the debt-equity ratio provided for in this Section shall be subject to the following conditions as of the Reoptimization Closing Date:

(i) payment in full of all Rent then due and owing under this Agreement and the other Operative Documents;

(ii) no Default, Event of Default, or Event of Acceleration shall have occurred and be continuing under the Lease or the Indenture, as the case may be;

(iii) no material adverse change shall have occurred in the business, operations, or financial condition of Lessee since December 31, XXXX;

(iv) Lessee, the Owner Trustee, the Indenture Trustee, and each Participant hereto shall have received such opinions of counsel, including, without limitation, opinions as to tax matters and to Section 1110 of the Bankruptcy Code, certificates and other documents as it may reasonably request, each in form and substance satisfactory to such person;

(v) all necessary authorizations, approvals, and consents shall have been obtained;

(vi) the Assumed Tax Benefits shall be modified to reflect the Tax Law Change that gave rise to the adjustment to Basic Rent; and

(vii) the documents implementing the adjustments made pursuant to this Section 18 shall be satisfactory in form and substance to the parties and amendments to the Operative Documents shall be filed, as appropriate, with the FAA.

The Lessee shall pay all costs and expenses of each party to the Participation Agreement, including the reasonable fees and expenses of their respective counsel, incurred in connection with such restructuring, whether or not the transaction is consummated.

Section 19. [Intentionally omitted.]

Section 20. Lessee's Right of Quiet Enjoyment

Each party to this Agreement acknowledges notice of, and consents in all respects to, the terms of the Lease, and expressly, severally and as to its own actions only, agrees that, notwithstanding any other provision of any of the Operative Documents, so long as Lessee is in compliance with its obligations under the Lease (including applicable grace periods) and no Event of Default has occurred and is continuing (except within the cure periods permitted by the Operative Documents), it shall not take or cause to be taken any action contrary to Lessee's rights under the Lease, including the right to possession and use of the Aircraft.

Section 21. Limitations of Liability of Owner Trustee

(a) It is expressly understood and agreed by and among the Owner Trustee, the Loan Participants, the Owner Participant, Lessee, and the Indenture Trustee that except as otherwise expressly provided herein, (i) this Participation Agreement is executed and delivered by the Owner Trustee not in its individual capacity but solely as trustee under the Trust Agreement in the exercise of the power and authority conferred and vested in it as such Owner Trustee, (ii) each of the representations, undertakings, and agreements made herein by the Owner Trustee are not personal representations, undertakings, and agreements, but are binding only on the Trust Estate and the Owner Trustee, as trustee, (iii) actions to be taken by the Owner Trustee pursuant to its obligations hereunder may, in certain instances, be taken by the Owner Trustee only upon specific authority of the Owner Participant, (iv) nothing herein contained shall be construed as creating any liability of the Owner Trustee, in its individual capacity, or any incorporator or any past, present, or future subscriber to the capital stock of, or stockholder, officer, or director of, the Owner Trustee in its individual capacity to perform any covenant either express or implied contained herein, all such liability, if any, being expressly waived by the Loan Participant, the Owner Participant, Lessee, and the Indenture Trustee and by any Person claiming by, through, or under them, and (v) so far as the Owner Trustee in its individual capacity is concerned, the Loan Participant, the Owner Participant, Lessee, the Indenture Trustee and any Person claiming by, through or under them shall look solely to the Trust

Estate and the Estate for the performance of any obligation under any of the instruments referred to herein; provided, however, that nothing in this Section shall be construed to limit in scope or substance the liability of the Owner Trustee (A) in its individual capacity to the Owner Participant under the Trust Agreement, (B) in respect of the representations, warranties, and agreements of the Owner Trustee in its individual capacity as set forth herein (including, without limitation, Section 7A hereof) or in any other Operative Document to which it is a party, and (C) in its individual capacity and as Owner Trustee for the consequences of its own gross negligence or willful misconduct.

Section 22. Miscellaneous

(a) Notices. Unless otherwise specifically provided herein, all notices required or permitted by the terms hereof shall be in writing. Any written notice shall become effective when received. Any written notice shall either be mailed, certified or registered mail, return receipt requested with proper postage for airmail prepaid, or sent in the form of a telex, telegram, or telecopy, or by overnight delivery service or delivered by hand. Any written notice shall be directed (i) to Lessee, the Participants, the Owner Trustee or the Indenture Trustee, to the respective addresses set forth in Schedule 2 hereto, or to such other address or telex or telecopy number as any such party may designate by notice given to the other parties to this Agreement or (ii) if to any subsequent holder of a Loan Certificate at such address as such holder shall have furnished by notice to the parties hereto. Notwithstanding any of the provisions hereof or of any other Operative Document, Lessee shall not be required to give notice to any holder of a Loan Certificate unless Lessee shall have first received notice of the identity of such holder and the address to which notices are to be sent.

(b) Counterparts. This Agreement may be executed by the parties hereto in separate Counterparts, each of which when so executed and delivered shall be an original, but all such counterparts shall together constitute but one and the same instrument.

(c) Amendments. Neither this Agreement nor any of the terms hereof may be terminated, amended, supplemented, waived, or modified orally, but only by an instrument in writing signed by the party against which the enforcement of the termination, amendment, supplement, waiver, or modification is sought.

(d) Headings. The table of contents and headings of the various sections of this Agreement are for convenience of reference only and shall not modify, define, expand, or limit any of the terms or provisions hereof.

(e) Governing Law. This Agreement shall in all respects be governed by, and construed in accordance with, the laws of the State of ________, including all matters of construction, validity, and performance. This Agreement is being delivered in the State of ________.

(f) Benefit and Binding Effect. The terms of this Agreement shall be binding upon, and shall inure to the benefit of, Lessee and its permitted Successors and assigns, each Participant and its successors and permitted assigns, including, without limitation, each holder of a Loan Certificate, the Owner Trustee and its successors as Owner Trustee under Trust Agreement, the Indenture Trustee and its successors as Indenture Trustee under the Indenture.

Section 23. Survival of Certain Obligations Under this Agreement

The agreements and indemnities contained in Sections 14, 16, and 17 hereof shall survive the termination of this Agreement and the Lease and the repayment of the Loan Certificates. Notwithstanding any other provision of any of the Operative Documents, all of Lessee's other obligations hereunder shall, if not previously terminated, terminate at the end of the Term.

IN WITNESS WHEREOF, the parties hereto have caused this Agreement to be duly executed by their respective officers thereunto duly authorized as of the day and year first above written.

AATX LIFE INSURANCE COMPANY, Loan Participant

By: ______________________________

Title: ______________________________

COMMONWEALTH LIFE INSURANCE COMPANY, Loan Participant

By: ______________________________

Title: ______________________________

ABLE RE-INSURANCE COMPANY, Loan Participant

By: ______________________________

Title: ______________________________

PEACHTREE SECURITY LIFE INSURANCE COMPANY, Loan Participant

By: ______________________________

Title: ______________________________

SYNX LIFE ASSURANCE COMPANY OF CANADA (U.S.), Loan Participant

By: ______________________________

Title: ______________________________

SYNX LIFE ASSURANCE COMPANY OF CANADA, Loan Participant

By: ______________________________

Title: ______________________________

STATE OF NEW YORK INVESTMENT BOARD, Loan Participant

By: ______________________________

Title: ______________________________

MARTIN TRUST COMPANY, Owner Trustee, not in its individual capacity except as other wise expressly provided herein.

By: ______________________________

Title: ______________________________

THE RHODE ISLAND BANK AND TRUST COMPANY, NATIONAL ASSOCIATION, Indenture Trustee

By: ______________________________

Title: ______________________________

PBC LEASING CORPORATION, Owner Participant

By: ______________________________

Title: ______________________________

Appendix A

Planet Aviation Inc., Lease Financing of One New Blackhawk 555-300 Aircraft Bearing

Registration No. N777P

Definitions Relating to the Participation Agreement, Lease, Indenture, Trust Agreement, Tax Indemnity Agreement and Assignment, Dated as of September 15, XXXX, and Supplements Thereto

The definitions stated herein shall apply equally to both the singular and plural forms of the terms defined.

"Additional Fixed Rate" means the rate per annum (based on a 360-day year consisting of twelve 30-day months) equal to the sum of 175 basis points with respect to the Series A Loan Certificates and 200 basis points with respect to the Series B Certificates plus the yield to maturity on the hypothetical U.S. Treasury Note due May, XXXX referred to in Section 2(k) of the Indenture with respect to the Series A Loan Certificates and on the hypothetical U.S. Treasury Note due February, XXXX referred to in Section 2(k) of the Indenture with respect to the Series B Loan Certificates, in each case determined at the close of business on the fifth Business Day prior to the Reoptimization Closing Date by reference to the "ask" price published in *The Wall Street Journal*.

"Additional Loan Certificates" means Loan Certificates issued by the Owner Participant pursuant to Section 2(b)(ii) of the Indenture to each Loan Participant, in an amount equal to such Loan Participant's Additional Participation, bearing interest at the rate and payable as provided in said Section 2(b)(ii).

"Additional Participation" of each Loan Participant means the amount by which such Loan Participant's initial Commitment is increased pursuant to Section 18 of the Participation Agreement.

"Agreement", "this Agreement", "herein", "hereby", or other like terms shall mean the Operative Document in which such term is used, unless the context indicates otherwise.

"Aircraft" means the Airframe to be delivered and leased under the Lease (or any airframe substituted therefore pursuant to Section 9 of the Lease) together with the two Engines delivered in connection therewith as indicated in the lease Supplement covering the Aircraft (or any Engine substituted for any of said Engines pursuant to Section 9 of the Lease), whether or not any of such initial or substitute Engines may from time to time be installed on the Airframe or may be installed on any other airframe or on any other aircraft.

"Airframe means (A) the Blackhawk 555-300 aircraft bearing Registration No. N777P (except the Engines or engines from time to time installed thereon) to be delivered and leased under the Lease, identified by manufacturer's serial number and registration number in a Lease Supplement; and (B) except as otherwise provided in Section 8 of the

Lease, any and all Parts so long as the same shall be incorporated or installed in or attached to the Airframe, or so long as title thereto shall remain vested in Lessor in accordance with the terms of Section 8 of the Lease, after removal from the Airframe.

"Applicable Law" means all applicable laws, treaties, judgments, decrees, injunctions, writs, and orders of any court, governmental agency, or authority and rules, regulations, orders, directives, licenses, and permits of any governmental body, instrumentality, agency, or authority.

"Assignment" means the Assignment of Rights under Purchase Agreement dated as of September 15, XXXX between the Lessee and the Owner Trustee in substantially the form of Exhibit I to the Participation Agreement, as the same may be amended or supplemented from time to time pursuant to the terms thereof, together with the Consent and Agreement executed by the Manufacturer substantially in the form attached thereto.

"Assumed Tax Benefits" means the Owner Participant's assumed tax benefits as set forth in Section 1 of the Tax Indemnity Agreement.

"Basic Rent" means the rent payable on Basic Rent Payment Dates throughout the Basic Term for the Aircraft pursuant to Section 3(c) of the Lease, and rent payable during any Renewal Term pursuant to Section 14(a) of the Lease.

"Basic Rent Payment Date" means each January 2.

"Basic Tax Assumptions" means all of the tax assumptions stated in Section 1 of the Tax Indemnity Agreement.

"Basic Term" has the meaning specified in Section 3(a) of the Lease.

"Bills of Sale" means, collectively (with respect to initially delivered Aircraft only and not with respect to Replacement Aircraft), (i) the FAA Bill of Sale for the Aircraft and (ii) Lessee's Bill of Sale for the Aircraft.

"Business Day" means any day other than a Saturday, Sunday, or day on which commercial banking institutions in the cities in which the principal office of the Indenture Trustee (as long as the Indenture has not been discharged), the Owner Participant or Lessee are authorized by law to be closed.

"Certificated Air Carrier" means a United States "air carrier" within the meaning of the Federal Aviation Act, operating pursuant to a certificate issued under Section 401 of such Act, or a carrier of comparable status under any successor law or provision.

"Code" means the United States Internal Revenue Code of 1954, as amended from time to time, or any similar legislation of the United States enacted to supersede, amend, or supplement such Code and any reference to a provision or provisions of the Code shall also mean and refer to any successor provisions, however designated or distributed.

"Commitment" of each Loan Participant means the amount of the loan required to be made by such Loan Participant pursuant to Section 2(a) of the Participation Agreement; "Commitment" of the Owner Participant means the amount of the equity investment required to be made by the Owner Participant pursuant to Section 2(a) of the Participation Agreement.

"Consent and Agreement" means the Consent and Agreement dated as of September 15, XXXX executed by the Manufacturer in substantially the form contained in Exhibit I to the Participation Agreement.

"Default" means an event which but for the giving of notice or the lapse of time or both would constitute an Event of Default.

"Delivery Date" means the date the Aircraft is delivered to, and accepted by, Lessor pursuant to Section 3 of the Participation Agreement.

"Department of Transportation" means the United States Department of Transportation and any agency or instrumentality of the United States Government succeeding to its functions.

"Engine" means: (A) each of the two CFM International 56-3-B1 engines listed by manufacturer's serial number in a Lease Supplement relating to the Airframe covered by such Lease Supplement, whether or not from time to time thereafter installed on such Airframe or installed on any other aircraft; (B) any engine that may from time to time be substituted, pursuant to Sections 6 or 9 of the Lease, for such Engine; and (C) except as otherwise provided in Section 8 of the Lease, any and all Parts (other than Engines or engines) incorporated or installed in or attached thereto or any and all Parts removed therefrom so long as title thereto shall remain vested in Lessor in accordance with the terms of Section 8 of the Lease after removal from such Engine. The term "Engines" means, as of any date of determination, all Engines then leased under the lease.

"ERISA" means the Employee Retirement Income Security Act of 1974, as amended.

"Estate" means all estate, right, title, and interest of the Indenture Trustee in and to the Aircraft, the Lease, the Participation Agreement, Subleases, the Purchase Agreement, and the Assignment including all amounts of Rent, insurance proceeds, proceeds from requisition, and other payments of any kind for or with respect to the Aircraft. The Estate includes the properties referred to in the Granting Clauses of the Indenture, but excludes the Excepted Property.

"Event of Acceleration" has the meaning given in Section 12(a) of the Indenture.

"Event of Default" has the meaning given in Section 17 of the Lease.

"Event of Loss" with respect to the Aircraft, Airframe, or any Engine means any of the following events with respect to such property:

(a) destruction, damage beyond repair, or rendition of such property permanently unfit for normal use;

(b) any event that results in an insurance settlement on the basis of an actual or constructive total loss;

(c) theft or disappearance for a period in excess of 60 days;

(d) with respect to the Aircraft or Airframe, (i) the condemnation, confiscation, requisition, or taking of title or (ii) the condemnation, confiscation, requisition, or taking of use (A) for a period in excess of 90 consecutive days by any foreign government or instrumentality or agency thereof, or (B) for a period in excess of 12 consecutive months by the United States government or any agency or instrumentality thereof or, in the case of either clause (A) or (B), for a period that extends beyond the end of the Term; or

(e) with respect to an Engine, the requisition for use by any government, and any divestiture of title deemed an Event of Loss pursuant to Section 6 of the Lease.

(f) as a result of any rule, regulation, order or other action by the FAA, or other governmental body having jurisdiction, the use of the Aircraft in the normal course of air transportation of persons shall have been prohibited for a period of not less than six consecutive months, unless Lessee, prior to the expiration of such six-month period, shall have undertaken and shall be diligently carrying forward all steps which are necessary to permit the normal use of the Aircraft, or, in any event, if such use shall have been prohibited for a period of 18 consecutive months.

(g) with respect to the Aircraft or Airframe, the Aircraft or Airframe has been subleased to a Permitted Foreign Air Carrier and Lessee is unable to obtain return of the Aircraft or Airframe (i) within 60 days after the terms of the Sublease require it to be returned to Lessee following a termination of the Sublease or (ii) as a result of a condemnation, confiscation, requisition, or taking of title to the Aircraft by the home government of the Permitted Foreign Air Carrier.

An Event of Loss with respect to the Aircraft shall be deemed to have occurred if an Event of Loss has occurred with respect to the Airframe of the Aircraft.

"Excepted Property" means (i) all public liability insurance and any proceeds thereof payable as a result of claims paid or losses suffered by the Owner Participant, (ii) proceeds of permitted insurance separately maintained by and for the benefit of the Owner Participant, so long as the separate maintenance of such insurance does not reduce the coverage or amounts payable under any insurance constituting a part of the Estate, (iii) any indemnity or other amount payable in favor of the Owner Participant pursuant to the Tax Indemnity Agreement and Sections 16 and 17 of the Participation Agreement, (iv) the rights of the Owner Participant to enforce payment of any of the foregoing amounts, (v) the rights of the Owner Participant to compromise or waive any such right or to modify, amend, or waive any provision conferring any such right, and (vi) all proceeds of the foregoing.

"FAA" means the United States Federal Aviation Administration, the Administrator thereof, and any agency or instrumentality of the United States government succeeding to their functions.

"FAA Bill of Sale" means a bill of sale for the Aircraft or Replacement Aircraft on AC Form 8050–2 or such other form as may be approved by the FAA on the Delivery Date for the Aircraft or Replacement Closing Date for each Replacement Aircraft executed by Lessee in favor of the Owner Trustee and dated the Delivery Date of each such Aircraft, or by the owner of such Replacement Aircraft in favor of the Owner Trustee and dated the Replacement Closing Date for each such Replacement Aircraft, as the case may be.

"Fair Market Sales Value" or "Fair Market Rental Value" of the Airframe or any Engine shall mean the value which would be obtained in an arms-length transaction between an informed and willing lessee-user or buyer-user (other than a lessee currently in possession or a used equipment dealer) under no compulsion to lease or buy, as the case may be, and an informed and willing lessor or seller, as the case may be, under no compulsion to lease or sell, as the same shall be specified by agreement between Lessor and Lessee or, if not agreed to by Lessor and Lessee within a period of 15 days after either party requests a determination, then as specified in an appraisal mutually agreed to by two recognized independent aircraft appraisers, one of which shall be appointed by Lessor and the other of which shall be appointed by Lessee, or, if such appraisers cannot agree on such appraisal, an appraisal arrived at by a third independent recognized appraiser chosen by the mutual consent of the two aircraft appraisers. If either party should fail to appoint an appraiser within 30 days (or 10 days in the case of an appraisal pursuant to Section 18 of the Lease) of receiving notice of the appointment of an appraiser by the other party, then such appraisal shall be made by the appraiser appointed by the first party. If the two appraisers cannot agree on such appraisal and fail to appoint a third independent recognized aircraft appraiser within 30 days after the appointment of the second appraiser, then either party may apply to the American Arbitration Association, to make such appointment. In making the appraisal, it will be assumed that the Aircraft is in the condition and overhaul status in which it is required to be returned to Lessor pursuant to Section 13 of the Lease and that Lessee has removed all Parts which it is entitled to remove pursuant to Section 8 of the Lease; provided, however, that an appraisal for purposes of Section 18 of the Lease will be on an "as-is, where-is" basis. Except as otherwise expressly provided in the Lease, the appraisal costs will be shared equally by Lessor and Lessee.

"Federal Aviation Act" means the Federal Aviation Act of 1958, as amended, as in effect on September 15, XXXX, or any subsequent legislation that amends, supplements, or supersedes the Federal Aviation Act.

"Fixed Rate" means 9.5% per annum based on a 360-day year consisting of twelve 30-day months.

"Indemnified Person" has the meaning given in Section 17 of the Participation Agreement.

"Indemnitee" has the meaning specified in Section 16 of the Participation Agreement.

"Indenture" means the Trust Indenture and Security Agreement dated as of September 15, XXXX between the Owner Trustee and the Indenture Trustee, in substantially the form of Exhibit III to the Participation Agreement, as the same may be modified or supplemented from time to time pursuant to the terms thereof.

"Indenture Supplement" means any Trust Indenture Supplement substantially in the form of Exhibit A to the Indenture, which shall describe with particularity the Aircraft owned by the Owner Trustee and leased to Lessee by reference to the Lease Supplement executed and delivered pursuant to the Lease with respect to such Aircraft and which, pursuant to the Granting Clauses of the Indenture, shall create a first mortgage on such Aircraft and the Engines which are part of such Aircraft and assign and pledge such Lease Supplement to the Indenture Trustee as part of the Estate.

"Indenture Trustee" means The Rhode Island Bank and Trust Company, National Association, a national banking association, and its successors under the Indenture.

"Independent Aircraft Appraisal" means a written report by an independent aircraft consultant of national recognized standing, which is experienced in appraising used aircraft and is familiar with maintenance standards generally, which report states that such appraiser has inspected the Aircraft and Engines in question, has reviewed the records relating thereto and has read the maintenance requirements of the Lease.

"Interim Rent" means the rent payable for the Aircraft pursuant to Section 3(b) of the Lease during the Interim Term.

"Interim Term" has the meaning given in Section 3(a) of the Lease.

"Lease" means the Lease Agreement dated as of September 15, XXXX between Lessor and Lessee, in substantially the form of Exhibit IV to the Participation Agreement, as the same may be modified or supplemented from time to time pursuant to the terms thereof. The term "Lease" shall also include each Lease Supplement entered into pursuant to the terms of the Lease.

"Lease Supplement" means any Lease Supplement, substantially in the form of Exhibit A to the Lease, entered into between Lessor and Lessee for the purpose of leasing the Aircraft, under and pursuant to the terms of the Lease, including any amendment thereto entered into subsequent to the Delivery Date for such Aircraft.

"Lessee" means Planet Aviation, Inc., a New Jersey corporation, and its permitted successors and assigns.

"Lessee's Bill of Sale" means a full warranty bill of sale for the Aircraft executed by Lessee in favor of the Owner Trustee and dated the Delivery Date of the Aircraft.

"Lessor" means the Owner Trustee and its successors and permitted assigns.

"Lessor's Cost" means $28,000,000.

"Lessor's Liens" means any Liens arising as a result of (i) claims against or affecting Lessor in its individual capacity or as Owner Trustee or the Owner Participant not related to the transactions contemplated by the Operative Documents, or (ii) acts or omissions of Lessor, in its individual capacity or as Owner Trustee, or the Owner Participant not related to the transactions contemplated by the Operative Documents or not contemplated by the Operative Documents, or (iii) Taxes imposed against Lessor, in its individual capacity or as Owner Trustee, the Owner Participant which Lessee has not agreed to indemnify against pursuant to the Participation Agreement or the Tax Indemnity Agreement, or (iv) claims against Lessor, in its individual capacity or as Owner Trustee, or the Owner Participant arising out of the voluntary transfer (without the consent of Lessee and, if the Indenture has not been discharged, the Indenture Trustee) of all or any part of its interest in any Aircraft, other than a transfer pursuant to Sections 9, 15, or 18 of the Lease, or (v) liens provided for in the last sentence of Section 3(h) of the Lease with regard to any outstanding Reimbursement Amount, as defined therein.

"Lien" means any mortgage, pledge, lien, charge, encumbrance, lease, exercise of rights, or security interest.

"Loan Certificates" shall mean the Series A Loan Certificates and the Series B Loan Certificates.

"Loan Participants" means AATX Life Insurance Company, a Rhode Island corporation; ABLE Re-Insurance Company, a Delaware corporation; Cooper Life Insurance Company, a Delaware corporation; Peachtree Security Life Insurance Company, a New Jersey corporation; Synx Life Assurance Company of Canada (U.S.), a Delaware corporation; Synx Life Assurance Company of Canada, a Canadian corporation; and State of New York Investment Board, an independent state agency of the State of New York; and their respective successors and assigns, including any subsequent holder of a Loan Certificate from time to time outstanding under the Indenture.

"Loss Payment Date" means each date listed in the column entitled "Loss Payment Date" in Exhibit B to the Lease.

"Majority in Interest of Holders" as of a particular date of determination shall mean the holders of more than 66 2/3% in aggregate unpaid principal amount of all Loan Certificates outstanding as of such date, provided, however, that for purposes of Section 12(a) of the Indenture, and for the purposes of directing the Indenture Trustee to exercise any of the rights and powers and pursue any of the remedies pursuant to Section 12(b) of the Indenture or Section 18 of the Lease, "Majority in Interest of Holders" shall mean the holders of more than 50% in aggregate unpaid principal amount of all Loan Certificates at the time outstanding, provided, further, that there shall be excluded from the foregoing calculations any Loan Certificates held by Lessee, the Owner Trustee, the Owner Participant, or any affiliate of any of the foregoing (unless all Loan Certificates then outstanding are held by Lessee, the Owner Trustee, the Owner Participant, or any affiliate of the foregoing).

"Manufacturer" means The Blackhawk Company, a Delaware corporation, and its successors and assigns.

"Mortgaged Property" means all of the properties, rights, and privileges subjected or intended to be subjected to the Lien of the Indenture.

"Net Economic Return" means the Owner Participant's after-tax rate of return on investment computed using the multiple investment sinking fund method and total after-tax cash flow assumed by the Owner Participant on the Delivery Date.

"Officer's Certificate" means as to any company a certificate signed by the Chairman, the Vice Chairman, the President, any Vice President, any Assistant Vice President, the Treasurer, the Secretary, or by any Assistant Treasurer or Assistant Secretary duly authorized to execute such certificate.

"Operative Documents" means, collectively, the Lease, any Lease Supplement, the Participation Agreement, the Bills of Sale, the Indenture, the Trust Agreement, any Indenture Supplement, the Tax Indemnity Agreement, the Assignment, and the Loan Certificates.

"Overdue Rate" means 10.5%.

"Owner Participant" means PBC Leasing Corporation, a Florida corporation, and its successors and permitted assigns.

"Owner Trustee" means Martin Trust Company, a New York trust company, not in its individual capacity, but solely as trustee under the Trust Agreement, except as otherwise expressly provided, and any successor under the Trust Agreement.

"Participants" means, collectively, the Owner Participant and the Loan Participants; "Participant" means, individually, such a Participant.

"Participation Agreement" means the Participation Agreement, dated as of September 15, XXXX, among Lessee, the Owner Participant, the Owner Trustee, the Loan Participants, and the Indenture Trustee, as such Participation Agreement may be modified or supplemented from time to time pursuant to the terms thereof.

"Parts" means any and all appliances, parts, instruments, appurtenances, accessories, furnishings, seats, and other equipment of whatever nature (other than Engines or engines and temporary replacement parts as provided in Section 8 of the Lease), which may from time to time be incorporated or installed in or attached to the Airframe or any Engine, exclusive of any items leased by Lessee from third parties and not required in the navigation of the Aircraft.

"Percentage Commitment" of each Participant means the percentage set forth opposite such Participant's name in Schedule I to the Participation Agreement in the column entitled "Percentage Commitment."

"Permitted Investment" means (i) direct obligations of the United States of America, (ii) obligations fully guaranteed by the United States of America, (iii) certificates of deposit issued by, or bankers' acceptances of, or time deposits with, any bank, trust company, or national banking association incorporated or doing business under the laws of the United States of America or one of the states thereof (but not exceeding $15,000,000 in principal amount or in deposits at any given time for any one bank, trust company, or national banking association) having a combined capital and surplus of at least $225,000,000 (excluding any Participant), or (iv) commercial paper of finance companies incorporated or doing business under the laws of the United States of America or one of the states thereof (but not exceeding $15,000,000 in principal amount at any given time for any one finance company) and in each case having a rating assigned to such commercial paper by Standard & Poor's Corporation or Moody's Investors Service, Inc. (or, if neither such organization shall rate such commercial paper at any time, by any nationally recognized rating organization in the United States of America) equal to the highest rating assigned by such organization, provided that any such obligations of the types described in clauses (i) through (iv) above shall not have a maturity in excess of 210 days and shall not be invested in obligations issued by the Indenture Trustee, the Owner Trustee, or any Participant or any affiliate of any of the foregoing.

"Permitted Foreign Air Carrier" means an air carrier which (i) is duly organized and operating pursuant to a license issued under the laws of its home country and (ii) is listed on Schedule I to the Lease, as the same may be amended from time to time pursuant to Section 23 of the Lease.

"Permitted Liens" has the meaning given in Section 11 of the Lease.

"Person" means an individual, partnership, corporation, business trust, joint stock company, trust, unincorporated association, joint venture, governmental authority, or other entity of whatever nature.

"Purchase Agreement" means Purchase Agreement No. 22, dated as of April 21, XXXX, between the Manufacturer and Lessee (as heretofore amended, modified, and supplemented), providing, among other things, for the manufacture and sale by the Manufacturer to the Lessee of a number of Blackhawk 555-300 aircraft, as such Purchase Agreement may hereafter be amended, modified or supplemented to the extent permitted by the terms of the Assignment and the Indenture, and including, without limitation, as part of such Purchase Agreement, any and all change orders from time to time entered into with respect thereto, but solely as such Purchase Agreement, as amended, modified, and supplemented, relates to the Aircraft.

"Regulations" means the Treasury Regulations, as amended from time to time. promulgated under the Code by the United States Treasury Department.

"Renewal Term" has the meaning given in Section 14(a) of the Lease.

"Rent" means Interim Rent, Basic Rent, and Supplemental Rent.

"Reoptimization Closing Date" has the meaning given in Section 18 of the Participation Agreement.

"Replacement Aircraft" means the Aircraft of which a Replacement Airframe is part.

"Replacement Airframe" means a Blackhawk 555-300 aircraft (except Engines or engines from time to time installed thereon) which shall have been leased pursuant to Section 9 of the Lease.

"Replacement Closing Date" has the meaning given in Section 9(b) of the Lease.

"Replacement Engine" means a CFM International 56-3-SI engine (or engine of the same or another manufacturer of a comparable or an improved model and suitable for installation and use on an Airframe) which shall have been leased pursuant to Section 6 or 9 of the Lease. "Responsible Officer" means any officer of the corporate trust department of the Owner Trustee (when used with respect to the Owner Trustee).

"Series A Loan Certificates" means the Series A Loan Certificates (including the Additional Loan Certificates, if any) issued by the Owner Participant to the Loan Participants under the Indenture and any Loan Certificates issued in exchange therefor or in replacement thereof in accordance with the Indenture.

"Series B Loan Certificates" means the Series B Loan Certificates (including the Additional Loan Certificates, if any) issued by the Owner Participant to the Loan Participants under the Indenture and any Loan Certificates issued in exchange therefor or in replacement thereof in accordance with the Indenture.

"Stipulated Loss Value" for the Aircraft as of any date of determination (which in the case of an Event of Loss, shall be the date on which such Event of Loss occurs) means the sum of (x) an amount determined by multiplying the Lessor's Cost by the percentage set forth in Exhibit B to the Lease opposite the Loss Payment Date next succeeding such date of determination (or, if such date of determination is a Loss Payment Date by the percentage set forth opposite such Loss Payment Date), plus (y) an amount equal to interest on the amount determined pursuant to clause (x) at the Fixed Rate then payable on the Loan Certificates from and including such Loss Payment Date to but excluding the date of payment. Anything contained in the Lease or in the Participation Agreement to the contrary notwithstanding, Stipulated Loss Value shall be an amount which will be at least sufficient to pay in full as of the date of payment thereof (after giving effect to any installment of Basic Rent due on that date) the aggregate unpaid principal amount of the outstanding Loan Certificates, together with all unpaid interest thereon accrued and to accrue to such payment date.

"Sublease" means any sublease described by subclause 4 of the Granting Clauses contained in the Indenture.

"Supplemental Rent" means all amounts, liabilities, and obligations (other than Basic Rent and Interim Rent) that Lessee assumes or agrees to pay under the Operative Documents to Lessor or others, including, without limitation, Stipulated Loss Value and Termination Value payments with respect to the Aircraft.

"Tax" means all license and registration fees and all taxes, levies, imposts, duties, charges, assessments, or withholdings of any nature whatsoever together with any penalties, additions to tax, fines, or interest thereon.

"Tax Indemnity Agreement" means the Tax Indemnity Agreement dated as of September 15, XXXX between Lessee and the Owner Participant, in substantially the form of Exhibit IV to the Participation Agreement, as may be modified or supplemented from time to time pursuant to the terms thereof.

"Tax Law Change" means (a) any change in or to the Code enacted by the ____th Congress of the United States that affects the Assumed Tax Benefits or (b) any change in or to the Treasury Regulations with respect to or arising from any such change in the Code enacted by the ____th Congress, excluding in both clauses (a) and (b), changes related to (i) a Corporate minimum tax or corporate alternative minimum tax and (ii) Section 861(e) of the Code.

"Term" has the meaning given in Sections 3(a) and 14(a) of the Lease.

"Termination Value" for the Aircraft as of any date of determination means the sum of (x) an amount determined by multiplying the Lessor's Cost by the percentage set forth in Exhibit C of the Lease opposite the Loss Payment Date next succeeding such date of determination (or, if such date of determination is a loss Payment Date, by the percentage set forth opposite such Loss Payment Date), plus (y) an amount equal to interest on the amount determined under clause (x) at the Fixed Rate payable on the Loan Certificates from and including such Loss Payment Date to but excluding the date of payment, and (z) any premium payable under Section 2(k) of the Indenture. Anything contained in the Lease or in the Participation Agreement to the contrary notwithstanding, Termination

Value shall be an amount which will be at least sufficient to pay in full as of the date of payment thereof (after giving effect to any installment of Basic Rent due and owing on that date) the aggregate unpaid principal amount of the outstanding Loan Certificates together with all unpaid interest thereon accrued and to accrue to such payment date and any premium payable under Section 2(k) of the Indenture.

"Transaction Costs" means all of the out-of-pocket costs, fees, and expenses incurred by the Participants, the Owner Trustee, and the Indenture Trustee in connection with the negotiation, preparation, execution, delivery, filing, and recording of the Operative Documents and the transactions contemplated thereby, including:

(i) the reasonable fees, expenses, and disbursements of (A) ________________, special counsel for the Loan Participants, (B) ________________, special counsel for the Owner Participant, (C) ________________, special counsel for the Indenture Trustee, (D) ________________, special FAA counsel, (E) ________________, New York counsel, for the Owner Trustee, and (F) ________________, special counsel for the Lessee (but only insofar as such fees, expenses, and disbursements relate to preparation of documentation);

(ii) the cost of filing and recording documents with the FAA and filing financing statements;

(iii) the initial fees (constituting the fee of the Indenture Trustee for the entire term of the loan evidenced by the Loan Certificates) and expenses of the Indenture Trustee;

(iv) the initial fees (constituting the fee of the Owner Trustee for the entire Term) and expenses of the Owner Trustee;

(v) the cost of the appraisal referred to in Section 4 of the Participation Agreement:

(vi) the Equity Placement Fee of Pertson, Inc.;

(vii) the Debt Placement Fee of New York Investment Corporation; and

(viii) reimbursement to the Lessee of amounts paid to the Participants pursuant to Section 2(d)(ii) of the Participation Agreement.

"Trust Agreement" means the Trust Agreement, dated as of September 15, XXXX, between the Owner Participant and the Owner Trustee, in substantially the form of Exhibit II to the Participation Agreement, as the same may be modified or supplemented from time to time pursuant to the terms thereof.

"Trust Agreement and Indenture Supplement" means a supplement to the Indenture and to the Trust Agreement substantially in the form of Exhibit A to the Indenture, which shall describe with particularity the Aircraft included in the property of the Owner Trustee covered by the Trust Agreement by reference to the Lease Supplement executed and delivered pursuant to the Lease and which, pursuant to the Granting Clauses of the Indenture, shall create a first mortgage on the Aircraft and the Engines which are part of the Aircraft and assign and pledge Such Lease Supplement to the Indenture Trustee as part of the Estate.

"Trust Estate" means all estate, right, title, and interest of the Owner Trustee in and to the Aircraft, any Engines, the Operative Documents (except the Tax Indemnity Agreement), and any other property contributed by the Owner Participant including, without limitation, all amounts of Rent, insurance proceeds and requisition, indemnity, or other payments of any kind, but specifically excluding any Excepted Property.

Schedule I to Participation Agreement

Commitment Schedule

Participant	*Percentage*
Owner Participant	41.000000%
PBC Leasing Corporation	
Subtotal	41.000000%
Loan Participants	11.000000%
Series A	
AATX Life Insurance Company	
Able Re-Insurance Company	11.000000
State of NEW YORK Investment Board	14.000000
Subtotal	37.000000%
Series B	11.000000%
Cooper Life Insurance Company	
Peachtree Security Life Insurance Company	7.000000
Synx Life Assurance Company of Canada (U.S.)	5.000000
Synx Life Assurance Company of Canada	1.000000
Subtotal	24.000000%
Total	100.000000%

Schedule II to Participation Agreement

Schedule of Addresses and Payment Instructions

1. If to Planet:
2. If to AATX Life Insurance Company:
3. If to Able Re-Insurance Company:
4. If to Cooper Life Insurance Company:
5. If to Peachtree Security Life Insurance Company:
6. (a) If to Synx Life Assurance Company of Canada (U.S.) by Wire Transfer:
7. If to State of New York Investment Board:
8. If to Martin Trust Company:
9. If to The Rhode Island Bank and Trust Company:
10. If to PBC:

Form: I-04c
Disk File Name: I-04c.rtf

Trust Indenture and Security Agreement

Form Purpose

A leveraged lease trust indenture and security agreement in which all parties to the leveraged lease transaction set forth the terms and conditions of lending arrangement. This form is integrated with a Participation Agreement, a Trust Agreement, an Assignment of Rights under Purchase Agreement, a Lease Agreement, and a Tax Indemnity Agreement.

Executing Parties

The owner trustee.
The indenture trustee.

See:

Assignment of Rights Under Purchase Agreement, Form I-04a
Leveraged Lease Agreement, Form I-04
Participation Agreement, Form I-04b
Trust Agreement, Form I-04d
Tax Indemnity Agreement, Form I-04e

TRUST INDENTURE AND SECURITY AGREEMENT

dated as of September 15, XXXX

between

MARTIN TRUST COMPANY,

not in its individual capacity, but
solely as Owner Trustee under the Trust Agreement
except as otherwise expressly provided herein,

and

THE RHODE ISLAND BANK AND TRUST COMPANY,
NATIONAL ASSOCIATION,
Indenture Trustee.

Covering One New Blackhawk
Model 555-300 Aircraft
Registration Number N777P

Table of Contents

Trust Indenture and Security Agreement

This TRUST INDENTURE AND SECURITY AGREEMENT, dated as of September 15, XXXX, between MARTIN TRUST COMPANY, a New York trust company, not in its individual capacity, but solely as Owner Trustee under the Trust Agreement, Owner Trustee, and THE RHODE ISLAND BANK AND TRUST COMPANY, NATIONAL ASSOCIATION, a national banking association, Indenture Trustee.

WITNESSETH:

WHEREAS, simultaneously with the execution and delivery of this Indenture, Lessee is selling the Aircraft to and leasing the Aircraft from the Owner Trustee;

WHEREAS, in connection with the purchase of the Aircraft from Lessee, the Owner Trustee desires by this Indenture, among other things, (i) to provide for the issue by the Owner Trustee to the Loan Participants of Loan Certificates evidencing each Loan Participant's Commitment for the financing of the Aircraft as provided in the Participation Agreement, and (ii) to provide for the assignment, mortgage, and pledge by the Owner Trustee to the Indenture Trustee, as part of the Estate hereunder, among other things, of all of the Owner Trustee's right, title, and interest in and to the Aircraft, the Lease (except as qualified herein), the Purchase Agreement, the Assignment, and all payments and other amounts received hereunder or thereunder, in accordance with the terms hereof, in trust, as security for the Owner Trustee's obligations to the holders of the Loan Certificates, for the benefit and security of such holders; and

WHEREAS, all things necessary to make this Indenture the legal, valid, and binding obligation of the Owner Trustee and the Indenture Trustee for the uses and purposes herein set forth, in accordance with its terms, have been done and performed and have happened;

NOW, THEREFORE, to secure the prompt payment of the principal of and interest on all the Loan Certificates from time to time outstanding hereunder and all other amounts payable hereunder and the performance and observance by the Owner Trustee of all the agreements, covenants, and provisions contained herein and in the Participation Agreement and in the Loan Certificates for the benefit of the holders of the Loan Certificates, and for the uses and purposes and subject to the terms and provisions hereof, and in consideration of the premises and covenants herein contained and of the acceptance of the Loan Certificates by the Loan Participants, and of the sum of $1 paid to the Owner Trustee by the Indenture Trustee at or before the delivery hereof, the receipt whereof is hereby acknowledged:

Granting Clauses

The Owner Trustee has sold, assigned, transferred, pledged, and confirmed and does hereby sell, assign, transfer, pledge, and confirm unto the Indenture Trustee, its successors and assigns, in the trust hereby created for the security and benefit of the holders from time to time of the Loan Certificates, a security interest in and lien on all right, title, and interest of the Owner Trustee in and to the following property, rights, and privileges (which property, rights, and privileges, including all property, rights, and privileges hereafter subjected to the Lien of this Indenture by any Indenture Supplement or any mortgage supplemental hereto, are included in the Estate), to wit:

(1) the Lease, including, without limitation, all amounts of Interim Rent, Basic Rent, Supplemental Rent, insurance proceeds, requisition, indemnity, and other payments of any kind for or with respect to the Aircraft or the Lease or payable by the Lessee under the Participation Agreement, including (but subject to Section 5[b] hereof) all rights of the Owner Trustee to exercise any option or election or to make any decision or determination or to give any notice, consent, waiver, or approval under or in respect of the Lease or to accept surrender of the Aircraft or any part thereof and all rights, powers, and remedies of the Owner Trustee, whether arising under the Lease or by statute or law or in equity or otherwise arising out of any Default or Event of Default and including all rights, powers, and remedies of the Owner Trustee under the Lease not otherwise specifically reserved in the Owner Trustee pursuant hereto;

(2) the Aircraft including the Airframe and Engines and all Parts thereof, and the Bills of Sale with respect thereto, and all additions, modifications, or alterations thereto and replacements of parts thereof, together with all logs, manuals, certificates, data and inspection, modification and overhaul records pertaining to the Aircraft, all as more particularly described in the Indenture supplement(s) executed and delivered with respect to the Aircraft as provided in this Indenture;

(3) all right, title, and interest of the Owner Trustee in, to, and under the Purchase Agreement, to the extent specified in the Assignment and in and to said Assignment;

(4) all right, title, and interest of the Owner Trustee in, to, and under any sublease entered into from time to time with respect to the Aircraft or Engines;

(5) all monies and securities deposited or required to be deposited with the Indenture Trustee pursuant to any term of this Indenture, the Lease, or the Participation Agreement or required to be held by the Indenture Trustee hereunder or thereunder; and

(6) all tolls, rents, issues, profits, products, revenue, and other income of the foregoing and all estate, right, title, and interest of the Owner Trustee in and to the same and every part thereof;

(7) all proceeds of the foregoing.

BUT EXCLUDING, however, from the property, rights, and privileges subject to these Granting Clauses, all Excepted Property.

(Concurrently with the delivery hereof, the Owner Trustee is delivering to the Indenture Trustee the original executed counterpart of the Lease (to which a chattel paper receipt is attached), an executed counterpart of the Assignment and a copy of the Purchase Agreement and each amendment to or modification of the Purchase Agreement, certified by Lessee as a true copy.)

To have and to hold all and singular the aforesaid property unto the Indenture Trustee, its successors and assigns, in trust for the benefit and security of the holders from time to time of the Loan Certificates, without any priority of any one Loan Certificate over any other, and for the uses and purposes, and subject to the terms and provisions, set forth in this Indenture.

A. In order to more clearly effectuate the foregoing and to secure payment, performance, and observance, for the same consideration as set forth above, the Owner Trustee has transferred, assigned, granted, bargained, sold, conveyed, mortgaged, hypothecated, and pledged, and does hereby transfer, assign, grant, bargain, sell, convey, mortgage, hypothecate, and pledge, to the Indenture Trustee, its successors and assigns, in the trust hereby created for the security and benefit of the holders from time to time of the Loan Certificates, the Aircraft, including the Airframe and the Engines which are part of the Aircraft, to be hereafter specifically subjected to the lien hereof as provided in the Indenture Supplement(s) creating a first mortgage on the Aircraft, the Airframe, and the Engines described therein, whether or not such Engines shall be installed in or attached to an Aircraft or any other aircraft.

B. In order to more clearly effectuate the foregoing and to secure payment, performance, and observance, for the same consideration as set forth above, the Owner Trustee has sold, assigned, transferred, and set over and does hereby sell, assign, transfer, and set over unto the Indenture Trustee, and its successors and assigns, in the trust hereby created for the security and benefit of the holders from time to time of the Loan Certificates, all of the right, title, and interest of the Owner Trustee (other than Excepted Property) under, in, and to (i) the Lease, as from time to time supplemented or amended, including any Lease Supplements thereto, except for such rights, powers, and remedies thereunder specifically reserved to the Owner Trustee pursuant hereto, (ii) all moneys and claims for moneys due and to become due to the Owner Trustee under the Lease, and all claims for damages, in respect of any Event of Loss with respect to the Aircraft, either with or without Engines or engines installed thereon, and the Engines, and all other payments of any kind due to the Owner Trustee under the Lease for or with respect to the Aircraft and the Engines, (iii) the Purchase Agreement and the Assignment, (iv) the Subleases, and (v) all monies and claims for monies due or to become due to the Owner Trustee from Lessee under the Participation Agreement and all rights of the Owner Trustee to enforce payment of any such amounts thereunder. The security interest created by the foregoing assignment attaches upon the delivery hereof.

It is expressly agreed that all of the property of the Owner Trustee subject to the Lien of this Indenture, including without limitation the Aircraft, Airframe, and each Engine, is security for any and all obligations secured by this Indenture, including without limitation all obligations in respect to any Loan Certificate (whether or not such Loan Certificate was issued in connection with the Aircraft, Airframe, or Engine), and, upon the happening of any Event of Acceleration, the Indenture Trustee shall, subject to the provisions of Section 11(a) hereof, be entitled to exercise the remedies herein provided with respect to any and all of such property.

It is expressly agreed that, anything herein contained to the contrary notwithstanding, the Owner Trustee shall remain liable under the Lease, the Participation Agreement, and the Assignment to perform all of the obligations, if any, assumed by it thereunder, all in accordance with and pursuant to the terms and provisions thereof, and the Indenture Trustee shall have no obligation or liability under the Lease by reason of or arising out of this assignment, nor shall the Indenture Trustee be required or obligated in any manner to perform or fulfill any obligations of the Owner Trustee under or pursuant to the Lease, the Participation Agreement, and the Assignment or, except as herein expressly provided, to make any payment, or to make any inquiry as to the nature or sufficiency of any payment received by it, or present or file any claim, or take any action to collect or enforce the payment of any amounts which may have been assigned to it or to which it may be entitled at any time or times.

The Owner Trustee does hereby irrevocably constitute the Indenture Trustee the true and lawful attorney of the Owner Trustee, with full power (in the name of the Owner Trustee or otherwise) to ask, require, demand, receive, and compound any and all monies and claims for monies due and to become due under or arising out of the Lease, the Subleases, the Participation Agreement, the Purchase Agreement, and the Assignment (to the extent such monies and claims under each such agreement are assigned to the Indenture Trustee pursuant to this Indenture), to endorse any checks or other instruments or orders in connection therewith and to file any claims or take any action or institute any proceedings which the Indenture Trustee may deem necessary or advisable in the performance of its duties hereunder, all to the extent provided in this Indenture.

The Owner Trustee has directed Lessee, and Lessee has agreed, to make all payments of Rent (other than Excepted Property), and all other amounts required to be paid to or deposited with the Owner Trustee pursuant to the Lease, directly to the Indenture Trustee at such address as the Indenture Trustee may from time to time specify.

The Owner Trustee does hereby warrant and represent that it has not assigned or pledged, and hereby covenants that it will not assign or pledge, so long as this Indenture shall remain in effect, any of its right, title, or interest hereby assigned, to anyone other than the Indenture Trustee, and that it will not, except as provided in this Indenture [including, without limitation, Section 5(b) hereof], (i) enter into any agreement amending or supplementing, or granting any consent or approval or giving any notice with regard to, the Lease, the Participation Agreement, the Subleases, the Purchase Agreement, or the Assignment, or (ii) accept any payment assigned hereunder, or (iii) settle or compromise any claim assigned hereunder arising under the Lease, the Participation Agreement, the Purchase Agreement, the Subleases, or the Assignment, or (iv) submit or consent to the submission to arbitration of any dispute, difference, or other matter arising under or in respect of the Lease, the Participation Agreement, the Purchase Agreement, the Subleases, or the Assignment, in each case to the extent assigned hereunder.

The Owner Trustee does hereby ratify and confirm the Lease and the Assignment, and acknowledge the existence of the Purchase Agreement and does hereby agree that it will not, except as provided in this Indenture, take any action altering, or omit to take any action required to prevent the alteration of, the Lease, the Participation Agreement, the Purchase Agreement, the Assignment or this assignment or any of the rights created by the Lease, the Participation Agreement, the Purchase Agreement, the Assignment or the assignment hereunder.

Notwithstanding the Granting Clause or any of the preceding paragraphs, (i) there is hereby excluded from the foregoing sale, transfer, assignment, grant, pledge, and security interest all Excepted Property, and (ii) the rights of the Indenture Trustee and the holders of the Loan Certificates are hereby expressly made subject to the rights of the Owner Participant referred to in Section 5(b) hereof.

It is hereby covenanted and agreed by and between the parties hereto as follows:

Section 1. Definitions

Unless the context otherwise requires, all capitalized terms used herein shall have the meanings set forth in Appendix A hereto for all purposes of this Indenture.

Section 2. The Loan Certificates

(a) Form of Loan Certificates. The Loan Certificates shall be substantially in the form set forth below:

[Form of Series A Loan Certificate]

MARTIN TRUST COMPANY, NOT IN ITS INDIVIDUAL CAPACITY BUT SOLELY AS OWNER TRUSTEE UNDER THE TRUST AGREEMENT DATED
AS OF SEPTEMBER 15, XXXX

SERIES A LOAN CERTIFICATE DUE JANUARY 2, XXXX*

Issued in connection with Aircraft bearing
U.S. Registration Number N777P

No. ______________________ New York, New York

$ ______________________________ October, XXXX

MARTIN Trust Company, a New York corporation, not in its individual capacity but solely as trustee under that certain Trust Agreement dated as of September 15, XXXX ("Owner Trustee"), hereby promises to pay to ______________________________, or registered assigns, the principal amount of $ ______________________, in lawful currency of the United States of America, in ____ installments as set forth in Annex A hereto*, commencing on January 2, XXXX, and payable on the dates specified in Annex A hereto of each year thereafter to and including January 2, XXXX**, each such installment to be in an amount equal to the corresponding percentage of the principal hereof set forth in Annex A hereto, together with interest on the unpaid principal hereof from time to time outstanding from the date hereof until final maturity at the rate of ____ %***

*Series B will read "Series B Loan Certificate due July 2, 2XXX."

*The principal amortization schedule to be initially attached to each Loan Certificate issued on the Delivery Date is attached to this Indenture as Exhibit B. Such amortization schedule is subject to change as set forth in Section 2(b) of the Indenture. The principal amortization schedule to be attached to each Additional Loan Certificate will be as agreed to by the parties to the Participation Agreement prior to the issuance of such Additional Loan Certificate.

**Series B will read "July 2, XXXX."

***Series A will read "8.XX%" and Series B will read "9.XX%."

per annum, payable in arrears on July 2 and January 2 of each year commencing on January 2, XXXX. All interest shall be computed on the basis of a 360-day year comprised of twelve 30-day months. In addition, the Owner Trustee promises to pay, under certain circumstances, a premium on the prepayment of principal as set forth in Section 2(k) of the Indenture (as hereinafter defined).

In any event, the payment made on this Loan Certificate on January 2, XXXX**** shall be in an amount sufficient to discharge the accrued interest and premium, if any, on, and the unpaid principal amount of this Loan Certificate, together with any other amounts then owing hereunder or under the Trust Indenture and Security Agreement dated as of September 15, XXXX (as the same may from time to time be amended, modified, or supplemented, herein called the "Indenture"; Capitalized terms used herein having the meanings assigned to them in the Indenture) between the Owner Trustee and The Rhode Island Bank and Trust Company, National Association, as Indenture Trustee thereunder for the holder of this Series A* Loan Certificate and the holders of other Loan Certificates outstanding thereunder (herein in such capacity called the "Indenture Trustee"). Interest at the Overdue Rate on any overdue principal and premium, if any, and (to the extent permitted by applicable law) overdue interest, shall be paid from the due date thereof until the date such amount is paid in full, payable on demand.

Except as set forth in Section 7(1) of the Participation Agreement, all payments of principal, interest, and premium, if any, to be made hereunder and all payments to be made under the Indenture are nonrecourse to the Owner Participant and the Owner Trustee and shall be made only from the income and proceeds from the Estate and only to the extent that the Indenture Trustee shall have sufficient income or proceeds from the Estate to make such payments in accordance with the terms of Section 3 of the Indenture, and each holder hereof, by its acceptance of this Series A* Loan Certificate, agrees that it will look solely to the income and proceeds from the Estate to the extent available for distribution to the holder hereof as provided in the Indenture and that the Owner Participant, the Owner Trustee, and the Indenture Trustee are not personally liable to the holder hereof for any amounts payable under this Series A* Loan Certificate or the Indenture.

Payments with respect to the principal hereof, premium, if any, and interest hereon shall be payable in U.S. dollars in immediately available funds at the principal corporate trust office of the Indenture Trustee, or as otherwise provided in the Indenture. Each such payment shall be made on the date such payment is due and without any presentment or surrender of this Series A* Loan Certificate, except that in the case of any final payment with respect to this Series A* Loan Certificate, this Series A* Loan Certificate shall be surrendered to the Owner Trustee for cancellation upon payment in full of such final payment. Whenever any payment to be made hereunder or under the Indenture shall be stated to be due on a day which is not a Business Day, the due date thereof shall be extended to the next succeeding Business Day and, if paid on such Business Day, without penalty or additional interest.

Each holder hereof, by its acceptance of this Series A* Loan Certificate, agrees that each payment received by it hereunder prior to an Event of Acceleration shall be applied, first, to the payment of accrued interest on this Series A* Loan Certificate to the date of such

****Series B will read "July 2, XXXX."

payment, second, to the payment of the unpaid principal of this Series A* Loan Certificate then due and third, to the payment of any premium then due.

Each holder hereof, by its acceptance of this Series A* Loan Certificate, agrees that the amortization schedule attached hereto may be changed pursuant to Section 2(b)(iii) of the Indenture.

This Series A* Loan Certificate is one of the Loan Certificates referred to in the Indenture which have been or are to be issued by the Owner Trustee pursuant to, and subject to the terms of, the Indenture. The Estate is held by the Indenture Trustee as security for the Loan Certificates. Reference is hereby made to the Indenture for a statement of the rights of the holder of, and the nature and extent of the security for, this Series A* Loan Certificate and of the rights of the holders of, and the nature and extent of the security for, the other Loan Certificates, as well as for a statement of the terms and conditions of the trusts created by the Indenture, to all of which terms and conditions in the Indenture each holder hereof agrees by its acceptance of this Series A* Loan Certificate.

This Series A* Loan Certificate and interest on the unpaid principal is not subject to prepayment except as specifically provided in the Indenture.

Unless the certificate of authentication hereon has been executed by or on behalf of the Indenture Trustee by manual signature, this Series A* Loan Certificate shall not be entitled to any benefit under the Indenture or be valid or obligatory for any purpose.

IN WITNESS WHEREOF, the Owner Trustee has caused this Series A* Loan Certificate to be executed by one of its authorized officers as of the date hereof.

MARTIN TRUST COMPANY,
Not in its individual
capacity, but solely as
Owner Trustee

By: ______________________________

Title: ______________________________

*Series B will read "Series B."
*Series B will read "Series B."

[Form of Indenture Trustee's Certificate of Authentication]

This is one of the Series A* Loan Certificates referred to in the within-mentioned Indenture.

THE RHODE ISLAND BANK AND TRUST COMPANY, NATIONAL ASSOCIATION, Indenture Trustee

By: ______________________________
Authorized Officer

*Series B will read "Series B."

Annex A to Series A* Loan Certificate

Schedule of Principal Payments

Payment Date	*Percentage of Principal to be paid*

Payments Received

Date of Payment	*Interest Paid*	*Principal Paid*	*Principal Remaining Unpaid*	*Notation Made By*

(b) Terms of Loan Certificates

(i) On the Delivery Date of the Aircraft, there shall be issued and delivered to each Loan Participant, as provided in the Participation Agreement, one or more Loan Certificates, each dated the Delivery Date, designated as having been issued in connection with the Aircraft, and payable to such Loan Participant or such other Person as such Loan Participant may specify to the Owner Trustee at least one Business Day prior to the Delivery Date for the Aircraft. The Loan Certificate or Loan Certificates issued to each such Loan Participant with respect to the Aircraft shall be Series A or Series B Loan Certificates as set forth in Schedule I to the Participation Agreement, shall be in a principal amount or aggregate principal amount, as the case may be, equal to such Loan Participant's Commitment with respect to the Aircraft and each such Loan Participant shall be entitled to receive a single Loan Certificate in a principal amount equal to such Loan Participant's Commitment or such greater number of Loan Certificates in denominations of not less than $1,000,000 as such Loan Participant may specify to the Owner Trustee at least one Business Day prior to the Delivery Date. The Loan Certificates issued in connection with the delivery of the Aircraft shall bear interest at the rate of 8.XX% with respect to the Series A Loan Certificates and 9.XX% with respect to the Series B Loan Certificates on the principal amount thereof from time to time outstanding from and including the date thereof until due and payable (computed on the basis of a 360-day year comprised of twelve 30-day months). The principal of and interest on each Loan Certificate shall be initially payable as set forth in the form thereof contained in Section 2(a) hereof and, with respect to premium, if any, payable in accordance with Section 2(k) hereof. The initial principal amortization schedule shall be subject to reoptimization on or prior to September 1, XXXX in accordance with Section 18 of the Participation Agreement. Upon the request of the Indenture Trustee, the Owner Trustee shall furnish to the Indenture Trustee a copy of each Loan Certificate issued pursuant to the provisions of this Indenture.

(ii) On the Reoptimization Closing Date, if any, there shall be issued and delivered to each Loan Participant, as provided in the Participation Agreement, one or more Additional Loan Certificates of the same Series of Loan Certificate as originally issued to such Loan Participant pursuant to Section 2(b)(i) hereof, each dated the Reoptimization Closing Date, designated as having been issued in connection with the Aircraft, and payable to such Loan Participant or such other person as such Loan Participant may specify to the Owner Trustee at least one Business Day prior to the Reoptimization Closing Date. The Additional Loan Certificate or Additional Loan Certificates issued to each such Loan Participant shall be in a principal amount or aggregate principal amount, as the case may be, equal to such Loan Participant's Additional Participation and each Loan Participant shall be entitled to receive a single Additional Loan Certificate in a principal amount equal to such Loan Participant's Additional Participation or such greater number of Additional Loan Certificates in denominations of not less than $200,000 as such Loan Participant may specify to the Owner Trustee at least one Business Day prior to such Reoptimization Closing Date. Each Additional Loan Certificate shall bear interest at the Additional Fixed Rate on the principal amount thereof from time to time outstanding from and including the date thereof (computed on the basis of a 360-day year comprised of twelve 30-day months). The principal amortization schedule with respect to each Additional Loan Certificate shall be as determined pursuant to Section 18 of the Participation Agreement. Upon the request of the Indenture Trustee, the Owner

Trustee shall furnish to the Indenture Trustee a copy of each Additional Loan Certificate issued pursuant to the provisions of this Indenture.

(iii) If the principal amortization schedule attached hereto is reoptimized pursuant to the penultimate sentence of Section 2(b)(i) hereof, the Owner Trustee shall on the Reoptimization Closing Date furnish to each holder of a Loan Certificate and the Indenture Trustee an amortization schedule showing the amounts and allocation between interest and payment of principal with respect to each installment payable on its Loan Certificates. Each Loan Participant is hereby authorized, and by its acceptance of a Loan Certificate agrees, to substitute such new principal amortization schedule for such Schedule initially attached to its Loan Certificate(s). The Owner Trustee shall not be liable for any loss or harm resulting from a failure by a Loan Participant to substitute such principal amortization schedule.

(iv) No Loan Certificate shall be entitled to any benefit under this Indenture or be valid or obligatory for any purpose, unless it shall have been authenticated by or on behalf of the Indenture Trustee by manual signature.

(c) Payment from Estate Only. Anything to the contrary notwithstanding, except as set forth in Section 7(1) of the Participation Agreement, all payments to be made under the Loan Certificates and this Indenture shall be nonrecourse to the Owner Trustee and Owner Participant and shall be made only from the income and the proceeds from the Estate and only to the extent that the Indenture Trustee shall have received sufficient income or proceeds from the Estate to make such payments in accordance with the terms of Section 3 hereof. Except as set forth in Section 7(1) of the Participation Agreement, each holder of a Loan Certificate, by its acceptance of Such Loan Certificate, agrees that it will look solely to the income and proceeds from the Estate to the extent available for distribution to such holder as herein provided and that the Owner Participant, the Owner Trustee, and the Indenture Trustee are not personally liable to the holder of any Loan Certificate for any amounts payable under the Loan Certificates or this Indenture.

(d) Method of Payment; Payments on Nonbusiness Days

(i) The principal of, premium, if any, and interest on each Loan Certificate will be payable in immediately available funds at the principal corporate trust office of the Indenture Trustee as specified in Section 10(g) hereof. Such payments shall be made by 11:00 A.M. Eastern Time on the dates such payments are due. The Owner Trustee shall not have any responsibility for the distribution of such payments by the Indenture Trustee to the holders of the Loan Certificates. Notwithstanding the foregoing or any provision in any Loan Certificate to the contrary, the Indenture Trustee will pay, or cause to be paid, if so requested by any institutional holder of a Loan Certificate by written notice (which notice, in the case of Loan Participants named in the Participation Agreement shall be deemed given by the instructions set forth in Schedule I to the Participation Agreement) to the Owner Trustee and the Indenture Trustee, all amounts payable hereunder to such holder or a nominee thereof (including all amounts distributed pursuant to Section 3 of this Indenture) either (A) by transferring by wire in immediately available funds to an account maintained by such holder with a bank in the United States of America, the amount to be distributed to such holder or (B) by mailing a check, in the amount to be distributed to such holder, drawn on a bank in the City and State of New York or Providence, Rhode Island, or the place of business of the Indenture Trustee, to such holder at such address as such holder shall have specified in such notice, in any case without any presentment or surrender of any Loan Certificate, except that a holder of a Loan Certificate shall surrender such Loan Certificate to the Indenture Trustee upon the payment in full of the principal amount of, premium, if any, and interest on such Loan Certificate and all other sums payable to such holder hereunder and under such Loan Certificate and under the Participation Agreement. Amounts received by the Indenture Trustee pursuant to this Section 2(d) by 11:00 A.M. Eastern Time on any day shall be distributed to the Loan Participants as provided herein on the same day. In the case of any amount not so distributed in a timely manner by the Indenture Trustee, the Indenture Trustee in its individual capacity agrees that it Shall pay, and distribute to the Loan Participants on demand, interest with respect thereto at the Overdue Rate for each day until such amounts are distributed to the Loan Participants.

(ii) Whenever any payment to be made hereunder or under any Loan Certificate shall be stated to be due on a day which is not a Business Day, the due date thereof shall be extended to the next succeeding Business Day and, if paid on such Business Day, without penalty or additional interest.

(e) Application of Payments to Principal and Interest. In the case of each Loan Certificate, each payment of principal thereof, and interest thereon received prior to an Event of Acceleration shall be applied, first, to the payment of accrued but unpaid interest on such Loan Certificate then due thereunder, and second, to the payment of the unpaid principal amount of such Loan Certificate then due thereunder.

(f) Equally and Ratably Secured. All Loan Certificates are equally and ratably secured by all of the property subject to the Lien of this Indenture. All Loan Certificates at any time outstanding under this Indenture shall be equally and ratably secured hereby without preference, priority, or distinction on account of the date or dates or the actual time or times of the issue or maturity of such Loan Certificates so that all Loan Certificates at any time issued and outstanding hereunder shall have the same rights, Liens, and preferences under and by virtue of this Indenture.

(g) Termination of Interest in Estate. A holder of a Loan Certificate shall have no further interest in, or other right with respect to, the Estate when and if the principal of, premium, if any, and interest on all Loan Certificates held by such holder and all other sums payable to such holder hereunder and under such Loan Certificates and under the Participation Agreement shall have been paid in full.

(h) Transfer of Loan Certificates. The Indenture Trustee shall maintain at its principal office in Providence, Rhode Island, a register for the purpose of registering transfers and exchanges of Loan Certificates. A holder of a Loan Certificate intending to transfer any Loan Certificate held by such holder to a new payee, or to exchange any Loan Certificate held by such holder for a Loan Certificate or Loan Certificates of a different denomination or denominations, but not for a different Series of Loan Certificate, may surrender such Loan Certificate or Loan Certificates to the Indenture Trustee at such principal office, together with a written request from such holder for the issuance of a new Loan Certificate or Loan Certificates, specifying the denomination or denominations [each of which shall be not less than $500,000 (or $200,000 in the case of Additional Loan Certificates) or such lesser amount as shall constitute the entire principal amount of a Loan Certificate held by such holder] of the same and the amount of all payments or prepayments of principal and interest previously made on the Loan Certificate being surrendered, and, in the case of a surrender for registration of transfer, the name and address of the payee or payees. Promptly upon receipt of such documents from the Indenture Trustee, and without assessing service or other charges to the holder of such Loan Certificates, the Owner Trustee will issue a new Loan Certificate or Loan Certificates, which Loan Certificate or Loan Certificates the Indenture Trustee shall authenticate, in the same aggregate principal amount, dated the same date or dates, designated as issued in connection with the same Aircraft, and of the same Series of Loan Certificate as the Loan Certificate or Loan Certificates surrendered, in such denomination or denominations and payable to such payee or payees as shall be specified in the written request from such holder. All Loan Certificates issued upon any registration of transfer or exchange of Loan Certificates shall be the valid obligations of the Owner Trustee evidencing the same respective obligations, and entitled to the same security and benefits under this Indenture, as the Loan Certificates surrendered upon such registration of transfer or exchange. The Indenture Trustee shall make a notation on each new Loan Certificate or Loan Certificates of the pro rata amount of all payments or prepayments of principal and interest previously made on the old Loan Certificate or Loan Certificates with respect to which such new Loan Certificate or Loan Certificates is or are issued. From time to time, the Indenture Trustee will provide the Lessee with such information as it may request as to the registered holders of Loan Certificates. The Owner Trustee shall not be required to exchange any surrendered Loan Certificates as above provided during the 10-day period preceding the due date of any payment on such Loan Certificates.

Prior to the due presentment for registration of transfer of a Loan Certificate, the Owner Trustee and the Indenture Trustee may deem and treat the registered holder of such Loan Certificate as the absolute owner and holder of such Loan Certificate for the purpose of receiving payment of all amounts payable with respect to such Loan Certificate and for all other purposes and shall not be affected by any notice to the contrary.

(i) Mutilated, Destroyed, Lost, or Stolen Loan Certificates. If any Loan Certificate shall become mutilated, destroyed, lost, or stolen, the Owner Trustee shall, upon the written request (a copy of which request shall be sent by such holder to the Indenture Trustee) of the holder of such Loan Certificate, and without assessing a service or other charge to such holder, execute and deliver in replacement thereof a new Loan Certificate, which the Indenture Trustee shall authenticate, payable to the same holder in the same principal amount, dated the same date and of the same Series of Loan Certificate as the Loan Certificate so mutilated, destroyed, lost, or stolen. If the Loan Certificate being replaced has become mutilated, such Loan Certificate shall be surrendered to the Indenture Trustee and forwarded to the Owner Trustee by the Indenture Trustee. If the Loan Certificate being replaced has been destroyed, lost, or stolen the holder of such Loan Certificate shall furnish to the Owner Trustee and the Indenture Trustee such security or indemnity as may be required by them to hold the Owner Trustee and the Indenture Trustee harmless and evidence satisfactory to the Owner Trustee and the Indenture Trustee of the destruction, loss, or theft of such Loan Certificate and of the ownership thereof; provided, however, that if the holder of such Loan Certificate is a Loan Participant named in the Participation Agreement or is an institutional holder, the written undertaking of such Loan Participant or institutional holder delivered to and reasonably satisfactory to the Owner Trustee and the Indenture Trustee shall be sufficient security and indemnity for the purposes of this Section 2(i).

(j) Payment of Transfer Taxes. Upon the transfer of any Loan Certificate or Loan Certificates pursuant to Section 2(h) hereof, the Owner Trustee or the Indenture Trustee may require from the party requesting such new Loan Certificate or Loan Certificates payment of a sum to reimburse the Owner Trustee or the Indenture Trustee for, or to provide funds for the payment of, any tax or other governmental charge in connection therewith.

(k) Prepayments.

(i) Except as otherwise provided in this Indenture the Loan Certificates may not be prepaid.

(ii) On the date of termination of the Lease with respect to the Aircraft pursuant to Section 15(a) thereof, all of the Loan Certificates issued in connection with the Aircraft shall be prepaid at a price, in addition to any other amounts payable to the holders of such Loan Certificates under this Indenture. equal to the aggregate unpaid principal amount of such Loan Certificates, together with all accrued interest thereon, but without premium.

(iii) On the date of termination of the Lease pursuant to Section 15(b) thereof, all of the Loan Certificates shall be prepaid at a price, in addition to any other amounts payable to the holders of such Loan Certificates under this Indenture, equal to the aggregate unpaid principal amount of such Loan Certificates, together with all accrued interest thereon. There shall be no premium as a result of Such prepayment unless (i) a change in accelerated depreciation and/or the corporate tax rate resulting from a Tax Law Change has occurred which would require an upward adjustment to Basic Rent under Section 3(e)(B) of the Lease in an aggregate amount over the then remaining period of the Basic Term the present value of which discounted at the Fixed Rate shall be 500 basis points or more greater than the present value of the aggregate rental payments otherwise payable over the remaining period of the Basic Term discounted at the Fixed Rate (hereinafter referred to as a "Burdensome Adjustment") or (ii) (A) a Tax Law Change has occurred which, exclusive of any loss of investment credit, change in accelerated depreciation or change in the corporate tax rate resulting from such Tax Law Change, would require a Burdensome Adjustment and (B) such termination occurs at the earlier of five Business Days after the close of the XXth Congress or January 31, XXXX. In the circumstances described in clause (i) or (ii) of the preceding sentence, the Series A and Series B Loan Certificates (respectively) shall be prepaid with a premium ("Yield Differential Premium") if, on the day five Business Days preceding the date of termination (x) in the case of the Series A Loan Certificates, the interpolated yield for a hypothetical U.S. Treasury bond due May, XXXX (interpolated with respect to U.S. Treasury 7-1/4% bonds due July, XXXX and U.S. Treasury 7-3/8% bonds due May, XXXX) is less than 7.125% and (y) in the case of the Series B Loan Certificates, the interpolated yield for a hypothetical U.S. Treasury bond due February, XXXX (interpolated with respect to U.S. Treasury 7-3/8% bonds due May, XXXX and U.S. Treasury 9-3/8% bonds due February, XXXX) is less than 7.95% (such difference in both cases being referred to herein as the "Yield Differential"). The yield an such bonds shall be as determined, on any date of determination required by this Section 2(k)(iii), by the Federal Reserve Bank of New York City and published as the "ask" price by *The Wall Street Journal.* The Yield Differential Premium for either series of Loan Certificates shall be equal to the present value (using a discount rate per annum equal to the interest rate on the respective series of Loan Certificates minus the respective Yield Differential) as of the date of prepayment of all scheduled installments of principal and interest which would have been payable but for such prepayment with respect to the principal amount of the Loan Certificates to be prepaid, less the outstanding principal amount of Such Loan Certificates at the time of prepayment.

(iv) On the date of termination of the Lease with respect to the Aircraft as a result of an Event of Loss with respect to the Aircraft under Section 9 of the Lease, the Loan Certificates issued with respect to the Aircraft shall be prepaid at a price, in addition to any other amounts payable to the holders of such Loan Certificates under this Indenture, equal to the aggregate unpaid principal amount of such Loan Certificates, together with all accrued interest thereon, but without premium.

(l) Withholding. The Indenture Trustee shall make any deduction required by law from any payment to any holder of a Loan Certificate hereunder for any withholding of taxes imposed by the United States. If the holder of a Loan Certificate has obtained an exemption from U.S. withholding tax, which would otherwise be imposed on payments made to such holder under the Loan Certificate, it shall provide the Indenture Trustee with a copy of the exemption. The Indenture Trustee shall obtain a tax receipt with respect to any such withholding of taxes and shall furnish such a receipt to such holder promptly after the Indenture Trustee has received the same.

(m) Loan Certificates in Respect to Replacement Aircraft. Upon the execution and delivery of an Indenture Supplement covering a Replacement Aircraft and/or Replacement Engine, each Loan Certificate issued in connection with the Aircraft and/or Engine being replaced shall be deemed to have been issued in connection with the Replacement Aircraft and/or Replacement Engine and each Loan Certificate issued thereafter upon a transfer or exchange of, or as a replacement for, such a Loan Certificate, shall be designated as having been issued in connection with the Replacement Aircraft and/or Replacement Engine, but without any other change therein except as provided for in this Section 2.

Section 3. Receipt, Distribution, and Application of Income from the Estate

(a) Distribution of Basic Rent and Owner Payments. Except as otherwise provided in Section 3(c) hereof, each installment of Interim Rent and Basic Rent as well as any installment of interest on overdue installments of Interim Rent and Basic Rent, and any other monies paid over by the Owner Trustee or the Owner Participant to the Indenture Trustee for such purpose, shall be distributed as promptly as possible (it being understood that any payments of Interim Rent and Basic Rent received by the Indenture Trustee on a timely basis and in accordance with the provisions of Section 3[g] of the Lease shall be distributed on the date received out of the funds so received and if not so distributed the Indenture Trustee in its individual capacity shall pay, and distribute to the Loan Participants on demand, interest with respect thereto at the Overdue Rate for each day or part thereof until such amounts are distributed to the Loan Participants), in the following order of priority: first, so much of such installment as shall be required for the purpose shall be distributed and paid to the holders of the Loan Certificates to pay in full the aggregate amount of the payment or payments of principal and interest (as well as any interest on overdue principal or interest (to the extent permitted by Applicable Law) to the extent that installments of interest on overdue installments of Interim Rent and Basic Rent are received as set forth above) then due, such distribution to be made ratably, without priority of one over the other, in the proportion that the amount of such payment or payments then due under each such Loan Certificate bears to the aggregate amount of payments then due under all such Loan Certificates; and second, the balance, if any, of such installment remaining thereafter shall be distributed to the Owner Participant; provided, however, that, if an Event of Acceleration shall have occurred and be continuing, then such balance shall not be distributed (unless otherwise directed by a Majority in Interest of Holders) to the Owner Participant as provided in this clause "second" but shall be held by the Indenture Trustee as part of the Estate until the earliest to occur of (x) the date on which any such Event of Acceleration shall have been cured, in which event such balance shall be distributed in accordance with the provisions of this clause "second," or (y) the date on which Section 3(c) hereof shall become applicable, in which event such balance shall be distributed in accordance with the provisions of Section 3(c) hereof, or (z) unless an event described in paragraph (e), (f) or (g) of Section 17 of the Lease or paragraph (v), (vi) or (vii) of Section 12(a) hereof shall exist, the 180th day following the day on which such balance was received by the Indenture Trustee, in which event such balance shall be distributed in accordance with the provisions of this clause "second." The portion of each such installment distributed to a holder of a Loan Certificate shall be applied by such holder in payment of such Loan Certificate in accordance with the terms of Section 2(e) hereof.

(b) Payments for Lost or Terminated Aircraft

(i) Except as otherwise provided in Section 3(b)(ii) and Section 3(c) hereof, any amount received or receivable pursuant to Sections 9, 15(a), or 15(b) of the Lease shall in each case be distributed and paid in the following order of priority: first, so much of such amount as shall be required to reimburse Indenture Trustee for any expenses not reimbursed by Lessee in connection with the Collection or distribution of such amount shall be applied by the Indenture Trustee to reimburse itself; second, so much of such amount remaining as shall be required to pay the aggregate unpaid principal amount of all of the Loan Certificates and premium thereon, if any, plus (in all cases) the accrued but unpaid interest on such Loan Certificates to the date of distribution, shall be distributed to the holders of all Loan Certificates, without priority of one over any other, in the proportion that the aggregate unpaid principal amount of all Loan Certificates held by each holder, plus the accrued but unpaid interest thereon to the date of distribution, bears to the aggregate unpaid principal amount of all Loan Certificates, plus the accrued but unpaid interest thereon to the date of distribution; third, in the manner provided in clause "second" of Section 3(c) hereof; fourth, in the manner provided in clause "fourth" of Section 3(c) hereof; and fifth, in the manner provided in clause "fifth" of Section 3(c) hereof, except that in the event any Reimbursement Amount shall be owed to Lessee pursuant to Section 3(h) of the Lease, such amount shall first be distributed to Lessee.

(ii) Except as otherwise provided in Section 3(c) hereof, any amounts received directly or through Lessee from any governmental authority or other party pursuant to Section 9 of the Lease with respect to the Airframe or the Airframe and the Engines or engines then installed on the Airframe as the result of an Event of Loss, to the extent that such amounts are not at the time required to be paid to Lessee pursuant to said Section 9, and any amounts of insurance proceeds for damage to the Estate received directly or through Lessee from any insurer pursuant to Section 10 of the Lease with respect thereto, to the extent such amounts are not at the time required to be paid to Lessee pursuant to said Section 10, shall, except as otherwise provided in the next sentence, be applied in reduction of Lessee's obligation to pay Stipulated Loss Value and Termination Value, in each case for the Aircraft of which the Airframe or Engines are a part, as provided in the Lease. Any portion of any such amount referred to in the preceding sentence that is not required to be so paid to Lessee pursuant to the Lease, solely because a Default under Sections 17(a), (e), (f) or (g) of the Lease or an Event of Default shall have occurred and be continuing shall be held by the Indenture Trustee as security for the obligations of Lessee under the Lease and at such time as there shall not be continuing any such Default or Event of Default, such portion shall be paid to Lessee, unless the Indenture Trustee (as assignee from the Owner Trustee of the Lease) shall have theretofore declared the

Lease to be, or the Lease shall have become, in default pursuant to Section 18 thereof, in which event such portion shall be distributed forthwith upon such declaration in accordance with the provisions of Section 3(c) hereof.

(c) Payments after Event of Default or Event of Acceleration. Except as specifically provided in Section 3(e) hereof, all payments received and amounts realized by the Indenture Trustee after an Event of Default or an Event of Acceleration shall have occurred and be continuing hereunder and after the Indenture Trustee has declared (as assignee from the Owner Trustee of the Lease) the Lease to be, or the Lease shall have become, in default pursuant to Section 18 thereof or has declared the Loan Certificates to be, or they shall have become, accelerated pursuant to Section 12(a) hereof, as the case may be, or has elected to foreclose or otherwise enforce its rights under this Indenture (including any amounts realized by the Indenture Trustee from the exercise of any remedies pursuant to Section 18 of the Lease, or Section 4 or Section 12 hereof), as well as all payments or amounts then held or thereafter received by the Indenture Trustee as part of the Estate while such Event of Default or Event of Acceleration shall be continuing, shall be distributed forthwith by the Indenture Trustee in the following order of priority: first, so much of such payments or amounts as shall be required to reimburse the Indenture Trustee for any tax, expense, or other loss incurred by the Indenture Trustee (to the extent not previously reimbursed and to the extent incurred in connection with its duties as Indenture Trustee) and any unpaid ongoing fees of the Indenture Trustee shall be distributed to the Indenture Trustee; second, so much of such payments or amounts as shall be required to reimburse the then existing or prior holders of the Loan Certificates for payments made by them to the Indenture Trustee pursuant to Section 5(c) hereof (to the extent not previously reimbursed), shall be distributed to the then existing or prior holders of the Loan Certificates, without priority of one over the other, in accordance with the amount of the payment or payments made by each such then existing or prior holder pursuant to said Section 5(c); third, so much of such payments or amounts as shall be required to pay in full the aggregate unpaid principal amount of all Loan Certificates, plus the accrued but the unpaid interest thereon to the date of distribution, shall be distributed to the holders of the Loan Certificates, and in case the aggregate amount so to be distributed shall be insufficient to pay in full as aforesaid, then, ratably, without priority of one over the other, in the proportion that the aggregate unpaid principal amount of all Loan Certificates held by each such holder, plus the accrued but unpaid interest thereon to the date of distribution, bears to the aggregate unpaid principal amount of all Loan Certificates, plus the accrued but unpaid interest thereon to the date of distribution; and fourth, so much of such payments or amounts as shall be required to pay the holders of the Loan Certificates any and all other amounts then due and payable to them under the Loan Certificates, this Indenture or the Participation Agreement shall be distributed to the holders of the Loan Certificates entitled thereto, ratably without priority of any such holder over any other, in the proportion that the amount of such payment to which each such holder is entitled bears to the aggregate amount of such payments to which all such holders are entitled; and fifth, the balance, if any, of such payments or amounts remaining thereafter shall be distributed to the Owner Participant.

(d) Other Payments. Except as otherwise provided in Section 3(c) hereof, any payments received by the Indenture Trustee for which no provision as to the application thereof is made in the Lease or the Participation Agreement or elsewhere in this Section 3 shall be distributed forthwith by the Indenture Trustee in the following order of priority: first, in the manner provided in the clause "first" of Section 3(c) hereof; second, in the manner provided in clause "second" of Section 3(c) hereof; third, in the manner provided in clause "fourth" of Section 3(c) hereof; and fourth, in the manner provided in clause "fifth" of Section 3(c) hereof; provided, however, that, if an Event of Acceleration shall have occurred and be continuing, then such balance shall not be distributed (unless otherwise directed by a Majority in Interest of Holders) to the Owner Trustee as provided in this clause "fourth" but shall be held by the Indenture Trustee as part of the Estate until the earliest to occur of (x) the date on which such Event of Acceleration shall have been cured, (y) the date on which Section 3(c) hereof shall become applicable or (z) unless an event described in Sections 17(e), (f), or (g) of the Lease or paragraphs (v), (vi), or (vii) of Section 12(a) hereof shall exist, the 180th day following the day on which such funds were received by the Indenture Trustee, in which event such balance shall be distributed in accordance with the provisions of clause "second" of Section 3(a) hereof.

Any payments received by the Indenture Trustee for which provision as to the application thereof is made in the Lease or the Participation Agreement but not elsewhere in this Indenture shall be applied to the purposes for which such payments were made in accordance with the provisions of the Lease or the Participation Agreement, as the case may be.

(e) Distribution of Excepted Property. Any other provision of this Indenture to the contrary notwithstanding, all amounts constituting Excepted Property received by the Indenture Trustee shall be paid by the Indenture Trustee to the Person or Persons entitled thereto.

(f) Certain Payments. Anything in this Section 3 to the contrary notwithstanding (but subject, however, to the provisions of the proviso to the first sentence of Section 3[a] hereof and the proviso to Section 3[d] hereof), after the Indenture Trustee shall have knowledge of an Event of Default or an Event of Acceleration or other event which, after lapse of time or notice or both would become an Event of Default or an Event of Acceleration, all amounts which, but for the provisions of this Section 3(f), would otherwise be distributable by the Indenture Trustee to Owner Trustee, Lessee, or the Owner Participant shall be held by the Indenture Trustee as part of the Estate and, if such Event of Default or Event of Acceleration or other event shall cease to be continuing prior to the time such amounts may become distributable pursuant to Section 3(c) hereof, such amounts shall be distributable as provided elsewhere in this Section 3.

(g) Notice of Distributions. Distributions to the Loan Participants by the Indenture Trustee hereunder shall be made to the addresses set forth on Schedule II to the Participation Agreement or such other addresses as any Loan Participant or any other holder may specify in writing to the Indenture Trustee from time to time and concurrently therewith, the Indenture Trustee shall give notice of Such distributions to the Loan Participants and such holders at the addresses set forth on Schedule II to the Participation Agreement or as otherwise specified pursuant to Section 11(g) hereof.

Section 4. Right of Owner Participant to Purchase Loan Certificates

(a) Purchase of Loan Certificates

(i) At any time after (A) an Event of Default under clauses (e), (f), or (g) of Section 17 of the Lease has occurred and is continuing or (B) two aggregate Events of Default but not consecutive with respect to Basic Rent have occurred and are continuing under clause (a) of Section 17 of the Lease and the Owner Participant then delivers an Independent Aircraft Appraisal to the effect that the value of the

Aircraft is materially declining because the Aircraft is not being maintained in accordance with the requirements of the Lease; or (ii) at any time after the Indenture Trustee, (A) has taken action to foreclose the Lien of this Indenture, or otherwise exercised any of the remedies pursuant to this Indenture or the Lease, other than those described in the next sentence of this Section 4(a), or (B) has notified the Owner Participant in writing that it intends to do so, and upon receipt of the written agreement of the Owner Participant to purchase (or cause prepayment of) all Loan Certificates then outstanding (for the amount, or at the price, hereinafter referred to) addressed to all holders of Loan Certificates at the time outstanding hereunder, each such holder shall upon receipt, within seven days of receipt of such agreement, of an amount equal to the aggregate unpaid principal amount of all Loan Certificates then held by such holder, together with accrued interest thereon to the date of payment, plus all other sums then due and payable to such holder hereunder or under the Participation Agreement or the Lease or under such Loan Certificates, (including, without limitation, all reasonable fees, costs, and expenses (including legal fees and expanses) incurred by or on behalf of the holders of the Loan Certificates and the Indenture Trustee in connection with such Event of Default or Event of Acceleration) forthwith sell, assign, transfer, and convey to the Owner Participant (without recourse or warranty except against liens arising by, through or under such Holder) all of the right, title, and interest of such holder in and to the Estate, this Indenture, all Loan Certificates held by such holder and the Participation Agreement, and the Owner Participant shall assume all of such holder's obligations under the Participation Agreement and this Indenture. The Owner Participant shall not be entitled to so purchase or cause the prepayment of the Loan Certificates if the Indenture Trustee shall (x) seize and hold physical possession of the Aircraft unless the Indenture Trustee shall retain such possession for a period exceeding 60 days or (y) make demand on the Lessee to perform, or bring a Court action to enforce, the provisions of the Lease (other than those in Section 18 thereof), so long as in either the case of clause (x) or clause (y), the Indenture Trustee shall not be exercising other remedies or taking action to foreclose the Lien of this Indenture and so long as there is no reasonable danger that the Owner Participant's title to the Aircraft will be lost. In any event the Indenture Trustee agrees to give the Owner Participant at least 10 days notice of its intention to sell the Aircraft pursuant to any action referred to in clause (ii)(A) above except that with respect to those actions described in clauses (x) and (y) of the preceding sentence of this Section 4(a), as to which the Indenture Trustee shall give concurrent notice. Notwithstanding the foregoing, nothing shall preclude the Owner Participant from purchasing any Loan Certificates on such terms as the holders of such Loan Certificates and the Owner Participant may agree, provided that the Owner Participant offers to purchase all other Loan Certificates then outstanding on the same terms and that after the purchase thereof the Owner Trustee shall proceed diligently under the Lease to exercise remedies dispossessing the Lessee of possession of the Aircraft.

Section 5. Duties of the Indenture Trustee

(a) Notice of Event of Default or Event of Acceleration. If any amounts of Interim Rent or Basic Rent, or payments of the principal of, interest or premium (if any) on the Loan Certificates, due and payable on any Interim Rent or Basic Rent Payment Date shall not have been paid in full on such payment date, the Indenture Trustee shall give telephonic notice within one Business Day (followed by prompt written notice) to the Owner

Trustee specifying the amount and nature of such deficiency in payment [provided, that failure of the Indenture Trustee to give such notice in a timely fashion shall not impair its rights hereunder or under the Lease, except to the extent that such failure shall deprive the Owner Trustee of knowledge of such default, in which case the running of the Owner Trustee's *cure* rights, if any, pursuant to Section 12(a) hereof shall be tolled until the Owner Trustee shall have such knowledge or the Indenture Trustee shall give such notice]. In the event the Indenture Trustee shall have knowledge of an Event of Default or an Event of Acceleration or shall hold a balance of an installment of Interim Rent or Basic Rent under the proviso to Section 3(a) hereof or shall hold any funds pursuant to Section 3(d) hereof, the Indenture Trustee shall give prompt notice of such Event of Default or Event of Acceleration or such retention to each holder of a Loan Certificate, the Owner Trustee, the Manufacturer, Lessee, and the Owner Participant by telex, telegraphic, facsimile transfer, or telephonic notice (confirmed, in the case of telephonic notice, in writing sent by first class registered mail, postage prepaid or sent by an overnight delivery service or hand delivered) unless such Event of Default or Event of Acceleration shall have been remedied or such retained funds shall have been distributed before the giving of such notice (provided, that failure of the Indenture Trustee to give such notice in a timely fashion shall not impair its rights hereunder or under the Lease, except to the extent that such failure shall deprive the Owner Trustee of knowledge of such default, in which case the running of the Owner Trustee's cure rights, if any, pursuant to Section 12(a) hereof shall be tolled until the Owner Trustee shall have such knowledge or the Indenture Trustee shall give such notice). Subject to the terms of Section 5(c) hereof, in accordance with written instructions received from a Majority in Interest of Holders, the Indenture Trustee shall, if an Event of Acceleration referred to in Section 12(a)(i) exists, declare the Lease to be in default pursuant to Section 18 thereof or the Loan Certificates to be accelerated pursuant to Section 12(a) hereof. If the Indenture Trustee shall not have received instructions as above provided within 20 days after giving notice of such Event of Default or Event of Acceleration to the holders of the Loan Certificates by the Indenture Trustee, the Indenture Trustee may, subject to instructions received pursuant to the preceding sentence, take such action, or refrain from taking such action, but shall be under no duty to take or refrain from taking any action, with respect to such Event of Default or Event of Acceleration as it shall determine advisable in the best interests of the holders of the Loan Certificates. If the Indenture Trustee shall at any time declare the Lease to be in default pursuant to Section 18 thereof, the Indenture Trustee in its discretion may, or upon receipt of a written demand therefor from a Majority in Interest of Holders shall, subject to and pursuant to the terms of Section 12 hereof, declare the unpaid principal amount of all Loan Certificates together with the premium, if any, and accrued interest thereon to be immediately due and payable, upon which declaration and automatically upon the occurrence of an event described in paragraphs (v), (vi), or (vii) of Section 12(a) hereof such principal amount, premium, and interest shall immediately become due and payable without further act or notice of any kind. In the event the Indenture Trustee shall at any time elect to foreclose the Lien of this Indenture or otherwise take action to dispose of any of the Estate, the unpaid principal amount of all Loan Certificates then outstanding with accrued interest thereon to the date of payment shall immediately become due and payable without further act or notice of any kind. If the Indenture Trustee shall at any time declare the Lease to be in default pursuant to Section 18 thereof or shall elect to foreclose or otherwise enforce the Lien of this Indenture or shall declare the Loan Certificates to be due and payable, the Indenture Trustee shall forthwith notify the Owner Participant, the Owner Trustee, Lessee, and each holder of Loan Certificates (provided, that failure of the Indenture Trustee to give such notice in a timely fashion shall not impair its right hereunder or under the Lease, except to the extent that such failure deprives the Owner Trustee of knowledge of an Event of Default under the Lease related to such action by the Indenture Trustee, in which case the running of the Owner Trustee's cure rights, if any, with respect to such Events of Default pursuant to Section 12[a] hereof shall be tolled until the Owner Trustee shall have such knowledge or the Indenture Trustee shall give such notice). For all purposes of this Indenture, in the absence of actual knowledge of an officer in the corporate trust department of the Indenture Trustee, the Indenture Trustee shall not be deemed to have knowledge of an Event of Default or of an Event of Acceleration, or of any event which with giving of notice or the lapse of time or both would constitute an Event of Default or an Event of Acceleration, unless notified in writing by one or more holders of Loan Certificates; provided, that the Indenture Trustee shall be deemed to have notice of the nonpayment of Interim Rent or Basic Rent on the date due, and not later than one Business Day after Such nonpayment the Indenture Trustee shall give telephonic notice of such nonpayment to Lessee, the Owner Trustee, the Owner Participant and each holder of a Loan Certificate promptly confirmed by telex, telegram, or telecopy sent to such parties (provided, that failure of the Indenture Trustee to give such notice in a timely fashion shall not impair its rights hereunder or under the Lease, except to the extent that such failure shall deprive the Owner Trustee of knowledge of such default, in which case the running of the Owner Trustee's cure rights, if any, pursuant to Section 12(a) hereof shall be tolled until the Owner Trustee shall have such knowledge or the Indenture Trustee shall give such notice.) All obligations of the Indenture Trustee hereunder with respect to any such Event of Default or Event of Acceleration or other event shall be subject to the Indenture Trustee having knowledge thereof pursuant to the foregoing.

(b) Action Upon Instructions. Subject to the terms of Sections 5(a) and 5(c) hereof, upon the written instructions at any time and from time to time of a Majority in Interest of Holders, the Indenture Trustee shall take such of the following actions as may be specified in such instructions (subject to the rights of the other parties hereto, except to the extent assigned hereunder): (i) give such notice, waiver, direction, or consent, or exercise such right, remedy, or power hereunder or under the Lease, the Participation Agreement, the Purchase Agreement, or the Assignment or in respect of any part or all of the Estate or take such other action as shall be specified in such instructions; and (ii) approve as satisfactory to it all matters required by the terms of the Lease to be satisfactory to the Owner Trustee as Lessor thereunder, it being understood that without the written instructions of a Majority in Interest of Holders the Indenture Trustee shall not take any action described in clauses (i) and (ii) above. Unless and until an Event of Acceleration shall have occurred and be continuing:

(A) the Owner Trustee, to the exclusion of the Indenture Trustee, may exercise all rights, powers, and privileges under, or with respect to, and may consent to or approve any matter subject to the consent, approval, or satisfaction of Lessor referred to in Sections 3(e), 10(f), 13(f), 14 (as to the determination of Fair Market Sales Value or Fair Market Rental value), 15(a) (solely in respect of exercising the right to solicit and make bids thereunder), and 19 of the Lease; provided that nothing herein shall be deemed to permit the Owner Trustee to amend, modify, or otherwise alter any of such Sections without the prior written consent of the Indenture Trustee;

(B) the exercise of all other rights, powers, and privileges of Lessor under or with respect to the Lease shall only be exercised jointly by the Indenture Trustee, acting upon instructions as aforesaid, and by the Owner Trustee (provided that, except in the case of Excepted Property, the Indenture Trustee shall have the right, to the exclusion of the Owner Participant to the extent provided in this Indenture, to receive money under the Lease and to exercise any rights under Section 18 of the Lease);

(C) the Indenture Trustee shall have an independent right (but not exclusive of the rights of Lessor) to exercise all rights, powers, and privileges of Lessor under Sections 12, 17, and 23 of the Lease; and

(D) any other matter referred to in the Lease as requiring or being subject to the consent, approval, or satisfaction of Lessor shall be consented to, approved by or satisfactory to both the Indenture Trustee, acting upon instructions as aforesaid, and the Owner Trustee (provided that, except in the case of Excepted Property, the Indenture Trustee shall have the right, to the exclusion of the Owner Trustee to the extent provided in this Indenture, to receive money under the Lease and to exercise any rights under Section 18 of the Lease). Upon the receipt of instructions from the Majority of Interest of Holders, the Owner Trustee, the Owner Participant or Lessee, the Indenture Trustee shall execute and file such financing statements (and such continuation statements with respect to any such financing statement) or any other similar document relating to the Estate or to the security interests and assignments created by this Indenture.

Notwithstanding the foregoing, the Owner Trustee may at any time exercise its rights under Section 19 of the Lease; provided that as between the Owner Trustee and the Indenture Trustee such exercise shall not be a cure of Lessee's default unless such exercise is in compliance with the provisions of Section 12(a) of this Indenture.

Upon the expiration or earlier termination of the Term and after payment in full of the principal amount of and interest on all Loan Certificates, and all other amounts owed under the Participation Agreement, this Indenture, and the Loan Certificates, the Indenture Trustee shall in each case, upon the written request of the Owner Trustee, execute and deliver to, or as directed in writing by, the Owner Trustee an appropriate instrument (in due form for recording) releasing the Aircraft from the Lien of this Indenture.

(c) Indemnification

(i) The Indenture Trustee shall not be required to take any action or refrain from taking any action under Section 5(a) or 5(b) or Sections 4 or 12 hereof unless it shall have been indemnified in manner and form satisfactory to the Indenture Trustee against any liability, cost, or expense (including counsel fees) which may be incurred in connection therewith; and if a Majority in Interest of Holders shall have directed Indenture Trustee to take any such action or refrain from taking any action, the holders constituting such Majority in Interest of Holders shall furnish promptly such indemnity as shall be required. The Indenture Trustee shall not be required to take any action under Section 5(a) or 5(b) or Sections 4 or 12 hereof, nor shall any other provision of this Indenture be deemed to impose a duty on the Indenture Trustee to take any action, if the Indenture Trustee shall have been advised in writing by independent counsel that such action is contrary to the terms hereof or of the Lease, the Participation Agreement, the Purchase Agreement, or the Assignment or is otherwise contrary to law.

(ii) Except as provided in the last sentence of Section 5(d) hereof, nothing contained in this Indenture shall require the Indenture Trustee to expend or risk its own funds or otherwise incur any financial liability in the performance of any of its duties hereunder or in the exercise of any of its rights or powers if it shall have reasonable grounds for believing that repayment of such funds or adequate indemnity against such risk or liability is not reasonably assured to it. Without limiting the generality of the foregoing, if an Event of Default occurs and is continuing and the Indenture Trustee shall have obtained possession of or title to the Aircraft or Engines, the Indenture Trustee shall not be obligated to use or operate the Aircraft or Engines or cause the Aircraft or Engines to be used or operated directly or indirectly by itself or through agents or other representatives or to lease, license, or otherwise permit or provide for the use or operation of the Aircraft or Engines by any other person unless (A) the Indenture Trustee shall have been able to obtain insurance in kinds, at rates, and in amounts satisfactory to it in its discretion to protect the Estate and the Indenture Trustee against any and all liability for loss or damage to the Aircraft or Engines and for public liability and property damages resulting from use or operation of the Aircraft or Engines and (B) funds are available in the Estate to pay for all such insurance or, in lieu of such insurance, the Indenture Trustee is furnished with indemnification from the holders of the Loan Certificates or any other person upon terms and in amounts satisfactory to the Indenture Trustee in its discretion to protect the Estate and the Indenture Trustee against any and all such liabilities.

(d) No Duties Except as Specified in Indenture or Instructions. The Indenture Trustee shall not have any duty or obligation to manage, control, use, sell, dispose, of or otherwise deal with the Aircraft or any other part of the Estate, or to otherwise take or refrain from taking any action under, or in connection with, this Indenture, the Lease, the Participation Agreement, the Purchase Agreement, or the Assignment, except as expressly provided by the terms of this Indenture or as expressly provided in written instructions received pursuant to the terms of Section 5(a) or 5(b) hereof; and no implied duties or obligations shall be read into this Indenture against the Indenture Trustee. The Indenture Trustee nevertheless agrees that it will, in its individual capacity and at its own cost and expense, promptly take such action as may be necessary to duly discharge any Liens on any part of the Estate, or on any properties of the Owner Trustee assigned, pledged, or mortgaged as part of the Estate, which result from claims against or affecting it or from acts or omissions of the Indenture Trustee, in each case not related to the administration of the Estate or any other transaction pursuant to this Indenture or any document included in the Estate.

(e) No Action Except Under Lease, Indenture, or Instructions. The Indenture Trustee agrees that it will not manage, control, use, sell, dispose of, or otherwise deal with the Aircraft or other property constituting part of the Estate except (i) as required by the terms of the Lease and the Participation Agreement, (ii) in accordance with the powers granted to, or the authority conferred upon, the Indenture Trustee pursuant to this Indenture, or (iii) in accordance with the express terms hereof or with written instructions pursuant to Section 5(a) or 5(b) hereof.

(f) Replacement Airframe and Engines. At any time and from time to time prior to the expiration of the Term, the Airframe or Engine which the provisions of Section 9 of the Lease require to be disposed of may be disposed of in accordance with the provisions of this Section 5(f) and the provisions of the aforementioned Section of the Lease, and the Owner Trustee shall, from time to time, direct the Indenture Trustee to execute and deliver to, or as directed in writing by, the Owner Participant, an appropriate instrument releasing the Airframe or Engine from the Lien of this Indenture and, but only in respect of such Airframe or Engine, from the assignment and pledge thereof hereunder and the Indenture Trustee shall execute and deliver such instrument as aforesaid, but only upon receipt by or deposit with the Indenture Trustee of the following:

(i) A written request from the Owner Trustee, requesting such release and describing the Airframe or Engine so to be released.

(ii) In the case of the Airframe, evidence satisfactory to the Indenture Trustee that there has been full compliance with Sections 9(a) and (b) of the Lease.

(iii) In the case of an Engine, a certificate signed by the Chairman of the Board or by the President, or by any Senior Vice President or any other Vice President signing with the Treasurer or an Assistant Treasurer or the Secretary or an Assistant Secretary, of Lessee stating the following:

(A) a description of the Engine to be released, which shall be identified by its manufacturer's serial number;

(B) a description, including the manufacturer's serial number, of the Replacement Engine to be received as consideration for the Engine to be released pursuant to the provisions of Section 9(c) of the Lease;

(C) that such release, in the opinion of the signers, will not impair the security of this Indenture in contravention of the provisions of this Indenture;

(D) that no Default or Event of Default under the Lease has occurred which has not been remedied or waived, or will occur as a result of the making and granting of the request for release;

(E) that the release of the Engine so to be released and the subjecting of such Replacement Engine to the Lien of this Indenture will not be inconsistent with any of the provisions of this Indenture; and

(F) that all provisions of Section 9(c) of the Lease have been complied with.

(iv) The appropriate instruments transferring title to the Replacement Engine to be received as consideration for the Engine to be released to the Owner Trustee, subjecting such Replacement Engine to the Lease and subjecting such Replacement Engine to the lien of this Indenture.

(v) The opinion of counsel to Lessee satisfactory to the Indenture Trustee:

(A) stating that the certificates, opinions, and other instruments or property which have been or are therewith delivered to and deposited with the Indenture Trustee conform to the requirements of this Indenture and the Lease and that, upon the basis of such application, the property so sold or disposed of may be lawfully released from the lien of this Indenture, and that all conditions precedent herein provided for relating to such release have been complied with;

(B) stating that the Lease Supplement pertaining to the Replacement Engine has been duly authorized, executed, and delivered by Lessee; and

(C) stating that the Owner Trustee has good and marketable title to the Replacement Engine to be received as consideration for the Engine to be released, free of all Liens whatsoever, except Permitted Liens, that such Replacement Engine has been validly subjected to the Lien of this Indenture and is covered by the Lease, that the instruments subjecting such Replacement Engine to the Lease and to the Lien of this Indenture have been duly filed for recordation pursuant to the Federal Aviation Act and that no further action, filing, or recording of any document is necessary or advisable in order to establish and perfect the title of the Owner Trustee to and the Lien of this Indenture on such Replacement Engine.

(g) Replacements After Default

In case an Event of Default under the Lease shall have occurred and be continuing, Lessee, while in possession of the Aircraft and other property covered by the Lease, may do any of the things enumerated in Section 5(f) hereof (to the extent set forth therein) if the Indenture Trustee in its discretion shall consent to such action, in which case the certificate mentioned in Section 5(f) need not contain the Statement required by clause (D) of paragraph (iii) thereof.

(h) Indenture Supplements for Replacements. In the event of a Replacement Airframe or Replacement Engine being substituted as contemplated by Section 9 of the Lease, the Owner Trustee and the Indenture Trustee agree for the benefit of the holders of Loan Certificates and Lessee, subject to fulfillment of the conditions precedent and compliance by Lessee with its obligations set forth in Section 9 of the Lease, to execute and deliver an Indenture Supplement substantially in the form of Exhibit A hereto and, provided no Event of Default shall have occurred and be continuing, execute and deliver to Lessee an appropriate instrument releasing the Airframe or Engine being replaced from the Lien of this Indenture.

(i) Effect of Replacements. In the event of the substitution of a Replacement Airframe, with or without Replacement Engines, as contemplated by Section 9(a) of the Lease or of a Replacement Engine pursuant to Section 9(c) of the Lease, all provisions of this Indenture relating to the Airframe or Engine or Engines being replaced shall be applicable to such Replacement Airframe or Replacement Engine or Engines with the same force and effect as if such Replacement Airframe or Replacement Engine or Engines were the same airframe or engine or engines, as the case may be, as the Airframe or Engine or Engines being replaced but for the Event of Loss with respect to the Airframe or Engine or Engines being replaced.

Section 6. The Owner Trustee and the Indenture Trustee

(a) Acceptance of Trust and Duties. The Indenture Trustee accepts the trusts hereby created and applicable to it and agrees to perform the same but only upon the terms of this Indenture and agrees to receive and disburse all monies received by it constituting part of the Estate in accordance with the terms hereof. The Indenture Trustee shall not be answerable or accountable under any circumstances, except for its own willful misconduct or negligence or breach of any of its representations or warranties set forth herein or in the Participation Agreement or its covenant in the last sentence of Section 5(d) hereof, and the Indenture Trustee shall not be liable for any action or inaction of the Owner Trustee.

(b) Absence of Duties. Except in accordance with written instructions or requests furnished pursuant to Section 5(b) and except as provided in, and without limiting the generality of, Section 5(d) hereof or as may otherwise expressly be provided in the Operative Documents, the Indenture Trustee shall have no duty (i) to see to any registration of the Aircraft or any recording or filing of the Lease, or of this Indenture or any other document, or to see to the maintenance of any such registration, recording, or filing, (ii) to see to any insurance on the Aircraft or to effect or maintain any such insurance, whether or not Lessee shall be in default with respect thereto, (iii) to see to the payment or discharge of any tax, assessment, or other governmental charge or any Lien owing with respect to, or assessed or levied against, any part of the Estate, (iv) to confirm, verify, or inquire into the failure to receive any financial statements of Lessee or (v) to inspect the Aircraft at any time or ascertain or inquire as to the performance or observance of any of Lessee's covenants under the Lease with respect to the Aircraft. The Indenture Trustee will furnish to each holder of a Loan Certificate at the time outstanding and to the Owner Trustee, promptly upon receipt thereof, duplicates or copies of all reports, notices, requests, demands, certificates, and other instruments furnished to the Indenture Trustee under the Lease or this Indenture, to the extent that the same shall not have been furnished to such holder or the Owner Trustee pursuant to the Lease or this Indenture.

(c) No Representations or Warranties as to the Aircraft or Documents. THE OWNER TRUSTEE IN ITS INDIVIDUAL CAPACITY OR OTHERWISE AND THE INDENTURE TRUSTEE MAKE (i) NO REPRESENTATION OR WARRANTY, EXPRESS OR IMPLIED, AS TO THE TITLE, AIRWORTHINESS, CONDITION, VALUE, DESIGN, OPERATION, MERCHANTABILITY, OR FITNESS FOR USE OF ANY AIRCRAFT, AS TO THE ABSENCE OF LATENT OR OTHER DEFECTS, WHETHER OR NOT DISCOVERABLE, AS TO THE ABSENCE OF ANY INFRINGEMENT OF ANY PATENT, TRADEMARK, OR COPYRIGHT, AS TO THE ABSENCE OF OBLI GATIONS BASED ON STRICT LIABILITY IN TORT OR AS TO THE QUALITY OF THE MATERIAL OR WORKMANSHIP OF THE AIRCRAFT, OR ANY OTHER REPRESENTATION OR WARRANTY, EXPRESS OR IMPLIED, WITH RESPECT TO THE AIRCRAFT WHATSOEVER, except that the Owner Trustee hereby represents and warrants that on the Delivery Date for the Aircraft the Owner Trustee shall have received whatever title to the Aircraft was conveyed to it by Lessee and that the Aircraft shall be free of Lessor's Liens attributable to it in its individual capacity, and (ii) no representation or warranty as to the validity, legality, or enforceability of this Indenture, the Participation Agreement, the Loan Certificates, the Lease, the Trust Agreement, the Purchase Agreement, Assignment, the Lease Supplement, or the Indenture Supplement or any other document or instrument or as to the correctness of any statement contained in any thereof, except that the Owner Trustee hereby represents and warrants to the holders of the Loan Certificates as set forth in Section 7 of the Participation Agreement, and except that the Indenture Trustee hereby represents and warrants to the holders of the Loan Certificates as set forth in Section 9 of the Participation Agreement.

(d) No Segregation of Monies; No Interest; Investments

(i) Subject to Section 6(d)(ii), no monies received by the Indenture Trustee hereunder need be segregated in any manner except to the extent required by law, and any such moneys may be deposited under such general conditions as may be prescribed by law applicable to the Indenture Trustee, and, except as otherwise agreed by the Indenture Trustee, the Indenture Trustee shall not be liable for any interest thereon.

(ii) Any amounts held by the Indenture Trustee pursuant to the express terms of this Indenture or the Lease shall be invested and reinvested by the Indenture Trustee from time to time in Permitted Investments at the direction and at the risk and expense of Lessee, except that (i) after an Event of Default shall have occurred and be continuing, such amounts shall be so invested and reinvested at the direction of a Majority in Interest of Holders and at the risk and expense of Lessee, and (ii) any amounts held pursuant to the proviso to the first sentence of Section 3(a) or 3(d) hereof shall be so invested and reinvested at the direction of a Majority in Interest of Holders and at the risk and expense of the holders. Any net income or gain realized as a result of any such investments or reinvestments shall be held as part of the Estate and shall be applied by the Indenture Trustee at the same time, and the same conditions and in the same manner as the amounts in respect of which such income or gain was realized are required to be distributed in accordance with the provisions hereof or of the Lease pursuant to which such amounts were required to be held. Any such Permitted Investments may be sold or otherwise reduced to cash (without regard to maturity date) by the Indenture Trustee whenever necessary to make any application as required by such provisions. If any sale (or any payment at maturity) of any such investment produces a net sum less than the cost (including accrued interest paid as such) of the investment so sold or paid (the difference between such cost and such net sum, an "Investment Loss") the Indenture Trustee shall give written notice to the Owner Trustee and the Owner Trustee shall promptly pay to the Indenture Trustee from funds provided by Lessee, an amount equal to the Investment Loss, which payment shall become part of the Estate. The Indenture Trustee shall have no liability for any loss resulting from any such investment or reinvestment other than by reason of the willful misconduct or gross negligence of the Indenture Trustee.

(e) Reliance; Agents; Advice of Counsel. The Owner Trustee and the Indenture Trustee shall incur no liability to anyone by acting upon any signature, instrument, notice, resolution, request, consent, order, certificate, report, opinion, bond, or other document or paper reasonably believed by them to be genuine and reasonably believed by them to be signed by the proper party or parties. The Owner Trustee and the Indenture Trustee may accept a copy of a resolution of the Board of Directors of any party to the Participation Agreement, certified by the Secretary or an Assistant Secretary of such party as duly adopted and in full force and effect, as conclusive evidence that such resolution has been duly adopted by said Board and that the same is in full force and effect. As to any fact or matter the manner of ascertainment of which is not specifically described herein, the Owner Trustee and the Indenture Trustee may for all purposes hereof rely on a certificate, signed by an officer of Lessee, as to such fact or matter, and such certificate shall constitute full protection to the Owner Trustee and the Indenture Trustee for any action taken or omitted to be taken by them in good faith in reliance thereon. The Indenture Trustee shall furnish to the Owner Trustee upon request such information and copies of such documents as the Indenture Trustee may have and as are necessary for the Owner Trustee to perform its duties under Section 2 hereof. In the administration of the trust hereunder, the Indenture Trustee may execute any of the trusts or powers hereof and perform its powers and duties hereunder directly or through agents or attorneys and may, at the expense of the Estate, consult with independent counsel, accountants and other skilled persons to be selected and employed by it, and the Indenture Trustee shall not be liable for anything done, suffered, or omitted in good faith by them in accordance with the advice or opinion of any such independent counsel, accountants or other skilled Persons acting within such Person 's area of competence (so long as the Indenture Trustee shall have exercised reasonable care in selecting such Persons).

(f) No Compensation from Estate. The Indenture Trustee agrees that it shall have no right against the holders of the Loan Certificates or, except as provided in Sections 3(c), 7, and 11(c) hereof, the Estate, for any fee as compensation for its services hereunder.

(g) Covenants of Owner Trustee

(i) The Owner Trustee will duly and punctually pay the principal of, and interest on and other amounts due under the Loan Certificates and hereunder in accordance with the terms of the Loan Certificates and this Indenture and all amounts payable by it to the holders of Loan Certificates under the Participation Agreement.

(ii) The Owner Trustee will furnish to the Indenture Trustee and to each of the Loan Participants named in the Participation Agreement, so long as such Loan

Participant or its nominees shall hold any of the Loan Certificates, and to each holder of at least 10% of the aggregate principal amount of the Loan Certificates at the time outstanding, promptly upon receipt thereof, duplicates or copies of all reports, notices, requests, demands, certificates, financial statements, and other instruments furnished to the Owner Trustee under the Lease, including, without limitation, a copy of each report or notice from an insurer received pursuant to Section 10 of the Lease, to the extent that the same shall not have been furnished to the Indenture Trustee, the Loan Participants, and to such other holders of Loan Certificates pursuant to the Lease.

(iii) The Owner Trustee will, from time to time, execute and deliver any and all such instruments of further assurance and other instruments as the Indenture Trustee shall deem necessary or advisable to effectuate and maintain the Lien and security interest purported to be granted by this Indenture as the Indenture Trustee may reasonably request. Upon the instructions at any time and from time to time of the Indenture Trustee, the Owner Trustee shall execute for filing any financing statement (and any continuation statement with respect to such financing statement) or any other similar document relating to the security interests created by this Indenture, as may be specified in such instructions.

(h) Not Acting in Individual Capacity. The Owner Trustee acts hereunder solely as trustee under the Trust Agreement and not in its individual capacity and all persons having any claim against the Owner Trustee by reason of the transactions contemplated hereby shall look only to the Estate for payment or satisfaction, provided that the foregoing shall not release the Owner Trustee from liability it would otherwise have in its individual capacity for gross negligence or willful misconduct.

Section 7. Indemnification of Indenture Trustee

(a) Scope of Indemnification. The Indenture Trustee, and its successors, assigns, agents, and servants, shall be entitled to indemnification from the Estate from and against any and all liabilities, obligations, losses, damages, penalties, taxes (excluding any taxes payable by the Indenture Trustee on or measured by any compensation received by the Indenture Trustee for its services under this Indenture), claims, actions, suits, costs, expenses, or disbursements (including legal fees and expenses) of any kind and nature whatsoever which may be imposed on, incurred by, or asserted against the Indenture Trustee (whether or not also indemnified against by any other person under any other document) in anyway relating to or arising out of this Indenture, the Lease, the Participation Agreement, the Purchase Agreement, or the Assignment or the enforcement of any of the terms of any thereof, or in any way relating to or arising out of the manufacture, purchase, acceptance, nonacceptance, rejection, ownership, delivery, lease, possession, use, operation, condition, sale, return, or other disposition of the Aircraft or any Engine (including, without limitation, latent and other defects, whether or not discoverable, and any claim for patent, trademark, or copyright infringement), or in any way relating to or arising out of the administration of the Estate or the action or inaction of the Indenture Trustee hereunder, except only (i) in the case of willful misconduct or negligence of the Indenture Trustee in the performance of its duties hereunder, (ii) breach of (A) any representation or warranty made herein or in the Participation Agreement or (B) its covenant contained in the last sentence of Section 5(d) hereof and (iii) items for which the Indenture Trustee is not Indemnified under Sections 16(c) and 17(d) of the Participation Agreement and, to secure the same, the Indenture Trustee shall have a Lien on the Estate prior to any interest therein of the holders of the Loan Certificates or the Owner Participant. The Indenture Trustee agrees that it will look only to the Estate and Lessee for payment or satisfaction of any claim it may have under this Section 7 provided that the Indenture Trustee agrees to first look to the Lessee for such payment or satisfaction. The indemnities contained in this Section 7 shall survive the termination of this Indenture.

Section 8. Successor Trustees

(a) Resignation of Indenture Trustee; Appointment of Successor.

(i) The Indenture Trustee or any successor thereto may resign at any time without cause by giving at least 30 days' prior written notice to the Owner Trustee and to each holder of a Loan Certificate, such resignation to be effective on the acceptance of the trusteeship by a successor Indenture Trustee. In addition, a Majority in Interest of Holders may at any time remove the Indenture Trustee without cause by an instrument in writing delivered to the Owner Trustee and the Indenture Trustee, and the Owner Trustee shall promptly notify Lessee and each holder of a Loan Certificate thereof in writing. In the case of the resignation or removal of the Indenture Trustee, a Majority in Interest of Holders may appoint a successor Indenture Trustee by an instrument signed by such holders. If a successor Indenture Trustee shall not have been appointed within 30 days after such resignation or removal, the Indenture Trustee or any holder of a Loan Certificate may apply to any court of competent jurisdiction to appoint a successor Indenture Trustee. If a successor Indenture Trustee shall not have been appointed within 60 days after such resignation or removal, the Owner Participant may apply to any court of competent jurisdiction to appoint a successor Indenture Trustee. Any successor Indenture Trustee so appointed by such court shall immediately and without further act be superseded by any successor Indenture Trustee appointed as provided in the third sentence of this paragraph (i) within one year from the date of the appointment by such court.

(ii) Any successor Indenture Trustee, whether appointed by a court, the Owner Participant, or by a Majority in Interest of Holders shall execute and deliver to the Owner Participant and to the predecessor Indenture Trustee an instrument accepting such appointment, and thereupon such successor Indenture Trustee, without further act, shall become vested with all the estates, properties, rights, powers, duties, and trusts of the predecessor Indenture Trustee hereunder in the trusts hereunder applicable to it with like effect as if originally named the Indenture Trustee herein; but nevertheless, upon the written request of such successor Indenture Trustee, such predecessor Indenture Trustee shall execute and deliver an instrument transferring to such Indenture Trustee, upon the trusts herein expressed applicable to it, all the estates, properties, rights, powers, and trusts of such predecessor Indenture Trustee, and such Indenture Trustee shall duly assign, transfer, deliver, and pay over to such successor Indenture Trustee all monies or other property then held by such predecessor Indenture Trustee hereunder.

(iii) Any successor Indenture Trustee, however appointed, shall be a "citizen of the United States" within the meaning of Section 101(16) of the Federal Aviation Act and shall also have a combined capital and surplus of at least $100,000,000, if there be such an institution willing, able, and legally qualified to perform the duties of the Indenture Trustee hereunder upon reasonable or customary terms.

(iv) Any corporation into which the Indenture Trustee may be merged or converted or with which it may be consolidated, or any corporation resulting from any merger, conversion, or consolidation to which the Indenture Trustee shall be a party, or any corporation to which substantially all the trust business of the Indenture Trustee may be transferred, shall, subject to the terms of paragraph (iii) of this Section, be the Indenture Trustee under this Indenture without further act.

Section 9. Supplements and Amendments to this Indenture and Other Documents

(a) Instructions of Majority; Limitations. At any time and from time to time but only upon the written request of a Majority in Interest of Holders and (prior to the existence and continuation of an event of Acceleration) subject to the consent of the Owner Trustee at the direction of the Owner Participant in its discretion, (i) the Indenture Trustee shall execute such supplements hereto for the purpose of adding provisions to, or changing or eliminating provisions of, this Indenture as specified in such request and as the Owner Trustee may agree to and (ii) the Indenture Trustee shall consent to such written amendment of or supplement to the Lease, or the Assignment, as the other parties thereto, as the case may be, may agree to, and as may be specified in such request, or execute and deliver such written waiver or modification of the terms of the Lease or the Assignment, as may be specified in such request and as the Owner Trustee, at the direction of the Owner Participant, may agree to [provided that the Indenture Trustee shall give the Owner Trustee prior notice of any such amendment or supplement, but the Indenture Trustee's failure to do so shall not affect its rights hereunder except to the extent that such failure shall adversely affect the Owner Trustee's rights under Section 4(a) hereof]; provided, however, that, without the consent of each holder of a Loan Certificate then outstanding no such supplement to this Indenture or amendment of or supplement to the Lease or the Assignment or waiver or modification of the terms of any thereof, shall (A) modify any of the provisions of this Section 9(a) or the definition of "Majority of Interest of Holders" or change the percentages required to take any action under any provision hereof, (B) reduce the amount of or extend or contract the time of payment of, any amount of principal or Interest owing or payable under any Loan Certificate or alter or modify the provisions of Section 3 hereof with respect to the order of priorities in which distributions thereunder shall be made as between the holders of Loan Certificates and the Owner Trustee, (C) reduce, modify, or amend any indemnities in favor of the Participants or any holders of Loan Certificates, (D) reduce the amount or extend the time of payment of the Basic Rent, Supplemental Rent, Stipulated Loss Value, or Termination Value for the Aircraft as set forth in the Lease or any Lease Supplement, (E) consent to any assignment of the Lease, (F) release Lessee from its obligations in respect to the payment of the Basic Rent, Supplemental Rent, Stipulated Loss Values, and Termination Value for the Aircraft or change the absolute and unconditional character of such obligations as set forth in Section 4 of the Lease, (G) affect the Lessee's obligations under Section 10 of the Lease, (H) affect the recording or priority of the Lien of this Indenture, or (I) modify or affect any of the provisions of the Participation Agreement; provided, further, that without the consent of each holder of a Loan Certificate then outstanding, no such supplement to this Indenture or waiver or modification of the terms thereof shall permit the creation of any Lien on the Estate or any part thereof, except as herein expressly permitted, or deprive the holder of any Loan Certificate then outstanding of the benefits of the Lien of this Indenture on the Estate; provided, further, that without the consent of Lessee, no such supplement to this Indenture or waiver or modification of the terms hereof shall alter or modify the provisions of the proviso of Section 12(b) hereof or Lessee's rights under this proviso.

(b) Indenture Trustee Protected. If in the opinion of the Indenture Trustee any document required to be executed pursuant to the terms of Section 9(a) hereof affects any right, duty, liability, immunity, or indemnity in favor of the Indenture Trustee under this Indenture, the Participation Agreement, or the Lease, the Indenture Trustee may in its discretion decline to execute such document.

(c) Request of Substance, Not Form. It shall not be necessary for any written request of the holders of Loan Certificates furnished pursuant to Section 9(a) hereof to specify the particular form of the proposed documents to be executed pursuant to said Section 9(a).

(d) Documents Mailed to Holders. Promptly after the execution by the Indenture Trustee of any document entered into pursuant to Section 9(a) hereof, the Indenture Trustee shall mail, by first-class mail, postage prepaid, a conformed copy thereof to each holder of a Loan Certificate at its address last known to the Indenture Trustee, but the failure of the Indenture Trustee to mail such conformed copies shall not impair or affect the validity of such document.

(e) No Request Necessary for Lease Supplements or Indenture Supplements. No written request of the holders of Loan Certificates pursuant to Section 9(a) hereof shall be required to enable the Owner Trustee to enter into any Lease Supplement with Lessee pursuant to the terms of the Lease, to execute and deliver any Indenture Supplement pursuant to the terms hereof, in each case for the purpose of adding property to the Lease or subjecting property to the Lien hereof, or to enter into such amendments or other documents as are necessary to implement any of the adjustments contemplated by Section 3(e) of the Lease and/or the Tax Indemnity Agreement.

Section 10. Agreements of Owner Trustee

(a) Liability of Owner Trustee Under Other Documents. Except as otherwise expressly provided herein, the Owner Trustee shall remain liable hereunder, under the Lease, each Lease Supplement, the Assignment, and the Participation Agreement, to perform all of the obligations assumed by it hereunder and thereunder, all in accordance with and pursuant to the terms and provisions hereof and thereof.

(b) Appointment of Indenture Trustee as Attorney. The Owner Trustee hereby constitutes the Indenture Trustee the true and lawful attorney of the Owner Trustee, irrevocably, with full power (in the name of the Owner Trustee or otherwise) to ask, require, demand, receive, compound, and give acquittance for any and all monies and claims for monies due and to become due under or arising out of the Lease, any Lease Supplement, or the Participation Agreement, to endorse any checks or other instruments or orders in connection therewith and to file any claims or take any action or institute any proceedings which the Indenture Trustee may deem to be necessary or advisable in the premises.

(c) Payment of Monies to Indenture Trustee. The Owner Trustee agrees that promptly on receipt thereof, it will transfer to the Indenture Trustee any and all monies from time to time received by it constituting part of the Estate, for distribution or retention by the Indenture Trustee pursuant to this Indenture, except that the Owner Trustee shall accept for distribution pursuant to this Indenture any amounts distributed to it by the Indenture Trustee under this Indenture.

(d) Further Assurances; Financing Statements. At any time and from time to time, upon the request of the Indenture Trustee, the Owner Trustee shall promptly and duly execute and deliver any and all such further instruments and documents as the Indenture Trustee may deem desirable in obtaining the full benefits of the security interests and assignment created or intended to be created hereby and of the rights and powers herein granted. Upon the instructions at any time and from time to time of the Indenture Trustee, and upon receipt of the form or document to be filed pursuant to such instructions, the Owner Trustee shall execute and file any financing statement (and any continuation statement with respect to any such financing statement) or any other similar document relating to the security interests and assignments created by this Indenture, as may be specified in such instructions.

(e) Limitations on Actions of Owner Trustee. Except as otherwise provided in Section 5(b) hereof, the Owner Trustee agrees that, except upon the instructions of the Indenture Trustee, it will take no action with respect to any part of the Estate. Except as otherwise provided in Section 5(b) hereof, the Owner Trustee shall exercise any such election or option or make any decision or determination under or give any notice, consent, waiver, or approval under or in respect of the Lease and shall take such other steps to exercise all rights, powers, and remedies on the part of the Owner Trustee under or with respect to the Lease as the Owner Trustee may be instructed to take by the Indenture Trustee pursuant to the terms of this Indenture. The Owner Trustee warrants and represents that it has not assigned or pledged, and hereby covenants that it will not assign or pledge, so long as this Indenture shall remain in effect, any of its estate, right, title, or interest hereby assigned, to anyone other than the Indenture Trustee, and that it will not, except as provided in this Indenture, (a) enter into any agreement amending or supplementing the Lease or any Lease Supplement, or (b) accept any payment from, or settle or compromise any claim against, the Lessee or any other Person arising under any of such agreements, (c) submit or consent to the submission. to arbitration of any dispute, difference, or other matter arising under or in respect to any of such agreements or the rights of the Indenture Trustee hereunder or thereunder or (d) take or omit to take any action, the taking or omission of which might result in an alteration or impairment of any of such agreements or the rignts of the Indenture Trustee hereunder or thereunder or the Security interest and assignment created or intended to be created hereby or of any of the rights created hereby or thereby.

(f) Registration of Aircraft. The Owner Trustee shall take such action as may be necessary and appropriate or requested by the Indenture Trustee or the Lessee to cause the Aircraft to become and remain fully registered in the name of the Owner Trustee under the Federal Aviation Act (except as otherwise required under such Act), and shall complete, at the request of and on the basis of information supplied by the Lessee, and promptly submit (and furnish the Indenture Trustee and each Loan Participant with a duplicate or copy of) any and all reports required to be filed with any governmental authority.

(g) Notice of Event of Acceleration; Furnishing of Documents. In the event an officer of the corporate trust department of the Owner Trustee ("Responsible Officer") shall have knowledge of an Event of Acceleration, the Owner Trustee shall give prompt telegraphic or telephonic notice (confirmed by written notice sent in the manner provided in Section 11[g] hereof) of such Event of Acceleration to the Manufacturer, the Indenture Trustee, and each Loan Participant, which notice shall set forth in reasonable detail the circumstances surrounding such Event of Acceleration (if such default is not a Default or Event of Default) and shall describe in reasonable detail the action the Owner Trustee is taking or proposes to take in respect thereto. The Owner Trustee shall furnish to the Indenture Trustee and to each Loan Participant, promptly upon receipt thereof, a duplicate or copy of all reports, notices, requests, demands, certificates, financial statements, and other instruments furnished to the Owner Trustee under the Lease or the Participation Agreement, including, without limitation, a copy of each insurance certificate, report, or notice or other evidence received pursuant to the Lease, unless the Owner Trustee shall reasonably believe that the Indenture Trustee and each such holder shall have received copies thereof.

Section 11. Miscellaneous

(a) Termination of Indenture. This Indenture and the trusts created hereby shall terminate and this Indenture shall be of no further force or effect upon the payment in full of the principal amount of and interest on all Loan Certificates outstanding hereunder and all other sums payable to the Indenture Trustee and the holders of the Loan Certificates hereunder and under such Loan Certificates and under the Participation Agreement or the sale or other final disposition by the Indenture Trustee of all property constituting part of the Estate and the final distribution by the Indenture Trustee of all money or proceeds constituting part of the Estate in accordance with the terms of Section 3 hereof, whereupon all monies or proceeds constituting part of the Estate shall be distributed in accordance with the terms of Section 3 hereof; otherwise this Indenture and the trusts created hereby shall continue in full force and effect in accordance with the terms hereof.

(b) No Legal Title to Estate in Holders. No holder of a Loan Certificate shall have legal title to any part of the Estate. No transfer, by operation of law or otherwise, of any Loan Certificate or Other right, title, and interest of any holder of a Loan Certificate in and to the Estate or hereunder shall operate to terminate this Indenture or the trusts hereunder or entitle any successor or transferee of such holder to an accounting or to the transfer to it of legal title to any part of the Estate.

(c) Sale of Aircraft by Indenture Trustee Is Binding. Any sale or other conveyance of the Aircraft by the Indenture Trustee made pursuant to the terms of this Indenture or the Lease shall bind the holders of the Loan Certificates and shall be effective to transfer or convey all right, title, and interest of the Indenture Trustee, the Owner Trustee, and such holders in and to the Aircraft. No purchaser or other grantee shall be required to inquire as to the authorization, necessity, expediency, or regularity of such sale or conveyance or as to the application of any sale or other proceeds with respect thereto by the Indenture Trustee.

(d) Remedies Cumulative. Each and every right, power, and remedy herein specifically given to the Indenture Trustee or otherwise in this Indenture shall be cumulative and shall be in addition to every other right, power, and remedy herein specifically given or now or hereafter existing at law, in equity or by statute, and each and every right, power, and remedy whether specifically herein given or otherwise existing may be exercised from time to time and as often and in such order as may be deemed expedient by the Indenture Trustee, and the exercise or the beginning of the exercise of any power or remedy shall not be construed to be a waiver of the right to exercise at the time or thereafter any other right, power, or remedy. No delay or omission by the Indenture Trustee in the exercise of any right, remedy, or power or in the pursuance of any remedy shall impair any such right, power, or remedy or be construed to be a waiver of any default on the part of the Owner Trustee or Lessee or to be an acquiescence therein.

(e) Discontinuance of Proceedings. In case the Indenture Trustee shall have proceeded to enforce any right, power, or remedy under this Indenture by foreclosure, entry, or otherwise, and such proceedings shall have been discontinued or abandoned for any reason or shall have been determined adversely to the Indenture Trustee, then and in every such case the Owner Trustee, the Indenture Trustee, and Lessee shall be restored to their former positions and rights hereunder with respect to the property subject to the Lien of this Indenture, and all rights, remedies, and powers of the Indenture Trustee shall continue as if no such proceedings had been undertaken (but otherwise without prejudice).

(f) Indenture and Loan Certificates for Benefit of Owner Participant, Owner Trustee, Indenture Trustee, and Holders Only. Nothing in this Indenture, whether express or implied, shall be construed to give to any Person other than the Owner Participant, the Owner Trustee, the Indenture Trustee (individually and as trustee), and the holders of the Loan Certificates any legal or equitable right, remedy, or claim under or in respect of this Indenture or any Loan Certificate.

(g) Notices. Unless otherwise expressly specified or permitted by the terms hereof, all notices shall be in writing, shall become effective when received, and shall either be mailed by first-class, certified or registered mail, return receipt requested, with proper postage prepaid or sent by overnight delivery service or hand delivered, or by telex, telegram, facsimile transfer, or its equivalent, and (i) if to the Owner Trustee, addressed to it at its office at ______________________________; (ii) if to the Indenture Trustee, addressed to it at its office at ______________________________, and (iii) if to any holder of a Loan Certificate, addressed to such holder at such address as such holder shall have furnished by notice to the Owner Trustee and the Indenture Trustee or, until an address is so furnished, addressed to such holder at its address set forth in the Participation Agreement.

Notwithstanding the foregoing provisions, for purposes of Sections 5(a), 5(b), and 11(a), hereof, written notice shall be deemed given when it is in fact received (by mail or otherwise) by any addressee at the respective addresses specified above.

(h) Separate Counterparts. This Indenture may be executed by the parties hereto in separate counterparts, each of which when so executed and delivered shall be an original, but all such counterparts shall together constitute but one and the same instrument.

(i) Successors and Permitted Assigns. All covenants and agreements contained herein shall be binding upon, and inure to the benefit of, the Owner Trustee and its successors and permitted assigns, and the Indenture Trustee and its successors and permitted assigns, and each holder of a Loan Certificate, all as herein provided. Any request, notice, direction, consent, waiver, or other instrument or action by any holder of a Loan Certificate shall bind the successors and assigns of such holder.

(j) Headings. The headings of the various Sections herein are for convenience of reference only and shall not define or limit any of the terms or provisions hereof.

(k) Governing Law. This Indenture shall in all respects be governed by, and construed in accordance with, the laws of the State of New York, including all matters of construction, validity, and performance. This Indenture is being delivered in the State of New York.

(l) Normal Commercial Relations. Anything contained in this Indenture to the contrary notwithstanding, the Owner Trustee or any affiliate of the Owner Trustee may enter into commercial banking or other financial transactions, and conduct banking or other commercial relationships, with Lessee fully to the same extent as if this Indenture were not in effect, including without limitation, the making of loans or other extensions of credit to Lessee for any purpose whatsoever.

(m) Reorganization Proceedings with Respect to the Owner Trustee. If (i) the Owner Trustee becomes a debtor subject to the reorganization provisions of Title II of the United States Bankruptcy Code, or any successor provision, (ii) pursuant to such reorganization provisions the Owner Trustee is held to have recourse liability directly or indirectly, to make payment on account of any amount payable as principal of, or interest on the Loan

Certificates and (iii) any holder of a Loan Certificate or the Indenture Trustee, as the case may be, actually receives any Excess Amount (as hereinafter defined) which reflects any payment by the Owner Trustee on account of the recourse liability referred to in clause (ii) above then, to the extent it may lawfully do so, such holder or the Indenture Trustee, as the case may be, shall refund such Excess Amount, as promptly as possible, without interest, to the Owner Trustee after receipt by such holder or the Indenture Trustee, as the case may be, of a written request for such refund by the Owner Trustee (which request shall specify the amount of such excess amount and shall set forth in detail the calculation thereof). For purposes of this Section 11(m), "Excess Amount" means the amount by which such payment exceeds the amount which would have been received by such holder and the Indenture Trustee if the Owner Trustee had not become subject to the recourse liability referred to in clause (ii) above. Nothing contained in this Section 11(m) shall prevent the Indenture Trustee or the holders from enforcing and retaining the proceeds of any personal recourse obligation of the Owner Trustee under the Participation Agreement.

Section 12. Remedies of the Indenture Trustee Upon an Event of Acceleration

(a) Events of Acceleration. The following events shall constitute "Events of Acceleration" (whether any such event shall be voluntary or involuntary or come about or be effected by operation of law or pursuant to or in compliance with any judgment, decree or order of any court or any order, rule, or regulation of any administrative or governmental body):

(i) an Event of Default (other than an Event of Default by reason of a default by Lessee in, making any payment of any amounts that are part of the Excepted Property unless notice is given by the Owner Trustee to the Indenture Trustee that such default shall constitute an Event of Default) shall exist;

(ii) a default by the Owner Participant pursuant to Section 7(1) of the Participation Agreement or a default by the Owner Trustee in making any payment when due (whether at stated maturity, by notice of prepayment or otherwise) of principal of or premium, if any, or interest on, any Loan Certificate or Loan Certificates, and the continuance of such default unremedied for five Business Days;

(iii) any other failure by the Owner Participant or the Owner Trustee to observe or perform any other covenant or obligation of the Owner Participant or the Owner Trustee, in this Indenture or the Loan Certificates or in the Participation Agreement, if, but only if, such failure is not remedied within a period of 30 days after written notice specifying such failure has been given to the Owner Participant, or the Owner Trustee and Lessee by the Indenture Trustee or any holder of a Loan Certificate; or

(iv) any representation or warranty made by the Owner Participant or the Owner Trustee herein, in the Participation Agreement or in any other document furnished to the Loan Participants or the Indenture Trustee pursuant to the Operative Documents shall prove to be incorrect when made in any respect material to the rights and remedies of the Loan Participants or of the holders of the Loan Certificates hereunder or under the Loan Certificates, the Participation Agreement, or the Lease and shall remain material; or

(v) a decree or order for relief shall be entered by a court having jurisdiction in the premises in respect of the Owner Trustee or the Owner Participant, in an involuntary case under any applicable bankruptcy, insolvency, or other similar law now or hereafter in effect, or appointing a receiver, liquidator, custodian, trustee, sequestrator (or similar official) of the Owner Trustee or the Owner Participant, or for any substantial part of its property, or ordering the winding-up or liquidation of its affairs of either of them, or granting to the Owner Trustee or the Owner Participant a suspension of payments and the continuance of any such decree or order shall be unstayed and remain in effect for a period of 60 consecutive days thereafter; or

(vi) the Owner Trustee or the Owner Participant shall commence a voluntary case under any applicable federal or state bankruptcy, insolvency, or other similar law now or hereafter in effect, or shall consent to the entry of an order for relief in an involuntary case under any such law, or shall consent to the appointment of or taking of possession by a receiver, liquidator, trustee, custodian, sequestrator (or other similar official) for or of the Owner Trustee or the Owner Participant or any substantial part of its property shall make a general assignment for the benefit of creditors, or shall fail generally to pay its debts as such debts become due; or

(vii) a court or governmental authority of competent jurisdiction shall enter an order appointing, without consent by the Owner Participant or the Owner Trustee, as the case may be, a custodian, receiver, liquidator, trustee, or other officer with similar powers with respect to it or with respect to any substantial part of its properties, or constituting an order for relief or approving a petition for relief or reorganization or any other petition in bankruptcy or for liquidation or to take advantage of any bankruptcy or insolvency law of any jurisdiction with respect to the Owner Participant or the Owner Trustee, or ordering the dissolution, winding-up, or liquidation of the Owner Participant or the Owner Trustee, or if any such petition shall be filed against the Owner Participant or the Owner Trustee and the continuance of any such order or decree shall be unstayed and remain in effect for a period of 60 consecutive days thereafter.

Upon the occurrence of any Event of Acceleration and at any time thereafter so long as the same shall be continuing (subject to the cure rights as aforesaid), the Indenture Trustee or a Majority in Interest of Holders may declare the Loan Certificates to be accelerated by giving written notice to the Owner Trustee and upon such declaration of acceleration and automatically following the occurrence of an event described in paragraphs (v), (vi), or (vii) of Section 12(a) hereof the entire unpaid principal amount of all the Loan Certificates, together with all accrued but unpaid interest thereon, shall become immediately due and payable without further act or notice of any kind. At any time thereafter, so long as the Owner Participant or the Owner Trustee shall not have remedied all outstanding Events of Acceleration to the extent permitted by this Section, the Indenture Trustee may exercise one or more of the remedies referred to in Sections 12(b) and 12(c) hereof, provided, however, that the Indenture Trustee shall not make any such declaration of acceleration, if the Owner Participant or the Owner Trustee has (1) in the case of an Event of Acceleration arising from a default in the payment of Basic Rent or Interim Rent (but not more than two defaults [not to be consecutive defaults] during the Term in payment of Basic Rent or Interim Rent), paid to the Indenture Trustee an amount equal to the installment of principal and interest on the Loan Certificates included in such Basic Rent or Interim Rent plus interest on account of such payment being overdue or (2) in the case of an Event of Acceleration arising from any other default by Lessee in the performance of its obligations under the Lease or the Participation Agreement which can be cured by the payment of money, paid, by exercise of the Owner Trustee's rights under Section 19 of the Lease or otherwise, an amount sufficient to cure such Event of Acceleration, in either case within five Business Days after the later of the receipt by the Owner Participant of written notice from the Indenture Trustee or any Loan Participant specifying such Default and the expiration of any grace period applicable to such Default. Notwithstanding the foregoing, such right to cure under clause (2) above shall not be in effect during any period during which the Owner Participant has expended an unreimbursed aggregate amount pursuant to clause (2) above equal to the sum of $__. Any payment by the Owner Participant pursuant to, and in compliance with, clause (1) above shall be deemed to remedy any such default in the payment of Interim Rent or Basic Rent; and any performance by Owner Participant or the Owner Trustee of Lessee's obligations under the Lease pursuant to, and in compliance with, clause (2) above shall be deemed to remedy any such default by Lessee under the Lease (but shall not relieve Lessee of any of its obligations under the Lease). In each such case the Owner Participant or the Owner Trustee shall be subrogated to the rights of the Indenture Trustee to receive such payment of Basic Rent or Interim Rent or other payment of money and, provided that no Default or Event of Default shall have occurred and is continuing, the Owner Trustee or the Owner Participant (as the case may be) shall have the right to proceed against Lessee to recover such payments and shall be entitled to retain the same (but if any monies shall be received by the Owner Participant or the Owner Trustee in payment of such subrogated claim during the continuance of any Event of Acceleration, such money shall be paid over to the Indenture Trustee and shall be distributed in accordance with the provisions of Section 3 hereof), and the payment of interest on account of its being overdue, and shall, if no other Event of Acceleration shall have occurred and be continuing, be entitled to receive such payment upon receipt by the Indenture Trustee.

(b) Remedies with Respect to Mortgaged Property. Subject to the cure rights under Section 12(a) hereof and/or the prepayment rights under Section 4(a) hereof, after an Event of Acceleration shall have occurred and so long as such Event of Acceleration shall be continuing, then and in every such case the Indenture Trustee or a Majority in Interest of Holders may, and to the extent required pursuant to the provisions of Section 5 hereof shall, exercise any or all of the rights and powers and pursue any and all of the remedies pursuant to Section 18 of the Lease and this Section 12 and may take possession of all or any part of the Mortgaged Property and may exclude the Owner Participant and the Owner Trustee and all persons claiming under it wholly or partly therefrom; provided, however, that nothing in this Indenture shall permit or require the Indenture Trustee to take any action contrary to, or to disturb, Lessee's rights under the Lease, except in accordance with the provisions of the Lease.

(c) Return of Aircraft, etc. Subject to Section 12(b), the Owner Trustee agrees, to the full extent that it lawfully may, that, in case one or more of the Events of Acceleration shall have occurred and be continuing, then, and in every such case, the Indenture Trustee may take possession of all or any part of the Mortgaged Property and may exclude the Owner Trustee and the Owner Participant, Lessee, and all persons claiming under them wholly or partly therefrom. In addition, the Indenture Trustee may (i) obtain a judgment conferring on the Indenture Trustee the right to immediate possession and collection and requiring the Owner Trustee to deliver such instruments of title and other documents as the Indenture Trustee may deem necessary or advisable to enable the Indenture Trustee or an agent or representative designated by the Indenture Trustee, at such time or times and place or places as the Indenture Trustee may specify, to obtain possession of all or any part of the Mortgaged Property, to the entry of which judgment the Owner Trustee hereby specifically consents, and (ii) pursue all or part of the Mortgaged Property wherever it may be found and may enter any of the premises of Lessee wherever the Mortgaged Property may be or be supposed to be and search for the Mortgaged Property and take possession of and remove the Mortgaged Property. Upon every such taking of possession, the Indenture Trustee may, from time to time, at the expense of the Mortgaged Property, make all such expenditures for maintenance, insurance, repairs, replacements, alterations, additions, and improvements to and of the Mortgaged Property, as it may deem proper. In each such case, the Indenture Trustee shall have the right to use, operate, store, control, or manage the Mortgaged Property, and to carry on business and exercise all rights and powers of the Owner Trustee and the Owner Participant relating to the Mortgaged Property, as the Indenture Trustee shall deem best, including the right to enter into any and all such agreements with respect to the maintenance, operation, leasing, or storage of the Mortgaged Property or any part thereof as the Indenture Trustee may determine; and the Indenture Trustee shall be entitled to collect and receive all tolls, rents, revenues, issues, income, products, and profits of the Mortgaged Property and every part thereof, without prejudice, however, to the right of the Indenture Trustee under any provision of this Indenture to collect and receive all cash held by, or required to be deposited with, the Indenture Trustee hereunder. Such tolls, rents, revenues, issues, income, products, and profits shall be applied to pay the expenses of holding and operating the Mortgaged Property and of conducting the business thereof, and of all maintenance, repairs, replacements, alterations, additions, and improvements, and to make all payments which the Indenture Trustee may be required or may elect to make, if any, for taxes, assessments, insurance, or other proper charges upon the Mortgaged Property or any part thereof, and all other payments which the Indenture Trustee may be required or authorized to make under any provision of this Indenture, as well as just and reasonable compensation for the services of the Indenture Trustee, and of all Persons properly engaged and employed by the Indenture Trustee, including the reasonable expenses of the Indenture Trustee.

IN WITNESS WHEREOF, the parties hereto have caused this Indenture to be duly executed by their respective officers thereunto duly authorized, as of the day and year first above written.

MARTIN TRUST COMPANY, Owner
Trustee, not in its individual
capacity, but solely as Owner
Trustee

By: ______________________________

Title: ______________________________

THE RHODE ISLAND BANK AND TRUST COMPANY, NATIONAL ASSOCIATION,
Indenture Trustee

By: ______________________________

Title: ______________________________

Exhibit A
to
Indenture

Trust Indenture Supplement No. I

TRUST INDENTURE SUPPLEMENT No. 1, dated October 1, XXXX, of MARTIN TRUST COMPANY, Owner Trustee, not in its individual capacity but solely as Owner Trustee (the "Owner Trustee") under the Trust Indenture and Security Agreement (the "Indenture") dated as of September 15, XXXX between the Owner Trustee and the Indenture Trustee named therein.

WITNESSETH:

WHEREAS, the Indenture provides for the execution and delivery of a Supplement thereto substantially in the form hereof, which Supplement shall particularly describe the Aircraft (such term and other defined terms in the Indenture being herein used with the same meanings), by having attached thereto a copy of the Lease Supplement covering such Aircraft, and shall specifically mortgage such Aircraft to the Indenture Trustee, and

WHEREAS, the Indenture relates to the Airframe and Engines described in the copy of the Lease Supplement of even number and date attached hereto and made a part hereof, and a counterpart of the Indenture is attached to and made a part of this Trust Indenture Supplement.

NOW, THEREFORE, this Supplement witnesseth, that to secure the prompt payment of the principal of and interest on all of the Loan Certificates from time to time outstanding under the Indenture and the performance and observance by the Owner Trustee of all the agreements, covenants, and provisions in the Indenture for the benefit of the holders of the Loan Certificates and in the Loan Certificates contained, subject to the terms and conditions of the Indenture, and in consideration of the premises and covenants contained in the Indenture and the acceptance of the Loan Certificates by the holders thereof, and of the sum of $1.00 paid to the Owner Trustee by the Indenture Trustee at or before the delivery hereof, the receipt of which is hereby acknowledged, the Owner Participant (i) has transferred, assigned, granted, bargained, sold, conveyed, mortgaged, hypothecated, and pledged, and does hereby transfer, assign, grant, bargain, sell, convey, mortgage, hypothecate, and pledge, the property comprising the Airframe and Engines described in the aforementioned copy of the Lease Supplement attached hereto, whether or not such Engines shall be installed on or attached to the Airframe or any other aircraft, and (ii) has sold, assigned, transferred, and set over, and does hereby sell, assign, transfer, and set over, all of the right, title, and interest of the Owner Trustee under, in, and to the Lease Supplement of even number and date, referred to above, in each case excluding Excepted Property, to the Indenture Trustee, its successors and assigns, in the trust created by the Indenture for the benefit of the holders from time to time of the Loan Certificates.

To have and to hold all and singular the aforesaid property unto the Indenture Trustee, its successors and assigns, in trust for the benefit and security of the holders from time to time of the Loan Certificates and for the uses and purposes and subject to the terms and provisions set forth in the Indenture.

This Supplement shall be construed as supplemental to the Indenture and shall form a part thereof, and the Indenture is hereby incorporated by reference herein and ratified, approved, and confirmed.

This Supplement is being delivered in the State of ________________.

This Supplement may be executed by the Owner Trustee in separate counterparts, each of which when so executed and delivered is an original, but all such counterparts shall together constitute but one and the same supplement.

IN WITNESS WHEREOF, the Owner Trustee has caused this Supplement to be duly executed by its officer thereunto duly authorized, as of the day and year first above written.

MARTIN TRUST COMPANY, Owner
Trustee, not in its individual capacity, but solely as Owner Trustee

By: ______________________________

Title: ____________________________

Exhibit B
to Indenture

Amortization Schedule

Series A Loan Certificates

Payment Date	*Percentage of Principal Repayment*

Exhibit B
to Indenture

Amortization Schedule

Series B Loan Certificates

Payment Date	*Percentage of Principal Repayment*

Form: l-04d
Disk File Name: l-04d.rtf

TRUST AGREEMENT

Form Purpose

A leveraged lease trust agreement in which the lending party in the leveraged lease transaction sets forth the terms and conditions of trust arrangement. This form is integrated with a Participation Agreement, a Trust Indenture and Security Agreement, an Assignment of Rights Under Purchase Agreement, a Lease Agreement, and a Tax Indemnity Agreement.

Executing Parties

The owner participant.
The indenture trustee.

See:

Assignment of Rights Under Purchase Agreement, Form l-04a
Leveraged Lease Agreement, Form l-04
Participation Agreement, Form l-04b
Trust Indenture and Security Agreement, Form l-04c
Tax Indemnity Agreement, Form l-04e

Trust Agreement

Dated as of September 15, XXXX

between

PBC LEASING CORPORATION,
Owner Participant

and

MARTIN TRUST COMPANY,
Owner Trustee

One New Blackhawk Model 555-300 Aircraft
Registration Number: N777P

Table of Contents

TRUST AGREEMENT, dated as of ________, XXXX, between PBC LEASING CORPORATION, a Florida corporation, and MARTIN TRUST COMPANY, a New York trust company (hereunder the "Owner Trustee").

In consideration of the mutual agreements herein contained and other good and valuable consideration, receipt of which is hereby acknowledged, the parties hereto, intending to be legally bound hereby, agree as follows:

Section 1. Definitions and Terms

Unless the context otherwise requires, all Capitalized terms used herein shall have the meanings set forth in Appendix A to the Participation Agreement entered into by the parties hereto, dated ________.

Section 2. Authority to Execute and Perform Various Documents; Declaration of Trust by Owner Trustee

(a) Authority to Execute and Perform Various Documents. The Owner Participant hereby authorizes and directs the Owner Trustee (i) to execute and deliver the Participation Agreement, the Lease, the Indenture, the Assignment, the Loan Certificates, and any other agreement or instrument relating to the Aircraft or any Engine as the Owner Participant may from time to time direct (collectively, the "Trustee Documents") and to accept delivery of the Aircraft and the Bills of Sale; (ii) to execute and deliver all other agreements, instruments, and certificates contemplated by the Trustee Documents including, without limitation, an aircraft registration application for the Aircraft and an affidavit pursuant to 14 C.F.R. Section 47.7(c)(2)(ii) for the Aircraft and take such other action as may be necessary to register the Aircraft and to maintain such registration; (iii) to take whatever action shall be required to be taken by the Owner Trustee by the terms of and subject to the terms of, this Agreement and the Trustee Documents and to take whatever action shall be required to be taken by the Owner Trustee by the terms of, and exercise its rights and perform its duties under, each of the agreements, instruments, and certificates referred to in clauses (i) and (ii) above as set forth in such agreements, instruments, and certificates and (iv) subject to the terms of this Agreement, to take such other action in connection with the foregoing as the Owner Participant may from time to time direct.

(b) Declaration of Trust by Owner Trustee. The Owner Trustee hereby declares that it will hold all estate, right, title, and interest of the Owner Trustee in and to the Aircraft, the Engines, the Operative Documents (except the Tax Indemnity Agreement), and any other property contributed by the Owner Participant, including without limitation all amounts of Rent, insurance proceeds and requisition, indemnity, or other payments of any kind, but specifically excluding any Excepted Property (collectively, the "Trust Estate"), upon the trusts set forth herein and for the use and benefit of the Owner Participant.

Section 3. Payments

(a) Payments from Trust Estate Only. All payments to be made by the Owner Trustee under this Agreement shall be made only from the income and the proceeds from the Trust Estate and only to the extent that the Owner Trustee shall have received income or proceeds from the Trust Estate. The Owner Participant agrees that it will look solely to the income and proceeds from the Trust Estate to the extent available for payment as herein provided and that, except as specifically provided in Section 6(a) hereof, the Owner Trustee shall not be liable in its individual capacity to the Owner Participant for any amounts payable under this Agreement and shall not be subject to any liability in its individual capacity under this Agreement.

(b) Method of Payment. All amounts payable to the Owner Participant pursuant to this Agreement shall be paid by the Owner Trustee to the Owner Participant or a nominee therefor by crediting, or causing the Indenture Trustee to credit, the amount to be distributed to the Owner Participant to an account maintained by the Owner Participant or such nominee with the Owner Trustee or the Indenture Trustee, as the case may be, in immediately available funds or by transferring such amount in immediately available funds to a banking institution with bank wire transfer facilities for the account of the Owner Participant or such nominee, as instructed from time to time by the Owner Participant.

Section 4. Distributions

Subject to the terms and requirements of the Operative Documents, all payments and amounts received by the Owner Trustee shall be distributed forthwith upon receipt in the following order of priority: first, so much of such payment or amount as shall be required to pay or reimburse the Owner Trustee for any fees or expenses not otherwise paid or reimbursed to the Owner Trustee as to which the Owner Trustee is entitled to be paid or reimbursed hereunder, or indemnified from the Trust Estate pursuant to the last sentence of Section 7(a) hereof, shall be retained by the Owner Trustee; and, second, the balance, if any, of such payment or amount remaining thereafter shall be distributed to the Owner Participant.

Section 5. Duties of the Owner Trustee

(a) Notice of Event of Default. In the event the Owner Trustee shall have actual knowledge of an Event of Acceleration or an Event of Default or any event which with the passage of time or giving of notice or both would constitute an Event of Acceleration or an Event of Default, the Owner Trustee shall give prompt written notice thereof to the Owner Participant, the Manufacturer, the Lessee and the Indenture Trustee. Subject to the terms of Section 5(c) hereof, the Owner Trustee shall take or refrain from taking such action, not inconsistent with the provisions of the Operative Documents, with respect thereto as the Owner Trustee shall be instructed in writing by the Owner Participant. If the Owner Trustee shall not have received instructions as above within 20 days after mailing notice of such event to the Owner Participant, the Owner Trustee may, subject to instructions received pursuant to the preceding sentence and to the provisions of the Operative Documents, take or refrain from taking such action, but shall be under no duty to, and shall have no liability for its failure or refusal to, take or refrain from taking any action with respect thereto as it shall deem advisable and in the best interests of the Owner Participant. For all purposes of this Agreement, in the absence of actual knowledge of an officer in the corporate trust department of the Owner Trustee, the Owner Trustee shall not be deemed to have knowledge of an Event of Acceleration or an Event of Default or any event which with the passage of time or giving of notice or both would constitute an Event of Acceleration or an Event of Default unless it receives written notification thereof given by or on behalf of the Owner Participant, the Lessee, the Indenture Trustee, or any holder of a Loan Certificate.

(b) Action Upon Instructions. Subject to the terms of Sections 5(a) and 5(c) hereof, upon the written instructions of the Owner Participant, the Owner Trustee will take or refrain from taking such action or actions, not inconsistent with the provisions of the Operative Documents, as may be specified in such instructions.

(c) Indemnification. The Owner Trustee shall not be required to take or refrain from taking any action under this Agreement or any of the Operative Documents [other than the actions specified in the first sentence of Section 5(a) hereof] unless the Owner Trustee shall have been indemnified by the Lessee or, if the Owner Trustee reasonably believes such indemnity to be inadequate, by the Owner Participant, in manner and form satisfactory to the Owner Trustee, against any liability, fee, cost, or expense (including reasonable attorneys' fees) which may be incurred or charged in connection therewith; and, if the Owner Participant shall have directed the Owner Trustee to take or refrain from taking any action under any Operative Document, the Owner Participant agrees to furnish such indemnity as shall be satisfactory to the Owner Trustee and in addition to pay the reasonable compensation of the Owner Trustee for the services performed or to be performed by it pursuant to such direction. The Owner Trustee shall not be required to take any action under any Operative Document if the Owner Trustee shall reasonably determine, or shall have been advised by counsel, that such action is likely to result in personal liability or is contrary to the terms hereof or of any document contemplated hereby to which the Owner Trustee is a party or is otherwise contrary to law.

(d) No Duties Except as Specified in Trust Agreement or Instructions. The Owner Trustee shall not have any duty or obligation to manage, control, use, make any payment in respect of, register, record, insure, inspect, sell, dispose of, or otherwise deal with the Aircraft, the Airframe, or an Engine or any other part of the Trust Estate, or otherwise to take or refrain from taking any action under, or in connection with, any document contemplated hereby to which the Owner Trustee is a party, except as expressly provided by the terms of this Agreement or in written instructions from the Owner Participant received pursuant to Section 5(a) or 5(b) hereof; and no implied duties or obligations shall be read into this Agreement against the Owner Trustee. The Owner Trustee nevertheless agrees that it will, in its individual capacity and at its own cost and expense, promptly take all action as may be necessary to discharge any Liens on any part of the Trust Estate which result from Lessor's Liens attributable to the Owner Trustee in its individual capacity. The Owner Trustee in its individual capacity agrees to indemnify, protect, save, and keep harmless the Owner Participant from and against any loss, cost, or expense (including legal fees and expenses) incurred by the Owner Participant, as a result of the imposition or enforcement of any Lessor's Lien against the Aircraft, any interest therein or on the Trust Estate or the Estate resulting from any Lessor's Liens attributable to the Owner Trustee in its individual capacity.

(e) No Action Except Under Specified Documents or Instructions. The Owner Trustee agrees that it will not manage, control, use, sell, dispose of, or otherwise deal with the Aircraft or an Engine or any other part of the Trust Estate except (i) as required by the terms of the Operative Documents, (ii) in accordance with the powers granted to, or the authority conferred upon, the Owner Trustee pursuant to this Agreement or (iii) in accordance with the express terms hereof or with written instructions from the Owner Participant pursuant to Section 5(a) or 5(b) hereof.

(f) Absence of Duties. Except in accordance with written instructions furnished pursuant to Section 5(b) hereof, and without limitation of the generality of Section 5(d) hereof, the Owner Trustee shall have no duty (i) to file, record, or deposit any Operative Document, the Bills of Sale, any financing statements or this Agreement, or to maintain any such filing, recording, or deposit or to refile, rerecord, or redeposit any such document, (ii) to obtain insurance on the Aircraft or any Engine or to effect or maintain any such insurance, (iii) to maintain or mark the Aircraft or an Engine, (iv) to pay or discharge any tax, assessment, or other governmental charge or any lien or encumbrance of any kind owing with respect to or assessed or levied against any part of the Trust Estate, except as provided in the last sentence of Section 5(d) hereof, (v) to confirm, verify, investigate, or inquire into the failure to receive any reports of financial statements of the Lessee, (vi) to inspect the Aircraft or an Engine at any time or to ascertain or inquire as to the performance or observance of any covenants of Lessee under any Operative Document with respect to the Aircraft or an Engine or (vii) to manage, control, use, sell, dispose of, or otherwise deal with the Aircraft or an Engine or any part thereof or any other part of the Trust Estate except as provided in Clauses (i), (ii), and (iii) of Section 5(e) hereof.

Section 6. The Owner Trustee

(a) Acceptance of Trusts and Duties. The Owner Trustee accepts the trusts hereby created and agrees to perform the same but only upon the terms of this Agreement. The Owner Trustee also agrees to disburse all monies actually received by it constituting part of the Trust Estate upon the terms of this Agreement. The Owner Trustee shall not be answerable or accountable under any circumstances in its individual capacity, except (i) for its own willful misconduct or gross negligence, (ii) in the case of the inaccuracy of any representation or warranty contained in Section 6(c) hereof or any representation or warranty of the Owner Trustee in its individual capacity contained in the Participation Agreement, (iii) for liabilities arising from the failure by the Owner Trustee to perform obligations expressly undertaken by it in the penultimate sentence of Section 5(d) hereof or obligations expressly taken by it in its individual capacity in the last sentence of Section 5(d) or in the Participation Agreement or (iv) for taxes, fees, or other charges on, based on, or measured by any fees, commissions, or Compensation received by the Owner Trustee for acting as trustee in connection with any of the transactions contemplated by the Operative Documents.

(b) Furnishing of Documents. The Owner Trustee will furnish to the Owner Participant, promptly upon receipt thereof, duplicates or copies of all reports, notices, requests, demands, certificates, financial statements, and any other instruments furnished to the Owner Trustee hereunder or under the Operative Documents, unless by the express terms of any Operative Document a copy of the same is required to be furnished by some other Person directly to the Owner Participant or the Owner Trustee shall have determined that the same has already been furnished to the Owner Participant.

(c) No Representations or Warranties as to the Aircraft or an Engine or Documents. THE OWNER TRUSTEE MAKES (i) NO REPRESENTATION OR WARRANTY, EXPRESS OR IMPLIED, AS TO THE TITLE, AIRWORTHINESS, VALUE, CONDITION, DESIGN, OPERATION, MERCHANTABILITY, OR FITNESS FOR USE OF THE AIRCRAFT, AS TO THE ABSENCE OF LATENT OR OTHER DEFECTS, WHETHER OR NOT DISCOVERABLE, AS TO THE ABSENCE OF ANY INFRINGEMENT OF ANY PATENT, TRADEMARK, OR COPYRIGHT, AS TO THE ABSENCE OF OBLIGATIONS BASED ON STRICT LIABILITY IN TORT, OR AS TO THE QUALITY OF THE MATERIAL OR WORKMANSHIP OF THE AIRCRAFT OR ANY OTHER REPRESENTATION OR WAR-

RANTY, EXPRESS OR IMPLIED, WITH RESPECT TO THE AIRCRAFT OR AN ENGINE WHATSOEVER, except that the Owner Trustee, in its individual capacity, hereby represents and warrants to the Owner Participant that it will comply with the last sentence of Section 5(d) hereof, and (ii) no representation or warranty as to the validity or enforceability of any Operative Document, the Bills of Sale, or as to the correctness of any statement contained in any thereof, except that the Owner Trustee, in its individual capacity, hereby represents and warrants to the Owner Participant that this Agreement has been and (assuming due authorization, execution, and delivery of this Agreement by the Owner Participant) each of such other documents which contemplates execution thereof by the Owner Trustee has been or will be executed and delivered by its officers who are or will be duly authorized to execute and deliver such document on its behalf.

(d) No Segregation of Monies; No Interest. Except as otherwise provided herein or in any of the Operative Documents, monies received by the Owner Trustee hereunder need not be segregated in any manner except to the extent required by law and may be deposited under such general conditions as may be prescribed by law, and the Owner Trustee shall not be liable for any interest thereon.

(e) Reliance; Advice of Counsel. The Owner Trustee shall incur no liability to anyone in acting upon any signature, instrument, notice, resolution, request, consent, order, certificate, report, opinion, bond, or other document or paper reasonably believed by it to be genuine and reasonably believed by it to be signed by the proper party or parties. The Owner Trustee may accept a certified copy of a resolution of the board of directors or other governing body of any corporate party as conclusive evidence that such resolution has been duly adopted by such body and that the same is in full force and effect. As to any fact or matter the manner of ascertainment of which is not specifically prescribed herein, the Owner Trustee may for all purposes hereof rely on an officer's certificate of the relevant party, as to such fact or matter, and such Certificate shall constitute full protection to the Owner Trustee for any action taken or omitted to be taken by it in good faith in reliance thereon. In the administration of the trusts hereunder, the Owner Trustee may execute any of the trusts or powers hereof and exercise its powers and perform its duties hereunder directly or through agents or attorneys and may consult with counsel, accountants, and other skilled persons to be selected and employed by it, and the Owner Trustee shall not be liable for anything done, suffered, or Omitted in good faith by it in accordance with the advice or opinion of any such counsel, accountants, or other skilled persons appointed by it with reasonable care hereunder and not contrary to this Agreement.

(f) Not Acting in Individual Capacity. Except as provided in this Section 6, in accepting the trusts hereby created the Owner Trustee acts solely as trustee hereunder and not in its individual capacity; and all Persons other than the Owner Participant as provided herein and the Indenture Trustee as provided in the Indenture having any claim against the Owner Trustee by reason of the transactions contemplated by the Operative Documents shall look only to the Trust Estate (or a part thereof, as the case may be) for payment or satisfaction thereof, except as specifically provided in this Section 6.

(g) Books and Records. The Owner Trustee shall be responsible for the keeping of all appropriate books and records relating to the receipt and disbursement of all monies under this Trust Agreement or any agreement contemplated hereby. The Owner Trustee shall not be responsible for preparing or filing any income tax returns required to be filed and the Owner Participant shall be responsible for causing to be prepared all income tax returns required to be filed with respect to the trust created hereby, and the Owner Trustee shall execute and file such returns as directed.

Section 7. Indemnification of Owner Trustee by Owner Participant

(a) Owner Participant to Indemnify Owner Trustee. The Owner Participant agrees to pay (or reimburse the Owner Trustee for) all reasonable expenses of the Owner Trustee hereunder, including, without limitation, the reasonable compensation, expenses, and disbursements of such agents, representatives, experts, and counsel as the Owner Trustee may employ in connection with the exercise and performance of its rights and duties under the Operative Documents unless and to the extent that the Owner Trustee receives payment or reimbursement from the Lessee, whether or not the transactions contemplated hereby are consummated. The Owner Participant agrees to assume liability for, and does hereby indemnify the Owner Trustee in its individual capacity only, and its successors, assigns, agents, and servants, against and from any and all liabilities (including, without limitation, any liability of the Owner Participant, any liability without fault and any strict liability), obligations, losses, damages, penalties, taxes, claims, actions, suits, costs, expenses, and disbursements (including, without limitation, reasonable legal fees and expenses) of any kind and nature whatsoever (collectively, "Expenses") which may be imposed on, incurred by, or asserted at any time against the Owner Trustee (whether or not indemnified against by other parties) in any way relating to or arising out of the administration of the Trust Estate or the action or inaction of the Owner Trustee hereunder or under the Operative Documents or the enforcement of any of the terms of any thereof, or in any way relating to or arising out of the manufacture, purchase, acceptance, nonacceptance, rejection, ownership, delivery, lease, possession, use, operation, condition, sale, return, or other disposition of the Aircraft or an Engine (including, without limitation, latent and other defects, whether or not discoverable, and any claim for patent, trademark, or copyright infringement), or in any way relating to or arising out of the administration of the Trust Estate or the action or inaction of the Owner Trustee hereunder, except only that the Owner Participant shall not be required to indemnify the Owner Trustee for expenses arising or resulting from any of the matters described in the last two sentences of Section 6(a) hereof. The indemnities contained in this Section 7(a) shall survive the termination of this Agreement. In addition, if necessary, the Owner Trustee shall be entitled to indemnification from the Trust Estate, subject to the lien of the Indenture, for any liability, obligation, loss, damage, penalty, tax, claim, action, suit, cost, expense, or disbursement indemnified against pursuant to this Section 7(a) to the extent not reimbursed by the Lessee, the Owner Participant or others, but without releasing any of them from their respective agreements of reimbursement; and to secure the same, the Owner Trustee shall have a lien on the Trust Estate, subject to the lien of the Indenture, which shall be prior to any interest therein of the Owner Participant. The payer of any indemnity under this Section 7(a) shall be subrogated to any right of the person indemnified in respect of the matter as to which such indemnity was paid.

(b) Compensation and Expenses. The Owner Trustee shall receive as compensation for its services hereunder the fee referred to in Section 14 of the Participation Agreement, and pursuant to such Section, shall be reimbursed for its reasonable expenses hereunder (including legal fees and expenses) and shall be compensated reasonably for any extraordinary services rendered hereunder.

Section 8. Termination of Trust Agreement

(a) Termination of Trust Agreement. This Agreement and the trusts created hereby shall terminate and the Trust Estate shall, subject to the Participation Agreement, the

Indenture, and Section 4 hereof, be distributed to the Owner Participant, and this Agreement shall be of no further force or effect, upon the earlier of (i) the sale or other final disposition by the Owner Trustee of all property constituting part of the Trust Estate and the final distribution by the Owner Trustee of all monies or other property or proceeds constituting part of the Trust Estate in accordance with the terms of Section 4 hereof and (ii) 21 years less one day after the death of the last survivor of all of the descendants living on the date of this Agreement of the present members of the Boards of Directors of the Owner Trustee and Owner Participant, but if any such rights, privileges, or options shall be or become valid under applicable law for a period subsequent to the 21st anniversary of the death of such last survivor (or, without limiting the generality of the foregoing, if legislation shall become effective providing for the validity or permitting the effective grant of Such rights, privileges, and options for a period in gross exceeding the period for which such rights, privileges, and options are hereinabove stated to extend and be valid), then such rights, privileges, or options shall not terminate as aforesaid but shall extend to and continue in effect, but only if such nontermination and extension shall then be valid under applicable law, until such time as the same shall, under applicable law, cease to be valid.

(b) Termination at Option of Owner Participant. The provisions of Section 8(a) hereof notwithstanding, this Agreement and the trusts created hereby shall terminate and the Trust Estate shall be distributed to the Owner Participant, and this Agreement shall be of no further force and effect, upon the election of the Owner Participant by notice to the Owner Trustee, if such notice shall be accompanied by the written agreement of the Owner Participant assuming all the obligations of the Owner Trustee under or contemplated by the Operative Documents and all other obligations of the Owner Trustee incurred by it as trustee hereunder; provided, however, that no such election shall be effective until the Lien of the Indenture on the Estate has been released and until full payment of the principal of, premium (if any), and interest on the Loan Certificates has been made. Such written agreement shall be satisfactory in form and substance to the Owner Trustee and shall release the Owner Trustee from all further obligations of the Owner Trustee hereunder and under the agreements and other instruments mentioned in the preceding sentence.

Section 9. Successor Owner Trustees, Co-Owner Trustees and Separate Owner Trustees

(a) Resignation of Owner Trustee; Appointment of Successor.

(i) The Owner Trustee may resign at any time without cause by giving at least 30 days' prior written notice to the Owner Participant, such resignation to be effective on the acceptance of appointment by a successor Owner Trustee under Section 9(a)(ii) hereof. In addition, the Owner Participant may at any time remove the Owner Trustee without cause by an instrument in writing delivered to the Owner Trustee, such removal to be effective upon the acceptance of appointment by a successor Owner Trustee under Section 9(a)(ii) hereof. In case of the resignation or removal of the Owner Trustee, the Owner Participant may appoint a successor Owner Trustee by an instrument signed by the Owner Participant. If a successor Owner Trustee shall not have been appointed within 30 days after the giving of written notice of such resignation or the delivery of the written instrument with respect to such removal, the Owner Trustee, the Indenture Trustee, or the Owner Participant may apply to any court of competent jurisdiction to appoint a successor Owner Trustee to act until such time, if any, as a successor shall have been appointed as above provided. Any successor Owner Trustee so appointed by such court shall immediately and without further act be superseded by any successor Owner Trustee appointed as above provided within one year from the date of the appointment by such court.

(ii) Any successor Owner Trustee, however appointed, shall execute and deliver to the predecessor Owner Trustee an instrument accepting such appointment, and thereupon such successor Owner Trustee, without further act, shall become vested with all the estates, properties, rights, powers, duties, and trusts of the predecessor Owner Trustee in the trusts hereunder with like effect as if originally named the Owner Trustee herein: but nevertheless, upon the written request of such successor Owner Trustee, such predecessor Owner Trustee shall execute and deliver an instrument transferring to such successor Owner Trustee, upon the trusts herein expressed, all the estates, properties, rights, powers, duties, and trusts of such predecessor Owner Trustee, and such predecessor Owner Trustee shall duly assign, transfer, deliver, and pay over to such successor Owner Trustee all monies or other property then held by such predecessor Owner Trustee upon the trusts herein expressed.

(iii) Any successor Owner Trustee, however appointed, a "citizen of the United States" within the meaning of Section 101(16) of the Federal Aviation Act of 1958, as amended, and shall also be a bank or trust company (not an affiliate of the Owner Participant) incorporated and doing business within the United States of America and having a combined capital and surplus of at least $50,000,000, if there be such an institution willing, able, and legally qualified to perform the duties of the Owner Trustee hereunder upon reasonable or customary terms.

(iv) Any corporation into which the Owner Trustee may be merged or converted or within which it may be consolidated, or any corporation resulting from any merger, conversion, or consolidation to which the Owner Trustee shall be a party, or any corporation to which substantially all the corporate trust business of the Owner Trustee may be transferred, shall, subject to the terms of Section 9(a)(iii) hereof, be the Owner Trustee under this Agreement without further act.

(b) Co-Trustees and Separate Trustees. Whenever the Owner Trustee or the Owner Participant shall deem it necessary or prudent in order either to conform to any law of any jurisdiction in which all or any part of the Trust Estate shall be situated or to make any claim or bring any suit with respect to the Trust Estate or any Operative Document, or the Owner Trustee or the Owner Participant shall be advised by counsel satisfactory to it that it is so necessary or prudent, the Owner Trustee and the Owner Participant shall execute and deliver an agreement supplemental hereto and all other instruments and agreements, and shall take all other action, necessary or proper to constitute one or more persons (and the Owner Trustee may appoint one or more of its officers) (any and all of which shall be a "citizen of the United States" as defined in Section 101(16) of the Federal Aviation Act of 1958, as amended) either as co-trustee or co-trustees jointly with the Owner Trustee of all or any part of the Trust Estate, or as separate trustee or separate trustees of all or any part of the Trust Estate, and to vest in such persons, in such capacity, such title to the Trust Estate or any part thereof, and such rights or duties as may be necessary or desirable, all for such period and under such terms and conditions as are satisfactory to the Owner Trustee and the Owner Participant. In case any co-trustee or separate trustee shall die, become incapable of acting, resign, or be removed, the title to the Trust Estate and all rights and duties of such co-trustee or separate trustee shall, so far as permitted by law, vest in and be exercised by the Owner Trustee, without the appointment of a successor to such co-trustee or separate trustee.

Section 10. Supplements and Amendments

(a) Supplements and Amendments. Subject to any applicable provisions of the Participation Agreement and to the Indenture, at the written request of the Owner Participant, this Agreement shall be amended by a written instrument signed by the Owner Trustee and the Owner Participant, but if in the opinion of the Owner Trustee any instrument required to be so executed adversely affects any right, duty, or liability of, or immunity or indemnity in favor of the Owner Trustee under this Agreement or any of the documents contemplated hereby to which the Owner Trustee is a party, or would cause or result in any conflict with or breach of any terms, conditions, or provisions of, or default under, the charter documents or by-laws of the Owner Trustee or any document contemplated hereby to which the Owner Trustee is a party, the Owner Trustee may in its sole discretion decline to execute such instrument.

(b) Limitation on Amendments. The provisions of Section 10(a) notwithstanding, the Owner Trustee shall not be required to execute any amendment which might result in the trusts created hereunder being terminated prior to the release of the lien of the Indenture on the Estate or prior to the payment in full of the principal of, premium (if any), and interest on the Loan Certificates.

Section 11. Miscellaneous

(a) No Legal Title to Trust Estate in Owner Participant. The Owner Participant shall not have legal title to any part of the Trust Estate. No transfer, by operation of law or Otherwise, of any right, title, and interest of the Owner Participant in and to the Trust Estate or hereunder shall operate to terminate this Agreement or the trusts hereunder or entitle any successor or transferee to an accounting or to the transfer to it of legal title to any part of the Trust Estate.

(b) Sale of Aircraft or an Engine, etc. by Owner Trustee Is Binding. Any sale or other conveyance of the Aircraft or an Engine or any part thereof by the Owner Trustee made pursuant to the terms of this Agreement or any Operative Document shall bind the Owner Participant and shall be effective to transfer or convey all right, title, and interest of the Owner Trustee and the Owner Participant in and to the Aircraft or an Engine or any part thereof, as the case may be. No purchaser or other grantee shall be required to inquire as to the authorization, necessity, expediency or regularity of such sale or conveyance or as to the application of any sale or other proceeds with respect thereto by the Owner Trustee.

(c) Limitations on Rights of Others. Except as provided in Section 7(k) of the Participation Agreement, nothing in this Agreement, whether express or implied, shall be construed to give to any Person other than the Owner Trustee, the Indenture Trustee, and the Owner Participant any legal or equitable right, remedy, or claim under or in respect of this Agreement, any covenants, conditions, or provisions contained herein or the Trust Estate.

(d) Notices. Unless otherwise expressly specified or permitted by the terms hereof, all notices shall be in writing and delivered by hand or mailed by first-class mail, postage prepaid, if to the Owner Trustee, addressed to it at ______________________________ ______________________________, or to such other address as the Owner Trustee may have set forth in a written notice to the Owner Participant, and, if to the Owner Participant, addressed to it at ______________________________, or such other address as the Owner Participant may have set forth in a written notice to the Owner Trustee. Whenever any notice in writing is required to be given by the Owner Participant, such notice shall be deemed given and such requirement satisfied if such notice is mailed by first-class mail, postage prepaid, addressed as provided above. All notices to other parties shall be transmitted and directed as required by Section 22(a) of the Participation Agreement.

(e) Severability. Any provision of this Agreement which is prohibited or unenforceable in any jurisdiction shall, as to such jurisdiction, be ineffective to the extent of such prohibition or unenforceability without invalidating the remaining provisions hereof, and any such prohibition or unenforceability in any jurisdiction shall not invalidate or render unenforceable such provision in any other jurisdiction.

(f) Limitation on Owner Participant's Liability. The Owner Participant shall not have any liability for the performance of this Agreement except as expressly set forth herein.

(g) Separate Counterparts. This Agreement may be executed by the parties hereto in separate counterparts, each of which when so executed and delivered shall be an original, but all such counterparts shall together constitute but one and the same instrument.

(h) Successors and Assigns. All covenants and agreements contained herein shall be binding upon, and inure to the benefit of, the Owner Trustee and its successors and assigns and the Owner Participant and its successors and assigns, all as herein provided. Any request, notice, direction, consent, waiver, or other instrument or action by the Owner Participant shall bind the successors and assigns of such Owner Participant.

(i) Headings. The Table of Contents and headings of the various Sections herein are for convenience of reference only and shall not define or limit any of the terms or provisions hereof.

(j) Governing Law. This Agreement shall in all respects be governed by, and construed in accordance with, the laws of the State of ________________, including all matters of construction, validity, and performance.

(k) Performance by Owner Participant. Any obligation of the Owner Trustee hereunder or under any Operative Document or other document contemplated herein may be performed by the Owner Participant and any such performance shall not be construed as a revocation of the trusts created hereby.

(l) Conflict with Operative Documents. If this Agreement shall require that any action be taken with respect to any matter and any Operative Document shall require that a different action be taken with respect to such matter, and such actions shall be mutually exclusive, the provisions of such Operative Document in respect thereof shall control.

IN WITNESS WHEREOF, the parties hereto have caused this Trust Agreement to be duly executed by their respective officers hereunto duly authorized, as of the day and year first above written.

PBC LEASING CORPORATION	MARTIN TRUST COMPANY
By: ______________________	By: ______________________
Title: ______________________	Title: ______________________

Form: I-04e
Disk File Name: I-04e.rtf

TAX INDEMNITY AGREEMENT

Form Purpose

A leveraged lease tax indemnity agreement in which the lessor sets forth the terms and conditions of the tax indemnity arrangement. This form is integrated with a Participation Agreement, a Trust Indenture and Security Agreement, a Trust Agreement, an Assignment of Rights Under Purchase Agreement, and a Lease Agreement.

Executing Parties

The owner participant.
The equipment lessee.

See:

Assignment of Rights Under Purchase Agreement, Form I-04a
Leveraged Lease Agreement, Form I-04
Participation Agreement, Form I-04b
Trust Indenture and Security Agreement, Form I-04c
Trust Agreement, Form I-04d

[*Author's note:* The following tax indemnity agreement is provided merely as an overview example. The tax attributes for each transaction must be reviewed by competent tax counsel and adjustments made as applicable.]

Tax Indemnity Agreement Covering One Blackhawk Model 555-300 Aircraft Registration Number N777P

THIS TAX INDEMNITY AGREEMENT, dated as of September XX, XXXX (this "Agreement"), is between PBC Leasing Corporation, a Florida corporation (together with its successor and permitted assigns, the "Owner Participant"), and Planet Aviation, Inc., a New Jersey corporation (together with its permitted successors and assigns, the "Lessee").

RECITALS

A. Contemporaneously with the execution and delivery of this Agreement, (i) the Lessee and the Owner Participant are entering into a Participation Agreement dated as of ____________________ (the "Participation Agreement") with Martin Trust Company, as Owner Trustee, AATX Life Insurance Company, Able Re-Insurance Company, Cooper Life Insurance Company, Peachtree Security Life Insurance Company, SYNX Life Assurance Company of Canada (U.S.), Synx Life Assurance Company of Canada, and State of New York Investment Board, as Loan Participants and The Rhode Island Bank and Trust Company, National Association, as Indenture Trustee, and (ii) the Owner Participant and the Lessee are entering into a Lease Agreement dated as of ____________________, (the "Lease"). Unless otherwise herein defined or unless the context hereof otherwise requires, the capitalized terms used herein shall have the respective meanings specified in Appendix A of the Particpation Agreement.

B. The Rent payable by the Lessee under the Lease has been determined in part based on the assumption that the Owner Participant will be entitled to certain federal and Florida state income tax benefits identified or referred to below as a result of entering into the transactions contemplated by the Participation Agreement and the Lease.

C. The Owner Participant and the Lessee wish to set forth their agreement with respect to certain federal and Florida income tax consequences of the transactions contemplated by the Participation Agreement and the Lease, including without limitation, the circumstances under which the Lessee shall be required to pay to the Owner Participant indemnity for the loss of federal and Florida income tax benefits.

NOW, THEREFORE, as a further inducement to the Owner Participant to enter into the transactions contemplated by the Participation Agreement and the Lease and in consideration thereof and of the mutual covenants and agreements contained herein and in the Participation Agreement and the Lease and the other Operative Documents, and of other good and valuable consideration, receipt of which is hereby acknowledged, the Owner Participant and the Lessee agree as follows:

Section 1. Assumed Tax Benefits. It is assumed for federal and Florida income tax purposes [the assumptions set forth in paragraph (a) being applicable only for federal income tax purposes, the assumption set forth in paragraph (b) being applicable for Florida income tax purposes only, and each of the other assumptions being applicable directly for federal income tax purposes and derivatively for Florida income tax purposes] that:

(a) The Owner Participant will be entitled to cost recovery deductions with respect to the Aircraft equal to the following percentages of the unadjusted basis of the Aircraft (reduced as required by Section 48[q] of the Code) in the years indicated (the "Cost Recovery Deductions"):

19XX 15%
20XX 22%
20XX 21%
20XX 21%
20XX 21%

(b) The Owner Participant will be entitled to depreciation deductions with respect to the Aircraft for Florida income tax purposes computed by employing the 150% declining balance method of depreciation (changing to the straight-line method at such time as will result in the most rapid recovery of basis), a useful life of 9.5 years, application of the half-year convention described in Treas. Reg. Section 1.167(a)-11(c)(2)(iii), and no salvage value;

(c) For purposes of determining the amount of the Cost Recovery Deductions, the Owner Participant's basis for the Aircraft will at least equal the Lessor's Cost therefor;

(d) The indebtedness evidenced by the Loan Certificates will constitute indebtedness of the Owner Participant, and the Owner Participant shall be entitled to deductions under Section 163 of the Code for interest paid or accrued on the Loan Certificates (the "Interest Deductions");

(e) The marginal federal income tax rate applicable to the Owner Participant will be ____ %, the marginal Florida state income tax rate applicable to the Owner Participant will be ____ % and in computing Owner Participant's federal income tax liability, Florida state income taxes will be deductible against income taxed at a ____ % tax rate;

(f) The Owner Participant will be entitled to amortize Transaction Costs on a straight-line basis over a period not longer than the period comprising the Interim Term and the Basic Term (the Transaction Expense Deductions");

(g) For federal and Florida income tax purposes, the Lease will be treated as a "true lease" of the Aircraft between the Owner Participant as owner and lessor thereof and the Lessee as the lessee thereof;

(h) The Owner Participant will compute its taxable income under the accrual method of accounting using as its taxable year the calendar year; and

(i) The Owner Participant will not be required to include in its gross income any amount attributable to the transactions contemplated by the Operative Documents other than (i) Interim Rent and Basic Rent in the amounts and in the respective years to which such Rent is allocated under the Lease, (ii) amounts attributable to improvements made to the Aircraft at the termination of the Term of the Lease, (iii) amounts to the extent that they are offset by deductions in the same taxable year in which such amounts were includible in gross income, and (iv) any amount not described in clauses (i), (ii), and (iii) of this paragraph (j) that is payable to the Owner Participant if, and to the extent that, such amount is calculated so as to include an indemnification for taxes payable by the Owner Participant by reason of receiving or accruing such amount.

In the event a Tax Law Change occurs that results in adjustments to Basic Rent, Stipulated Loss Values, and Termination Values pursuant to Section 3(e) of the Lease, the Assumed Tax Benefits shall be modified, if appropriate, to reflect the Tax Law Change that gives rise to such adjustment.

Section 2. Agreement with Respect to Federal and State Income Tax Consequences. The Lessee agrees that neither it nor any person controlled by it, in control of it, or under common control with it, directly or indirectly (an "Affiliate"), will at any time file any federal, state, or local income tax return in the United States that is inconsistent with the assumptions set forth in Section 1 hereof or with the representations and warranties set forth in Section 3 hereof or file any other document in a manner that causes a Tax Loss. The Lessee and each Affiliate will file such returns, execute such documents, and take such actions as may be reasonable and necessary to facilitate accomplishment of the intent hereof. The Lessee will maintain sufficient records to enable the Owner Participant to determine and verify its federal and Florida state income tax liability with respect to the transactions contemplated by the Operative Documents and to determine and verify its potential tax liability with respect to each other taxing jurisdiction. In addition, within 60 days after written request therefor (or within 30 days after written request therefor if Owner Participant so requires in order to fulfill its obligations, as described below), the Lessee shall provide such information as the Owner Participant may reasonably request from the Lessee to enable the Owner Participant to fulfill its tax return filing obligation (including but not limited to its federal and Florida income tax return filing obligations), to respond to requests for information, to verify information in connection with any income tax audit and to participate effectively in any tax contest. Nothing in this Section 2 shall be construed to limit the Lessee's use and operation of the Aircraft under the Lease.

Section 3. Lessee's Representations and Warranties. The Lessee represents and warrants to the Owner Participant that:

(a) On the Delivery Date, the Aircraft will constitute "recovery property" within the meaning of Section 168(c)(l) of the Code and "5-year property" within the meaning of Section 168(c) (2) (B) of the Code;

(b) At the time the Aircraft is delivered and accepted under the Operative Documents, the Lessee, all shareholders of the Lessee, and all affiliates and other Persons related to the Lessee (within the meaning of Section 318 of the Code) shall have been fully reimbursed by the Owner Participant for all amounts paid by them (directly or indirectly) to the manufacturer or to the manufacturer's subsidiary, or any other supplier with respect to the Aircraft, including all amounts paid by them to suppliers with respect to the buyer-furnished equipment;

(c) Neither the Lessee nor any affiliate of the Lessee (i) has claimed or will claim the Cost Recovery Deductions with respect to the Aircraft, (ii) will claim the Interest Deductions or the Transaction Expense Deductions or (iii) has made or will make any election with respect to any depreciation which would be binding upon the Owner Participant;

(d) When delivered and accepted under the Operative Documents, the Aircraft will not require any improvements, modifications, or additions (other than ancillary items of removable equipment of a kind customarily selected and furnished by purchasers or lessees of similar aircraft) in order to be rendered complete for its intended use by the Lessee;

(e) The Owner Participant will not be required to include any amount in its gross income that is attributable to any improvements made to the Aircraft prior to the termination of the Term of the Lease;

(f) All information in regard to the Aircraft furnished by the Lessee in writing to the Owner Participant, the Owner Participant's agents, or any person retained by the Owner Participant to appraise the Aircraft was accurate at the time given; and

(g) No member of the "lessee group" (within the meaning of Rev. Proc. 75–21, 1975-1 C. B. 715) will acquire any interest in any Loan Certificates during the Interim Term or the Basic Term;

Section 4. Income Tax Indemnification. (a) The following events (both singly and collectively) are referred to herein as a "Tax Loss". The Owner Participant shall, for federal income tax purposes, lose the right to claim, or shall not claim as the result of its good faith determination that such claim is not properly allowable, or shall suffer a disallowance or deferral of, or shall be required, for federal income tax purposes, to recapture all or any portion of, the Cost Recovery Deductions, the Transaction Expense Deductions, or the Interest Deductions or shall be required to include in its gross income for federal income tax purposes with respect to the transactions contemplated by the Operative Documents any amount other than such amounts at such times as referred to above in Section 1(i) (and other than rent paid by the Lessee pursuant to Section 3[e] of the Lease) primarily and directly as the result of:

(i) the inaccuracy or breach of any representation or warranty of the Lessee contained in Section 3 of this Agreement; or

(ii) the Lessee, an affiliate, assignee, or sublessee of the Lessee or any user or Person in possession of the Aircraft or Airframe or any Engine (v) committing any act, irrespective of whether such act is required or permitted by the Operative Documents, (including but not limited to any improvement, modification, addition, alteration, substitution, or replacement of the Aircraft or Airframe or any Engine or Part), or operating the Aircraft in such a manner that it is deemed to be used predominantly outside the United States within the meaning of Section l68(f)(2) of the Code), (w) failing to take any action required under this Agreement, the Participation Agreement, or any other Operative Document, or (x) failing to take any other action (unless such failure is due to reasonable cause).

(b) If a Tax Loss shall occur, the Lessee shall from time to time pay to the Owner Participant an indemnity with respect to each taxable year of the Owner Participant in an amount which after deduction of all taxes required to be paid by the Owner Participant in respect of the receipt of payment of such amount (taking into account the assumptions set forth in Section 4[e] hereof) shall be equal to the sum of (y) the product obtained by multiplying (I) the amount of the deduction that is the subject of such Tax Loss, or the amount of income that is the subject of such Tax Loss, by (II) the Owner Participant's combined federal and Florida state income tax rate (taking into account deductibility of Florida state income taxes for federal income tax purposes) in the taxable year for which such computation is made, and (z) the amount of any interest, penalties, or additions to tax (including any additions to tax because of underpayment of estimated tax) payable by the Owner Participant in respect of such Tax Loss.

(c) Notwithstanding anything to the contrary in this Agreement, no amount shall be payable to the Owner Participant as an indemnity under this Agreement to the extent the Tax Loss in question results directly and primarily from:

(1) A disposition of the Aircraft or any part thereof by Lessor (if such disposition is not pursuant to or in connection with the exercise of any remedy available to the Owner Participant under Section 18 of the Lease, or available to any Person claiming any right through the Owner Participant upon the occurrence of an Event of Default);

(2) The occurrence of a voluntary termination, an Event of Loss or an Event of Default as a result of which the Lessee is required to pay the Owner Participant an amount equal to or in excess of Stipulated Loss Value, Termination Value, or Fair Market Sale Value (provided that such payment is made);

(3) A failure by the Owner Participant to timely or properly claim the Cost Recovery Deductions, the Transaction Expense Deductions, or the Interest Deductions on its tax returns (unless Owner Participant shall have previously obtained a written opinion from Messrs. Merriweather & Sailing or other counsel selected by the Owner Participant and reasonably acceptable to the Lessee to the effect that substantial authority does not exist in favor of making such claim (the cost of such opinion to be borne by the Lessee, except that the Lessee will not bear such cost unless the Owner Participant has previously informed the Lessee that it intends not to claim such tax benefit and the Lessee has failed to agree within 15 days of receipt of such notice to Owner Participant's not claiming such tax benefit) or is due to the Lessee's failure (after a written request by the Owner Participant) to provide the Owner Participant with timely information required by Section 2(b) hereof);

(4) The failure of the Owner Participant to have sufficient liability for federal income tax against which to benefit from the Cost Recovery Deductions, the Transaction Expense Deductions, or the Interest Deductions;

(5) The failure of the Lease to be treated as a "true lease" for federal income tax purposes [except with respect to a Tax Loss arising primarily and directly as a result of (a) an act or omission of Lessee described in Section 4(a) of this Agreement or (b) the breach or inaccuracy of one or more of the representations or warranties contained in Sections 3(b), 3(c), 3(d), 3(f), or 3(g) of this Agreement];

(6) The application of Section 467 of the Code or the regulations promulgated thereunder;

(7) The inclusion in the Owner Participant's gross income upon termination of the Term of the Lease of amounts attributable to improvements to the Aircraft; or

(8) Any amendment to the Code or Treasury Regulations which is enacted or promulgated after delivery and acceptance of the Aircraft pursuant to the Operative Documents (but nothing in this clause [8] shall preclude adjustments to Basic Rent as provided for in the Lease).

(d) If, as a result of a Tax Loss in any taxable year, the Owner Participant shall, from time to time, (i) be entitled to claim any credits or deductions as a result of such Tax Loss in excess of the deductions which it would otherwise have been entitled to claim or (ii) be entitled to exclude from its federal taxable income any amount as a result of such Tax Loss in excess of the amount which it would otherwise have been entitled to exclude then the Owner Participant shall, from time to time, pay to the Lessee an amount, with respect to an increased deduction or exclusion resulting from a Tax Loss described in Section 4(b)(B), (taking into account the assumptions set forth in Section 4[e] hereof) equal to the sum of (A) the product obtained by multiplying (y) the amount by which the deduction or the amount of the exclusion is increased by (z) the Owner Participant's combined federal and Florida state income tax rate (taking into account the deductibility of Florida state income taxes for federal income tax purposes) in the taxable year for which such computation is made, and (B) the amount of any federal and state income tax savings realized by the Owner Participant in respect of such payment; provided, however, that (a) the aggregate amount paid by the Owner Participant to the Lessee under this paragraph shall not exceed the aggregate amount paid by the Lessee to the Owner Participant under Section 4(b) hereof and (b) any disallowance or reduction of such additional tax benefits subsequent to the year of realization by the Owner Participant shall be treated as a Tax Loss and subject to the provisions of this Agreement. Anything to the contrary herein notwithstanding the Owner Participant shall not be obligated to make any payments to the Lessee hereunder if, and so long as, an Event of Default shall have occurred and be continuing, but this restriction shall cease to apply when the Event of Default no longer continues.

(e) All calculations of amounts required to be paid by the Lessee or the Owner Participant pursuant to paragraphs (b) and (d) of this Section 4 (including any so-called "gross-up" of a basic indemnity payment) shall be made utilizing the tax assumptions set forth in Section 1 of this Agreement (excluding the assumption set forth in Sections 1[b] and 1[e] of this Agreement), and the further assumptions that (1) the Owner Participant is entitled to Florida state depreciation deductions computed in the same manner as the Cost Recovery Deductions, (2) the Owner Participant would have been able to utilize the Cost Recovery Deductions, the Transaction Expense Deductions, and the Interest Deductions, which were the subject of a Tax Loss, if such Tax Loss had not occurred, (3) the Owner Participant can utilize fully on a current basis any tax benefits resulting from the transactions giving rise to the Tax Loss, and (4) the Owner Participant is at all times subject to taxation at the highest marginal federal, state, and local income tax rates in effect for the taxable year for which the computation is made.

The parties acknowledge and agree that the provisions of this Section 4 are intended to, and shall, operate in a manner such that, utilizing the assumptions set forth in this Agreement and the highest, marginal federal income tax rate for each tax year for which a computation of Tax Loss, or an amount payable by the Owner Participant pursuant to paragraphs (b) and (d) of this Section 4, is to be made, items of deduction shall be deemed utilized regardless of actual utilization of such items.

(f) Any amount payable to the Owner Participant pursuant to Section 4(b) shall be paid within thirty (30) days after receipt of a written demand therefor from the Owner Participant accompanied by a written statement describing in reasonable detail the Tax Loss (and any interest, penalties, or additions to tax) that is the subject of and the basis for such indemnity, and the computations of the amount so payable but not prior to (i) the date of payment (or if no payment is made by reason of an offset against a tax refund the filing of a return reflecting the Tax Loss) of the additional income tax, interest, penalties, or additions to tax that become due as the result of the Tax Loss, and (ii) in the case of amounts which are being contested in accordance with Section 5, the date of settlement of such claim or a decision of a court of competent jurisdiction with respect to such claim which has become final after either (i) exhaustion of allowable appeals (to the extent required to be taken pursuant to Section 5 hereof) or (ii) expiration of time to take any such appeal with respect to the claim (any such settlement or decision being referred to herein as a "Final Determination"), except as otherwise provided in Section 5. Any payment due to the Lessee from the Owner Participant pursuant to Section 4(d) shall be paid within thirty (30) days after the Owner Participant files a tax return reflecting the additional tax benefit resulting from this transaction (regardless of whether such additional benefit results in an actual reduction in the tax liability of Owner Participant).

(g) All computations required to be made under this Section 4 shall be made in good faith by the Owner Participant, and the results of such computations, together with a statement describing in reasonable detail the manner in which such computations were made, shall be delivered to the Lessee in writing. Within fifteen (15) days following the Lessee s receipt of such computation, the Lessee may request that an independent public accounting firm of recognized national standing selected by the Owner Participant and reasonably acceptable to the Lessee (provided that, if selected by the Owner Participant, the independent public accounting firm that regularly audits the financial statements of the Owner Participant (or the affiliated group of which it is a member) shall be deemed to be reasonably acceptable to the Lessee) (the "Independent Accountants") verify whether such computations are correct. Such accounting firm shall be requested to make its determination within thirty (30) days. If such accounting firm shall determine that the Owner Participant's computations are not correct, then such firm shall determine what it believes to be the correct computations. The computations of the Owner Participant or the Independent Accountants, whichever is applicable, shall be final, binding, and conclusive upon the Lessee. Any information provided to the Independent Accountants shall be for the confidential use of such accountants and shall not be disclosed to the Lessee or any other person and the Lessee shall have no right to inspect the books, records, tax returns, or other documents of or relating to the Owner Participant to verify such computations or for any other purpose. All fees and expenses payable under this paragraph shall be borne solely by the Lessee except that such fees shall be borne by the Owner Participant if the computations provided by the Independent Accountants are different from those provided by the Owner Participant (and the difference is in favor of the Lessee) and the difference is greater than the lesser of (i) 8% of the amount computed by the Owner Participant and (ii) $100,000.

Section 5. Contest Provisions. (a) In the event the Owner Participant receives written notice of a claim for additional taxes by the Internal Revenue Service, which, if sustained, would require the payment by the Lessee of an indemnity pursuant to Section 4(a), the Owner Participant will notify the Lessee in writing of such claim within thirty (30) days after its receipt (but the failure to so notify the Lessee shall not impair the Owner Participant's right to indemnification under this Agreement unless the Lessee's contest rights with respect to such claim are adversely affected by such failure). If permitted by law, and if doing so will not cause it material adverse detriment, Owner Participant will not pay the tax claimed for at least thirty (30) days after giving such notice to the Lessee. If (a) within 30 days after notice by the Owner Participant to the Lessee of such claim, the Lessee (i) agrees in writing that the Lessee is obligated to indemnify the Owner Participant with respect to such claim pursuant to Section 4 hereof, (ii) requests in writing that such claim be contested, (iii) furnishes the Owner Participant with a written opinion of independent counsel selected by the Lessee and approved by the Owner Participant, which approval will not be unreasonably withheld ("Tax Counsel"), to the effect that there is a reasonable basis for contesting such claim, and (iv) agrees in writing to pay the Owner Participant within five (5) days of written demand therefor all out-of-pocket costs, fees, expenses, and penalties which the Owner Participant may incur in connection with contesting such claim, the Owner Participant shall contest such adjustment, provided, however, that the Owner Participant shall not be required to undertake judicial action with respect to a claim unless the proposed adjustment would result in an indemnity payment of at least $40,000 for the year or years to which the proposed adjustment pertains and the Owner Participant shall not be required to undertake any action at the administrative level with respect to a claim unless the proposed adjustment would result in an indemnity payment of at least $20,000 for the year or years to which the proposed adjustment pertains.

(b) The Owner Participant shall keep Lessee informed as to the progress of any litigation, consider in good faith suggestions made by the Lessee as to the method of conducting a contest pursuant to this Section 5 and shall not release, waive, or settle such contest without the express written consent of the Lessee except as provided in paragraph (d) of this Section 5, but, except as provided in the following sentence, the Owner Participant shall determine in its sole discretion the nature of all actions to be taken to contest such proposed adjustment, including without limitation (i) whether the contest shall initially be by way of judicial or administrative proceedings, or both, (ii) whether the proposed adjustment shall be contested by resisting payment thereof or by paying the same and seeking a refund thereof, and (iii) if the Owner Participant shall undertake judicial action, the Court or other judicial body before which such action shall be commenced. The Owner Participant, in its sole discretion. may forego any and all administrative appeals, proceedings, hearings, and conferences with the Internal Revenue Service in respect of such claim; provided, however, that the Owner Participant shall not be entitled to forego any such administrative appeals, proceedings, hearings, or conferences with respect to such claim (but only if the amount of such claim is at least $20,000 for the year or years to which the proposed adjustment pertains) for so long as (and only for so long as) the Owner Participant is contesting other items for the same taxable year in such administrative proceedings, hearings, or conferences.

(c) In the event the Owner Participant chooses to Contest a claim by paying the tax deficiency asserted and then seeking a refund thereof, the Owner Participant shall notify the Lessee, and the Lessee shall within five (5) days of demand therefor make an interest-free loan to the Owner Participant in the amount of such tax deficiency plus any interest, penalties, and additions to tax relative thereto. In the event of a Final Determination that results in an indemnity payment under Section 4 hereof, any such advance shall be applied against the amount of such indemnity.

(d) At any time, whether before or after commencing to take any action pursuant to this Section 5, the Owner Participant may decline to take such action with respect to any or all issues that form part of a claim by notifying the Lessee in writing that it is released from its obligations to indemnify the Owner Participant with respect to such issue or issues, as the case may be, but in no event shall the Lessee be relieved of the obligation to pay any related costs, fees, and expenses described in clause (iv) of paragraph (a) of this Section 5 (excluding penalties).

(e) If the Owner Participant shall have contested a proposed adjustment through lower court proceedings and the lower court shall have rendered a judgment adverse to the Owner Participant in whole or in part, then the Owner Participant shall not be obligated to appeal such adverse determination unless it receives an opinion from Tax Counsel, the costs of which shall be borne solely by Lessee to the effect that it is more likely than not that such adverse determination will be reversed. The Owner Participant shall not be obligated to appeal a decision to the United States Supreme Court unless (i) it receives a second opinion from Tax Counsel, the costs of which shall be borne solely by Lessee, similar to the opinion described above and (ii) the proposed adjustment (for all open taxable years) would result in a tax liability of at least $300,000.

(f) In the event the Owner Participant shall release, waive, or settle any claim (with respect to which it requires the Lessee's written consent for such action pursuant to paragraph [b] of this Section 5) without the express written consent of the Lessee, Lessee's obligation to indemnify the Owner Participant with respect to such claim (but not any related costs, fees, and expenses described in clause [iv] of paragraph [a] of this Section 5 [excluding penalties]) shall terminate.

Section 6. Refunds. If, after a loan by the Lessee to the Owner Participant pursuant to Section 5, the Owner Participant shall, without the consent of the Lessee, release, waive, or settle any or all issues that form part of a claim with respect to a proposed adjustment which it is obliged to contest pursuant to Section 5, the Owner Participant shall pay the Lessee the entire amount advanced by the Lessee with respect to such issue or issues (other than the costs, fees, and expenses described in clause [iv] of paragraph [a] of Section 5 of this Agreement, excluding penalties). If, after a loan by the Lessee to the Owner Participant pursuant to Section 5, there shall be a Final Determination of the claim, the Owner Participant shall pay the Lessee the excess, if any, of the amount advanced by the Lessee pursuant to Section 5 with respect to such claim (plus the amount of interest that would have been received by the Owner Participant from the United States Government if such claim were the sole matter involved in the dispute) over the amount of the indemnity payable in respect of the Final Determination.

Section 7. Loss and Termination Value Recomputation. If any amount is paid by the Lessee to Owner Participant pursuant to this Agreement, the Owner Participant shall adjust the Stipulated Loss Values and Termination Values if, and as, appropriate to avoid or eliminate duplication of payments. Any dispute between Lessee and the Owner Participant regarding adjustments to Stipulated Loss Values and Termination Values shall be settled in accordance with the procedure described in Section 4(g) hereof. Anything to the contrary in this Agreement notwithstanding, none of the Stipulated Loss Values or the Termination Values shall be decreased to an amount which is less than the amount sufficient to pay in full as of the date of payment thereof the aggregate unpaid principal amount of the Loan Certificates then outstanding, and the accrued and unpaid interest thereon.

Section 8. No Setoff. No payment required to be made by the Lessee pursuant to this Agreement shall be subject to any right of setoff, counterclaim, defense, abatement, suspension, deferment, or reduction.

Section 9. Survival of Agreement. The obligations and liabilities of the Lessee and the Owner Participant arising under this Agreement shall continue in full force and effect, notwithstanding the expiration or other termination of the Participation Agreement, the Lease, or any other Operative Documents, until all such obligations have been met and such liabilities have been paid in full. The obligations and liabilities of the Lessee and the Owner Participant arising under this Agreement are expressly made for the benefit of, and shall be enforceable by, the Owner Participant and the Lessee and their successors, assigns, and agents.

Section 10. (a) Payments. Any payments made to any party pursuant to this Agreement shall be in U.S. dollars and shall be made directly to such party (and shall not constitute part of the Estate) by wire transfer of immediately available funds to such banks and/or account as specified by the payee in written directions to the payer, or, if no such direction shall have been given, by check of the payer payable to the order of such payee and mailed to such party by certified mail, postage prepaid, at its address as set forth in the Lease.

(b) Late Payments. In the case of any late payment of an amount due hereunder, the relevant party shall promptly pay interest in respect thereof at the Overdue Rate (computed on the basis of a 360-day year of twelve 30-day months) for the period from the date such amount was due to the date on which payment thereof is made.

Section 11. Affiliated Group. The term "Owner Participant" shall be deemed to include every member of the "affiliated group" (within the meaning of Code Section 1504) of which the Owner Participant is or becomes a member if such group files consolidated returns for federal income tax purposes.

Section 12. Governing Laws. This Agreement shall be governed by and construed in accordance with the laws of the State of ____________________.

Section 13. Notices. Any notice required to be given by either party under this Agreement shall be deemed to have been properly given or made if delivered personally to, or mailed by certified mail, return receipt requested, addressed as follows:

If to the Owner Participant:

If to the Lessee:

Section 14. Counterparts. This Agreement may be executed in any number of counterparts, each of which when executed shall be deemed to be an original and such counterparts together shall constitute and be one of the same instrument.

PBC LEASING CORPORATION

By: ______________________________

Title: ____________________________

PLANET AVIATION, INC.

By: ______________________________

Title: ____________________________

Loan Documents

[See also Forms a-05 and p-02.]

Form: l-05
Disk File Name: l-05.rtf

LOAN AND SECURITY AGREEMENT—SHORT FORM

Form Purpose

A short form equipment loan and security agreement setting forth a nonrecourse loan arrangement between a lender and an equipment leasing company, the proceeds of which are to be used by the leasing company to pay for equipment subject to lease. By deleting the nonrecourse limitation, the form can be used to document a recourse loan arrangement. This form references a promissory note and an assignment, both of which have been integrated with this form.

Executing Parties

The borrower (equipment lessor).
The lender.

See:

Promissory Note, Form p-02
Assignment, Form a-05

Loan and Security Agreement

This Loan and Security Agreement, dated ____________________, XXXX, (the "Agreement") by and between ____, a (insert jurisdiction of incorporation) (the "Borrower"), with a place of business at ______________________________________, and ______________________________, a (insert jurisdiction of incorporation) (the "Lender"), with a place of business at ______________________________________.

Subject to the terms and conditions of this Agreement, Lender agrees to lend to Borrower on or before ____________________, an aggregate amount (the "Loan") equal to _____ % of the purchase price of certain newly manufactured equipment, as described in Exhibit A hereto (the "Units") which are subject to an Equipment Lease Agreement dated as of ________________ between Borrower, as lessor, and ______________________________, as lessee (the "Lessee") (said lease together with its (two) equipment schedules, hereinafter referred to as the "Lease").

1. Use of Loan Proceeds. The proceeds of the Loan shall be applied toward the cost to Lessor of the Units (the "Purchase Price") which are the subject of the Lease.

2. Closing; Conditions Precedent. It is anticipated that the Loan will be made in (two) installments. The first will be made on (insert appropriate date) with respect to Units accepted for lease by Lessee prior to such date. The second installment will be made on (insert appropriate date) with respect to all other Units leased by Lessee. On each such date that an installment is made (a "Closing Date"), Borrower will deliver to Lender a promissory note substantially in the form annexed hereto as Exhibit A [*Author's Note:* For promissory note integrated with this Loan and Security Agreement, see Form p-02], in the principal amount of the loan being made on such Closing Date (a "Note"). The obligation of Lender to make the Loan hereunder is subject to the performance by Borrower of all of its respective covenants, agreements, and other obligations required to be performed under this Agreement, and to the following further conditions:

(a) On or prior to the first Closing Date, Lender shall have received:

(i) an assignment executed by Borrower in substantially the form annexed hereto as Exhibit B [*Author's Note:* For assignment agreement integrated with this form, see Form a-05] (the "Assignment);

(ii) an opinion of counsel for Borrower, in form and substance satisfactory to Lender, to the effect that (A) Borrower is a corporation duly organized and existing and in good standing under the laws of the jurisdiction of its incorporation, with adequate power to enter into and perform this Agreement and the Lease and (B) this Agreement, the Lease, the Assignment, and the Notes have been duly authorized, executed, and delivered by Borrower and are (or will be in the case of the Notes) legal, valid, and binding instruments enforceable in accordance with their respective terms (which opinion of counsel may be subject to appropriate qualifications as to applicable bankruptcy law and other similar laws affecting creditors' rights generally);

(iii) Lessor's executed copy of the Lease; and

(iv) such other documents as Lender shall reasonably request.

(b) In respect of each Closing Date Lender shall have received:

(i) notice of Lessee's acceptance of Units for lease, the date of such acceptance and the amount of the Purchase Price of the Units to be paid by Borrower for such Units, and (ii) a Note in the principal amount of the Loan being made on such Closing Date and payable to Lender.

(c) The first Closing shall be held at the offices of ______________ or as otherwise agreed to by the parties. Each Loan shall be made by a bank wire transfer or by a certified or official bank check in New York Clearing House funds payable to the order of Borrower. On each Closing Date Borrower shall execute and deliver to Lender a single Note in the principal amount of the Loan being made on such date.

3. Repayment. The principal amount of each Note shall be repaid by Borrower to Lender in such number of installments and on such dates ("Payment Dates") as are specified in the Note. The unpaid balance of the Note shall bear interest from the Closing Date in respect thereof at the rate of ____ % per annum. Interest shall be payable on each Payment Date and on such other dates as are set forth in the Note. The principal amount of the Note payable on each Payment Date shall be calculated so that the aggregate of the principal and interest payable on each of the Payment Dates shall be substantially equal and the aggregate of all such payments will completely amortize the Loan. Interest under the Notes shall be determined on the basis of a 360-day year of twelve 30-day months. Borrower will pay Lender interest, computed at a rate per annum equal to ____ %, on all installments of principal and, to the extent legally enforceable, interest remaining unpaid after the same shall have become due and payable. All payments shall be made in lawful money of the United States of America. Lender agrees to furnish Borrower as a schedule to each Note, an amortization table showing the respective amounts of principal and interest payable on each Payment Date and the unpaid principal amount outstanding ("Loan Schedules").

It is anticipated that once all Units have been accepted for lease, Borrower and Lessee will consolidate the various (quarterly) rental payment schedules with respect to all Units. In such event, Borrower and Lender will consolidate the Notes based on the amount of unamortized principal into a single Note which shall be amortized with Payment Dates concurrent with the consolidated lease payment dates.

In the event that Lessee shall pay amounts in respect of a casualty occurrence or condemnation or seizure of any Units as set forth in the Lease, a sum equal to such payment shall be applied to the prepayment without penalty of the applicable Note secured by such Units. Each such prepayment shall be applied, first, to the payment of all accrued and unpaid interest under such Note to the date of such prepayment and, second, to the pro rata reduction of the respective principal amounts of the remaining unpaid installments of the Note, and the amount of interest included in each future installment shall be correspondingly reduced to reflect such reductions in principal amount. Borrower shall pay such amounts together with an amount equal to interest at ____ % per annum compounded monthly from the date said accelerated payments are due to and including the date of receipt.

Upon acceleration of a Note as provided in this Agreement, Borrower shall pay an amount equal to interest at a rate of ____ % per annum compounded monthly from the date said amounts are due and payable to the date of receipt.

Borrower hereby authorizes Lender (i) to collect all payments to be made by Lessee under the Lease and (ii) to separate and retain for Lender's account the applicable payments as and when due to Lender. Borrower agrees to direct Lessee to make all payments to be made by it under the Lease, directly to Lender. Borrower agrees that should it receive any such payments with respect to the Units or the Lease that have been assigned to Lender pursuant to the Assignment, it will promptly forward such payments to Lender for disbursement in accord with the terms hereof. Lender agrees to apply amounts from time to time received by it (from Lessee, Borrower, or otherwise) with respect to the Lease or the Units, to the extent such amounts have been assigned to Lender pursuant to the Assignment, first to the payment of the principal of and interest on any Note then due and any other amounts then due and payable under this Agreement, and then, if no event of default hereunder shall have occurred and be continuing, promptly to pay any balance to Borrower no later than the day after receipt of such payment by depositing such payments to the account of Borrower in Borrower's account at ______________________________ or such other account as Borrower may designate in writing. Any payments Lender receives with respect to the Lease or Units that have not been assigned to Lender shall be remitted by Lender to the said account of Borrower.

4. Security. Borrower hereby grants to Lender a security interest in the Units (subject to the rights to the use of the Units by Lessee pursuant to the Lease) and in the Lease, and for such purpose, assigns to Lender the Lease and all payments due or to become due thereunder pursuant and subject to the terms of the Assignment, to secure obligations of Borrower hereunder and under the Notes. Borrower hereby authorizes Lender to file or record this Agreement, the Assignment or financing statements with respect to Lender's security interest in the Units and the Lease with any appropriate governmental office in order to perfect such security interest. The security interest created thereunder will terminate when all obligations of Borrower hereunder and under the Notes are discharged, and Lender, at the request of Borrower, will then execute termination statements and such other documents as may be necessary or appropriate to make clear upon the public records the termination of such security interest.

Borrower hereby appoints Lender its true and lawful attorney, with full power of substitution, to enforce Borrower's rights as Lessor under the Lease, and to take any action which Lender may deem necessary or appropriate to protect and preserve the security interest of Lender.

5. Limitation on Liability. The liability of Borrower with respect to the payments specified in Section 3 hereof shall be nonrecourse to the Buyer and shall be limited to the Units, the Lease, and "income and proceeds therefrom," but Borrower's liability hereunder shall not be so limited in respect of any breach or inaccuracy of the covenants, warranties, and agreements contained in Section 6 hereof. As used herein the phrase "income and proceeds therefrom" shall mean:

(i) all Rent (as defined in the Lease) and any other sums due or to become due under the Lease which have been assigned to Lender, including but not limited to all proceeds of insurance, or payments due as a result of a casualty occurrence or condemnation, and

(ii) any and all payments or funds received by Borrower or Lender for or with respect to the Units as a result of the sale or other disposition thereof.

Notwithstanding the limitation on liability of Borrower otherwise herein contained, the obligation of Borrower to pay the principal of and interest on the Loan and all other amounts payable to Lender hereunder shall be fully enforceable (by appropriate proceedings against Borrower in law or in equity or otherwise) against Borrower's right, title, and interest in the Units, the Lease, the Rent, and any other assigned sums due or to become due under the Lease, and nothing contained herein limiting the liability of Borrower shall derogate from the right of Lender to enforce its security interest in the Units or the Lease for the unpaid principal of and interest on the Loan and all other amounts payable to Lender hereunder and under the Notes, including, without limitation, the right to accelerate the maturity of payments on the Loan as provided herein upon an event of default hereunder and to proceed against Lessee under the Lease and to realize upon the Units.

6. Covenants, Warranties, and Agreements of Borrower.

Borrower covenants, warrants, and agrees that:

(a) it will not, except with the prior written consent of Lender, agree to modify any material provision of the Lease or give any consent thereunder;

(b) on each Closing Date Borrower will have good and marketable title to the subject Units and the interest of Borrower in the Units, the Lease, the Rent, and any other assigned sums due or to become due under the Lease will continue to be held free and clear of security interests, liens, claims, encumbrances, and rights of others (excepting only the rights of Lender hereunder and of Lessee under the Lease);

(c) this Agreement, the Assignment, and the Loan have been duly authorized by Borrower;

(d) the execution and delivery of this Agreement, the Assignment, the Notes, the Lease, and the carrying out of the transactions contemplated hereby and thereby do not and will not constitute a default under, or result in the creation of any lien, charge, encumbrance, or security interest upon any assets of Borrower under, any agreement, (except this Agreement) or instrument to which Borrower is a party or by which its assets may be bound or affected;

(e) Borrower, at its expense, will fulfill all its obligations under the Lease and, upon default, will, upon the request of Lender, enforce all its rights as Lessor under the Lease or such of such rights as Lender shall request;

(f) Borrower will maintain, preserve, and keep in full force and effect its corporate existence and all rights and qualifications necessary for the enforcement of the Lease by Borrower or Lender; and

(g) except for the Lease and this Agreement, Borrower will not sell, loan, pledge, mortgage, assign, or otherwise dispose of, or create or suffer to be created any levies, liens, or encumbrances on the Units, the Lease, or any interest or part thereof.

7. Representations of Lender. Lender represents that except as heretofore disclosed in writing to special counsel for Lender, it is acquiring the Notes for its own account for investment and not with a view to, or for sale in connection with, any distribution thereof, but subject, nevertheless, to any requirement of law that the disposition of its property shall at all times be within its control. Lender understands that the Notes to be issued hereunder have not been registered under the Securities Act of 1933, as amended.

Lender hereby agrees that any transfer or assignment of the Notes or of all or any part of its interest hereunder shall be on the express condition that the transferee or assignee shall be bound by the terms of this Agreement.

8. Default.

(a) Any of the following events shall constitute an event of default hereunder:

(i) payment of any part of the principal of or interest on the Note shall not be made when and as the same shall become due and payable (irrespective of the limitations contained in Section 5 hereof), and such default shall continue unremedied for 10 days;

(ii) Borrower shall default in the due observance or performance of any other covenants, conditions, or provisions hereof or of the Assignment or the Lease and such default shall continue for more than 10 days after written notice from Lender specifying the default and demanding the same to be remedied;

(iii) Borrower shall cease doing business as a going concern, make an assignment for the benefit of creditors, admit in writing its inability to pay its debts as they become due, file a voluntary petition in bankruptcy, be adjudicated a bankrupt or an insolvent, file a petition seeking for itself any reorganization, arrangement, composition, readjustment, liquidation, dissolution, or similar arrangement under any present or future statute, law, or regulation or file an answer admitting the material allegations or a petition filed against it in any such proceeding, or consent to or acquiesce in the appointment of a trustee, receiver, or liquidator of it or all or any substantial part of its assets or properties, or if any of them shall take action looking to its dissolution or liquidation or if any, within 30 days after the commencement of any proceedings against Borrower seeking reorganization, arrangement, readjustment, liquidation, dissolution, or similar relief under any present or future statute, law, or regulation, such proceedings shall not have been dismissed, or if within 30 days after the appointment without Borrower's consent or acquiescence of any trustee, receiver, or liquidator of it or of all or any substantial part of its assets or properties, such appointment shall not be vacated; and

(v) an Event of Default (as the term is defined in the Lease) shall have occurred and be continuing under the Lease.

In case an event of default shall have occurred and be continuing hereunder, Lender may declare the entire unpaid principal amounts of the Notes outstanding and unpaid interest thereon and any other sums owed hereunder immediately due and payable, subject, however, to the limitations as to the liability of Borrower contained in Section 5 hereof, and Lender shall have all the rights and remedies of a secured party under the Uniform Commercial Code. If an Event of Default shall have occurred and be continuing under the Lease, Lender may exercise all rights and remedies of Borrower, as Lessor under the Lease and apply any amounts realized in consequence thereof against the unpaid principal amount of the Note and unpaid interest thereon.

(b) Notwithstanding the foregoing, an Event of Default under the Lease resulting from nonpayment of Rent due thereunder on a specific Payment Date shall not be an event of default hereunder provided that (i) Borrower shall have paid the full amount of such defaulted Rent within ten days of notification to Borrower of such nonpayment (notwithstanding the limitation of Borrower's obligation set forth in Section 5 hereof), (ii) Lender shall have reasonably determined that the delaying of a declaration of such an event of default would not have a materially adverse effect on the exercise or realization of Lender's rights hereunder with respect to the

Units or (iii) Lessee shall have made the next preceding payment of Rent when due, together with the payment of Rent then in arrears.

9. Notes. Lender, upon payment to it of all amounts payable to it hereunder and under the Notes, will surrender the Notes to Borrower. Lender shall be entitled to all payments due hereunder and under the Notes without being required to surrender the Notes. However, Lender agrees to make appropriate notation on the Notes before any transfer thereof to reflect all payments of principal and interest theretofore received.

10. Notice. All notices required or permitted to be delivered hereunder shall be in writing and shall be deemed given when delivered or when deposited in the United States mails, certified, postage prepaid and addressed with the full name and address of the appropriate party set forth below:

If to Borrower:

If to Lender:

11. Execution; Controlling Law; Successors and Assigns. This Agreement may be executed in one or more counterparts, each of which, when so executed, shall be deemed to be an original, and such counterparts, together shall constitute one and the same agreement, which shall be sufficiently evidenced by one of such original counterparts. This Agreement shall be governed by and be construed in accordance with the laws of the State of ____________________ and shall inure to the benefit of and be binding upon, Borrower and Lender and the permitted successors and assign.

Borrower:

(Insert name of borrower)

By: ____________________________________

Title: __________________________________

Lender:

(Insert name of lender)

By: ____________________________________

Title: __________________________________

Exhibit A

[Insert equipment description.]

Exhibit B

Form of Promissory Note

[See Form p-02.]

Exhibit C

Form of Assignment

[See Form a-05.]

Form: I-06
Disk File Name: I-06.rtf

Loan and Security Agreement—Long Form (Railcars/General)

Form Purpose

A comprehensive long-form loan and security and loan agreement for railcar lending. This form contemplates a nonrecourse loan arrangement with respect to two separate equipment lease transactions. With minor modifications, the form may be used for any type of equipment, as well as cover a recourse loan arrangement. Collateral documents necessary to complete the loan transaction are integrated with this form (see below).

Executing Parties

The borrower.
The lender.

See:

Promissory Note, Form l-06a
Guaranty, Form l-06b
Bill of Sale, Form l-06c
Certificate of Acceptance, Form l-06d
Certificate of Cost, Form l-06e
Legal Opinion for Lessee-Counsel for Lessee and Guarantor, Form l-06f
Legal Opinion for Lessee-Special Counsel, Form l-06g

Loan and Security Agreement

Between

(insert name of borrower)

and

(insert name of lender)

Dated as of ____________________, XXXX.

Filed and recorded with the Interstate Commerce Commission pursuant to Section ___, Title ______________________, United States Code on ______________________, XXXX at ____, Recordation No. ________.

Table of Contents

LOAN AND SECURITY AGREEMENT, dated as of ______________, XXXX, between (insert name of borrower), a (insert jurisdiction of incorporation of borrower) corporation (the "Company"), with a principal place of business at ______________ ______________ and (insert name of lender), a (insert incorporation jurisdiction of lender) corporation (the "Lender'"), with a principal place of business at ______________.

WITNESSETH:

WHEREAS, the Company is engaged, among other things, in the business of purchasing and owning railroad box-cars for lease to others; and

WHEREAS, the Company desires to obtain a loan from the Lender in order to finance a portion of the purchase price of (insert number of box-cars here) box-cars on order from (insert name of box-car vendor or manufacturer), (insert number of box-cars) of such box-cars to be leased to (insert the name of the prospective lessee number 1) under the First Lessee Lease (as hereinafter defined) and (insert number of box-cars) of such box-cars to be leased to (insert name of prospective lessee number 2) under the Second Lessee Lease (as hereinafter defined); and

WHEREAS, the Company will evidence its borrowing hereunder by the issuance of its promissory note which, together with the Company's obligations and liabilities under this Agreement, will be secured by, inter alia, a lien on and security interest in such box-cars and the rights of the Company under the First Lessee Lease and the Second Lessee Lease; and

WHEREAS, the Lender is agreeable to making the loan on the terms and conditions set forth in this Agreement;

NOW, THEREFORE, in consideration of the premises and of the mutual agreements contained herein, the parties hereto agree as follows:

Section 1. Definitions

1.1 Defined Terms. As used in this Agreement the following terms shall have the following meanings:

"Agreement" shall mean this Loan and Security Agreement, including all Schedules and all Exhibits hereto, as the same may from time to time be amended, supplemented, or otherwise modified.

"Box-Cars" shall mean at any time the box-cars which are described in Schedule I hereto, together with (i) any and all other box-cars which are subjected to the lien and security interest of this Agreement or intended so to be, (ii) any and all parts, mechanisms, devices, and replacements referred to in Subsection 6.17 hereof from time to time incorporated in or installed on or attached to any of such box-cars, (iii) any and all additions and improvements from time to time incorporated in or installed on or attached to any of such box-cars pursuant to requirement of law or governmental regulation, and (iv) any and all Nonremovable Improvements.

"Box-Car Cost" shall mean, for each Unit (other than a Replacement Unit), the actual cost thereof to the Company including all inspection fees and all applicable local or state sales taxes, if any, but excluding transportation charges in excess of $1,000, as set forth in the manufacturer's invoice with respect to such Unit. The "Box-Car Cost" of a Replacement Unit shall be the Box-Car Cost of the Unit which it replaced.

"Business Day" shall mean any day other than a Saturday, a Sunday, or a legal holiday under the laws of the State of (________________).

"Cash Collateral Account" shall have the meaning set forth in Subsection 5.2(b) hereof.

"Casualty Occurrence" shall mean any of the following events or conditions with respect to any Unit:

(i) such Unit shall become lost for a period of at least 30 consecutive days, or shall become stolen, destroyed, or damaged beyond economic repair from any cause whatsoever; or

(ii) the confiscation, condemnation, seizure, or forfeiture of, or other requisition of title to, or use of, such Unit by any governmental authority or any Person acting under color of governmental authority.

"Casualty Value" with respect to any Unit shall mean the amount obtained by multiplying the unpaid principal amount of the Note at the time Casualty Value is being determined by a fraction, the numerator of which is the Box-Car Cost of such Unit and the denominator of which is the aggregate Box-Car Costs of all Box-Cars which are then subject to the lien and security interest of this Agreement.

"Casualty Value Determination Date" shall have the meaning set forth in Subsection 6.16 (a) hereof.

"Collateral" shall mean the Box-Cars, the Leases, the monies at any time in the Cash Collateral Account and all other property, interests, and rights described or referred to in Subsection 5.1, 5.2, or 5.3 hereof or otherwise subjected to the lien and security interest created by this Agreement or intended so to be.

"Damaged Unit" shall mean any Unit which has suffered a Casualty Occurrence.

"Default" shall mean any of the events specified in Section 8 hereof, whether or not there has been satisfied any requirement in connection with such event for the giving of notice or the lapse of time, or both.

"Event of Default" shall mean any of the events specified in Section 8 hereof, provided that there has been satisfied any requirement in connection with such event for the giving of notice, or the lapse of time, or both.

"First Lessee" shall mean (insert the name of lessee number 1), a ________________ corporation.

"First Lessee Box-Cars" shall mean at any time the Box-Cars which are subject to the First Lessee Lease.

"First Lessee Lease" shall mean the Lease Agreement dated as of ________________, XXXX, between the Company and The First Lessee, as the same may from time to time be amended, supplemented, or otherwise modified.

"Guarantor" shall mean (insert name of any guarantor here), a ________________ corporation.

"Guaranty" shall mean the Guaranty of the Guarantor in favor of the Lender, substantially in the form of Exhibit B hereto.

"Installment Payment Date" shall mean each date on which an installment of principal and interest is due and payable under the Note.

"Leases" shall mean and include the First Lessee Lease and the Second Lessee Lease.

"Lessees" shall mean and include the First Lessee and the Second Lessee.

"Lien" shall mean any mortgage, pledge, hypothecation, assignment, security interest, lien, charge or encumbrance, priority or other security agreement, or arrangement of any kind or nature whatsoever (including, without limitation, any conditional sale or other title retention agreement, any lease having substantially the same economic effect as a conditional sale or other title retention agreement, and the filing of, or agreement to give, any financing statement under the Uniform Commercial Code or comparable law of any jurisdiction).

"Loan" shall mean the loan made by the Lender under this Agreement.

"Nonremovable Improvement" shall mean any addition or improvement incorporated in or installed on or attached to any Box-Car which is not readily removable without causing material damage to such Box-Car or without diminishing or impairing the utility or condition which such Box-Car would have had at the time of removal had such addition or improvement not been made.

"Note" shall mean the promissory note of the Company described in Subsection 2.3 hereof.

"Obligations" shall have the meaning set forth in Section 5 hereof.

"Permitted Liens" shall mean, with respect to any Unit, (i) the rights of the Lessee under the Lease of such Unit, (ii) Liens for taxes which are not yet due or the payment of which is not at the time required to be made in accordance with the provisions of Subsection 6.4 hereof, and (iii) materialmen's, mechanics, repairmen's and other like Liens arising in the ordinary course of business securing obligations which are not more than 30 days overdue or the payment of which is not at the time required to be made in accordance with the provisions of Subsection 6.4 hereof.

"Person" shall mean an individual, partnership, corporation, joint venture, trust, unincorporated organization, or government or any agency or political subdivision thereof.

"Proceeds" shall have the meaning assigned to it under the Uniform Commercial Code of the State of New York and, in any event, shall include, but not be limited to, (i) any and all proceeds of any insurance, indemnity, warranty, or guaranty payable to the Company from time to time with respect to any of the Collateral, (ii) any and all payments (in any form whatsoever) made or due and payable to the Company from time to time in connection with any requisition, confiscation, condemnation, seizure, or forfeiture of any of the Collateral by any governmental authority (or any Person acting under color of governmental authority), and (iii) any and all other amounts from time to time paid or payable under or in connection with any of the Collateral.

"Replacement Unit" shall have the meaning set forth in Subsection 6.16(c) hereof.

"Second Lessee" shall mean (insert name of lessee number 2), a ____________ corporation.

"Second Lessee Box-Cars" shall mean at any time the Box-Cars which are subject to the Second Lessee Lease.

"Second Lessee Lease" shall mean the Lease Agreement dated as of ________________ XXXX between the Company and the Second Lessee, as the same may from time to time be amended, supplemented, or otherwise modified.

"Subsidiary" shall mean, when used with respect to any person, any corporation more than 50% of the issued and outstanding shares of Voting Stock of which at the time is owned or controlled, directly or indirectly, by such Person or by one or more other Subsidiaries of such Person.

"Unit" shall mean one of the Box-Cars.

"Vendor" shall mean (insert the name of the railcar manufacturer or vendor), a ________________ corporation.

"Voting Stock" of a corporation shall mean stock having ordinary voting power for the election of a majority of the board of directors, managers, or trustees of such corporation, other than stock having such power only by reason of the happening of a contingency.

"Wholly-Owned Subsidiary" shall mean, when used with respect to any Person, any Subsidiary, all the issued and outstanding shares (except for directors' qualifying shares, if required by law) of Voting Stock of which at the time are owned by such Person or by one or more Wholly-Owned Subsidiaries of such Person.

1.2 Use of Defined Terms. All terms defined in this Agreement shall have their defined meanings when used in the Note, or in any certificates, reports, or other documents made or delivered pursuant hereto.

1.3 Other Definitional Provisions.

(a) The words "hereof", "herein", and "hereunder" and words of similar import when used in this Agreement shall refer to this Agreement as a whole and not to any particular provision of this Agreement.

(b) Terms defined in the singular shall have a comparable meaning when used in the plural and vice versa.

Section 2. Amount and Terms of Loan

2.1 Commitment. Subject to the terms and conditions of this Agreement, the Lender agrees to make a loan to the Company on any Business Day from the date hereof to and including (insert date on which lender is obligated to loan funds through), in a principal amount not to exceed $ (insert maximum dollar amount of loan), to finance a portion of the aggregate purchase price of (insert number of box-cars) box-cars to be purchased by the Company from Vendor and leased under the Leases; provided, however, that the amount of such loan shall in no event exceed the sum of (i) (insert maximum percentage) % of the aggregate Box-Car Costs of the First Lessee Box-Cars plus (ii) (insert maximum percentage) % of the aggregate Box-Car Costs of the Second Lessee Box-Cars. The Company shall give the Lender at least 5 Business Days' prior written notice (effective upon receipt) of the borrowing hereunder.

2.2 Use of Proceeds. The Company will use the proceeds of the Loan solely to pay, or to reimburse, the Company for payments made by it with respect to, up to (insert maximum percentage) % of the aggregate Box-Car Costs of the First Lessee Box-Cars and up to (insert maximum percentage) % of the aggregate Box-Car Costs of the Second Lessee Box-Cars.

2.3 The Note. The Loan shall be evidenced by a secured promissory note of the Company substantially in the form of Exhibit A hereto with appropriate insertions therein. The Note shall (a) be dated the date on which the Loan is made, (b) be in the principal amount of the Loan, (c) bear interest on the unpaid principal amount thereof from the date thereof at the rate of (insert the interest rate) % per annum, provided that whenever any such unpaid principal amount shall become due and payable (whether at the stated maturity, by prepayment, by acceleration, or otherwise), interest thereon shall thereafter be payable at the rate of (insert the late interest rate) % per annum until such overdue principal amount shall be paid in full, and (d) be payable in (insert the total number of payments to be made, such as 120) consecutive monthly installments of principal and interest, commencing on the day of the first calendar month after the date of the Note corresponding with the date of the Note and on the same day of each calendar month thereafter (or, if any such month does not have a corresponding day, then on the last day of such month), the 1st through the (insert the second to the last payment number, such as 119th) of such installments each being in an amount equal to (insert the appropriate percentage, such as 1.184131%) of the original principal amount of the Note and the (insert the number of the last payment, such as 120th) of such installments being in an amount equal to (insert the final percentage payment, such as 53.536308%) of the original principal amount of the Note, provided that, in any event, the (insert the number of the last payment, such as 120th) installment shall be in an amount sufficient to pay in full all accrued interest on, and the entire unpaid principal amount of, the Note. Installments received with respect to the Note shall be applied first to the payment of interest then due and then to the payment of principal.

2.4 Voluntary Prepayment With Premium. On any one Installment Payment Date subsequent to the (sixth) anniversary of the date of the Note, the Company may, at its Option, upon notice as provided in Subsection 2.6 hereof, prepay up to but not exceeding (40)% of then outstanding principal amount of the Note, provided that simultaneously with such prepayment the Company pays to the Lender (i) accrued interest on the outstanding principal amount of the Note to the date of such prepayment and (ii) a premium equal to (insert appropriate premium, such as 1%) of the outstanding principal amount of the Note being prepaid. Upon the making of any such prepayment of the Note by the Company, the Company shall have no further right to prepay the Note pursuant to this Subsection 2.4. Except as otherwise provided in this Subsection 2.4, the Note may not be voluntarily prepaid.

2.5 Casualty Occurrence Prepayment. In the event that any Unit shall suffer a Casualty Occurrence and the Company shall not replace such Unit pursuant to Subsection 6.16 hereof, the Company will prepay the Note without premium in accordance with the provisions of said Subsection 6.16.

2.6 Notice of Prepayment. The Company shall give written notice to the Lender of any prepayment of the Note not less than 10 days nor more than 30 days before the date fixed for such prepayment, specifying (a) the date fixed for such prepayment (which shall be an Installment Payment Date if the prepayment is to be made pursuant to Subsection 2.4

hereof), (b) the Subsection hereof under which such prepayment is to be made, (c) the principal amount of the Note to be prepaid, and (d) the premium, if any, and accrued interest applicable to such prepayment. Such notice of prepayment shall also certify all facts which are conditions precedent to such prepayment, including, if such prepayment is to be made pursuant to Subsection 2.5 hereof, the calculations used in determining the unpaid principal amount of the Note to be prepaid. Upon the giving of such notice, the unpaid principal amount of the Note to be prepaid, together with the premium, if any, and accrued interest thereon, shall become due and payable on the date fixed for such prepayment.

2.7 Adjustment of Installments. In the event any partial prepayment of the Note is made pursuant to Subsection 2.4 or 2.5 hereof, each installment due and payable under the Note after such partial prepayment shall be reduced in the same proportion as then outstanding Principal amount of the Note shall have been reduced by such partial prepayment.

2.8 Computation of Interest. Interest on the Note shall be calculated on the basis of a 360-day year of twelve 30-day months. All payments (including prepayments) by the Company on account of the principal of, premium, if any, and interest on the Note shall be made to the Lender at its office at (insert address of Lender's office), or at such other place as the Lender shall notify the Company in writing, in lawful money of the United States of America. If any such payment becomes due and payable on a day that is not a Business Day, the maturity thereof shall be extended to the next succeeding Business Day.

2.9 Release of Collateral. Upon any prepayment of the Note pursuant to Subsection 2.4 hereof, the Lender will promptly execute and deliver to the Company such instruments as shall be necessary to release from the lien and security interest of this Agreement, without recourse to, or representation or warranty by, the Lender, that number of Units which is equal to the number (disregarding any fraction) obtained by multiplying the total number of Box-Cars which are then subject to the lien and security interest of this Agreement by a fraction, the numerator of which is the principal amount of the Note so prepaid and the denominator of which is the original principal amount of the Note. The Lender shall have the right to designate the Units to be released.

Section 3. Representations and Warranties

In order to induce the Lender to enter into this Agreement and to make the Loan, the Company represents and warrants to the Lender that:

3.1 Corporate Existence and Business. The Company is a corporation duly organized, validly existing, and in good standing under the laws of the State of (insert state of incorporation). Neither the conduct of its business nor the ownership or lease of its properties requires the Company to qualify to do business as a foreign corporation under the laws of any jurisdiction. The Company has (no) Subsidiaries. The Company presently is engaged solely in the business of (insert description business of Company, such as "purchasing, leasing, and managing railroad cars.")

3.2 Power and Authorization; Enforceability; Consents. The Company has full power, authority and legal right to own its properties and to conduct its business as now conducted and presently proposed to be conducted by it and to execute, deliver, and perform this Agreement, the Note, and the Leases and to borrow under this Agreement on the terms and conditions hereof, to grant the lien and security interest provided for in this Agreement, and to take such action as may be necessary to complete the transactions contemplated by this Agreement, the Note, and the Leases, and the Company has taken all necessary corporate action to authorize the borrowing on the terms and conditions of this Agreement and the grant of the lien and security interest provided for in this Agreement and to authorize the execution, delivery, and performance of this Agreement, the Note, and the Leases. This Agreement has been duly authorized, executed, and delivered by the Company and constitutes, and the Note has been duly authorized by the Company and when executed and delivered by the Company will constitute, a legal, valid, and binding obligation of the Company enforceable in accordance with its terms. No consent of any Other party (including stockholders of the Company and the Guarantor) and no consent, license, permit, approval or authorization of, exemption by, or registration or declaration with, any governmental authority is required in connection with the execution, delivery, performance, validity, or enforceability of this Agreement and the Note except for the filing of this Agreement with the Interstate Commerce Commission and the filing of a financing statement with respect to the Lender's security interest in the Leases in the office of the Secretary of State of (insert appropriate state, such as "New Jersey").

3.3 No Legal Bar. The execution, delivery, and performance by the Company of this Agreement, the Note, and the Leases will not violate any provision of any existing law or regulation to which the Company is subject or of any order, judgment, award, or decree of any court, arbitrator, or governmental authority applicable to the Company or of the Articles of Incorporation, By-Laws, or any preferred stock provision of the Company or of any mortgage, indenture, contract, or other agreement to which the Company is a party or which is or purports to be binding upon the Company or any of its properties or assets, and will not constitute a default thereunder, and (except as contemplated by this Agreement) will not result in the creation or imposition of any Lien on any of the properties or assets of the Company. The Company is not in default in the performance or observance of any of the obligations, covenants, or conditions contained in any bond, debenture, or note, or in any mortgage, deed of trust, indenture, or loan agreement, of the Company.

3.4 No Material Litigation. There are no actions, suits, or proceedings (whether or not purportedly on behalf of the Company) pending or, to the knowledge of the Company, threatened against the Company or any of its properties or assets in any court or before any arbitrator of any kind or before or by any governmental body, which (i) relate to any of the Collateral or to any of the transactions contemplated by this Agreement, or (ii) would, if adversely determined, materially impair the right or ability of the Company to carry on its business substantially as now conducted and presently proposed to be conducted, or (iii) would, if adversely determined, have a material adverse effect on the operating results or on the condition, financial or other, of the Company. The Company is not in default with respect to any order, judgment, award, decree, rule, or regulation of any court, arbitrator, or governmental body.

3.5 No Default. No Default or Event of Default has occurred and is continuing under this Agreement.

3.6 Financial Condition. The unaudited financial statements of the Company as at (insert appropriate date, such as "January 31, XXXX"), and for the (insert any stub period, such as "six") months then ended, certified by the chief financial officer of the Company, copies of which have heretofore been delivered to the Lender, are complete and correct, have been prepared in accordance with generally accepted accounting principles consistently applied throughout the period involved and present fairly the financial position of the Company at (insert appropriate date, such as "January 31, XXXX"), and the results of its operations for the (insert any stub period, such as "six") months then ended. There has been no material adverse change in the condition, financial or other, of the Company since (insert appropriate date, such as "January 31, XXXX").

3.7 Payment of Taxes. The Company has filed all federal, state, and local tax returns and declarations of estimated tax which are required to be filed and has paid all taxes which have become due pursuant to such returns and declarations or pursuant to any assessments made against it, and the Company has no knowledge of any deficiency or additional assessment in connection therewith not adequately provided for on the books of the Company. In the opinion of the Company, all tax liabilities of the Company were adequately provided for as of (insert appropriate date, such as "January 31, XXXX"), and are now so provided for, on the books of the Company.

3.8 Force Majeure. Since (insert appropriate date, such as "January 31, XXXX"), the business, operations, properties, and assets of the Company have not been materially and adversely affected in any way as the result of any fire, explosion, earthquake, disaster, accident, labor disturbance, requisition or taking of property by governmental authority, flood, drought, embargo, riot, civil disturbance, uprising, activity of armed forces, or act of God or the public enemy.

3.9 Burdensome Provisions. The Company is not a party to any agreement or instrument, or subject to any charter or other corporate restriction or to any judgment, order, writ, injunction, decree, award, rule or regulation, which does or will materially and adversely affect the business, operations, properties, or assets or the condition, financial or other, of the Company.

3.10 Leases.

(a) Each Lease has been duly authorized, executed, and delivered by the Company and the Lessee thereunder and constitutes a valid and binding obligation of the Company and such Lessee, enforceable in accordance with its terms. No consent of any other party (including stockholders of the Company, the Guarantor, and each Lessee) and no consent, license, permit, approval or authorization of, exemption by, or registration or declaration with, any governmental authority is required to be obtained, effected, or given in connection with the execution, delivery, and performance of each Lease by each party thereto except for the filing of the Leases with the Interstate Commerce Commission which will have been duly effected on or before the making of the Loan hereunder and will be in full force and effect at all times thereafter.

(b) Neither the Company nor (to the best of the Company's knowledge) the Lessee under either Lease is in default in the performance or observance of any covenant, term, or condition contained in such Lease, and no event has occurred and no condition exists which constitutes, or which with the lapse of time or the giving of notice or both would constitute, a default under either Lease. The Company has fully performed all of its obligations under each Lease, and the right, title, and interest of the Company in, to and under each Lease is not subject to any defense, offset, counterclaim, or claim, nor have any of the foregoing been asserted or alleged against the Company as to either Lease. The Company has not received any payment of rent or any other amount under either of the Leases.

3.11 Title to Box-Cars; Specifications. At the time of the making of the Loan by the Lender under this Agreement (i) the Company will have good and valid title to, and will be the lawful owner of, each Unit described in Schedule I hereto, free and clear of all Liens whatsoever except the lien and security interest created by this Agreement, (ii) each Unit will conform to all Department of Transportation and Interstate Commerce Commission requirements and specifications and to all standards recommended by the Association of American Railroads, in each case applicable to railroad equipment of the same type as such Unit and (iii) each such Unit will be new and unused.

3.12 First Lien. Upon the filing of this Agreement and the Leases in the manner prescribed in Section 11303, Title 49, United States Code and in the related regulations of the Interstate Commerce Commission, and the filing of a financing statement with respect to the Lender's security interest in the Leases in the office of the Secretary of State of ____ , this Agreement will constitute a legal, valid, and perfected first lien on and first priority security interest in each of the Units (and any Proceeds thereof), each of the Leases (and the Proceeds thereof), and the Cash Collateral Account, as security for the Obligations, free and clear of all other Liens whatsoever. No security agreement, financing statement, equivalent security or lien instrument, or continuation statement covering all or any part of the Collateral is on file or of record with the Interstate Commerce Commission or with any other public office, except such as may have been filed by or on behalf of the Company in favor of the Lender pursuant to this Agreement.

3.13 Principal Office. The principal place of business, the chief executive office, and the place at which the books and records of the Company are kept is (insert address of the Company where records are kept).

Section 4. Conditions of Borrowing

The obligation of the Lender to make the Loan hereunder shall be subject to the fulfillment, to the satisfaction of the Lender, of the following conditions precedent:

(a) The Company shall have executed and delivered to the Lender a Note meeting the requirements of Subsection 2.3 hereof;

(b) There shall have been delivered to the Lender copies, certified by the Secretary of the Company on the date of the Loan, of the Certificate of Incorporation and By-Laws of the Company;

(c) There shall have been delivered to the Lender copies, certified by the Secretary of the Guarantor on the date of the Loan, of the Certificate of Incorporation and By-Laws of the Guarantor;

(d) There shall have been delivered to the Lender a copy, certified by the Secretary of the Company on the date of the Loan, resolutions of the Board of Directors of the Company approving the transactions contemplated by this Agreement and authorizing the execution, delivery, and performance by the Company of this Agreement, the Note, and the Leases and all other documents and instruments required hereby;

(e) There shall have been delivered to the Lender a copy, certified by the Secretary of the Guarantor on the date of the Loan, of the resolutions of the Board of Directors of the Guarantor authorizing the execution, delivery, and performance by the Guarantor of the Guaranty and all other documents and instruments required hereby or thereby;

(f) There shall have been delivered to the Lender a copy, certified by the Secretary or an Assistant Secretary of the First Lessee on the date of the Loan, of the resolutions of the Board of Directors of the First Lessee, authorizing the execution, delivery, and performance by the First Lessee of the First Lessee Lease;

(g) There shall have been delivered to the Lender a copy, certified by the Secretary or an Assistant Secretary of the Second Lessee on the date of the Loan, of the resolutions of the Board of Directors of the Second Lessee, authorizing the execution, delivery, and performance by the Second Lessee of the Second Lessee Lease.

(h) There shall have been delivered to the Lender a certificate, dated the date of the Loan, with respect to the incumbency and signatures of each of the officers of the Company executing this Agreement or any document relating hereto on behalf of the Company;

(i) There shall have been delivered to the Lender a certificate, dated the date of the Loan, with respect to the incumbency and signatures of each of the officers of the Guarantor executing the Guaranty or any other document relating hereto or thereto on behalf of the Guarantor;

(j) The Guaranty shall have been duly executed by the Guarantor and delivered to the Lender;

(k) There shall have been delivered to the Lender evidence that this Agreement has been duly filed, registered, and recorded with the Interstate Commerce Commission in accordance with Section 11303, Title 49, United States Code;

(l) All executed counterparts of each Lease in the possession of the Company or of any Person controlling, controlled by or under common control with the Company shall have been delivered to the Lender, and the Lender shall have received a certificate to the foregoing effect, dated the date of the Loan, and signed by a duly authorized officer of the Company;

(m) There shall have been delivered to the Lender evidence that each Lease has been duly filed, registered, and recorded with the Interstate Commerce Commission in accordance with Section 11303, Title 49, United States Code and that a financing statement with respect to the Lender's security interest therein has been filed in the office of the Secretary of State of (insert appropriate state);

(n) The Lender shall have received a certificate of each Lessee, dated the date of the Loan, in which such Lessee acknowledges notice of the assignment to the Lender of all of the Company's right, title, and interest in, to, and under its respective Lease, (ii) agrees to make payment of all moneys under or arising out of such Lease directly to the Cash Collateral Account until such time as it shall have received notice from the lender otherwise, (iii) agrees that each such payment shall be final and that such Lessee shall not seek to recover from the Lender for any reason whatsoever, any monies paid by such Lessee to the Lender by virtue of this Agreement and that it will not seek recourse against the Lender by reason of this Agreement or such Lease, and (iv) certifies to the effect that such Lease is in full force and effect and constitutes a valid and binding agreement of such Lessee, enforceable in accordance with its terms;

(o) The representations and warranties contained in Section 3 hereof shall be true and correct on and as of the date of the making of the Loan with the same effect as if made on and as of such date, and no Default or Event of Default shall be in existence on the date of the making of the Loan or would occur as a result of the Loan;

(p) There shall have been delivered to the Lender (i) a copy of the warranty bill of sale from Vendor with respect to the Box-Cars, substantially in the form of Exhibit C hereto, transferring to the Company good title to the Box-Cars free and clear of all Liens and (ii) copies of the Certificates of Acceptance of each Lessee with respect to the Box-Cars subject to its respective Lease, substantially in the form of Exhibit D hereto;

(q) There shall have been delivered to the Lender a Certificate of Cost with respect to the Box-Cars, substantially in the form of Exhibit E hereto, showing the principal amount of the Loan to be equal to or less than the sum of (i) (insert appropriate percentage) ____ % of the aggregate Box-Car Costs of the First Lessee Box-Cars plus (ii) (insert appropriate percentage) ____ % of the aggregate Box-Car Costs of the Second Lessee Box-Cars, and accompanied by true and complete copies of the invoice(s) from Vendor, identifying the Box-Cars and specifying the Box-Car Costs thereof;

(r) There shall have been delivered to the Lender evidence of insurance with respect to the Box-Cars, which indicates compliance by the Company with the provisions of Subsection 6.15 hereof;

(s) There shall have been delivered to the Lender a certificate, dated the date of the Loan and signed by the President or any Vice President of the Company, to the same effect as paragraph (o) of this Section 4 and to the further effect that (i) the Box-Cars have been delivered to and accepted by the Company; (ii) the Company has valid and legal title to, and is the lawful owner of, the Box-Cars, free and clear of all Liens except the lien and security interest created by this Agreement; and (iii) the Box-Cars have been duly leased to the Lessees under the respective Leases;

(t) There shall not have been, in the judgment of the Lender, any material adverse change in the financial condition or business operations of the Company, the Guarantor, the First Lessee, or the Second Lessee;

(u) There shall have been delivered to the Lender, an opinion of counsel for each Lessee, dated the date of the Loan and addressed to the Lender and the Company to the effect provided in Paragraph ________ of the respective Lease;

(v) There shall have been delivered to the Lender, an opinion of (insert name of Company and Guarantor counsel), counsel for the Company and the Guarantor, dated the date of the Loan and substantially in the form of Exhibit F hereto;

(w) There shall have been delivered to the Lender, an opinion of (insert name of any special counsel for the Company), special counsel for the Company, dated the date of the Loan and substantially in the form of Exhibit G hereto;

(x) There shall have been delivered to the Lender, an opinion of counsel for Vendor, dated the date of the Loan and addressed to the Lender and the Company, to the effect that (i) Vendor is a corporation duly organized, validly existing, and in good standing under the laws of its jurisdiction of incorporation and has all requisite corporate power and authority to own its property and to conduct its business as presently conducted; (ii) the purchase letter with respect to the Box-Cars has been duly authorized, executed, and delivered by Vendor and, assuming due authorization, execution, and delivery thereof by the Company, constitutes a legal, valid, and binding obligation of Vendor, enforceable against Vendor in accordance with its terms, except as enforceability may be limited by applicable bankruptcy, insolvency, reorganization, moratorium, and similar laws affecting the enforcement of creditors' rights generally; and (iii) Vendor's bill of sale relating to the Box-Cars has been duly authorized, executed, and delivered by Vendor and is effective to transfer to the Company good and marketable title to the Box-Cars, free and clear of all claims, charges, liens, security interests, and other encumbrances, except the rights of the Lender under this Agreement;

(y) The Lender shall have received any other documents, instruments, or certificates that the Lender may reasonably request; and

(z) All legal matters in connection with the Loan and the security therefor shall be satisfactory to (insert name of Lender's counsel), counsel for the Lender.

Section 5. Grant of Lien and Security Interest

As collateral security for (a) the prompt and complete payment when due (whether at the stated maturity, by prepayment, by acceleration, or otherwise) of the unpaid principal of, premium, if any, and interest on the Note, (b) the due and punctual payment and performance by the Company of all of its obligations and liabilities under or arising out of or in connection with this Agreement and (c) the prompt and complete payment when due (whether at the stated maturity, by prepayment, by acceleration or otherwise) of all other indebtedness, obligations, and liabilities of the Company to the Lender, whether now existing or hereafter incurred (all of the foregoing being hereinafter called the "Obligations"), and in order to induce the Lender to make the Loans hereunder:

5.1 Box-Cars. The Company does hereby assign, convey, mortgage, pledge, and transfer to the Lender, and does hereby grant to the Lender a continuing security interest in, all Box-Cars now owned or at any time hereafter acquired by the Company and any and all Proceeds thereof, provided that the Lender does not hereby consent to the sale or other disposal thereof.

5.2 Leases.

(a) The Company does hereby assign, convey, mortgage, pledge, and transfer to the Lender, and does hereby grant to the Lender a continuing security interest in, all of the right, title, and interest of the Company in, to and under each of the Leases, including, without limitation, all right, title, and interest of the Company in and to all rents, issues, profits, revenues, and other income arising under each of the Leases and other monies due and to become due to the Company under or arising out of each of the Leases, all accounts and general intangibles under or arising out of each of the Leases, all proceeds of each of the Leases and all claims for damages arising out of the breach of either of the Leases, the right of the Company to terminate each of the Leases and to compel Performance of the terms and provisions thereof, and all chattel paper, contracts, instruments, and other documents evidencing either of the Leases or any monies due or to become due thereunder or related thereto. Each and every copy of each of the Leases which the Company directly or indirectly has in its control or possession shall have attached thereto a notice indicating the Lender's interest therein.

(b) The Company agrees that (i) it will specifically authorize and direct the Lessee under each Lease to make payment of all amounts due and to become due to the Company under or arising out of such Lease directly to an account of the Lender, to be maintained by the Lender at the office of (insert name of Lender), located at (insert appropriate address) and entitled "(insert name of borrower)—Cash Collateral Account" (the "Cash Collateral Account"), (ii) it will hold in trust any such amounts received by it and forthwith pay the same to the Lender, and (iii) it hereby irrevocably authorizes and empowers the Lender to ask, demand, receive, receipt, and give acquittance for any and all such amounts which may be or become due and payable or remain unpaid to the Company by such Lessee at any time or times under or arising out of such Lease, to endorse any checks, drafts, or other orders for the payment of money payable to the Company in payment therefor, and in the Lender's discretion to file any claims or take any action or proceedings either in its own name or in the name of the Company or otherwise which the Lender may deem to be necessary or advisable in the premises.

(c) It is expressly agreed by the Company that, anything herein to the contrary notwithstanding, the Company shall remain liable under the Leases to observe and perform all the conditions and obligations to be observed and performed by it thereunder, all in accordance with and pursuant to the terms and provisions thereof. The Lender shall not have any obligation or liability under the Leases by reason of or arising out of this Agreement or the assignment of the Leases to the Lender or the receipt by the Lender of any payment relating to either Lease pursuant hereto, nor shall the Lender be required or obligated in any manner to perform or fulfill any of the obligations of the Company under or pursuant to either Lease, or to make any payment, or to make any inquiry as to the nature or the sufficiency of any performance by either Lessee under either Lease or to present or file any claim, or to take any action to enforce the observance of any obligations of either Lessee under either Lease.

5.3 Cash Collateral Account. The Company does hereby assign, convey, mortgage, pledge, and transfer to the Lender, and does hereby grant to the Lender a continuing security interest in, all monies at any time held in the Cash Collateral Account.

5.4 Application of Funds. The Lender hereby agrees that (i) it will apply the monies on deposit from time to time in the Cash Collateral Account to the payment of the installments of principal and interest under the Note as they become due and payable in accordance with the terms and provisions thereof, (ii) so long as no Default or Event of Default has occurred and is continuing, the Lender will pay or cause to be paid to the Company all amounts on deposit in the Cash Collateral Account in excess of the amounts due and payable or to become due and payable under the Note within 31 days of the date of determination, and (iii) when the Obligations shall have been paid, performed, and discharged in full, the Lender shall pay or cause to be paid to the Company all amounts then on deposit in the Cash Collateral Account and shall notify each Lessee to make all further payments under its Lease directly to the Company or as the Company shall direct. Nothing contained in Section 5 of this Agreement or elsewhere in this Agreement is intended or shall impair, diminish, or alter the obligation of the Company, which is absolute and unconditional, to pay to the Lender all principal of and interest on the Note and all amounts payable under this Agreement as and when the same shall become due and payable in accordance with their respective terms.

Section 6. Covenants

The Company hereby covenants and agrees that from the date of this Agreement and so long as any amount remains unpaid on account of the Note, unless the Lender shall otherwise consent in writing:

6.1 Financial Statements. The Company will furnish or cause to be furnished, or, in the case of paragraphs (h) and (j), use its best efforts to furnish or cause to be furnished, to the Lender:

(a) as soon as available, but in any event not later than 120 days after the end of each fiscal year of the Company, a balance sheet of the Company as at the end of such fiscal year and the related statements of income and of changes in financial position of the Company for such fiscal year, all in reasonable detail, prepared in accordance with generally accepted accounting principles applied on a basis consistently maintained throughout such fiscal year and accompanied by a report or opinion of ______________ ______________________ or other independent public accountants of recognized standing selected by the Company and satisfactory to the Lender;

(b) as soon as available, but in any event not later than 90 days after the end of each quarter, other than the last, of each fiscal year of the Company, an unaudited balance sheet of the Company as at the end of such quarter and the related unaudited statements of income and of changes in financial position of the Company for the period from the beginning of such fiscal year to the end of such quarter, all in reasonable detail, prepared in accordance with generally accepted accounting principles applied on a basis consistently maintained throughout the period involved and certified by the chief financial officer of the Company (subject to normal year-end audit adjustments);

(c) concurrently with the delivery of the financial statements referred to in clauses (a) and (b) above, a certificate of the chief financial officer of the Company stating that, to the best of his knowledge after due inquiry, the Company has observed and performed each and every covenant and agreement of the Company contained in this Agreement, the Note, and the Leases and that no Default or Event of Default has occurred during the period covered by such financial statements or is in existence on the date of such certificate or, if a Default or Event of Default has occurred or is in existence, specifying the same;

(d) concurrently with the delivery of the financial statements referred to in clause (a) above, a certificate of the independent public accountants who certified such statements to the effect that, in making the examination necessary for the audit of such financial statements, they obtained no knowledge of any Default or Event of Default, or, if they shall have obtained knowledge of any Default or Event of Default, specifying the same;

(e) as soon as available, but in any event not later than 120 days after the end of each fiscal year of the Guarantor, a consolidated balance sheet of the Guarantor and its Subsidiaries as at the end of such fiscal year and the related consolidated statements of income and of changes in financial position of the Guarantor and its Subsidiaries for such fiscal year, all in reasonable detail, prepared in accordance with generally accepted accounting principles applied on a basis consistently maintained throughout such fiscal year and accompanied by a report or opinion of Coopers & Lybrand or other independent public accountants of recognized standing selected by the Guarantor and satisfactory to the Lender;

(f) as soon as available, but in any event not later than 90 days after the end of each quarter, other than the last, of each fiscal year of the Guarantor, an unaudited consolidated balance sheet of the Guarantor and its Subsidiaries as at the end of such quarter and the related unaudited consolidated statements of income and of changes in financial position of the Guarantor and its Subsidiaries for the period from the beginning of such fiscal year to the end of such quarter, all in reasonable detail, prepared in accordance with generally accepted accounting principles applied on a basis consistently maintained throughout the period involved and certified by the chief financial officer of the Guarantor (subject to normal year-end audit adjustments);

(g) as soon as available, but in any event not later than April 30 of each year commencing (insert appropriate start date here) (i) a duplicate original of the annual report filed by the First Lessee with the Interstate Commerce Commission or any governmental authority succeeding to all or a part of the functions thereof and (ii) a copy of any annual report to shareholders for the most recent fiscal year made publicly available by the First Lessee;

(h) as soon as available, but in any event not later than 90 days after the end of each quarter, other than the last, of each fiscal year of the First Lessee, an unaudited consolidated balance sheet of the First Lessee and its Subsidiaries as at the end of such quarter and the related unaudited consolidated statements of income and of changes in financial position of the First Lessee and its Subsidiaries for the period from the beginning of such fiscal year to the end of such quarter, all in reasonable detail, prepared in accordance with generally accepted accounting principles applied on a basis consistently maintained throughout the period involved and certified by the chief financial office of the First Lessee (subject to normal year-end audit adjustments);

(i) as soon as available, but in any event not later than (insert appropriate date here) of each year commencing (insert appropriate date) (i) a duplicate original of the annual report filed by the Second Lessee with the Interstate Commerce Commission or any governmental authority succeeding to all or a part of the functions thereof and (ii) a copy of any annual report to shareholders for the most recent fiscal year made publicly available by the Second Lessee;

(j) as soon as available, but in any event not later than 90 days after the end of each quarter, other than the last, of each fiscal year of the Second Lessee, an unaudited consolidated balance sheet of the Second Lessee and its Subsidiaries as at the end of such quarter and the related unaudited consolidated statements of income and of changes in financial position of the Second Lessee and its Subsidiaries for the period from the beginning of such fiscal year to the end of such quarter, all in reasonable detail, prepared in accordance with generally accepted accounting principles applied on a basis consistently maintained throughout the period involved and certified by the chief financial officer of the Second Lessee (subject to normal year-end audit adjustments);

(k) during any period when the Company shall have one or more Subsidiaries, within the periods prescribed in clauses (a) and (b) above, financial statements of the character and for the period or periods and as of the date or dates specified in such clauses and certified or accompanied by a report or opinion of independent public accountants as therein provided, covering the financial condition, income, and changes in financial position of the Company and each of its Subsidiaries on a consolidated basis and, if requested by the Lender, a consolidating basis;

(l) during any period when the First Lessee or the Second Lessee, as the case may be, shall not be required to file annual reports with the Interstate Commerce Commission or any successor governmental authority, as soon as available, but in any event no later than 120 days after the end of each fiscal year of such Person, a balance sheet of such Person as at the end of such fiscal year and the related statements of income and of changes in financial position of such Person, all in reasonable detail, prepared in accordance with generally accepted accounting principles applied on a basis consistently maintained throughout such fiscal year and, in the case of the First Lessee, accompanied by a report or opinion of independent public accountants of recognized standing selected by the First Lessee and satisfactory to the Lender, or, in the case of the Second Lessee, certified by the chief financial officer of the Second Lessee;

(m) promptly upon request, such additional financial and other information with respect to the Company and the Guarantor and, consistent with its best efforts, the First Lessee and the Second Lessee, as the Lender may from time to time reasonably require.

6.2 Reports. (a) On or before March 31 in each year, commencing with the year (insert appropriate year), the Company shall furnish or cause to be furnished to the Lender a report, certified by the chief financial officer of the Company, (i) setting forth as of the preceding December 31 (A) the amount, description, and identifying numbers of all Units then subject to this Agreement and (B) the amount, description, and identifying numbers of all Units that have suffered a Casualty Occurrence or are then undergoing repairs (other than running repairs) or have been withdrawn from use pending repairs (other than running repairs) during the preceding calendar year (or since the date of this Agreement in the case of the first such report) and (ii) stating that, in the case of all Units repaired or repainted during the period covered by such report, the numbers and markings required by Subsection 6.21 hereof have been preserved or replaced.

(b) The Company will prepare and deliver to the Lender within a reasonable time prior to the required date of filing (or, to the extent permissible, file on behalf of the Lender) all reports (other than income tax returns), if any, relating to the maintenance, registration, and operation of the Box-Cars required to be filed by the Lender with any federal, state, or other regulatory agency by reason of the Lender's lien on and security interest in the Box-Cars or the Leases or the provisions of this Agreement.

6.3 Limitation on Fundamental Changes. The Company will not convey, sell, lease, transfer, pledge, or otherwise dispose of, in one transaction or a series of related transactions, all or any substantial part of its properties, assets, or business or change the form of organization of its business or liquidate or dissolve itself (or suffer any liquidation or dissolution). The Company will not enter into any transaction of merger or consolidation except that the Company may merge into or consolidate with the Guarantor or any Wholly-Owned Subsidiary of the Guarantor provided that immediately after giving effect to such transaction, the Company or the successor to the Company (if the successor shall not be the Company) shall not be in default in the performance or observance of any convenant, agreement, or condition contained in this Agreement.

6.4 Payment of Taxes. The Company will promptly pay and discharge or cause to be paid and discharged, before the same shall become in default, all lawful taxes, assessments, and governmental charges or levies imposed upon the Company, or upon any property, real, personal or mixed, belonging to the Company, or upon any part thereof, as well as all lawful claims for labor, materials, and supplies which, if unpaid, might become a Lien upon any such property or any part thereof; provided, however, that the Company shall not be required to pay and discharge or to cause to be paid and discharged any such tax, assessment, charge, levy, or claim so long as (i) the validity thereof shall be contested in good faith by appropriate proceedings, (ii) such proceedings do not involve any danger of the sale, forfeiture, or loss of such property or any part thereof, and (iii) the Company shall have set aside on its books adequate reserves with respect thereto.

6.5 Conduct of Business; Maintenance of Existence. The Company will engage primarily in the business presently conducted by it, and will do or cause to be done all things necessary to preserve and keep in full force and effect its corporate existence, rights, and franchises necessary to continue such business. The Company will qualify as a foreign corporation and remain in good standing under the laws of each jurisdiction in which it is required to be qualified by reason of the ownership of its assets or the conduct of its business.

6.6 Compliance with Laws and Rules. The Company will (i) comply, and use its best efforts to cause each Lessee and every user of the Box-Cars to comply, in all material respects (including, without limitation, with respect to the use, maintenance, and operation of the Box-Cars) with all laws of the jurisdictions in which its or such Lessee's or such user's operations involving the Box-Cars may extend, with the interchange rules of the American Association of Railroads and with all lawful rules of the Department of Transportation, the Interstate Commerce Commission, and any other governmental authority exercising any power or jurisdiction over the Box-Cars, to the extent that such laws or rules affect the title to, or the operation or use of, or the Lender's lien and security interest in, the Box-Cars, and in the event that such laws or rules require any alteration of, or any replacement or addition of or to any part on, any Unit, the Company will conform therewith at its own expense, and, (ii) comply in all material respects with all other applicable laws and regulations of any governmental authority relative to the conduct of its business or the ownership of its properties or assets, provided, however, that the Company may, in good faith, contest the validity or application of any such law or rule by appropriate proceedings which do not, in the opinion of the Lender, involve any danger of the sale, forfeiture, or loss of the Box-Cars or any part thereof.

6.7 Maintenance of Properties. The Company will at all times maintain and keep, or cause to be maintained and kept, in good repair, working order, and condition all property of the Company used or useful in the conduct of its business, and will from time to time make or cause to be made all needful and proper repairs, renewals, replacements, betterments, and improvements thereto, so that the business carried on in connection therewith may be properly and advantageously conducted at all times.

6.8 Principal Office. The Company will not change the location of its principal place of business, its chief executive office, or the place at which its books and records are kept from the address specified in Subsection 3.13 hereof unless it shall have given the Lender at least 90 days' prior written notice of such change, and the Company will at all times maintain its principal place of business, chief executive office, and the place at which its books and records are kept within the United States of America.

6.9 Indemnities, etc.

(a) In any suit, proceedings, or action brought by the Lender under either of the Leases or to enforce any provision thereof, the Company will save, indemnify, and keep the Lender harmless from and against all expense, loss, or damage suffered by reason of any defense, setoff, counterclaim, recoupment, or reduction of liability whatsoever of the Lessee thereunder, arising out of a breach by the Company of any obligation thereunder or arising out of any other agreement, indebtedness, or liability at any time owing to or in favor of such Lessee from the Company, and all such obligations of the Company shall be and remain enforceable against and only against the Company and shall not be enforceable against the Lender.

(b) The Company agrees to indemnify and hold the Lender harmless against any and all liabilities, obligations, losses, damages, claims, suits, costs, expenses, and disbursements (including reasonable legal fees and expenses) incurred by or asserted against the Lender with respect to claims for personal injury or property damage arising from its participation in the transactions contemplated by this Agreement, the Leases, or the Note except for claims arising due to the gross negligence or willful misconduct of the Lender or its employees or agents.

6.10 Performance of Leases. The Company will perform and comply in all material respects with all its obligations under each Lease and all other agreements to which it is a party or by which it is bound relating to the Collateral, and the Company will use its best efforts to cause each other party to any thereof to so perform and comply.

6.11 Preservation of Collateral.

(a) The Company will not create, permit, or suffer to exist, and will defend the Collateral against and take such other action as is necessary to remove, any Lien, claim, or right in or to the Collateral (other than the lien and security interest created by this Agreement and Permitted Liens), and will defend the right, title, and interest of the Lender in and to the Company's rights under the Leases and rights in the Box-Cars and in and to the Proceeds thereof against the claims and demands of all other Persons whomsoever.

(b) The Company will not sell, transfer, or otherwise dispose of any of the Collateral or attempt or offer to do so.

(c) The Company will not agree to or permit any amendment or other modification of, or any termination of, either Lease in whole or in part.

(d) The Company will advise the Lender promptly, in reasonable detail, of any Lien or claim made or asserted against any of the Collateral and of any event affecting the Lender's lien on and security interest in the Collateral.

6.12 Location of Box-Cars. The Company will not permit any of the Box-Cars to be located outside the continental United States of America at any time, except that not more than 10% of the Box-Cars may be temporarily or incidentally used in Canada or Mexico.

6.13 Further Assurances; Recordation and Filing. The Company will, at its sole cost and expense, do, execute, acknowledge, and deliver all further acts, supplements, mortgages, security agreements, conveyances, transfers, and assurances necessary or advisable for the perfection and preservation of the lien and security interest created by this Agreement in the Collateral, whether now owned or hereafter acquired. The Company will cause this Agreement and any supplements hereto, and all financing and continuation statements and similar notices requested by the Lender or required by applicable law, at all times to be kept, recorded, and filed at no expense to the Lender in such manner and in such places as may be required by law in order fully to preserve and protect the rights of the Lender hereunder.

6.14 ICC Jurisdiction. The Company will not take or permit to be taken any action within its control which would subject it to the jurisdiction of the Interstate Commerce Commission as a "carrier", "railroad carrier", or "common carrier", as such terms are defined in Title 49, United States Code, if such jurisdiction will adversely affect the ability of the Company to perform its obligations under this Agreement, the Note, or the Leases or adversely affect the validity or enforceability of this Agreement, the Note, or the Leases.

6.15 Maintenance of Insurance.

(a) Upon the delivery of any Box-Cars the Company will promptly effect and maintain or cause to be effected and maintained with (Insert name of insurance company) or other financially sound and reputable companies, insurance policies (i) insuring each such Box-Car against loss by fire, explosion, theft, and such other casualties as are usually insured against by companies engaged in the same or a similar business and with coverage in an amount at least equal to the Casualty Value of such Box-Car and (ii) insuring the Company and the Lender against liability for personal injury and property damage caused by or relating to such Box-Cars or their use with coverage in the amount of at least $ ________________, all such insurance policies to be in such form and to have such coverage as shall be satisfactory to the Lender, with losses payable to the Company and the Lender as their respective interests may appear.

(b) All insurance required by this Subsection 6.15 shall (I) be with the carriers designated above or other carriers acceptable to the Lender, (ii) name the Lender as an assured and loss-payee, as its interest may appear, (iii) provide for at least 30 days' prior written notice to the Lender before any cancellation, reduction in amount, or change in coverage thereof shall be effective, (iv) contain a breach of warranty clause in favor of the Lender and (v) provide that the Lender shall have no obligation or liability for premiums, commissions, assessments, or calls in connection with such insurance.

(c) The Company shall, if so requested by the Lender, deliver to the Lender within a reasonable time and as often as the Lender may reasonably request a report of a reputable insurance broker with respect to the insurance on the Box-Cars.

6.16 Casualty Occurrence.

(a) In the event of a Casualty Occurrence with respect to any Unit, the Company shall, promptly after it has knowledge of same, give the Lender written notice of such Casualty Occurrence, which notice shall (i) identify the Unit which has suffered the Casualty Occurrence, (ii) set forth the Casualty Value of such Damaged Unit (and the calculations used in the determination thereof) as of the date which is not less than 10 days nor more than 45 days after the date of such notice (the "Casualty Value Determination Date"), and (iii) specify whether the Company will, on the Casualty Value Determination Date, prepay the Note pursuant to paragraph (b) of this Subsection 6.16 or replace the Damaged Unit pursuant to paragraph (c) of this Subsection 6.16.

(b) If the notice given pursuant to paragraph (a) of this Subsection 6.16 specifies that the Company will prepay the Note on the Casualty Value Determination Date, the Company will, on such date, (i) prepay the Note in an aggregate principal amount equal to the Casualty Value of the Damaged Unit as of such date and (ii) pay the accrued interest on the principal amount so prepaid to the date of prepayment.

(c) If the notice given pursuant to paragraph (a) of this Subsection 6.16 specifies that the Company will replace the Damaged Unit, the Company will, on or prior to the Casualty Value Determination Date:

(i) replace the Damaged Unit with a box-car of the same type, which has a value and utility at least equal to, and which is in as good condition as, the Damaged Unit immediately prior to the Casualty Occurrence (assuming that such Damaged Unit was then in the condition required to be maintained by Subsection 6.17 hereof) and which is free and clear of all Liens other than Permitted Liens,

(ii) take all steps necessary to subject such replacement box-car (the "Replacement Unit") to the lien and security interest of this Agreement and to subject such Replacement Unit to the applicable Lease, and

(iii) deliver to the Lender such documents evidencing the foregoing as the Lender may reasonably request, including, without limitation, (A) a duly executed supplement to this Agreement, satisfactory in form and substance to Lender and its counsel, describing the Replacement Unit and subjecting the Replacement Unit to the lien and security interest of this Agreement, together with evidence that such supplement has been duly filed, registered, and recorded with the Interstate Commerce Commission in accordance with Section 11303, Title 49, United States Code, (B) a duly executed schedule, satisfactory in form and substance to Lender and its counsel, subjecting the Replacement Unit to the applicable Lease together with evidence that such schedule has been duly filed, registered, and recorded with the Interstate Commerce Commission in accordance with Section 11303, Title 49, United States Code, and (C) documents and opinions of counsel with respect thereto corresponding to those described in paragraphs (p), (r), (s), (v) and (w) of Section 4 hereof;

Upon the Company s compliance with the foregoing provisions of this Section 6.16, the Lender will, if no Default or Event of Default has occurred and is continuing, execute and deliver to the Company such instruments as shall be necessary to release such Damaged Unit from the lien and security interest of this Agreement (without recourse to, or representation or warranty by, the Lender).

6.17 Maintenance. The Company will, at no expense to the Lender, keep and maintain or cause to be kept and maintained, the Box-Cars in good repair, condition, and working order, eligible for interchange with other railroads pursuant to Association of American Railroads Interchange Standards, and will cause to be furnished all parts, mechanisms, devices, and servicing required therefor so that the value, condition, and operating efficiency thereof will at all times be maintained and preserved, ordinary wear and tear excepted.

6.18 Notice of Default; etc. The Company will promptly give written notice to the Lender of (a) the occurrence of any Default or Event of Default; (b) any litigation or proceedings relating to the Collateral; (c) any litigation or proceedings affecting the Company or any of its properties or assets which, if adversely determined, might have a material adverse effect upon the financial condition, business, or operations of the Company; and (d) any dispute between the Company and any governmental regulatory body that might materially interfere with the normal business operations of the Company.

6.19 Books and Records. The Company will keep proper books of record and account in which full, true, and correct entries in accordance with generally accepted accounting principles will be made of all dealings or transactions in relation to its business and activities.

6.20 Inspection. The Company will permit any person designated by the Lender to visit and inspect any of the properties, corporate books, and financial records of the Company and to discuss the affairs, finances, and accounts of the Company with its respective officers, all at such reasonable times and as often as the Lender may reasonably request.

6.21 Marking of Box-Cars. The Company will cause each Unit to be numbered at all times with the identification number set forth in Schedule I hereto pertaining to such Unit and will keep and maintain, plainly, distinctly, permanently, and conspicuously marked on each side of each Unit, in letters not less than one inch in height, the following words:

"TITLE TO THIS CAR SUBJECT TO DOCUMENTS RECORDED WITH INTERSTATE COMMERCE COMMISSION"

or other appropriate words designated by the Lender, with appropriate changes thereof and additions thereto as from time to time may be required by law in order to protect the Lender's interest in the Box-Cars and its rights under this Agreement. The Company will not permit any such Unit to be placed in operation or exercise any control or dominion over the same until such words shall have been so marked on both sides thereof and will replace or will cause to be replaced promptly any such words which may be removed, defaced, or destroyed. The Company will not permit the identifying number of any Unit to be changed except in accordance with a statement of new number or numbers to be substituted therefor, which statement previously shall have been delivered to the Lender and filed, recorded, and deposited by the Company in all public offices where this Agreement shall have been filed, recorded, or deposited.

Section 7. Power of Attorney

7.1 Appointment. The Company hereby irrevocably constitutes and appoints the Lender and any officer or agent thereof, with full power of substitution, as its true and lawful attorney-in-fact with full irrevocable power and authority in the place and stead of the Company and in the name of the Company or in its own name, from time to time in the Lender's discretion, for the purpose of carrying out the terms of this Agreement, to take any and all appropriate action and to execute any and all documents and instruments which may be necessary or desirable to accomplish the purposes of this Agreement and, without limiting the generality of the foregoing, the Company hereby gives the Lender the power and right, on behalf of the Company, without notice to or assent by the Company, to do the following:

(a) (i) to receive payment of and receipt for any and all monies, claims, and other amounts due and to become due at any time in respect of or arising out of any Collateral and (ii) to endorse any checks, drafts, or other orders for the payment of money payable to the Company in connection with the Collateral;

(b) upon default by the Company in the performance of Subsection 6.4 or 6.15, the Lender may, but shall not be obligated to, (i) effect any insurance called for by the terms of Subsection 6.15 and pay all or any part of the premiums therefor and the costs thereof and (ii) pay and discharge any taxes, liens, and encumbrances on the Collateral; and

(c) upon the occurrence and continuance of any Event of Default or of any Default specified in paragraph (i) of Section 8 hereof, (i) to sign and endorse any invoices, freight or express bills, bills of lading, storage or warehouse receipts, drafts against debtors, assignments, verifications, and notices in connection with accounts and other documents relating to the Collateral; (ii) to commence and prosecute any suits, actions, or proceedings at law or in equity in any court of competent jurisdiction to collect the Collateral or any thereof and to enforce any other right in respect of any of the Collateral; (iii) to defend any suit, action or proceeding brought against the Company with respect to any of the Collateral; (iv) to settle, compromise or adjust any suit, action, or proceeding described in clause (iii) above and, in connection therewith, to give such discharges or releases as the Lender may deem appropriate; and (v) generally to sell, transfer, pledge, make any agreement with respect to, or otherwise deal with any of the Collateral as fully and completely as though the Lender were the absolute owner thereof for all purposes, and to do, at the Lender's option and the Company's expense, at any time or from time to time, all acts and things which the Lender deems necessary to protect, preserve, or realize upon the Collateral and the Lender's security interest therein, in order to effect the intent of this Agreement, all as fully and effectively as the Company might do.

The Company hereby ratifies all that said attorneys shall lawfully do or cause to be done by virtue hereof. This power of attorney is a power coupled with an interest and shall be irrevocable.

7.2 No Duty. The powers conferred on the Lender hereunder are solely to protect its interests in the Collateral and shall not impose any duty upon it to exercise any such powers. The Lender shall be accountable only for amounts that it actually receives as a result of the exercise of such powers and neither it nor any of its officers, directors, employees, or agents shall be responsible to the Company for any act or failure to act, except for its or their own gross negligence or willful misconduct.

7.3 Additional Rights.

(a) The Company authorizes the Lender, at any time and from time to time, (i) to communicate in its own name with regard to the assignment of the Leases and other matters related thereto and (ii) to execute, in connection with the sale provided for in Section 9(b) of this Agreement, any endorsements, assignments, or other instruments of conveyance or transfer with respect to the Collateral.

(b) If the Company fails to perform or comply with any of its agreements contained herein, the Lender may itself perform or comply, or otherwise cause performance or compliance, with such agreement, and the expenses of the Lender incurred in connection with such performance or compliance, together with interest thereon at the rate of (18%) per annum, shall be payable by the Company to the Lender on demand and shall constitute part of the Obligations secured hereby.

Section 8. Events of Default

If any of the following Events of Default shall occur and be continuing:

(a) Failure to pay any principal of, premium, if any, or interest on the Note when due and the continuance of such failure for 10 days after notice thereof shall have been given to the Company by the Lender;

(b) Any representation or warranty made by the Company in this Agreement, by the Guarantor in the Guaranty, or by the Company or the Guarantor or any officer of either thereof in any document, certificate, or financial or other statement furnished at any time under or in connection with this Agreement or the Guaranty, shall prove to have been untrue or inaccurate in any material respect at the time when made;

(c) The default by the Company in the observance or performance of any covenant contained in Subsection 5.2(b), 6.3, 6.11(a), 6.11(b), 6.11(c), 6.12, 6.15(a), 6.15(b), 6.16, or 6.17 hereof;

(d) The default by the Company in the observance or performance of any other covenant or agreement contained in this Agreement and the continuance of such default for 30 days after written notice, specifying such default, shall have been given to the Company by the Lender;

(e) The Company or either Lessee shall breach or disaffirm any of its respective obligations under either Lease or either Lease shall cease to be in full force and effect;

(f) The Guarantor shall cease to be the record and beneficial owner of 80% or more of the issued and outstanding capital stock of the Company;

(g) The default by the Company or the Guarantor in any payment of principal of, or interest on, any obligation for borrowed money (other than the Note) or for the deferred purchase price of any property or asset or any obligation guaranteed by it or in respect to which it is liable, for a period equal to the period of grace, if any, applicable to such default, or in the performance or observance of any other term, condition, or covenant contained in any such obligation or in any agreement or instrument relating thereto if the effect of such default is to cause, or to permit the holder or holders of such obligation (or a trustee or agent on behalf of such holder or holders) to cause, such obligation to become due and payable prior to its stated maturity or to realize upon any collateral given as security therefor, unless the aggregate amount of all such obligations as to which any such default shall have occurred does not exceed $(200,000);

(h) The Guarantor shall breach or disaffirm any of its obligations or covenants under the Guaranty or the Guaranty shall cease to be in full force and effect;

(i) Filing by the Company or the Guarantor of a voluntary petition in bankruptcy or a voluntary petition or an answer seeking reorganization, arrangement, readjustment of its debts or for any other relief under any bankruptcy, insolvency, reorganization, liquidation, dissolution, arrangement, composition, readjustment of debt, or other similar act or law of any jurisdiction, domestic or foreign, now or hereafter existing, or any action by the Company or the Guarantor indicating its consent to, approval of, or acquiescence in, any such petition or proceeding; the application by the Company or the Guarantor for, or the appointment by consent or acquiescence of, a receiver or trustee for the Company or the Guarantor or for all or a substantial part of its property; the making by the Company or the Guarantor of an assignment for the benefit of creditors; the inability of the Company or the Guarantor, or the admission by the Company or the Guarantor in writing of its inability, to pay its debts as they mature;

(j) Filing of an involuntary petition against the Company or the Guarantor in bankruptcy or seeking reorganization, arrangement, readjustment of its debts, or for any other relief under any bankruptcy, insolvency, reorganization, liquidation, dissolution, arrangement, composition, readjustment of debt, or other similar act or law of any jurisdiction, domestic or foreign, now or hereafter existing; or the involuntary appointment of a receiver or trustee of the Company or the Guarantor or for all or a substantial part of its property; or the service on the Company or the Guarantor of a warrant of attachment, execution, or similar process against any substantial part of its property; and the continuance of any of such events for 60 days undismissed, unbonded, or undischarged;

(k) Final judgment for the payment of money in excess of $(50,000) shall be rendered against the Company or the Guarantor and the same shall remain undischarged for a period of 60 days during which execution shall not be effectively stayed; then, and in any such event, the Lender may exercise any and all remedies granted to it under this

Agreement and under applicable law, and may further, by notice of default given to the Company declare the Note to be forthwith due and payable, whereupon the unpaid principal amount of the Note, together with accrued interest thereon, shall become immediately due and payable without presentment, demand, protest, or other notice of any kind, all of which are hereby expressly waived, anything contained herein or in the Note to the contrary notwithstanding.

Section 9. Remedies

If an Event of Default shall occur and be continuing:

(a) All payments received by the Company in connection with or arising out of any of the Collateral shall be held by the Company in trust for the Lender, shall be segregated from other funds of the Company and shall forthwith upon receipt by the Company be turned over to the Lender, in the same form as received by the Company (duly endorsed by the Company to the Lender, if required); any and all such payments so received by the Lender (whether from the Company or otherwise) may, in the sole discretion of the Lender, be held by the Lender as collateral security for the Obligations, and/or then or at any time thereafter applied in whole or in part by the Lender against all or any part of the Obligations then due in such order as the Lender shall elect. Any balance of such payments held by the Lender and remaining after payment in full of all the Obligations shall be paid over to the Company or to whomsoever may be lawfully entitled to receive the same;

(b) The Lender may exercise in addition to all other rights and remedies granted to it in this Agreement and in any other instrument or agreement securing, evidencing, or relating to the Obligations, all rights and remedies of a secured party under the Uniform Commercial Code of the State of (insert appropriate state). Without limiting the generality of the foregoing, the Company expressly agrees that in any such event the Lender, without demand of performance or other demand, advertisement, or notice of any kind (except the notice specified below of time and place of public or private sale) to or upon the Company or any other Person (all and each of which demands, advertisements, and/or notices are hereby expressly waived), may forthwith collect, receive, appropriate, and realize upon the Collateral or any part thereof and may take possession of the Box-Cars and/or may forthwith sell, assign, give option or options to purchase, or sell, lease, or otherwise dispose of and deliver the Collateral, or any part thereof, in any manner permitted by applicable law (or contract to do so) in one or more parcels at public or private sale or sales, at the office of any broker or at any of the Lender's offices or elsewhere at such prices as it may deem best, for cash or on credit or for future delivery without assumption of any credit risk, with the right of the Lender upon any such sale or sales, public or private, to purchase the whole or any part of the Collateral so sold, free of any right or equity of redemption in the Company, which right or equity of redemption is hereby expressly waived or released. If any notification of intended disposition of any of the Collateral is required by law, such notification shall be deemed reasonably and properly given if mailed at least 15 days before such disposition, by registered or certified mail, postage prepaid, addressed to the Company at the address set forth in Subsection 10.2 hereof. The Company further agrees, at the Lender's request, to collect the Box-Cars and make them available to the Lender as hereinafter provided. The Lender shall apply the net proceeds of any such collection, recovery, receipt, appropriation, realization, and sale, after deducting all reasonable costs and expenses of every kind incurred therein or incidental to the care, safekeeping, or otherwise of any or all of the Collateral or in any way relating to the rights of the Lender hereunder, including reasonable attorney's fees and legal expenses, to the payment in whole or in part of the Obligations, in such order as the Lender may elect, the Company remaining liable for any deficiency remaining unpaid after such application, and only after so applying such net proceeds and after the payment by the Lender of any other amount required by any provision of law, including (insert appropriate section reference, such as Section 9-504(1)(c)) of the Uniform Commercial Code of the State of (insert appropriate state, such as New York), need the Lender account for the surplus, if any, to the Company. To the extent permitted by applicable law, the Company waives all claims, damages, and demands against the Lender arising out of the repossession, retention, or sale of the Collateral. The Company shall remain liable for any deficiency if the proceeds of any sale or disposition of the Collateral are insufficient to pay all amounts to which the Lender is entitled, the Company also being liable for the fees of any attorneys employed by the Lender to collect such deficiency. The Company hereby waives presentment, demand, protest, and any notice (to the extent permitted by applicable law) of any kind in connection with this Agreement or any Collateral; and

(c) In the event that the Lender shall request that the Box-Cars be collected as provided in paragraph (b) of this Section 9, the Company shall, at its own risk and expense (i) forthwith and in the usual manner (including, but not by way of limitation, giving prompt telegraphic and written notice to the Association of American Railroads and to all railroads to which any Unit or Units have been interchanged to return the Unit or Units so interchanged) place such Units upon such storage tracks as the Lender reasonably may designate; (ii) permit the Lender to store such Units on such tracks until such Units have been sold, leased, or otherwise disposed of by the Lender; and (iii) transport the same to any connecting carrier for shipment, all as directed by the Lender. The assembling, delivery, storage, and transporting of the Box-Cars as hereinbefore provided shall be at the expense and risk of the Company and are of the essence of this Agreement, and upon application to any court of equity having jurisdiction in the premises the Lender shall be entitled to a decree against the Company requiring specific performance of the covenants of the Company so to assemble, deliver, store, and transport the Box-Cars. During any storage period, the Company will, at its own cost and expense, maintain and keep the Box-Cars in good order and repair and will permit the Lender or any person designated by it, including the authorized representative or representatives of any prospective purchaser, lessor, or manager of any Unit, to inspect the same. The Company hereby expressly waives any and all claims against the Lender and its agent or agents for damages of whatsoever nature in connection with any retaking of any Unit in any reasonable manner.

(d) Beyond the use of reasonable care in the custody thereof the Lender shall not have any duty as to any Collateral in its possession or control or in the possession or control of any agent or nominee of it or as to any income therefrom.

Notwithstanding any provision of this Agreement to the contrary, the Lender shall not, so long as either Lessee is not in default under its Lease, take any action which would interfere with such Lessee's rights under its Lease, including the right to the possession and use of the Box-Cars subject thereto, except in accordance with the provisions of such Lease.

Section 10. Miscellaneous

10.1 Reimbursement of Lender, etc. The Company agrees, whether or not the transactions contemplated by this Agreement shall be consummated, to pay, or reimburse the Lender for, (i) all costs and expenses (including the reasonable legal fees and disbursements of counsel for the Lender in an amount not exceeding $10,000) incurred by the Lender in connection with the preparation and execution of this Agreement, the Note, and the Guaranty and (ii) all costs and expenses (including the reasonable legal fees and disbursements of counsel for the Lender) incurred by the Lender in connection with the enforcement (or the preservation of any rights hereunder) and any modification of this Agreement, the Note and the Guaranty. The Company also agrees to pay, and to save the Lender harmless from, any and all liabilities with respect to, or resulting from any delay in paying, documentary, excise, recording, filing, stamp or similar taxes, fees and other governmental charges (including interest and penalties), if any, which may be payable or determined to be payable in respect of the execution, delivery, or recording of this Agreement, the Note, or the Guaranty or any modification of any thereof or any waiver or consent under or in respect of any thereof. The obligations of the Company under this Subsection 10.1 shall survive payment of the Note and termination of this Agreement.

10.2 Notices. All notices, requests and demands to or upon the respective parties to this Agreement shall be in writing and shall be deemed to have been given or made when delivered by hand or deposited in the mail, by registered or certified mail, postage prepaid, addressed as follows or to such other address as may be hereafter designated in writing by the respective parties hereto:

The Company:

Attention:

With a copy to:

Attention:

The Lender:

Attention:

10.3 No Waiver; Cumulative Remedies. No failure to exercise and no delay in exercising, on the part of the Lender, any right, power, or privilege under this Agreement, the Note, the Guaranty, or any of the Collateral shall operate as a waiver thereof; nor shall any single or partial exercise of any right, power, or privilege hereunder or thereunder preclude any other or further exercise thereof or the exercise of any other right, power, or privilege. The rights and remedies provided herein and therein are cumulative and not exclusive of any rights or remedies provided by law.

10.4 Amendments and Waivers. The provisions of this Agreement may from time to time be amended, supplemented, or otherwise modified or waived only by a written agreement signed by the Company and the Lender.

10.5 Successors. This Agreement shall be binding upon and inure to the benefit of the Company and the Lender and their respective successors and assigns, except that the Company may not transfer or assign any of its rights hereunder without the prior written consent of the Lender.

10.6 Survival of Representations. All representations and warranties herein contained or made in writing in connection with this Agreement shall survive the execution and delivery of this Agreement and the making of the Loan hereunder and shall continue in full force and effect until all sums due and to become due hereunder and under the Note shall have been paid in full.

10.7 Construction. This Agreement and the rights and obligations of the parties hereunder shall be governed by, and construed and interpreted in accordance with, the laws of the State of (insert appropriate state, such as New York).

10.8 Severability. Any provision of this Agreement which is prohibited or unenforceable in any jurisdiction shall, as to such jurisdiction, be ineffective to the extent of such prohibition or unenforceability without invalidating the remaining provisions hereof, and any such prohibition or unenforceability in any jurisdiction shall not invalidate or render unenforceable such provision in any other jurisdiction.

10.9 Counterparts. This Agreement may be executed by one or more of the parties hereto in any number of separate counterparts and all of said counterparts taken together shall be deemed to constitute one and the same instrument.

IN WITNESS WHEREOF, the parties have caused this Agreement to be duly executed and delivered by their proper and duly authorized officers as of the day and year first above written.

(INSERT NAME OF BORROWER)

By: ______________________________

Title: ______________________________

(SEAL)

Attest:

By: ______________________________
Secretary

(INSERT NAME OF LENDER)

By: ____________________________

Title: ____________________________

(SEAL)

Attest:

By: ____________________________
Secretary

STATE OF ____________________________)

: ss.:

COUNTY OF ________________________)

On this ____ day of ________________________, XXXX, before me personally appeared ____________________________, to me known, who, being duly sworn, did depose and say that he resides at ____, that he is ____________________________ of ________________________, one of the corporations described in and which executed the foregoing document; that he knows the seal of said corporation; that one of the seals affixed to said instrument is such corporation's seal; that it was so affixed by authority of the Board of Directors of said corporation, and that he signed his name thereto by like order.

____
Notary Public

(NOTARIAL SEAL)

STATE OF ____________________________)

: ss.:

COUNTY OF ________________________)

On this ____ day of May, XXXX, before me personally appeared ____________________ __________, to me known, who, being duly sworn, did depose and say that he resides at ____; that he is a ____________________________ of ____________________________, one of the corporations described in and which executed the foregoing document; that he knows the seal of said corporation; that one of the seals affixed to said instrument is such corporation's seal; that it was so affixed by authority of the Board of Directors of said corporation, and that he signed his name thereto by like order.

____
Notary Public

(NOTARIAL SEAL)

Schedule I

Box-Cars

Number of Cars	*A.A.R. Mech. Design Description*	*Identifying Numbers (Both Inclusive)*

Form: I-06a
Disk File Name: I-06a.rtf

FORM OF NOTE

Form Purpose

A promissory note for use in connection with an equipment loan transaction. This form is integrated with Loan and Security Agreement, Form I-06.

Executing Parties

The borrower.

See:

Loan and Security Agreement, Form I-06

Exhibit A

[Form of Promissory Note]

(Insert name of borrower)

$ (Insert city, state)
, XXXX

FOR VALUE RECEIVED, (insert name of the borrower), a ____________________ corporation (the "Company"), hereby promises to pay to the order of (insert name of Lender) at its office located at ____________________, in lawful money of the United States of America, the principal amount of (insert principal amount of loan) Dollars ($ ____________), and to pay interest on the unpaid principal amount hereof, in like money, from the date hereof at the rate of (____) % per annum (calculated on the basis of a 360-day year of twelve 30-day months). Such principal and installments on the day of each month, commencing interest shall be due and payable in (____) consecutive (monthly) installments on the ________ day of each (month), commencing ____________________ XXXX. Each of the 1st through the (insert the number for the second to last installment) such installments shall be a payment of principal and interest in the amount of $ ____________ and the (insert the number of the last installment) such installment shall be a payment of principal and interest in the amount of $ ____________, provided that, in any event, the (insert the number of the last installment) such installment shall be in amount sufficient to pay in full all accrued interest on, and the entire unpaid principal amount of, this Note, and provided further, that in the event any partial prepayment of this Note is made pursuant to Subsection 2.4 or 2.5 of the Agreement referred to below, each installment due and payable on this Note after such partial prepayment shall be reduced in the same proportion as then outstanding principal amount of this Note shall have been reduced by such partial prepayment. Each installment of this Note, when paid, shall be first applied to the payment of interest on the unpaid principal amount of this Note, and the balance thereof to the payment of principal. Interest on any overdue principal of and premium, if any, on this Note shall be payable from the due date thereof at the rate of ____ % per annum for the period during which such principal or premium shall be overdue.

If any installment of principal and interest on this Note becomes due and payable on a Saturday, Sunday, or legal holiday under the laws of the State of (insert the appropriate state), the maturity thereof shall be extended to the next succeeding business day.

This Note is the Note of the Company issued pursuant to the Loan and Security Agreement dated as of ____________ between the Company and the payee hereof (herein, as the same may from time to time be amended, supplemented, or otherwise modified, called the "Agreement"), and is entitled to the benefits thereof. As provided in the Agreement, this Note is subject to prepayment, in whole or in part, in certain cases without premium and in other cases with a premium as specified in the Agreement.

This Note is secured by the Collateral described in the Agreement. Reference is made to the Agreement for a description of the nature and extent of the security for this Note and the rights of the holder hereof with respect to such security.

This Note shall be governed by, and construed and interpreted in accordance with, the laws of the State of ____________.

Upon the occurrence of any one or more of the Events of Default specified in the Agreement, the amounts then remaining unpaid on this Note may be declared to be immediately due and payable as provided in the Agreement.

(Insert name of borrower)

By: ________________________________

Title: ______________________________

Form: I-06b
Disk File Name: I-06b.rtf

Form of Guaranty

Form Purpose

A form of borrower guaranty for use in with an equipment loan transaction. This form is integrated with Loan and Security Agreement, Form I-06.

Executing Parties

Borrower's guarantor.

See:

Loan and Security Agreement, Form I-06

Exhibit B

[Form of Guaranty]

Guaranty

GUARANTY dated ________________, XXXX, made by (insert the name of the guarantor), a ____________________________ corporation (the "Guarantor") in favor of (insert the name of the Lender), a ____________________ corporation (the "Lender").

WITNESSETH:

WHEREAS, [insert the relationship of guarantor to borrower, such as "the Guarantor is the record and beneficial owner of all of the issued and outstanding shares of the capital stock of (insert the name of the borrower), a ________________________________ corporation (the "Company")];

WHEREAS, the Company has entered into a Loan and Security Agreement dated as of __________________ with the Lender (the "Loan Agreement"), pursuant to which the Lender has agreed, subject to the terms and conditions thereof, to make a loan to the Company in a principal amount not to exceed $ ____________ to finance a portion of the aggregate purchase price of (insert the numbered of rail cars to be financed) box-cars, such loan to be evidenced by a secured promissory note of the Company as provided in the Loan Agreement (the "Note");

WHEREAS, it is a condition precedent to the obligation of the Lender to make the loan under the Loan Agreement that the Guarantor execute and deliver this Guaranty to the Lender; and

WHEREAS, it is in the best interests of the Guarantor that the Company acquire the aforesaid box-cars and finance a portion of the purchase price thereof with the proceeds of the loan under the Loan Agreement;

NOW, THEREFORE, in consideration of the premises and in order to induce the Lender to make the loan as provided in the Loan Agreement, the Guarantor agrees as follows:

1. The Guarantor hereby unconditionally and irrevocably guaranties, as primary obligor and not merely as surety, to the Lender, its successors, endorsees, transferees, and assigns, the prompt and complete payment when due (whether at the stated maturity, by acceleration or otherwise) of (i) the unpaid principal amount of, and accrued interest on, the Note and (ii) all other obligations and liabilities of the Company to the Lender, now existing or hereinafter incurred, under the Loan Agreement and the Note, and under any renewals or extensions of either thereof (all of said principal amount, interest, obligations, and liabilities being hereinafter called the "Obligations"), and the Guarantor further agrees to pay any and all reasonable expenses which may be paid or incurred by the Lender in collecting any or all of the Obligations and/or enforcing any rights under this Guaranty or under the Obligations.

2. Notwithstanding any payment or payments made by the Guarantor hereunder, the Guarantor shall not be entitled to be subrogated to any of the rights of the Lender against the Company or any collateral security or guaranty or right of offset held by the Lender for the payment of the Obligations until all amounts owing to the Lender by the Company for or on account of the Obligations are paid in full.

3. The Guarantor hereby consents that, without the necessity of any reservation of rights against the Guarantor and without notice to or further assent by it, (a) any demand for payment of any of the Obligations may be rescinded by the Lender and any of the Obligations continued; (b) the Obligations may, from time to time, in whole or in part, be renewed, extended, modified, prematured, compromised, or released by the Lender; (c) the Loan Agreement and the Note may be amended, modified, or supplemented by the Lender and the provisions thereof may be waived by the Lender from time to time; and (d) any and all collateral security and/or lien or liens (legal or equitable) at any time, present or future, held, given, or intended to be given for the Obligations, and any rights or remedies of the Lender under the Loan Agreement and/or any other collateral security documents or in law or in equity or otherwise, may, from time to time, in whole or in part, be exchanged, sold, surrendered, released, modified, waived, or extended by the Lender and the Lender may permit or consent to any such action or the result of any such action; all as the Lender may deem advisable and all without impairing, abridging, releasing, or affecting the guaranty provided for herein.

4. The Guarantor hereby waives any and all notice of the acceptance of this Guaranty and any and all notice of the creation, renewal, extension, or accrual of any of the Obligations or the reliance by the Lender upon this Guaranty. The Obligations shall conclusively be deemed to have been created, contracted, and incurred in reliance upon this Guaranty and all dealings between the Company and the Lender shall likewise be conclusively presumed to have been had or consummated in reliance upon this Guaranty. To the extent permitted by law, the Guarantor waives protest, demand for payment and notice of default, dishonor or nonpayment to or upon it or the Company with respect to the Obligations or any of them.

5. This is a continuing, absolute, and unconditional guaranty of payment without regard to the validity, regularity, or enforceability of the Note, the Loan Agreement, or any other collateral security document or guaranty therefor or rights of offset with respect thereto and without regard to any defense, offset, or counterclaim which may at any time be available to or be asserted by the Company against the Lender and which constitutes, or might be construed to constitute, an equitable or legal discharge of the Company for the Obligations, or of the Guarantor under this Guaranty, in bankruptcy or in any other instance. This Guaranty shall remain in full force and effect and be binding in accordance with and to the extent of its terms upon the Guarantor, its successors and assigns until all of the Obligations have been paid in full.

6. The Guarantor hereby represents and warrants to the Lender that:

(a) The Guarantor is a corporation duly organized, validly existing, and in good standing under the laws of the State of ________________ and is duly qualified as a foreign corporation and in good standing under the laws of each jurisdiction in which the conduct of its business or the ownership or lease of its properties requires such qualification.

(b) The Guarantor has full power, authority, and legal right to own its properties and to conduct its business as now conducted and presently proposed to be conducted by it and to execute, deliver, and perform this Guaranty and to take such action as may be necessary to complete the transactions contemplated by the Loan Agreement and this Guaranty, and the Guarantor has taken all necessary corporate action to authorize the execution, delivery, and performance of this Guaranty.

(c) This Guaranty has been duly authorized, executed, and delivered by the Guarantor and constitutes a legal, valid, and binding obligation of the Guarantor enforceable in accordance with its terms.

(d) No consent of any other party (including stockholders of the Guarantor) and no consent, license, permit, approval, or authorization of, exemption by, or registration or declaration with, any governmental authority is required in connection with the execution, delivery, performance, validity, or enforceability of this Guaranty.

(e) The execution, delivery, and performance by the Guarantor of this Guaranty will not violate any provision of any existing law or regulation to which the Guarantor is subject or of any order, judgment, award, or decree of any court, arbitrator, or governmental authority applicable to the Guarantor or of the Articles of Incorporation, By-Laws, or any preferred stock provision of the Guarantor or of any mortgage, indenture, contract, or other agreement to which the Guarantor is a party or which is or purports to be binding upon the Guarantor or any of its properties or assets, and will not constitute a default thereunder, and will not result in the creation or imposition or any lien, charge, or encumbrance on, or security interest in, any of the properties or assets of the Guarantor or any of its subsidiaries. The Guarantor is not in default in the performance or observance of any of the obligations, covenants, or conditions contained in any bond, debenture, or note, or in any mortgage, deed of trust, indenture, or loan agreement, of the Guarantor.

(f) There are no actions, suits, or proceedings (whether or not purportedly on behalf of the Guarantor) pending or, to the knowledge of the Guarantor, threatened against the Guarantor or any of its subsidiaries or any of their respective properties or assets in any court or before any arbitrator of any kind or before or by any governmental body, which (i) relate to any of the transactions contemplated by this Guaranty or the Loan Agreement, or (ii) would, if adversely determined, materially impair the right or ability of the Guarantor to carry on its business substantially as now conducted and presently proposed to be conducted, or (iii) would, if adversely determined, have a material adverse effect on the operating results or on the condition, financial or other, of the Guarantor or any of its subsidiaries. The Guarantor is not in default with respect to any order, judgment, award, decree, rule, or regulation of any court, arbitrator, or governmental body.

(g) The consolidated financial statements of the Guarantor and its subsidiaries as at ____________________, and for the three years then ended, certified by ____________________, and the unaudited consolidated financial statements of the Guarantor and its subsidiaries as at ____________________, and for the (six) months then ended, certified by the chief financial officer of the Guarantor, copies of which have heretofore been delivered to the Lender, are complete and correct, present fairly the consolidated financial position of the Guarantor and its subsidiaries as of their respective dates and the results of their operations for the respective periods covered thereby, and have been prepared in accordance with generally accepted accounting principles consistently applied. There has been no material adverse change in the condition, financial or other, of the Guarantor since ____________, XXXX.

(h) Each of the Guarantor and each of its subsidiaries has filed all federal, state, and local tax returns and declarations of estimated tax which are required to be filed and has paid all taxes which have become due pursuant to such returns and declarations or pursuant to any assessments made against it, and the Guarantor has no knowledge of any deficiency or additional assessments in connection therewith not adequately provided for on the books of the Guarantor or the applicable subsidiary. In the opinion of the Guarantor, all tax liabilities of the Guarantor and its subsidiaries were adequately provided for as of ________________, XXXX, and are now so provided for, on the books of the Guarantor and its subsidiaries,

(i) Since ________________, XXXX, the business, operations, properties, and assets of the Guarantor and its subsidiaries have not been materially and adversely affected in any way as the result of any fire, explosion, earthquake, disaster, accident, labor disturbance, requisition, or taking of property by governmental authority, flood, drought, embargo, riot, civil disturbance, uprising, activity of armed forces, or act of God or the public enemy.

(j) The Guarantor is not a party to any agreement or instrument, or subject to any charter or other corporate restriction or to any judgment, order, writ, injunction, decree, award, rule, or regulation, which does or will materially and adversely effect the business, operations, properties, or assets or the condition, financial or other, of the Guarantor.

(k) The Guarantor owns of record and beneficially all of the issued and outstanding capital stock of the Company.

7. The Guarantor covenants and agrees that it will furnish to the Lender (a) as soon as available, but in any event not later than 120 days after the end of each fiscal year of the Guarantor, a consolidated balance sheet of the Guarantor and its subsidiaries as at the end of such fiscal year and the related statements of income and of changes in financial position of the Guarantor and its subsidiaries for such fiscal year, all in reasonable detail, prepared in accordance with generally accepted accounting principles applied on a basis consistently maintained throughout such fiscal year and accompanied by a report or opinion of ________________________________ or other independent public accountants of recognized standing selected by the Guarantor and satisfactory to the Lender; (b) as soon as available, but in any event not later than 90 days after the end of each quarter, other than the last, of each fiscal year of the Guarantor, an unaudited consolidated balance sheet of the Guarantor and its subsidiaries as at the end of such quarter and the related unaudited consolidated statements of income and of changes in financial position of the Guarantor and its subsidiaries for the period from the beginning of such fiscal year to the end of such quarter, all in reasonable detail, prepared in accordance with generally accepted accounting principles applied on a basis consistently maintained throughout the period involved and certified by the chief financial officer of the Guarantor (subject to normal year-end audit adjustments); and (c) promptly upon request, such additional financial information with respect to the Guarantor as the Lender may from time to time reasonably require.

8. This Guaranty shall continue to be effective, or be reinstated, as the case may be, if at any time payment, or any part thereof, of any of the Obligations is rescinded or must otherwise be restored or returned by the Lender upon the insolvency, bankruptcy, or reorganization of the Company or otherwise, all as though such payment had not been made.

9. No failure or delay in exercising any right, power, or privilege hereunder shall operate as a waiver thereof; nor shall any single or partial exercise of any right, power, or privilege hereunder preclude any other or further exercise thereof or the exercise of any other right, power, or privilege. All rights and remedies of the Lender hereunder and under the Note, and any other collateral security document or guarantee therefor shall be cumulative and may be exercised singly or concurrently and are not exclusive of any rights or remedies permitted by law.

10. This Guaranty may not be waived, altered, modified, or amended except in writing duly signed by the Lender. This Guaranty and the rights and obligations of the parties hereunder shall be governed by and construed in accordance with the laws of the State of ____________________.

11. All terms defined in the Loan Agreement and used herein shall have the meanings assigned to them therein unless the context requires otherwise.

IN WITNESS WHEREOF, the Guarantor has caused this Guaranty to be duly executed and delivered by its duly authorized officer on the day and year first above written.

(Insert the name of guarantor)

By: ____

Title: ______________________________________

Form: I-06c
Disk File Name: I-06c.rtf

FORM OF BILL OF SALE

Form Purpose

An equipment bill of sale for use in connection with an equipment loan transaction. This form is integrated with Loan and Security Agreement, Form I-06.

Executing Parties

The equipment vendor.

See:

Loan and Security Agreement, Form I-06

Exhibit C

[Form of Bill of Sale]

Bill of Sale

(INSERT THE NAME OF VENDOR) (the "Vendor"), in consideration of the sum of Ten Dollars and other good and valuable consideration paid by (insert the name of borrower/ purchaser) (the "Buyer"), receipt of which is hereby acknowledged, does hereby grant, bargain, sell, transfer, and set over unto the Buyer, its successors and assigns, the following described equipment which has been delivered by the Vendor to the Buyer, to wit:

Number of Units	*Description*	*Identification Numbers*
	(Insert information)	

TO HAVE AND TO HOLD all and singular the equipment above described to the Buyer, its successors and assigns, for its and their own use and behoof forever.

And the Vendor hereby warrants to the Buyer, its successors and assigns, that said equipment has been constructed from new components; that said equipment is new and unused upon delivery to the Buyer, that is, has never been placed in service prior to delivery to the Buyer; that said equipment has been constructed in accordance with Association of American Railroads or other U.S. governmental regulations applicable to said equipment; that at the time of delivery to the Buyer the Vendor is the lawful owner of said equipment; that title to said equipment is free from all prior claims, liens, and encumbrances suffered by or through the Vendor; and that the Vendor has good right to sell the same as aforesaid; and the Vendor covenants that it will warrant and defend such title against all claims and demands whatsoever.

(Insert the name of the vendor)

By: ______________________________

Title: ______________________________

Dated: ___________________________, XXXX

Form: I-06d
Disk File Name: I-06d.rtf

FORM OF CERTIFICATE OF ACCEPTANCE

Form Purpose

An equipment certificate of acceptance for use in connection with an equipment loan transaction. This is integrated with Loan and Security Agreement, Form I-06.

Executing Parties

The equipment lessee.

See:

Loan and Security Agreement, Form I-06

Exhibit D

[Form of Certificate of Acceptance]

Certificate of Acceptance

________________________, XXXX

(Insert the name and address of borrower)

Gentlemen:

The undersigned, being a duly authorized representative of (the "Lessee"), hereby accepts (insert the number of railcars) railcars ("Cars") bearing numbers as follows:

for the Lessee pursuant to the Lease Agreement, dated as of ____________, XXXX (the "Lease") between the Lessee and you and certifies that each of said Cars is plainly marked in stencil on both sides of each Car with the words

"TITLE TO THIS CAR SUBJECT TO DOCUMENTS RECORDED WITH INTERSTATE COMMERCE COMMISSION"

in readily visible letters not less than one inch (1") in height, and that each of said Cars conforms to, and fully complies with the terms of the Lease and is in condition satisfactory to the Lessee. Lessee hereby certifies that it is an interstate carrier by rail and that the Cars are intended for actual use and movement in interstate commerce.

By: ________________________

Title: ________________________

Form: I-06e
Disk File Name: I-06e.rtf

Form of Certificate of Cost

Form Purpose

A certificate of equipment cost for use in connection with an equipment loan transaction. This form is integrated with Loan and Security Agreement, Form I-06.

Executing Parties

The borrower.

See:

Loan and Security Agreement, Form I-06

Exhibit E

[Form of Certificate of Cost]

Certificate of Cost

Pursuant to paragraph (q) of Section 4 of the Loan and Security Agreement, dated as of _______________, XXXX (the "Agreement"), between (insert here the name of borrower), and (insert the name of the lender) (the "Lender"), the undersigned hereby certifies that the Box-Car Costs (as defined in the Agreement) of the Box-Cars being partially financed with the proceeds of the loan being made by the Lender to the undersigned on the date hereof are as follows:

Number of Units	*Description*	*Identification Nos.*	*Box-Car Costs*
	(insert information)		

Total Box-Car Cost: $__________

The undersigned hereby further certifies that attached hereto are true and complete copies of the invoices of (insert the name of Vendor here), identifying the Box-Cars described above and specifying the Box-Car Costs thereof.

IN WITNESS WHEREOF, the undersigned has duly executed and delivered this Certificate this ____ day of _______________, XXXX.

(Insert name of borrower)

By: ______________________________

Title: ______________________________

Form: l-06f
Disk File Name: l-06f.rtf

Form of Legal Opinion—General

Form Purpose

A form of legal opinion for use by counsel for borrower and its guarantor in connecton with an equipment loan transaction. This form is integrated with Loan and Security Agreement, Form l-06.

Executing Parties

Counsel for borrower and guarantor.

See:

Loan and Security Agreement, Form l-06

Exhibit F

[Form of Legal Opinion of Counsel to the Company and the Guarantor]

____________________________, XXXX

(Insert name and address of Lender)

Dear Sirs:

I have acted as counsel for (insert name of borrower), Inc., a ________________ corporation (the "Company"), in connection with the execution and delivery of the Loan and Security Agreement, dated as of ____________________________, between the Company and you (the "Agreement"), and for (insert the name of the Guarantor), a __________________________ corporation (the "Guarantor") in connection with the execution and delivery of the Guaranty, dated ________________, XXXX (the "Guaranty") made by the Guarantor in your favor.

This opinion is furnished to you pursuant to paragraph (v) of Section 4 of the Agreement. Terms used herein which are defined in the Agreement shall have the respective meanings set forth in the Agreement, unless otherwise defined herein.

In connection with this opinion, I have examined executed counterparts of the Agreement, the Leases, and the Guaranty, the executed Note delivered by the Company on the date hereof (the "Note"), and such corporate documents and records of the Company and the Guarantor, certificates of public officials and of officers of the Company and the Guarantor, and such other documents, as I have deemed necessary or appropriate for the purposes hereof.

Based upon the foregoing, I am of the opinion that:

1. Each of the Company and the Guarantor is a corporation duly organized, validly existing, and in good standing under the laws of the State of ________________. Neither the conduct of its business nor the ownership or lease of its properties requires the Company to qualify to do business as a foreign corporation under the laws of any jurisdiction. The Guarantor is duly qualified as a foreign corporation and in good standing under the laws of each jurisdiction in which the conduct of its business or the ownership or lease of its properties requires such qualification.

2. The Company has the corporate power and authority to own its properties and to transact the business in which it is presently engaged (including the purchase of the Box-Cars) and to execute, deliver, and perform the Agreement, the Note, and the Leases, to borrow under the Agreement on the terms and conditions thereof, to grant the lien and security interest created by the Agreement, and to take such action as may be necessary to complete the transactions contemplated by the Agreement, the Note, and the Leases and the Company has taken all necessary corporate action to authorize the borrowing on the terms and conditions of the Agreement and the grant of the lien and security interest created by the Agreement and to authorize the execution, delivery, and performance of the Agreement, the Note, and the Leases.

3. The Guarantor has the corporate power and authority to own its properties and to transact the business in which it is presently engaged and to execute, deliver, and perform the Guaranty and to take such action as may be necessary to complete the transactions contemplated by the Loan Agreement and the Guaranty, and the Guarantor has taken all necessary corporate action to authorize the execution, delivery, and performance of the Guaranty.

4. Each of the Agreement, the Note, and the Leases has been duly authorized, executed, and delivered by the Company and constitutes a legal, valid, and binding obligation of the Company enforceable in accordance with its terms, except as enforceability may be limited by applicable bankruptcy, insolvency, reorganization, moratorium, or similar laws affecting the enforcement of creditors' rights generally.

5. The Guaranty has been duly authorized, executed, and delivered by the Guarantor and constitutes a legal, valid, and binding obligation of the Guarantor enforceable in accordance with its terms, except as enforceability may be limited by applicable bankruptcy, insolvency, reorganization, moratorium, or similar laws affecting the enforcement of creditors' rights generally.

6. No consent of any other party (including the stockholders of the Company and the Guarantor) and no consent, license, permit, approval or authorization of, exemption by, or registration or declaration with, any governmental authority, is required in connection with the execution, delivery, performance, validity, or enforceability of the Agreement, the Note, or the Guaranty except for the filings and recordings referred to in paragraph 9 below.

7. The execution, delivery, and performance by the Company of the Agreement, the Note, and the Leases and by the Guarantor of the Guaranty will not violate any provision of, or constitute a default under, any existing law or regulation to which the Company or the Guarantor is subject, or any order, judgment, award, or decree of any court, arbitrator, or governmental authority applicable to the Company or the Guarantor, or the respective Articles of Incorporation, the respective By-Laws or any preferred stock provision of the Company or the Guarantor, or any mortgage, indenture, contract, or other agreement to which the Company or the Guarantor is a party or which is binding upon the Company or the Guarantor or any of their respective properties or assets, and will not result in the creation or imposition of any Lien (other than the lien on and security interest created by the Agreement) on any of the respective properties or assets of the Company or the Guarantor pursuant to the provisions of any such mortgage, indenture, contract, or other agreement.

8. To the best of my knowledge (having made due inquiry), there are no actions, suits, or proceedings (whether or not purportedly on behalf of the Company or the Guarantor) pending or threatened against the Company or the Guarantor or any of their respective properties or assets in any court or before any arbitrator or before or by any governmental body, which (i) relate to any of the Collateral or to any of the transactions contemplated by the Agreement or the Guaranty, or (ii) would, if adversely determined, materially impair the right or ability of the Company or the Guarantor to carry on its respective business substantially as now conducted, or (iii) would, if adversely determined, have a material adverse effect on the respective operating results or on the respective condition, financial or other, of the Company or the Guarantor.

9. The Agreement and each Lease have been duly filed and recorded with the Interstate Commerce Commission in accordance with Section 11303, Title 49, United States Code and no other agreement or document has been so filed or recorded as of the date

hereof asserting a grant by the Company of an interest in or a Lien on the Box-Cars or either Lease. A financing statement with respect to your security interest in the Leases has been duly filed in the office of the Secretary of State of ________________ and no other financing statement asserting the grant by the Company of a security interest in either Lease has been so filed. No other filing, registration, or recording or other action is necessary in Order to perfect, protect, and preserve, as security for the Note and the other Obligations, the lien on and security interest in the Box-Cars and the Leases created by the Agreement except that a continuation statement must be filed within six months prior to the expiration of each five-year period following the date of filing of the financing statement filed with the Secretary of State of ________________. The Agreement (i) constitutes a legal, valid, and perfected first lien on and first priority security interest in each of the Box-Cars (and the Proceeds thereof) and in each of the Leases (and the Proceeds thereof), as security for the Note and the other Obligations and (ii) constitutes a legal and valid lien on and security interest in the Cash Collateral Account, as security for the Note and the other Obligations, and upon each deposit of funds in such Account, such lien and security interest shall be perfected with respect to such funds, and the Lender shall have a first priority perfected security interest in such funds, as security for the Note and the other Obligations.

In rendering the opinions expressed in paragraph 9 above, I have relied as to matters governed by Title 49, United States and as to the filings and recordings with the Interstate Commerce Commission (or the lack of such filings and recordings), upon the opinion of ________________________________, delivered to you on the date hereof pursuant to paragraph (w) of Section 4 of the Agreement. Such opinion is satisfactory in form and substance to me, and I believe that I and you are justified in relying thereon.

Very truly yours,

Form: l-06g
Disk File Name: l-06g.rtf

Form of Legal Opinion—Special Counsel

Form Purpose

A form of legal opinion for use by special counsel for borrower in connection with an equipment loan transaction. This form is integrated with Loan and Security Agreement, Form l-06.

Executing Parties

Special counsel for borrower.

See:

Loan and Security Agreement, Form l-06

Exhibit G

[Form of Legal Opinion of Special
Counsel to the Company]

______________________, XXXX

(Insert name and address of lender)

Dear Sirs:

We have acted as special counsel for (insert name of borrower), a ______________ corporation (the "Company"), in connection with the execution and delivery of the Loan and Security Agreement dated as of ______________ XXXX between the Company and you (the "Agreement").

This opinion is furnished to you pursuant to paragraph (w) of Section 4 of the Agreement. Terms used herein which are defined in the Agreement shall have the respective meanings set forth in the Agreement, unless otherwise defined herein.

In connection with this opinion, we have examined executed counterparts of the Agreement and the Leases, the executed Note delivered by the Company on the date hereof (the "Note"), and such other documents as we have deemed necessary or appropriate for the purposes thereof.

Based upon the foregoing, we are of the opinion that:

1. The Agreement and each Lease have been duly filed and recorded with the Interstate Commerce Commission in accordance with Section 11303, Title 49, United States Code and no other agreement or document has been so filed or recorded as of the date hereof asserting a grant by the Company of an interest in or a Lien on the Box-Cars or either Lease. A financing statement with respect to your security interest in the Leases has been duly filed in the office of the Secretary of State of ______________ and no other financing statement asserting the grant by the Company of a security interest in either Lease has been so filed. No other filing, registration, or recording or other action is necessary in order to perfect, protect, and preserve, as security for the Note and the other Obligations, the lien on and security interest in the Box-Cars and the Leases created by the Agreement except that a continuation statement must be filed within six months prior to the expiration of each five-year period following the date of filing of the financing statement filed with the Secretary of State of ______________.

2. The Agreement constitutes a legal, valid, and perfected first lien on and first priority security interest in each of the Box-Cars (and the proceeds thereof) and in each of the Leases (and the proceeds thereof) as security for the Note and the other Obligations.

In rendering the opinions expressed above, we have relied as to matters governed by the Uniform Commercial Code and as to the filing with the Secretary of State of ______________ (or the lack of such filings) upon the opinion of ______________________________, delivered to you on the date hereof pursuant to paragraph (v) of Section 4 of the Agreement.

Very truly yours,

Form: l-07
Disk File Name: l-07.rtf

Loan and Security Agreement—Master Format

Form Purpose

Form of master equipment security and loan agreement. The master format allows future equipment loans to be easily added by means of a schedule, and is integrated with all collateral closing documents (see below).

Executing Parties

The borrower.
The lender.

See:

Loan Supplement, Form l-07a
Promissory Note, Form l-07b
Acknowledgment and Consent to Assignment of Equipment Lease, Form l-07c
Supplement, Form l-07d

Master Loan and Security Agreement

dated as of ______ XXXX

between

____

Lender

and

____

Borrower

Master Loan and Security Agreement

Table of Contents

Master Loan and Security Agreement

MASTER LOAN AND SECURITY AGREEMENT (the "Master Agreement") entered into as of the ____ day of ____________, XXXX by and between ____________________, a ______________________________ corporation having its principal place of business at ____
____ ("Lender") and ____________________, a ______________________________ corporation having its principal place of business at ______________________ ("Borrower").

WHEREAS, Borrower will be entering into arrangements from time to time for the purchase of certain equipment, which equipment will be, at the time of purchase, subject to various equipment leases between Borrower and various lessees;

WHEREAS, Borrower desires to obtain, from time to time, loans to finance a portion of the purchase price of certain Borrower specified equipment it will be purchasing and which will be subject to certain Borrower specified equipment leases; and

WHEREAS, pursuant to, and in accordance with, the terms of this Master Agreement Lender is willing to make loans, which loans meet Lender's lending criteria, to Borrower to purchase such equipment.

NOW, THEREFORE, In consideration of the foregoing and of the mutual covenants and conditions contained herein, Lender and Borrower hereby agree as follows:

Section 1. Definitions

The following terms shall have the respective meanings set forth below for all purposes of this Master Agreement (Terms defined in the singular shall have a comparable meaning when used in the plural and vice versa.):

1.1 Specific Definitions

"Business Day" shall mean a calendar day, excluding Saturdays, Sundays, and all days on which banking institutions in the State of ______________________ are authorized to be closed.

"Code" shall mean the Uniform Commercial Code, or comparable law, as now or hereafter in effect in any applicable jurisdiction.

"Collateral" with respect to a Loan shall have the meaning set forth in Section 9 of this Master Agreement.

"Cut-Off Date" shall mean the date specified in a Loan Supplement after which Lender shall not be obligated to make a Loan.

"Default" shall have the meaning set forth in Section 16 of this Master Agreement.

"Documents" shall have the meaning set forth in Section 23.1 of this Master Agreement.

"Equipment" shall mean the equipment described on a Loan Supplement together with all attachments, accessories, additions, parts, and equipment whenever affixed thereto.

"Equipment Lease" shall mean each equipment leasing agreement identified in a Loan Supplement, including without limitation all equipment schedules or supplements and all exhibits, and documents related, to the equipment lease.

"Event of Default" shall mean any of the events or conditions specified in Section 15 of this Master Agreement.

"Event of Loss" shall have the meaning set forth in a Loan Supplement.

"Governmental Body" shall have the meaning set forth in Section 12.8 of this Master Agreement.

"Item of Equipment" shall mean an item of equipment described in a Loan Supplement.

"Interim Loan Term" as to any Loan shall mean the period of time, if any, commencing on the Loan Closing Date and ending on the day immediately preceding the date that the Primary Loan Term begins.

"Lessee" shall mean the Lessee identified in a Loan Supplement, and any and each guarantor of such Lessee obligations under the applicable Equipment Lease.

"Lessee Consent" shall mean an Acknowledgment and Consent to Assignment of Equipment Lease, as Lender may require a Lessee to execute and deliver on a Loan Closing Date.

"Lien" shall mean any mortgage, pledge, hypothecation, assignment, security interest, lien, charge, or encumbrance, priority, or other security agreement or arrangement or other claim or right of any kind or nature whatsoever created by Borrower (including any conditional sale or other title retention agreement, any lease, and the filing of, or agreement to give, any financing statement under the Uniform Commercial Code or comparable law of any jurisdiction), other than the rights of Lessee under an Equipment Lease and the rights of Lender under a Loan Agreement.

"Loan" shall mean the amount of money which Lender lends Borrower on the Loan Closing Date pursuant to a Loan Agreement.

"Loan Agreement" shall mean a Loan Supplement and all documentation attached thereto or delivered pursuant thereto, together with the Master Agreement made a part thereof as the same may from time to time be amended, supplemented, or otherwise modified. Each Loan Supplement shall be considered a separate and enforceable agreement incorporating the terms and conditions of this Master Agreement.

"Loan Closing Date" shall mean the date on which Borrower shall have received Loan proceeds.

"Loan Commencement Date" with respect to each Loan shall mean the date on which the Loan Term shall begin, as specified in a Loan Supplement.

"Loan Fee" shall be that fee, if any, specified as such in a Loan Supplement.

"Loan Interest Rate" with respect to a Loan shall mean that per annum interest rate specified in a Loan Supplement.

"Loan Request" shall have the meaning set forth in Section 2.2 of this Master Agreement.

"Loan Supplement" shall mean each supplement, substantially in the form of Exhibit A hereto, which shall refer to this Master Agreement and which shall become a part hereof as executed from time to time by the parties hereto, covering one or more Loans.

"Loan Term" with respect to a Loan shall mean the Primary Loan Term and any Interim Loan Term.

"Manufacturer" as to each Item of Equipment shall mean the manufacturer or vendor thereof specified in a Loan Supplement.

"Note" shall mean each secured promissory note, substantially in the form of Exhibit A hereto, including any amortization schedule attached thereto, issued and delivered by Borrower to Lender in connection with a Loan and which evidences the Loan repayment obligation of Borrower to Lender.

"Order" shall have the meaning set forth in Section 12.3 of this Master Agreement.

"Overdue Rate" shall mean the per annum interest charge specified in a Loan Supplement.

"Permitted Early Equipment Lease Termination" shall have the meaning set forth in Section 7.3 of this Master Agreement.

"Primary Loan Term" with respect to a Loan shall mean that period of time commencing on, and including, the date specified in a Loan Supplement on which the Primary Term shall begin, and ending that period of time thereafter, as designated in the applicable Loan Supplement, unless earlier terminated pursuant to the provisions of the applicable Loan Agreement.

"Prime Rate" shall mean the rate publicly announced from time to time by Chemical Banking Corporation as its prime lending rate to its commercial customers. The Prime Rate for purposes of a Loan Agreement shall be determined at the close of business on the 15th day of each calendar month and shall become effective as of the first day of the calendar month succeeding such determination and shall continue in effect to, and including, the last day of said calendar month.

"Principal Amount" shall mean the principal amount of a Loan, as set forth in a Loan Supplement.

"Purchase Cost" as to each Item of Equipment shall mean the amount paid, or payable, by Borrower to Manufacturer for such Item of Equipment, and evidenced by one or more Manufacturer's invoices for such Item of Equipment, plus any additional cost so identified in a Loan Supplement, all as set forth in a Loan Supplement.

"Secured Obligations" with respect to a Loan shall have the meaning set forth in Section 9 of this Master Agreement.

"Term" shall mean the term of this Master Agreement which shall commence on the date of first execution and delivery of this Master Agreement by the parties hereto and continue in effect until all Notes have been paid in full and all other obligations, responsibilities, and liabilities, including Secured Obligations, of Borrower pursuant to this Master Agreement and all Loan Agreements have been fully satisfied and discharged.

"Total Equipment Cost" shall mean the aggregate Equipment Purchase Cost, plus additional costs and expenses, all as specified in a Loan Supplement.

1.2 General Word Definitions

"Hereof, "herein," and *"thereunder"* and words of similar import when used in this Master Agreement or in any Loan Supplement, Note, or other agreement shall refer to such agreement as a whole and not to any particular portion or provision thereof.

"Including" when used in this Master Agreement or in any Loan Supplement, Note, or other agreement shall mean including but not by way of limitation.

"Original" when used in this Master Agreement or in any Loan Supplement, Loan Agreement, or other agreement shall mean the execution copy of such document or, when executed in counterparts the counterpart of a document designated as such by Lender for collateral, security interest, filing, and/or any other purpose.

Section 2. Loan Request

2.1 General Borrowing

Borrower may request equipment loans from time to time during the Term of this Master Agreement in accordance with the procedure in Section 2.2 hereof.

2.2 Loan Request Procedure

In the event Borrower shall desire to obtain equipment loan financing, Borrower shall make a loan request by delivering to Lender a written request for a loan pursuant to the terms of this Master Agreement (hereinafter referred to as a "Loan Request") at least thirty (30) days prior to the Borrower's requested loan closing date, supplying such information as Lender shall require, including satisfactory-to-Lender financial statements and other credit information of the equipment lessee(s), a complete copy of the equipment lease agreement(s) and related documents, a detailed description of the type of equipment involved, and specifying the proposed Principal Amount, Loan Term, Loan repayment schedule, and Loan Closing Date.

Section 3. Loan

3.1 Equipment Loans

Subject to the terms and conditions of this Master Agreement, and each applicable Loan Supplement, Lender agrees to make one or more Loans to Borrower which will be used to finance a portion of the Purchase Cost of the Items of Equipment.

3.2 Loan Term and Principal Amount

Each Loan shall be for a Loan Term, and Principal Amount, as set forth in the applicable Loan Supplement.

3.3 Loan Repayment and Note

Each Loan shall be repayable in that number of consecutive periodic installments as set forth in the applicable Loan Supplement. Borrower's obligation to repay each Loan shall be evidenced by a Note. The Principal Amount of each Note will be repaid, together with interest accruing thereon at the Loan Interest Rate on the unpaid balance thereof, in that number of consecutive periodic installments set forth in the Note, in such amounts and at such times as specified in the Note.

3.4 Conditions Precedent

The obligation of Lender to make a Loan shall be subject to the following conditions:

3.4.1 Loan Request

Lender shall have received from Borrower a Loan Request in accordance with Section 2 of this Master Agreement, along with such additional information as Lender shall request to evaluate the Loan Request.

3.4.2 Lending Criteria Satisfied

The loan requested by Borrower pursuant to the Loan Request shall satisfy all lending criteria adopted from time to time by, and governing, Lender, as determined within its sole discretion.

3.4.3 Formal Notice

Lender shall have notified Borrower in writing that the loan as requested in the Loan Request has been approved by Lender.

3.4.4 Security Interest

Each Loan shall be based on, among other things, a satisfactory-to-lender and its legal counsel continuing first priority security interest in the applicable Equipment and Equipment Lease as specified in the applicable Loan Supplement.

3.4.5 No Financial Change

No material adverse change in the business or the financial condition of Borrower or any Lessee under the applicable Equipment Lease shall have occurred and be continuing since the respective dates of the most recent financial statements and other credit information furnished by each of them to Lender.

3.4.6 Approvals and Filings

All acts, conditions, and actions (including, without limitation, the obtaining of any necessary regulatory approvals and the making of any required filings, recordings, or registrations) required to be done or performed or to have happened prior to the execution, delivery, and performance of the Master Agreement and the Loan Agreement, and Note and Equipment Lease shall have been done and performed to the satisfaction of Lender and its legal counsel.

3.4.7 Corporate Authorization

All corporate and legal proceedings, and all documents and instruments, in connection with the authorization of the Master Agreement, Loan Agreement, Note, and Equipment Lease shall be delivered to Lender and shall be satisfactory in form and substance to Lender and its legal counsel, and Lender shall have received all other Lender requested and related documents and instruments, including records of corporate proceedings, which Lender and its legal counsel may reasonably have requested in connection therewith, such documents and instruments, where appropriate, to be certified by proper corporate or government authorities.

3.4.8 Equipment Lease

With respect to a Loan, Lender shall have received the sole original of each applicable Equipment Lease satisfactory in form and substance to Lender and Its legal counsel, and related documents, and the duly executed originals of the Loan Agreement and the Note and all ancillary documentation related thereto and delivered in connection therewith and shall have received all other documents, agreements, and instruments relating to any aspect of the transactions contemplated hereby, including the Supplement, substantially in the form of Exhibit C hereto, and the Acknowledgment and Consent to Assignment of Equipment Lease, substantially in the form of Exhibit D hereto (hereinafter referred to as the "Lessee Consent").

3.4.9 Insurance

Lender shall have received evidence of insurance as to the Equipment, satisfactory in form and amount to Lender and its legal counsel.

3.4.10 Borrower's Counsel's Opinion

Lender shall have received, in form and substance satisfactory to Lender and its counsel, the written opinion addressed to it of legal counsel for Borrower, as to matters contained in Section 12, Subsections 12.1 through 12.4 inclusive and 12.7 through 12.11 inclusive, and as to such other matters incident to the transactions contemplated by this Master Agreement as Lender may request.

3.4.11 Lessee's Counsel Opinion

Lender shall have received, in form and substance satisfactory to Lender and its counsel, a written opinion addressed to it of counsel for Lessee, as to matters incident to the transactions contemplated by the Loan Agreement as Lender may request.

3.4.12 Equipment Ownership

Borrower shall own the Equipment free and clear of all Liens (except for the first priority security interest of Lender created by the Loan Agreement, and the rights of the Lessee created by the applicable Equipment Lease) and Lender shall have received such lien searches, consents, waivers, releases, or the like as it shall deem necessary or desirable to establish the same and shall have received, in form and substance satisfactory to it, copies of such invoices, bills of sale, and evidence of payment, as it shall deem necessary or desirable as evidence of Borrower's ownership of the Equipment.

3.4.13 Transaction Matters Satisfactory

All legal, financial, and documentation matters, and all documents executed, in connection with the contemplated transaction shall be satisfactory in form and substance to Lender and its legal counsel.

Section 4. Place of Payment

Payment of principal, interest, and other sums due or to become due with respect to each Loan and all the Secured Obligations are to be made at the office of Lender referred to in Section 19 of this Master Agreement, in lawful money of the United States of America in immediately available funds.

Section 5. Loan Prepayment

Borrower may not prepay any Note unless otherwise specifically provided for in, and then only in accordance with the terms and conditions of, the applicable Loan Supplement.

Section 6. Payment From Lease Amounts Due; Limitation of Liability

6.1 Payment From Lease Amounts Due

Lender and Borrower agree that, except as otherwise provided in Section 16 hereof, payment due under each Note shall be made by the Lessee's payment of the rentals and other amounts due or to become due (including, without limitation amounts due as Equipment casualty or purchase payments, or as to any early lease termination permitted under the applicable Equipment Lease) under the applicable Equipment Lease, assigned as collateral security for such Note, directly to Lender; provided, however, that nothing contained herein shall be deemed to alter or diminish the Borrower's absolute and unconditional obligation to make the payments to Lender required under the terms of the Note.

6.2 Limitation of Borrower's Liability

Notwithstanding anything to the contrary in Section 6.1, and subject to the succeeding sentence, with respect to each Loan, Lender agrees that it will look solely to the Collateral for such Loan for repayment for the Loan, without recourse against Borrower, and that Borrower shall not be personally liable to Lender for any amounts payable under such Loan; *provided, however,* Borrower expressly agrees that Borrower shall have personal recourse liability to Lender for any damages suffered by Lender in the event any representation, covenant, or warranty made by Borrower contained in this Master Agreement, Loan Agreement, Note, or Equipment Lease shall prove to be untrue in any material respect when made or has been breached in any material respect; including any representation, covenant, or warranty as to the indemnity made in Section 14.3 hereof, any representations and warranties made in Section 12 hereof, any covenants made in Sections 11.1, 13, 18, 20, and 21 hereof, and for its own gross negligence or willful misconduct. The foregoing limitation of recourse liability shall not limit, restrict, or impair the rights of Lender to accelerate the maturity of any Note upon any Event of Default, or to exercise all rights and remedies provided under this Master Agreement, any Loan Agreement, Note, or Equipment Lease, or otherwise realize upon the Collateral.

Section 7. Lender Application of Amounts Received

7.1 Rent Payments

So long as no Default or Event of Default or event which with notice, lapse of time, or the happening of any further condition, event, or act would constitute an Event of

Default shall have occurred and be continuing, each payment of an installment of rent under each Equipment Lease (including each payment of interest on overdue installments of rent) received by Lender shall be applied (i) *first,* to the payment of the installments of principal and interest (including interest on overdue principal) on the applicable Note(s) which have become due or which become due on or before the day on which such installment of rent is due from the applicable Lessee, and (ii) *second,* the balance, if any, of such installment of rent shall be paid by Lender to Borrower.

7.2 Casualty Payments

So long as no Default or Event of Default or event which with notice, lapse of time, or the happening of any further condition, event, or act would constitute an Event of Default shall have occurred and be continuing, any amounts received by Lender as a result of an Event of Loss with respect to an Item of Equipment (including, without limitation, any payment of casualty or stipulated loss value, insurance or condemnation, or similar, proceeds) shall be applied (i) *first,* to the prepayment amounts required to be paid by any mandatory prepayment requirement in a Loan Agreement, (ii) *second,* to the payment in full of all other Secured Obligations which are then due and payable, and (iii) *third,* the balance, if any, shall be paid by Lender to Borrower for distribution in accordance with the terms of the applicable Equipment Lease.

7.3 Permitted Early Lease Termination

So long as no Default or Event of Default or event which with notice, lapse of time, or the happening of any further condition, event, or act would constitute an Event of Default shall have occurred and be continuing, any amounts received by Lender as a result of an early equipment lease termination permitted under an Equipment Lease with respect to an Item of Equipment ("Permitted Early Equipment Lease Termination"), including, without limitation, any payment of early termination value, or similar, proceeds, shall be applied (i) *first,* to the prepayment amounts required to be paid by any mandatory prepayment requirement in a Loan Agreement, (ii) *second,* to the payment in full of all other Secured Obligations which are then due and payable, and (iii) *third,* the balance, if any, shall be paid by Lender to Borrower for distribution in accordance with the terms of the applicable Equipment Lease.

7.4 Other Amounts

So long as no Default or Event of Default or event which with notice, lapse of time, or the happening of any further condition, event, or act would constitute an Event of Default shall have occurred and be continuing, all amounts from time to time received by Lender (other than amounts specified in Section 6 or Sections 7.1, 7.2, or 7.3), (i) if due to Lender pursuant to the terms of a Loan Agreement, shall be applied by Lender to the purpose for which such payment was made, (ii) if provision as to its application is made in this Master Agreement or in an Equipment Lease, Lender shall, in its sole discretion, either apply such payment to the purpose for which it was made or pay it to Borrower, which shall so apply it, and (iii) if due to Borrower or Lessee, pay it to Borrower for distribution by Borrower in accordance with the terms of the applicable Equipment Lease.

7.5 Application After Declaration

All payments received and amounts realized by Lender after an Event of Default or event which with notice, lapse of time, or the happening of any further condition, event, or act would constitute an Event of Default shall have occurred and be continuing and after Lender has either declared (as assignee from Borrower of the Equipment Lease) the Equipment Lease to be in default pursuant to the provisions thereof or declared the Notes to be due and payable pursuant to Section 16 hereof, as well as all payments or amounts then held by Lender as part of the Collateral, shall be applied pursuant to said Section 16.

7.6 Application After Event of Default

All payments received and amounts realized by Lender after an Event of Default or event which with notice, lapse of time, or the happening of any further condition, event, or act would constitute an Event of Default shall have occurred and be continuing, but prior to the declaration of an Equipment Lease to be in default or the acceleration of the Notes, which funds would, but for the provisions of this Section 7.6, be paid to Borrower, shall be held by Lender as part of the Collateral until such time as no Events of Default or event which with notice, lapse of time, or the happening of any further condition, event, or act would constitute an Event of Default shall be continuing thereunder (at which time such funds shall be paid to Borrower) or until such funds are applied pursuant to Section 16 hereof.

Section 8. Late Payments; Other Charges

If any installment or other amount due with respect to the repayment of a Loan or any portion of the Secured Obligations is not paid when the same shall be due, Borrower shall pay interest on any such overdue amount at the applicable Overdue Rate.

Section 9. Assignment and Grant of Security Interests

As collateral security for the prompt and complete payment when due (whether at the stated maturity, by prepayment, by acceleration, or otherwise) of all indebtedness and other obligations of Borrower to Lender under or arising out of each Loan Agreement and/or evidenced by each Note, including any extensions or renewals thereof, and for the payment of all obligations of each Lessee under each Equipment Lease (all of which are referred to collectively herein as the "Secured Obligations"), the Borrower hereby: (a) assigns, pledges, and hypothecates to Lender, its successors and assigns, and grants to Lender, a continuing first priority security interest in and to, all of its present and future right, title, and interest in, to and under each Equipment Lease identified in each applicable Loan Supplement (including any extensions or renewals thereof) and all rentals, other sums payable thereunder (including without limitation any amounts payable in connection with an Equipment casualty or Permitted Equipment Lease Early Termination), and any and all cash and noncash proceeds (including proceeds of insurance) thereof, and all rights, powers, and remedies (BUT NONE OF THE DUTIES OR OBLIGATIONS, IF ANY) of Borrower, as lessor, including without limitation the rights to give and receive any notice, consent, waiver, demand, or approval under or in respect to each applicable Equipment Lease, to exercise any election or option thereunder or in respect thereof, to accept a surrender of any of the applicable Equipment and to do all other things which the Borrower is entitled to do as lessor under each applicable Equipment Lease, and (b) assigns, pledges, and hypothecates to Lender, and grants to Lender a continuing first priority security interest in and to all Equipment and any and all accessories and additions thereto, substitutions and replacements therefor, and proceeds (including without limitation, insurance proceeds or condemnation awards) thereof. All of the property, rights, benefits, and interests referred to in clauses (a) and (b) of this Section 9 are referred to collectively herein as the "Collateral").

Section 10. Lender Appointment as Attorney-in-Fact

10.1 Lender Appointment

Borrower hereby irrevocably constitutes and appoints Lender and any officer or agent thereof, with full power of substitution, as its true and lawful attorney-in-fact with full irrevocable power and authority in the place and stead of Borrower and in the name of Borrower or in its own name, from time to time in Lender's discretion, for the purpose of carrying out the terms of each Loan Agreement, to take any and all appropriate action and to execute any and all documents or instruments which may be deemed necessary or desirable by Lender to protect and preserve, and/or exercise its rights and remedies with respect to, the Collateral and, without limiting the generality of the foregoing, hereby gives Lender the power and right, on behalf of Borrower and without notice to or assent by Borrower, to do the following: to demand, enforce, collect, receive, receipt, and give release for any monies due or to become due under or arising out of or with respect to, any of the Collateral, and to endorse all checks and other instruments, and to do and take all such other actions relating to any of the Collateral, to file any claims or institute any proceedings with respect to any of the foregoing which Lender deems necessary or desirable, and to compromise any such demand, claim or action.

10.2 Borrower Ratification

Borrower hereby ratifies all that Lender as attorney-in-fact shall lawfully do or cause to be done by virtue of this Section 10. This power of attorney is a power coupled with an interest and shall be irrevocable.

10.3 Right to Extend

Borrower consents and agrees that any of the liabilities of each Lessee under each Equipment Lease may be extended by Lender in whole or in part, without notice to Borrower and without affecting the liability of Borrower thereunder.

10.4 No Lender Duty

The powers conferred on Lender thereunder are solely to protect its interest in the Collateral and shall not impose any duty upon it to exercise any such powers. Lender shall be accountable only for amounts that it actually receives as a result of the exercise of such powers and neither it nor any of its officers, directors, employees, or agents shall be responsible to Borrower for any act or failure to act, except for its gross negligence or willful misconduct.

Section 11. Assignments; Encumbrances; Transfers

11.1 No Borrower Assignment

Borrower will not, without the prior written consent of Lender, assign, convey, transfer, sell, exchange, further lease, or otherwise dispose of any of its right, title, or interest in, to or under any of the Collateral, or this Master Agreement, any Loan Agreement, or any Note, or create, incur, or suffer to exist any Lien upon any of the Collateral (except the security interests and the assignments created by the applicable Loan Agreement).

11.2 Permitted Lender Assignment

Lender may, without notice to, or the written consent of, Borrower, assign, convey, transfer, sell, exchange, or otherwise dispose of any of its right, title, or interest in, to or under any of the Collateral, or this Master Agreement, any Loan Agreement, or any Note, or create, incur, or suffer to exist any Lien upon any of the Collateral; provided, however, any such action shall be subject to each applicable Lessee's right of quiet enjoyment as set forth in Section 17 of this Master Agreement.

Section 12. Borrower's Representations and Warranties

Borrower represents and warrants to Lender that as of the date of this Master Agreement, and (with respect only to the Loan being made as of such date) each Loan Closing Date as follows:

12.1 Not Insolvent

Borrower is not insolvent within the meaning of applicable state or federal law.

12.2 Good Standing

Borrower is a corporation duly organized and validly existing in good standing under the laws of the jurisdiction of its incorporation, (i) is duly qualified to do business and is in good standing in each jurisdiction (x) in which the location of its properties and any Equipment requires such qualification, and (y) where failure to qualify would materially and adversely affect Lender's ability to enforce its rights under any Equipment Lease or Loan Agreement, and (ii) has full power, authority, and legal right to purchase, own, and hold under lease its properties, and to transact the business in which it is engaged.

12.3 Loan Transaction Power and Authority

The (i) acquisition of the Equipment and the leasing of the Equipment to each Lessee pursuant to the applicable Equipment Lease(s), and (ii) execution, delivery, and performance by Borrower of this Master Agreement, and as of the applicable Loan Closing Date, each Loan Agreement, Note, and Equipment Lease, and any related documents and the transactions contemplated hereby and thereby have been duly authorized by all necessary action on the part of Borrower and do not, and will not, as the case may be, contravene any provisions of law applicable to Borrower or the certificate of incorporation or by-laws of Borrower, and do not conflict or are not inconsistent with, and will not result (with or without the giving of notice) in a breach of or constitute a default or require any consent under, or result in the creation of any Lien upon the Collateral pursuant to, the terms of any judgment, award, order, injunction, determination, direction, demand, writ, or decree of any court or Governmental Body (collectively "Order"), credit agreement, indenture, mortgage, purchase agreement, deed of trust, security agreement, guarantee, or other instrument to which Borrower is a party or by which Borrower may be bound or to which any of its property may be subject.

12.4 Transaction Document Binding Nature

This Master Agreement, and, as of each Loan Closing Date when executed and delivered by Borrower, each Note, and Loan Agreement is a legal, valid, and binding obligation of Borrower enforceable in accordance with its respective terms, except as limited by bankruptcy, insolvency, reorganization, moratorium, or other similar law or equitable principles relating to or affecting the enforcement of creditor's rights in general and subject to general principles of equity.

12.5 Binding Equipment Lease

As of the applicable Loan Closing Date, each Equipment Lease constitutes the legal, valid, and binding obligation of the respective Lessee, enforceable against such Lessee in accordance with its terms thereof, except as limited by bankruptcy, insolvency, reorganization, moratorium, or other similar law or equitable principles relating to or affecting the enforcement of creditor's rights in general and subject to general principles of equity.

12.6 No Financial Change

No material adverse change in the business or the financial condition of Borrower, or as of the applicable Loan Closing Date with respect to the applicable Lessee, shall have occurred and be continuing since the respective dates of the most recent financial statements and other credit information furnished by each of them to Lender.

12.7 No Adverse Proceedings

There is no action, suit, investigation, or proceeding (whether or not purportedly on behalf of Borrower) pending or, to Borrower's knowledge, threatened against or affecting Borrower or any of its assets in any court or before any arbitrator or before and/or by any federal, state, municipal, or other governmental department, commission, board, bureau, agency, or instrumentally, domestic or foreign (collectively, "Governmental Body"), (a) which involves any of the Equipment or any of the transactions contemplated by this Master Agreement, any Loan Agreement, Note, or Equipment Lease or (b) which, if adversely determined, would have a material adverse effect upon the financial condition, business, or operations of Borrower or upon the transactions contemplated by this Master Agreement, any Loan Agreement, Note, or Equipment Lease, and Borrower is not in material default with respect to any material Order of any Court, arbitrator, or Governmental Body.

12.8 Sales, Use, Property Taxes

All sales, use, property or other taxes, licenses, tolls, inspection or other fees, bonds, permits, or certificates which were or may be required to be paid or obtained in connection with the acquisition by Borrower of the Equipment or its subsequent lease to each applicable Lessee will have been, or when due will be, paid in full or obtained, as the case may be.

12.9 Good, Valid, and Marketable Title

Borrower has good, valid, and marketable title to the Collateral free and clear of all liens, claims, and encumbrances, except for (i) the rights of the Lessee as user of the applicable Equipment in accordance with the terms of each applicable Equipment Lease, and (ii) the liens, claims, and encumbrances in favor of Lender created by each Loan Agreement.

12.10. Perfected Security Interest

At the time each Loan is made, Lender will have a perfected continuing first priority security interest in and to all of the applicable Loan Collateral.

12.11 Tax Return Filings

Borrower has as of the date of execution of this Master Agreement, and as of each Loan Closing Date will have, filed all required tax returns in all jurisdictions in which such returns were required to be filed and has paid, or made provision for, all material taxes shown to be due and payable on such returns and all other material taxes and assessments that are payable by it, except for any taxes and assessments of which the amount, applicability, or validity is currently being contested in good faith and as to which any adverse determination in excess of any accruals to reflect potential liability would not materially adversely affect its ability to perform its obligations under this Master Agreement, any Loan Agreement, Note, or Equipment Lease.

12.12 Equipment Lease Counterparts

Any counterpart of any Equipment Lease which has not been delivered to Lender bears the following legend on the face and signature pages thereof: "Counterpart No. ________ of ____________________ manually executed counterparts. Only the manually executed counterpart numbered 1 is sufficient to transfer Lessor's interest, or to grant a security interest herein." Each such counterpart also bears a legend on the face and signature pages thereof specifying Lender as the assignee of the Equipment Lease.

12.13 Equipment Lease Statements Correct

All amounts, statements, and conditions of fact stated in each Equipment Lease are true and correct;

12.14 Lease Performance

As of each applicable Loan Closing Date, Borrower, and to the best of Borrower's knowledge, each Lessee, have performed and observed each term, provision, covenant, and condition contained in the applicable Equipment Lease to be performed or observed by Borrower, as lessor, and as lessee, respectively, up to and including such Loan Closing Date.

12.15 Entire Lease Agreement

As of each Loan Closing Date, each applicable Equipment Lease constitutes the entire agreement of Borrower and the applicable Lessee with respect to the Equipment and the lease thereof, and has not been amended, supplemented, or otherwise modified in any manner, and Borrower has not entered into any understanding or agreement (oral or in writing), relating to the Equipment, or to such Equipment Lease, the transactions contemplated thereby, or any other transactions contemplated or permitted by this Master Agreement or any applicable Loan Agreement, or Note, with any person or entity.

12.16 No Assignment

As of each Loan Closing Date Borrower has not theretofore alienated, assigned, granted a security interest in, or otherwise disposed of any interest in each applicable Equipment Lease, amounts due Lender or to become due Lender thereunder, Borrower's leasehold interest or the applicable Equipment.

12.17 No Defense; Setoff

As of each Loan Closing Date, there are no defenses, setoffs, or counterclaims which each applicable Lessee has, or may have, in connection with the applicable Equipment Lease, or, any such defense, claim, or setoff on the part of any entity in connection with any of the obligations set forth in such Equipment Lease, or of any event which with the passage of time or giving of notice or both would constitute a default with respect to any of the foregoing.

12.18 Borrower's Place of Business

The chief place of business and the chief executive office of Borrower and the office where Borrower keeps its records relating to the Collateral, is located at the address set forth in Section 19 hereof;

Section 13. Covenants of Borrower

Borrower covenants and agrees that from and after the date hereof and so long as any of the Secured Obligations are outstanding:

13.1 Loan Proceeds Use

The proceeds of each Loan will be used exclusively for commercial or business purposes to finance the acquisition of Equipment for which the Loan has been provided under a Loan Agreement.

13.2 Notices

Borrower will promptly give written notice to Lender of (i) the occurrence of any Event of Default or of any event which with notice, lapse of time, or both would constitute an Event of Default, of which it has knowledge, (ii) the occurrence of any Event of Loss of which it has knowledge, and (iii) the commencement or threat of any material litigation or other proceedings affecting Borrower or any Lessee or any other entity that involves any of the Collateral that might materially interfere with the normal business operations of Borrower or any Lessee.

13.3 Lessee Communications

Borrower will promptly deliver, no later than five (5) days after receipt thereof, to Lender a copy of each communication received from each Lessee with respect to each Equipment Lease or the transactions contemplated thereby.

13.4 Compliance With Laws; Corporate Existence; Governmental Approvals

Borrower will (i) duly observe and conform to all valid requirements of governmental authorities necessary to the performance of its obligations under this Master Agreement and each Loan Agreement, Note, and Equipment Lease, (ii) maintain its corporate existence and obtain and keep in full force and effect all rights, franchises, licenses, and permits which are necessary to the proper conduct of its business, and (iii) obtain or cause to be obtained as promptly as possible any governmental, administrative, or agency approval and make any filing or registration therewith which shall be required with respect to the performance of its obligations under this Master Agreement, and each Loan Agreement, Note, and Equipment Lease.

13.5 Performance of Equipment Leases

Borrower will duly observe and perform all covenants and obligations to be performed by it under each Equipment Lease and, subject to Section 13.10 hereof, will promptly take any and all action as may be necessary to enforce its rights under each such Equipment Lease or to secure the performance by the applicable Lessee of such Lessee's obligations under such Equipment Lease.

13.6 Equipment Location Change

Borrower shall cause the Equipment to be used solely by each Lessee in accordance with the terms of the applicable Equipment Lease, and shall not consent to a change in the location of any Item of Equipment as specified in the applicable Equipment Lease, without the prior written consent of Lender.

13.7 Equipment Insurance

Borrower shall cause each Lessee to provide insurance coverage with respect to the applicable Equipment in accordance with the terms of the applicable Equipment Lease; shall further cause each such Lessee to cause such insurance to be endorsed to provide that losses, if any, shall be payable to Borrower, Lender, and such Lessee, as their interest may appear; shall further cause it to be further endorsed to provide that such insurer will give Lender thirty (30) days' prior written notice of the effective date of any material alteration or cancellation or nonrenewal of any such policy; shall further cause it to provide that all provisions of such policy, except the limits of liability, will operate in the same manner as if there were a separate policy governing such additional insured; shall further cause it to provide that as to Lender's interest, such insurance shall not be invalidated by reason of any breach of representation or violation of warranty by Lessee to the insurer in connection with obtaining such policy to insurance or maintaining the same in full force and effect; and shall further cause such insurance to meet such other reasonable requirements as Lender may request from time to time.

13.8 Security Interest Filing Costs

Borrower will pay, or reimburse Lender for, any and all fees, costs, and expenses of whatever kind or nature incurred in connection with the creation, preservation, and protection of Lender's security interests in the Collateral, including, without limitation, all fees and taxes in connection with the recording or filing of instruments and documents in public offices, payment or discharge of any taxes or Liens of any nature upon or in respect of the Collateral, premiums for insurance with respect to the Collateral and all other fees, costs, and expenses in connection with protecting, maintaining, or preserving the Collateral and Lender's interests therein, whether through judicial proceedings or otherwise, or in defending or prosecuting any actions, suits, or proceedings arising out of or related to the Collateral; and all such amounts that are paid by Lender shall, until reimbursed by Borrower, constitute Secured Obligations of Borrower secured by the Collateral.

13.9 No Liens

Borrower will not create, assume, or suffer to exist any Lien of any kind upon any of the Collateral, of or by any individual (or association of individuals), entity or governmental instrumentality, claimed or asserted against, through or under Borrower, except the interest granted hereby to Lender, and any Liens expressly permitted by Lender pursuant to Section 11 hereof, and Borrower shall promptly notify, no later than five (5) days after the receipt thereof, Lender upon the receipt of any Lien, or judicial proceeding affecting any Equipment in whole or in part, and Borrower shall cause Lessee to maintain the Equipment free from all Liens, and legal processes of Lessee.

13.10 Restriction on Equipment Lease Actions

Borrower will not, without the prior written consent of Lender, declare a default under any Equipment Lease, exercise any remedies under any Equipment Lease or enter into or consent to or permit any cancellation, termination, amendment, supplement or modification of or waiver with respect to any Equipment Lease, and any such attempted declaration, exercise, cancellation, termination, amendment, supplement, modification, or waiver shall be void and of no effect.

13.11 Change in Office Location

Borrower will not change its principal place of business or chief executive office or remove its books and records concerning the Collateral from the address set forth in

Section 19 hereof unless it shall have given at least thirty (30) days' prior written notice of such change or removal to Lender, specifying the new address.

13.12 Further Assurances

Borrower will promptly, at any time and from time to time, at its sole expense, execute and deliver to Lender such further instruments and documents, and take such further action, as Lender may from time to time reasonably request in order to carry out the intent and purpose of this Master Agreement, and each Loan Agreement, Note, and Equipment Lease and to establish and protect the rights, interests, and remedies created, or intended to be created, in favor of Lender hereby and thereby, including, without limitation, the execution, delivery, recordation, and filing of financing statements and continuation statements with respect to the Collateral. Borrower hereby authorizes Lender, in such jurisdictions where such action is authorized or permitted by law, to effect any such recordation or filing without the signature of Borrower thereto, and Lender's expenses with respect thereto shall be payable by Borrower on demand.

13.13 Indemnification

Without limiting the generality of any other provision hereof, Borrower shall indemnify, protect, save, and keep harmless Lender from and against any reduction in the amount payable out of the Collateral to Lender with respect to the Secured Obligations, or any other loss, cost, or expense (including legal fees) incurred by Lender, as the result of Borrower's breach of Section 13.9 hereof.

Section 14. Indemnity

14.1 Fees, Assessments, and Taxes

Borrower agrees to pay when due, and to indemnify and hold Lender harmless from all license, filing and registration fees and assessments, and all sales, use, property, excise, and other taxes and charges (other than those measured by Lender's net income) now or hereafter imposed by any Governmental Body upon or with respect to (i) this Master Agreement, or any Loan Agreement, Note, or Equipment Lease, or the creation and continued perfection of the security interest created hereby or thereby, and (ii) any of the Collateral, including without limitation the use, possession, ownership, and operation of any of the Equipment.

14.2 Equipment Operation and Use Expenses

Borrower hereby assumes liability for, and indemnifies and holds Lender harmless against, all claims, costs, expenses (including reasonable legal fees), damages, and liabilities arising from or pertaining to the manufacture, assembly, installation, use, operation or sale, or disposition of, or in any way relating to, the Equipment or any interest therein.

14.3 Lawsuit Costs

Without limiting the generality of the foregoing, Borrower hereby agrees that in any suit, proceeding, or action brought by Lender under any Equipment Lease for any sum owing thereunder, or to enforce any provision thereof, Borrower will save, indemnify, and keep Lender harmless from and against all expense, loss, or damage suffered by reason of any defense, setoff, counterclaim, recoupment, or reduction of liability whatsoever of Lessee, arising out of a breach by Borrower of any obligation under such Equipment Lease or arising out of any other agreement, indebtedness, or liability at any time owing to or in favor of Lessee from Borrower.

14.4 Survival

The indemnities set forth in this Section 14 shall survive the expiration or earlier termination of this Master Agreement and each Loan Agreement, Note, and Equipment Lease with respect to acts or events occurring or alleged to have occurred prior to such expiration or earlier termination.

Section 15. Events of Default

During the Term of this Master Agreement, the occurrence of any of the following events shall constitute an "Event of Default":

15.1 Nonpayment

Borrower fails to pay, or cause to be paid, any amount owing pursuant to this Master Agreement, any Loan Agreement, or Note, including, but not limited to the principal or interest of any Note, when due (whether at the stated maturity, by acceleration or otherwise), and such failure shall continue for a period of ten (10) days.

15.2 Nonperformance

Borrower disaffirms or fails to perform or observe any other covenant, agreement, obligation, or undertaking under this Master Agreement or under any Loan Agreement, Note, or any Equipment Lease, or under any agreement contemplated hereby or thereby to which Borrower is a party, or under any other agreement or document given to evidence or secure any of the Secured Obligations, and such failure shall continue for a period of thirty (30) days.

15.3 Event of Default Occurrence

If an event of default (as therein defined) occurs under any Equipment Lease or a default by any Lessee of its obligations under its Lessee Consent occurs.

15.4 Breach of Representation or Warranty

Any representation or warranty, made by Borrower in connection with any transaction contemplated by this Master Agreement, any Loan Agreement, or any Note, whether contained in any Equipment Lease, any related document, in this Master Agreement, in any Loan Agreement, in any Note, or in any certificate or other related document delivered to Lender in connection herewith or therewith, shall prove to be incorrect or untrue in any material respect.

15.5 Bankruptcy Proceedings

Borrower institutes proceedings to be adjudicated a bankrupt or insolvent, or consents to the institution of bankruptcy or insolvency proceedings against it, or commences a voluntary proceeding or case under any applicable federal or state bankruptcy, insolvency, or other similar law, or consents to the filing of any such petition or to the appointment of or taking possession by a receiver, liquidator, assignee, trustee, custodian, or sequestrator (or other similar official) of Borrower or of any substantial part of its property, or makes any assignment for the benefit of creditors or the admission by it of its inability to pay its debts generally as they become due or becomes willing to be adjudicated a bankrupt or fails generally to pay its debts as they become due or takes any corporate action in furtherance of any of the foregoing or Borrower shall file any such proceeding, or any execution or writ of process shall be issued under any proceeding whereby any Item of Equipment may be taken or restrained.

15.6 Entered Decree or Order

A decree or order is entered for relief by a court having jurisdiction in respect of Borrower adjudging the Borrower a bankrupt or insolvent, or approving as properly filed a petition seeking a reorganization, arrangement, adjustment or composition of or in respect of Borrower in an involuntary proceeding or case under any applicable federal or state bankruptcy, insolvency, or other similar law, or appointing a receiver, liquidator, or assignee, custodian, trustee, or sequestrator (or similar official) of Borrower or of any substantial part of its property, or ordering the winding-up or liquidation of its affairs, and the continuance of any such decree or order unstayed and in effect for a period of thirty (30) days.

15.7 Business Cessation

Borrower shall cease doing business as a going concern or shall be dissolved.

Section 16. Remedies

Upon the occurrence of an Event of Default, and so long as such Event of Default shall be continuing, Lender may, at its option, declare this Master Agreement and/or any or all Loan Agreements in default (herein referred to as a "Default") and may exercise, at its option, one or more of the following remedies:

16.1 Right of Acceleration

Lender may accelerate the full amount of any or all of the then outstanding Secured Obligations in which event such amounts will become immediately due and payable by the Borrower without presentment, demand, protest, or other notice of any kind, all of which are hereby expressly waived, and Lender may thereafter pursue any or all of the rights and remedies with respect to the Collateral accruing to Lender thereunder or by operation of law as a secured creditor under the Code or other applicable law, as it may elect in its sole discretion, and all such available rights and remedies, to the full extent permitted by the law, shall be cumulative and not exclusive.

16.2 Additional Remedies

If an Event of Default shall occur and be continuing, Lender may exercise in addition to all other rights and remedies granted to it in this Master Agreement, in any Loan Agreement, Note, or Equipment Lease and in any other instrument or agreement securing, evidencing, or relating to the Secured Obligations, all rights and remedies of secured parties under the Code or under any other applicable law. Without limiting the generality of the foregoing, Borrower agrees that in any such event, Lender, without demand of performance or other demand, advertisement, or notice of any kind (except the notice specified below of time and place of public or private sale) to or upon Borrower or any other person (all and each of which demands, advertisements, and/or notices are hereby expressly waived), may forthwith collect, receive, appropriate, and realize upon the Collateral, or any part thereof, and may take possession of (subject to the right of quiet enjoyment with respect to any Lessee pursuant to Section 17 hereof) any or all Equipment or any part thereof and/or may forthwith sell, lease, assign, give option or options to purchase, or otherwise dispose of and deliver the Collateral (or contract to do so), or any part thereof, in one or more parcels at public or private sale or sales, at any exchange or broker's board or at any of Lender's offices or elsewhere at such prices as it may deem best, for cash or on credit or for future delivery without assumption of any credit risk. Lender shall have the right upon any such public sale or sales, and, to the extent permitted by law, upon any such private sale or sales, to purchase the whole or any part of the Collateral so sold, free of any right or equity of redemption in Borrower, which right or equity is hereby expressly waived or released to the extent permitted by law. Borrower further agrees (subject to the right of quiet enjoyment with respect to any Lessee pursuant to Section 17 hereof), at Lender's request, to assemble the Collateral, make it available to Lender at places which Lender shall reasonably select, whether at Borrower's premises or elsewhere. Lender shall apply the net proceeds of any such collection, recovery, receipt, appropriation, realization, and/or sale (after deducting all costs and expenses of every kind incurred therein or incidental to the care, safekeeping, or otherwise of any or all of the Collateral or in any way relating to the rights of Lender thereunder, including attorney's fees and legal expenses) to the payment in whole or in part of the Secured Obligations, in such order as Lender may elect and only after so applying such net proceeds and after the payment by Lender of any other amount required by any provision of law, need Lender account for the surplus, if any, to Borrower. To the extent permitted by applicable law, Borrower waives all claims, damages, and demands against Lender arising out of the repossession, retention, or sale of the Collateral, including any costs of valuation and/or appraisal of the Collateral or any part thereof. Borrower agrees that Lender need not give more than ten (10) days' prior written notice (which notification shall be deemed given when mailed, postage prepaid, addressed to Borrower at its address set forth in Section 19 hereof) of the time and place of any public sale or of the time after which a private sale may take place and that such notice is reasonable notification of such matters.

16.3 Lease Action

If an Event of Default referred to in Section 15.3 shall occur and be continuing, Lender (as assignee of Borrower) may declare the applicable Equipment Lease to be in default and may exercise all rights, powers, and remedies of Borrower under the applicable section of such Equipment Lease, either in Lender's own name or in the name of Borrower for the use and benefit of Lender.

16.4 Waiver of Presentment

Borrower hereby waives presentment, demand, protest, and (to the extent permitted by applicable law) notice of any kind in connection with this Master Agreement, each Loan Agreement, each Note, or any Collateral.

16.5 Rights, Powers, and Remedies Cumulative

All rights, powers, and remedies herein specifically given to Lender shall be cumulative and shall be in addition to all other rights, powers, and remedies herein specifically given or now or hereafter existing at law, in equity or by statue, and all rights, powers, and remedies whether specifically given herein or otherwise existing may be exercised from time to time and as often and in such order as may be deemed expedient by Lender and the exercise or the beginning of the exercise of any power or remedy shall not be construed to be a waiver of the waiver of the right to exercise at the same time or at any other time any other right, power, or remedy. No delay or omission by Lender in the exercise of any right, remedy, or power, or in the pursuance of any right, remedy, or power shall impair any such right, power, or remedy or be construed to be a waiver of any Event of Default on the part of Lender.

16.6 Discontinuance of Proceeding

In case Lender shall have proceeded to enforce any right, power, or remedy under, or arising out of, or in connection with, this Master Agreement, any Loan Agreement, Note, Equipment Lease or any other related agreement, document, by foreclosure, entry, or otherwise, any such proceeding or any portion thereof shall have been discontinued or abandoned for any reason or shall have been determined adversely to Lender, then and in every such case Borrower and Lender shall be restored to their former position and rights hereunder or thereunder with respect to the Collateral subject to such proceeding or portion thereof, and all rights, remedies, and powers of Lender shall continue as if no such proceeding or portion thereof had been taken.

Section 17. Lessee Quiet Enjoyment Right

So long as a Lessee is not in default of its obligations under the applicable Equipment Lease or of its obligations to Lender under the applicable Lessee Consent, Lender will not interfere with the Lessee's peaceful use and enjoyment of the applicable Equipment for its intended purposes as provided for by the terms of such Equipment Lease.

Section 18. Receipt of Funds by Borrower

Should Borrower, notwithstanding the assignment of the Equipment Leases and the granting to Lender of a first priority security interest in and to the Collateral, at any time while any of the Secured Obligations remain unsatisfied, receive any amount representing funds due, or proceeds of, any of the Collateral, such sums shall be held by Borrower in trust for Lender, shall be segregated from other funds of Borrower, and shall be immediately paid by Borrower to Lender in the form so received, together with any necessary endorsement thereon.

Section 19. Notices

Any notice or document or payment to be delivered thereunder to any of the persons designated below, except as otherwise expressly provided herein, shall be deemed to have been properly delivered if delivered personally or deposited with the United States Postal Service, registered or certified mail, return receipt requested, postage prepaid, to the following respective addresses:

If to Borrower:

If to Lender:

or such other address as may be furnished from time to time by any of the parties hereto upon at least thirty (30) days' prior written notice.

Section 20. Payment of Expenses and Taxes

Borrower agrees, whether or not the transactions contemplated by this Master Agreement and each Loan Agreement shall be consummated, to pay (i) all costs and expenses of Lender in connection with the negotiation, preparation, execution, and delivery of this Master Agreement, and the other documents relating hereto, including, without limitation, the reasonable fees and disbursements of counsel to Lender; (ii) all fees and taxes in connection with the recording of this Master Agreement and any Loan Agreement or Note or any other document or instrument required hereby; and (iii) all costs and expenses of Lender in connection with the enforcement of this Master Agreement, and each Loan Agreement and each Note, including all legal fees and disbursements arising in connection therewith. Borrower also agrees to pay, and to indemnify and save Lender harmless from any delay in paying, all taxes, including without limitation, sales, use, stamp, and personal property taxes (other than any corporate income, capital, franchise, or similar taxes payable by Lender with respect to the payments made to Lender hereunder and all license, filing, and registration fees and assessments and other charges, if any, which may be payable or determined to be payable in connection with the execution, delivery, and performance of this Master Agreement, each Loan Agreement, and each Note or any modification thereof.

Section 21. Performance by Lender of Borrower's Obligations

If Borrower fails to perform or comply with any of its agreements contained herein, or in any Loan Agreement or document related hereto or thereto, and Lender shall itself perform or comply, or otherwise cause performance or compliance, with such agreement, the expenses of Lender incurred in connection with such performance or compliance, together with interest thereon at the Overdue Rate provided for in the applicable Loan Agreement, shall be payable by Borrower to Lender on demand and until such payment shall constitute Secured Obligations secured hereby.

Section 22. Loan Request Right Termination

Without affecting any of Lender's rights, or Borrower's duties, obligations, or liabilities, under this Master Agreement, or any Loan Agreement, or Note, Lender may terminate Borrower's future right to submit Loan Requests pursuant to Section 2 of this Master Agreement, with or without cause, by sending a written notice to that effect to Borrower at Borrower's address specified in Section 19.

Section 23. Miscellaneous

23.1 Survival of Representations and Warranties

All representations and warranties made in, or pursuant to, this Master Agreement, any Loan Agreement, or Note and any documents, instruments, or certificates delivered pursuant hereto or thereto (collectively herein referred to as "Documents") shall survive the execution and delivery of the Documents, and the making of the Loans thereunder, and the agreements contained in Section 20 hereof, shall survive payment of the Notes until all obligations of Borrower to Lender are satisfied in full.

23.2 Modification, Waiver, and Consent

Any modification or waiver of any provision of this Master Agreement, any Loan Agreement, or Note, nor any terms hereof or thereof, or any consent to any departure by Lender or Borrower, as the case may be, therefrom, shall not be effective in any event unless the same is in writing and signed by the party to be charged, and then such modification, waiver, or consent shall be effective only in the specific instance and for the specific purpose given.

23.3 Headings

The headings of the Sections and Subsections are for convenience only, are not part of this Master Agreement and shall not be deemed to affect the meaning or construction of any of the provisions hereof.

23.4 Binding Effect

This Master Agreement and each Loan Agreement, and Note shall be binding upon and inure to the benefit of Borrower and Lender and their permitted respective successors and assigns.

23.5 Complete Statement of Rights

This Master Agreement, and each Loan Agreement, exclusively and completely states the rights and agreements with respect to the subject matter hereof and thereof, and supersedes all other agreements, oral or written, with respect thereto.

23.6 Law Governing

The terms and provisions of this Master Agreement, each Loan Agreement, and each Note and all rights and obligations thereunder shall be governed in all respects by the laws of the State of New York.

23.7 Construction

Any provision contained in this Master Agreement, in any Loan Agreement, or in any Note, or in any agreement or document delivered in connection therewith, or related thereto, which is prohibited or unenforceable in any jurisdiction shall, as to such jurisdiction, be ineffective to the extent of such prohibition or unenforceability without invalidating the remaining provisions hereof, and any such prohibition or unenforceability shall not invalidate or render unenforceable such provision in any other jurisdiction. To the extent permitted by law, Borrower hereby waives any provision of law which renders any provision hereof prohibited or unenforceable in any respect. A waiver by Lender of any right or remedy in any one instance shall not operate as a waiver of such right or remedy in any other instance, and a waiver by Lender of any breach of the terms hereof or Event of Default thereunder shall not be a waiver of any additional or subsequent breach or Event of Default.

23.8 Execution in Counterparts

This Master Agreement and each Loan Agreement may be executed by the parties hereto in any number of separate counterparts, each of which when so executed and delivered shall be an original, but all such counterparts shall together constitute but one and the same instrument.

IN WITNESS WHEREOF, Borrower and Lender have caused this Master Agreement to be executed on their behalf by their duly authorized representatives as of the day and year first above written.

____

Lender

By: ________________________________

Title: ______________________________

____

Borrower

By: ________________________________

Title: ______________________________

Form: I-07a
Disk File Name: I-07a.rtf

LOAN SUPPLEMENT

Form Purpose

A loan supplement to be used in connection with a master equipment security and loan agreement. This form is integrated with Loan and Security Agreement, Form I-07.

Executing Parties

The borrower.
The lender.

See:
Loan and Security Agreement, Form I-07

Exhibit A

Loan Supplement

Loan Supplement No. _____ ("Loan Supplement")
Dated as of ______________________________, XXXX

to Master Loan and Security Agreement,
("Master Agreement")
Dated as of ______________________________, XXXX

between
______________________________ ("Lender")
and
______________________________ ("Borrower")

1. Incorporation by Reference of Master Agreement

The Master Agreement and all documentation attached thereto, or delivered in connection therewith, or pursuant to thereto, including all terms and conditions thereof, are specifically incorporated herein by reference, and made a part hereof, as if set forth at length herein, as the same may from time to time be amended, supplemented, or otherwise modified. This Loan Supplement shall be considered a separate and enforceable agreement incorporating the terms and conditions of the Master Security Agreement and all documentation attached thereto, or delivered in connection therewith, or pursuant to thereto, and is referred to as a Loan Agreement.

2. Lessee

[Insert name]

3. Lessee Guarantor

[Insert name]

4. Description of Equipment Lease

[Insert description]

5. Equipment Description:

Qty. Manufacturer Model New/Used Description Install. Location I.D./Ser. # Purchase Cost Per Item Aggregate

[Insert description]

Total Equipment Cost $ ______________

6. Loan Principal Amount

The Principal Amount of the Loan to be extended pursuant to this Loan Supplement shall not be equal to $ ______________, but in no event shall it be less than $ ______________, nor shall it be greater than $ ______________, and shall be evidenced by a Note.

7. Loan Commencement Date

The Loan Commencement Date for the Note shall be the Loan Closing Date.

8. Loan Term

8.1 Primary Term

The Primary Loan Term shall commence on the Loan Closing Date, unless the Loan Closing Date shall not fall on the 1st day of a month, in which case the Primary Loan Term shall commence on the 1st day of the month immediately following the Loan Closing Date, and shall end on the anniversary date thereof ________ years thereafter.

8.2. Interim Term

If the Loan Closing Date does not fall on the 1st day of a month, there shall be an Interim Loan Term.

9. Loan Payment Dates

The Loan Payment Dates with respect to the Loan shall be the ________ day of each ____________ during the Loan Term, and, in the event there is an Interim Term, any Interim Loan Payment shall be made on the Loan Closing Date, all payments to be payable in lawful money of the United States and in immediately available funds.

10. Loan Interest Rate

10.1 Loan Interest Rate

The Note shall bear interest during the Primary Loan Term at a per annum interest rate equal to ____ % (calculated on the basis of a 360-day year and 30-day month).

10.2 Interim Loan Term Interest

The Note shall bear interest during any Interim Loan Term at an interest rate equal to the daily equivalent of the Primary Loan Term Interest Rate.

11. Loan Amortization Schedule

Attached hereto as Annex A is the Loan Amortization Schedule.

12. Loan Proceeds Instructions

Lender shall pay to Borrower the Principal Amount of the Loan by electronic wire transfer in accordance with written wire instructions from Borrower submitted prior to the Loan Closing Date.

13. Cutoff Date

Lender shall not be obligated to make the Loan provided for in this Loan Supplement unless the Loan Closing Date occurs on or before ________________________, 19 ____.

14. Loan Fee

15. Overdue Rate

The Overdue Rate (calculated on the basis of a 360-day year and 30-day month) for the Note shall be a per annum amount equal to two percent (2%) above the Prime Rate (not to exceed, however, the highest rate permitted by applicable law).

16. Loan Prepayment

16.1 Mandatory Prepayment in the Event of Loss

16.1.1 *Event of Loss Prepayment.* In the event that the Equipment or any item thereof subject to this Loan Supplement shall be lost, stolen, destroyed, damaged beyond repair, or rendered permanently unfit for normal use for any reason, or in the event of any condemnation, confiscation, seizure, or requisition of title to or use of any Item of Equipment as to result in the Lessee's loss of possession or use, or the Item of Equipment shall be deemed to have incurred a casualty loss under the applicable Equipment Lease (each of the foregoing being hereinafter called a "Event of Loss"), provided that Lessee is not replacing such Item of Equipment pursuant to any provisions permitting such replacement in the applicable Equipment Lease, Borrower shall make a prepayment on the Note in an amount equal to the sum of:

(i) that proportionate share of the then outstanding Principal Amount of such Note determined by multiplying the outstanding Principal Amount by a fraction, the numerator of which is the Borrower's Purchase Cost of the Item(s) of Equipment which was the subject of the Event of Loss and the denominator of which is the Total Equipment Cost of all Items of Equipment covered by the Loan Supplement to which the Note corresponds;

(ii) all accrued interest, late charges, if any, and any other sums which may be due Lender with respect to the Item(s) of Equipment which was the subject of the Event of Loss, to the date of such payment; and

(iii) a casualty prepayment fee equal to the product of (x) the principal amount prepaid and (y) the product obtained by multiplying 10% by a fraction, the numerator of which will be the number of installment payment dates with respect to such Note remaining after such date of prepayment (including the installment payment date on which such prepayment is made) and the denominator of which shall be the total number of installment payment dates with respect to such Note.

16.1.2 Mandatory Early Lease Termination Prepayment

[If an Early Equipment Lease termination is permitted, this subsection will incorporate the appropriate mandatory Note prepayment provision.]

17. Representations and Warranties

Borrower represents and warrants that:

(a) Its representations and warranties contained in Section 12 of the Master Agreement are true and accurate on and as of the date of this Loan Supplement as though made on and as of such date.

(b) It is not in Default under any of the terms, covenants, agreements, or other provisions of any Loan Agreement, Note, or Equipment Lease, or the Master Agreement, and no Event of Default, or event which with notice, lapse of time, or the happening of any further condition, event, or act would constitute an Event of Default shall have occurred and is continuing thereunder.

18. Term Definitions

The terms used in this Loan Supplement, where not defined herein to the contrary, shall have the same meanings as defined in the Master Agreement.

____

Lender

By: ____________________________

Title: ___________________________

____

Borrower

By: ____________________________

Title: ___________________________

Annex A
to
Loan Supplement No. ________________

Loan Amortization Schedule

(values to be inserted)

Exhibit B

Form of Promissory Note

[see Form 1-07b]

Exhibit C

Acknowledgment and Consent to Assignment of Equipment Lease

[see Form 1-07c]

Exhibit D

Supplement

[see Form 1-07d]

Form: I-07b
Disk File Name: I-07b.rtf

PROMISSORY NOTE

Form Purpose

A promissory note to be used in connection with a master equipment loan and security agreement. This form is integrated with Loan and Security Agreement, Form I-07.

Executing Parties

The borrower.

See:

Loan and Security Agreement, Form I-07

Exhibit B

Form of Promissory Note

New York, New York

$ ______________________, XXXX.

FOR VALUE RECEIVED, ______________________ ("the Undersigned") promises to pay to the order of ______________________ ("Lender") at its office at ______________________ in lawful money of the United States, the principal sum of ______________________ DOLLARS ($ __________) and to pay interest in like money on the unpaid principal amount thereof to maturity at the rate of interest of __________ percent (______%) per annum, computed on the basis of 360-day year consisting of twelve 30-day months. The principal and interest shall be paid in ______ equal consecutive installments of principal and interest, each in the amount of $ ______________, in accordance with the attached Loan Amortization Schedule. The first of such installments shall be due on ______________, and each of the remaining installments shall be due on the same day of each ______________ thereafter, continuing through ______________. Each installment of principal shall bear interest from and after the date due through the date payment is received by Lender at ____ %.

This Note is one of the Notes referred to in, and is issued pursuant to, a Loan Supplement, dated as of ______________, XXXX, (the "Loan Supplement") by and between the Undersigned and Lender, which Loan Supplement incorporates by reference the terms and conditions of a Master Loan and Security Agreement ("Master Agreement") by and between the Undersigned and Lender, dated as of __________, XXXX (the Loan Supplement and Master Agreement are collectively referred to herein as the "Loan Agreement") and the holder hereof is entitled to the benefits thereof. Terms defined in the Loan Agreement are used with the same meanings herein. This Note is secured as provided in the Loan Agreement, and is subject to prepayment only as provided therein. Reference is herein made to the Loan Agreement for a description of the provisions upon which the Note is issued and secured, and the nature and extent of the security and the rights of the holder hereof.

Upon the occurrence of any one or more of the Events of Default specified in the Loan Agreement, the unpaid principal balance of this Note, together with interest accrued to the date of payment, shall be immediately due and payable without notice or demand, although not yet due in accordance with the terms hereof.

The Undersigned hereby waives presentment, demand for payment, notice of dishonor, and any and all other notices or demands in connection with the delivery, acceptance, performance, default, or enforcement of this Note.

In the event that any holder shall institute any action for the enforcement or collection of this Note, there shall be immediately due and payable, in addition to the then unpaid principal balance hereof and any accrued interest, any late charges and all costs and expenses of such action including attorney's fees. The Undersigned and Lender in any litigation (whether or not relating to this Note) in which Lender and the Undersigned shall be adverse parties, waive trial by jury, and the Undersigned waives the right to interpose any setoff, counterclaim, or defense of any nature whatsoever.

This Note shall be governed by, and construed and interpreted in accordance with, the laws of the State of ________________.

____

Borrower

By: ____________________________

Title: ___________________________

Loan Supplement No. ______

Loan Amortization Schedule

(values to be inserted)

Form: I-07c
Disk File Name: I-07c.rtf

Acknowledgment and Consent to Assignment of Equipment Lease

Form Purpose

An acknowledgment and consent of assignment of an equipment lease agreement to be used in connection with a master equipment security and loan agreement. This form is integrated with Loan and Security Agreement, Form I-07.

Executing Parties

The borrower.
The equipment lender.
The equipment lessee.

See:

Loan and Security Agreement, Form I-07

Exhibit C

Acknowledgment and Consent to Assignment of Equipment Lease

Dated: ______________________________

[Insert name and address of Lender.]

Gentlemen:

Reference is made to that certain Equipment Leasing Agreement dated as of ________ ______________, XXXX (the Equipment Leasing Agreement together with all exhibits, attachments, and schedules thereof, and ancillary and related documents are herein referred to as the "Equipment Lease") between ______________________________ ("Lessor"), as lessor, and ______________________________ (the "Company"), as lessee.

The Company understands that Lessor and ______________________________ ("Lender") have entered into a Master Loan and Security Agreement, dated as of ______________, XXXX (the "Master Agreement"), and a Loan Supplement No. ____ dated as of ______________________________, XXXX, together with all exhibits, attachments, and schedules thereto, and ancillary and related documents thereto (collectively referred to herein as the "Loan Agreement") and that pursuant to the Loan Agreement, Lender shall make one or more loans to Lessor to finance its acquisition of Equipment (as hereinafter defined). In consideration of Lender's financing the acquisition of the Equipment, of the mutual covenants hereinafter set forth, and for other good and valuable consideration, receipt of which is hereby acknowledged, the Company hereby covenants and agrees with Lender as follows:

1. The Company hereby acknowledges and consents to the assignment by Lessor to Lender of all of Lessor's right, title, and interest in, to and under the Equipment Lease, including without limitation the right to receive all remaining rental payments payable under the Equipment Lease and all other monies from time to time payable to or receivable by Lessor under any of the provisions of the Equipment Lease (all such amounts hereinafter referred to as the "Monies"). The items of Equipment subject to the Equipment Lease are referred to hereinafter as the "Equipment".

The Company confirms that as of the date hereof, (a) the remaining term of the Equipment Lease is ______________ months, and the Company's remaining rental obligation thereunder is to pay the sum of $ ______________________________ in ______ consecutive ______________________ installments commencing ______________________ XXXX, and ending ______________________, XXXX, each in the amount of $______________________ exclusive of applicable taxes.

2. The Company hereby represents and warrants that the documents attached hereto as Exhibit A are true and correct copies of the Equipment Lease, that all dates, amounts, equipment descriptions, and other facts set forth therein are correct (and that the rental amounts set forth therein are exclusive of applicable taxes), and that the Equipment is in its possession and control at the addresses shown in the Equipment Lease. Further the Company represents and warrants that there are no agreements between Lessor and the Company relative to the Equipment or the lease thereof other than the Equipment Lease, and this Consent.

3. The Company agrees (i) to remit and deliver all rentals directly to Lender at the above address (or at such other address as may be specified in writing by Lender), ABSOLUTELY AND UNCONDITIONALLY, WITHOUT ABATEMENT, REDUCTION, COUNTERCLAIM, OR OFFSET, and (ii) to promptly deliver copies of all notices and other communications given or made by the Company pursuant to the Equipment Lease to Lender at the address shown above at the time as required for such delivery to Lessor, or other parties, under the Equipment Lease. The Company further agrees that (a) it shall not enter into any agreement amending, modifying, or terminating the Equipment Lease without the prior written consent of Lender, and (b) any such attempted agreement to amend, modify, or terminate the Equipment Lease without such consent shall be void.

4. Without limiting the generality of clause (i) of Paragraph 3 above, the Company hereby expressly affirms its understanding that notwithstanding any breach of or default under the Equipment Lease by Lessor, that the Company's obligations under the Equipment Lease are absolute and unconditional, and that the Company's recourse for any such breach by Lessor is solely against Lessor.

5. The Company hereby affirms that all representations and warranties made by it in the Equipment Lease are true and correct on the date hereof with the same force and effect as if made on the date hereof, and that Lender may rely upon the same.

6. The Company hereby affirms its understanding that the assignment made by Lessor to Lender is an assignment of rights, benefits, and remedies only and that Lender has not assumed any duties or obligations whatsoever as lessor under the Equipment Lease, and shall not, now or hereafter, have any duty or obligation as lessor under the Equipment Lease, notwithstanding its receipt of Payments due under the Equipment Lease or its exercise of any other rights and/or remedies of "Lessor" thereunder, and the Company hereby agrees that it shall not now or hereafter look to Lender for performance or satisfaction of any such duties or obligations.

7. The Company will furnish to Lender (a) as soon as available, but in any event not later than 120 days after the end of each fiscal year, its (a) consolidated balance sheet as at the end of such fiscal year, and consolidated statements of income and changes in financial position for such fiscal year, all in reasonable detail, prepared in accordance with generally accepted accounting principles applied on a basis consistently maintained throughout the period involved and certified by certified public accountants selected by the Company and acceptable to Lender; (b), if applicable, as soon as available, but in any event not later than 90 days after the end of each of the first three quarterly periods of each fiscal year, the Form 10-Q report filed by Lessee with the Securities and Exchange Commission for such quarterly period, certified by the chief financial officer of Lessee; and (c) promptly, such additional financial and other information as Lender may from time to time reasonably request.

8. Section ____ of the Equipment Lease is hereby amended by adding the following: (*Author's note:* this to be conformed as necessary)

9. The Equipment Lease is hereby amended by deleting Section [____] thereof and substituting the following:

10. The Company agrees to furnish to Lender, before Lender shall make any loan to Lessor pursuant to the terms of the Loan Agreement, (a) the written opinion of counsel for the Company, as to matters contained in paragraphs [______ through ______] inclusive of Lessee's Representations and Warranties set forth in the Equipment Lease, and as to such other matters incident to the transactions contemplated by the Equipment Lease and the Agreement as Lender may request; and (b), if applicable, the Form 10-Q

report filed by lessee with the Securities and Exchange Commission for such quarterly period ending ____________________ XXXX, in form and substance satisfactory to Lender and certified by the chief financial officer of Lessee.

11. The Company hereby affirms that it shall not voluntarily terminate the Equipment Lease for any reason whatsoever.

12. In consideration of the covenants and agreements made by the Company herein, Lender hereby agrees that so long as no Event of Default (as defined in the Equipment Lease) shall have occurred and be continuing, and the Company shall not be in default of its obligations hereunder to Lender, neither Lender nor any party claiming through or under Lender, will disturb the Company's quiet and peaceful possession of the Equipment and its unrestricted use thereof for its intended purpose under the terms of the Equipment Lease.

13. This Consent may not be changed, waived, discharged, or terminated orally, but only by an instrument in writing signed by the party against which enforcement of a change, waiver, discharge, or termination is sought. This Consent shall be binding upon and inure to the benefit of Lender and the Company and their respective successors and assigns. This Consent shall be governed by, and construed and interpreted in accordance with, the laws of the State of New York.

IN WITNESS WHEREOF, the Company has executed this Consent as of the ____ day of ____________, XXXX.

____

Company

By: ____________________________

(Insert name)

Title: __________________________

ACKNOWLEDGED AND AGREED:

____

Lessor

By: ____________________________

(Insert name)

Title: __________________________

____

Lender

By: ____________________________

(Insert name)

Title: __________________________

Form: l-07d
Disk File Name: l-07d.rtf

SUPPLEMENT

Form Purpose

A supplement to be used for individual loan takedowns in connection with a master equipment loan and security agreement. This form is integrated with Loan and Security Agreement, Form l-07.

Executing Parties

The borrower.

See:

Loan and Security Agreement, Form l-07

Exhibit D

Supplement

This Supplement is executed and delivered by ______________________ ("Borrower") pursuant to the terms of a Loan and Security Agreement ("Loan Agreement") dated as of ______________________, XXXX between Borrower and ______________________ ("Lender"). Terms defined in the Loan Agreement shall have the respective meanings given them in the Loan Agreement unless otherwise defined herein or unless the context otherwise requires.

1. Borrower hereby confirms that the proceeds of the Loan made this date shall be used to purchase the items of personal property ("Unit of Equipment") set forth below:

Qty	*Model*	*Mfgrs.*	*Description*	*Serial No.*	*Cost*

[Insert equipment information]

2. Borrower hereby represents and warrants that the above described items of personal property have been delivered to it, duly assembled, and are in good working order at ______________________.

3. Borrower hereby affirms that the representations and warranties set forth in Section 12 of the Loan Agreement are true and correct as of the date hereof.

4. Borrower hereby affirms that Lender has made a Loan to it for the purchase of the above described Unit of Equipment, which loan is evidenced by a Note, in the principal amount of $ ______________ dated ______________, XXXX.

5. Borrower hereby affirms that Lender has a security interest in the items of personal property described above as set forth in Section 9 of the Loan Agreement.

Borrower: ______________________

By: ______________________

Title: ______________________

Marketing Documents—Lessor

[Also see Form o-03.]

Form: m-01
Disk File Name: m-01.rtf

CREDIT APPLICATION

Form Purpose

Equipment leasing company credit approval guideline handout.

Able Leasing Company
Lessee Credit Application

Company Information

Legal Name: ______________________________

Trade Name: ______________________________

Address: ______________________________

____

Telephone Number: (____) ______________

Years in Business: ______________________________

Type of Business (Please Check One):

Proprietorship ____ **Partnership** ____ **Corporation** ____

Description of Business: ______________________________

Reference Credit Information

Bank Reference: ______________________________

Telephone Number: (____) ______________

Account Number: ______________

Contact: ______________________________

Trade Reference: ______________________________

Telephone Number & Contact: ______________________________

Trade Reference: ______________________________

Telephone Number & Contact: ______________________________

Trade Reference: ______________________________

Telephone Number & Contact: ______________________________

Owner Information

Name: ______________________________

Address: ______________________________

Social Security Number: ______________

Equipment Information

Equipment Description: ______________________________

Vendor: ______________________________

Cost: ______________ Term: ______________

Form: m-02
Disk File Name: m-02.rtf

CREDIT GUIDELINES—SMALL TICKET

Form Purpose

Equipment leasing company credit approval guideline handout.

Able Leasing Company
Lessee Credit Approval Guidelines

Your credit worthiness is the most important consideration in the lessor's decision. If you are aware of any credit problem you've had during your period in business, please bring it to our attention so we may work with you to package your financing and have presented in the best possible manner. Chances of a subsequent approval are reduced if a problem is discovered after you've submitted your financing package.

To qualify for financing under the ALC Quick Finance Program, your business must meet the following guidelines. If it does not, please call us to discuss your financing. We may be able to obtain an exception if credit augmentation is possible. Remember, we're here to work to get your business financing needs met.

Able Leasing Company will conduct a preliminary "lease acceptability review" before formally submitting a transaction to our Credit Committee to head off potential problems. Very often issues that could result in a turndown can be addressed to facilitate an approval before the application is submitted.

Guidelines

Minimum Time in Business

You must have a minimum verifiable time in business of two years. Three years is required in the case of applications over $25,000 and four years in the case of applications over $100,000.

Existing Banking Relationship

You must have a business bank relationship of at least two years and the bank account must show a minimum low four figure average balance. In the case of transactions exceeding $25,000, the minimum average account balance must be in the low five figures. There cannot be any overdrafts or check returns for insufficient funds.

Trade References

You must provide three significant business trade references, each of whose relationship goes back at least six months. COD trade references will not be acceptable.

Good Personal Credit

Personal credit reports must be forthcoming that contain no derogatory information.

Financial Statements

Financial statements must be supplied for transactions exceeding $25,000. Current assets must exceed current liabilities and, for transactions in excess of $50,000, a minimum equity of $75,000 must be present.

Form: m-03
Disk File Name: m-03.rtf

FINANCING INSTRUCTIONS—SMALL TICKET

Form Purpose

Equipment leasing company finance instruction handout.

Able Leasing Company
Financing Instructions

Your application for equipment financing can be processed quickly and your financing will be trouble-free, provided you carefully follow the instructions below. If you have any questions, don't guess. Call us and we'll help.

1. Check over the Lessee Credit Approval Guidelines.

If your business qualifies, go to Step 2. If it does not, we will be happy to explore with you any alternatives or credit augmentation in order for you to obtain financing.

2. Fill out, and fax, or mail, us the ALC Credit Application.

The application must be complete or it cannot be processed.

3. Tell us now about any personal or business credit problems.

If you have had, or now have, any credit problem, such as late credit card payments or judgments, describe them on a sheet included along with your credit application.

4. Complete all paperwork carefully.

When your financing is approved, you will receive the necessary paperwork for documenting the financing. Complete it exactly as indicated and return it to us in the return envelope.

5. Fill out and return the equipment lease acceptance form.

When your equipment arrives and you are satisfied that it is operating to your complete satisfaction, fill out and return to us the equipment acceptance-for-lease form included with your financing documentation.

6. Make sure you deliver your financing payments on time.

If you don't, it may damage your credit rating.

____

Able Leasing Company

Fax Number:
Telephone Number:
Address:
24 Hour OnLine HotLine:

Form: m-04
Disk File Name: m-04.rtf

Financing Lease Rate Sheet—Small Ticket

Form Purpose

Equipment leasing company lease rate sheet handout.

Able Leasing Company
Lessee Financing Rates and Terms

The Able Leasing Company lease financing rates and terms are as follows:

*Transaction Size**	*Lease Term*	
	3 Years	*5 Years*
$1,500 to 4,999	____ %	____ %
$5,000 to 24,999	____ %	____ %
$25,000 to 50,000	____ %	____ %

*Financing for transactions in excess of $50,000 will also be available. Various end-of-lease options will be offered, such as fair market and low fixed-price purchase and renewal options, as well as $1 buy-outs. The lease financing interest rates charged will vary with the option chosen; the lowest rates are typically provided by fair market end-of-lease option leases.

Form: m-05
Disk File Name: m-05.rtf

MORTGAGE—INDEMNITY

Form Purpose

A form of mortgage used to secure the obligations of the guarantor of equipment lease agreement obligations.

Executing Parties

The equipment lease guarantor.

See:

Guaranty, Forms g-01 through g-03

Indemnity Mortgage

THIS INDEMNITY MORTGAGE, made this ____ day of ________________, XXXX, by and between ______________________________, (the "Mortgager"), with a place of business at ______________________________ and ______________________________, (the "Mortgagee"), with a place of business at ______________________________.

WITNESSETH:

WHEREAS, Mortgagor has requested Mortgagee, as Lessor, to enter into a Lease or Leases [the "Lease(s)"] with respect to certain specified equipment;

WHEREAS, pursuant to Mortgagor's request, Mortgagee has or will enter into the Leases with certain specified lessees;

WHEREAS, in order to induce Mortgagee to enter into the Leases, Mortgagor, by Guaranty dated ________________, has agreed to guarantee Mortgagee from any loss it may sustain as a result of the Leases, and Mortgagor has agreed to secure the Guaranty by this Mortgage; and

WHEREAS, as a condition precedent to the making of the Leases, Mortgagee has required the execution of this Mortgage for purposes of securing the performance of the terms and conditions of the Indemnity of Mortgagor, and to secure Mortgagee from any loss it may sustain as a result of a Lessee default in any or all of the Leases (the "Mortgage Debt").

NOW, THEREFORE, in consideration of the premises and the sum of One Dollar ($1.00) and other good and valuable considerations, receipt whereof is hereby acknowledged, Mortgagor grants, assigns, and conveys unto Mortgagee, its successors and assigns, all that lot(s) of ground situate in ________________, State of ________________, known as ________________, said lot(s) being more particularly described on Schedule A attached hereto and made a part hereof.

TOGETHER with the building and improvements thereupon and all the rights, roads, alleys, ways, waters, privileges, easements, profits, and appurtenances thereunto belonging or in any wise appertaining, and including any right, title, interest, and estate hereafter acquired by Mortgagor in the Property (defined below) granted herein.

ALSO TOGETHER with and including as part of the buildings and improvements erected on the aforesaid lot of ground all building materials and other chattels on the premises intended to be incorporated in the improvements thereon, and all fixtures, equipment, accessories, and furniture which is attached to or affixed to the buildings and improvements, including kitchen cabinets, hot water heaters, gas and electric ranges, laundry equipment and tubs, medicine cabinets, lighting fixtures, heating plant, air-conditioning equipment, piping, tubing, duct work, radiators, storm windows, storm doors, screens, screen doors, window shades and awnings, all of which fixtures, accessories, and equipment now on or hereafter placed upon the lot or lots of ground are hereby declared to be by Mortgagor fixtures and permanent additions to the realty and intended to be included as part of the lot or lots of ground hereby mortgaged.

TO HAVE AND TO HOLD the said lot or lots of ground, improvements, and other property and rights described above (collectively, the "Property") unto Mortgagee, its successors and assigns, in fee simple.

PROVIDED, that if Mortgagor, their heirs, personal representatives, and assigns, shall cause to be paid the Mortgage Debt and interest thereon from the date hereof, and upon the termination, release, or other voidance of the Leases and payment to Mortgagee of all costs, charges, and expenses in connection therewith, without any loss or further liability on the part of Mortgagor, and shall perform all of the covenants and agreements herein on their part contained, then this Mortgage shall be void.

MORTGAGOR HEREBY COVENANTS:

A. To pay, when due, all ground rents, taxes, water rents, assessments, public and other dues and charges levied or assessed or which may be levied or assessed on the Property; and not to permit any lien or encumbrance on the Property except the lien of this Mortgage, any statutory lien of any kind except liens for taxes and benefit charges not then delinquent, or any lien and/or encumbrance listed on Schedule B attached hereto.

B. To keep the Property in good order, condition, and repair and to permit Mortgagee to enter upon and inspect the same; to make all proper renewals, replacements, and additions of and to the Property; not to permit or suffer any waste thereof; and not to tear down the improvements or materially change them or permit them to be torn down or materially changed, without the written consent of Mortgagee.

C. To keep the Property insured against loss or damage by fire and such other hazards, casualties, and contingencies as may be required from time to time by Mortgagee, such insurance to be written through an agent or broker selected by Mortgagor in such form and in such companies as may be approved by Mortgagee, and in amounts satisfactory to Mortgagee; to cause a standard mortgagee clause satisfactory to Mortgagee to be attached to such policy or policies providing that all payments thereunder shall be made to the order of Mortgagee as its interest may appear, and, at the request of Mortgagee, to deliver such policy or policies and all renewals thereof to Mortgagee at its place of business, or at such other place as it may designate in writing. All sums payable under such policy or policies shall be paid to Mortgagee and all sums received by Mortgagor on account of such policy or policies shall be paid over promptly to Mortgagee and Mortgagee at its discretion, may apply such sums, in whole or in part, to the repair, restoration, and replacement of the damaged or destroyed Property or toward the payment of the mortgage indebtedness. In the event of foreclosure of this Mortgage or other transfer of title to the Property or any parcel thereof in extinguishment of the Mortgage Debt, Mortgagee is authorized to cancel any insurance policy then in force and the unearned premium shall be applied to the payment of any sums due Mortgagee under the terms of this Mortgage.

D. To comply promptly with all laws, ordinances, and regulations affecting the Property or its use.

THE PARTIES HERETO FURTHER COVENANT AND AGREE:

1. Mortgagor warrant specially the Property hereby conveyed and will execute such further assurances thereof as may be requisite.

2. In the event of any default under the terms of this Mortgage or any letter of credit or other documents relating thereto, or in the event a receiver or trustee is appointed for the Property of Mortgagor, or any of them, either in bankruptcy or in equity, or in the event Mortgagor, or any of them, execute a deed of trust of their Property for the benefit of creditors, then the whole Mortgage Debt, at the option of Mortgagee, shall be and become due and payable.

3. It shall be deemed a default under this Mortgage, if, without the written consent of Mortgagee, (a) Mortgagor shall sell, cease to own, assign, transfer, or dispose of all or any part of the mortgaged Property, or (b) the mortgaged Property is abandoned.

4. In the event of any default in any of the covenants of this Mortgage, Mortgagor, in accordance with the general or local rules, regulations, or laws of the State of ____ relating to mortgages, including any amendments thereof or supplements or additions thereto which do not materially change or impair the remedy, do hereby (a) declare their assent to the passage of a decree for the sale of the Property and (b) authorize Mortgagee, its successors and assigns, to sell the Property. Any such sale, whether under the assent to a decree or power of sale, may be made by the person or persons authorized to sell either as an entirety or in such separate parcels and on such terms and at such places and in such manner as it, they, or he may deem advisable.

5. Upon any sale of the Property under this Mortgage, whether under the assent to a decree, the power of sale, or by equitable foreclosure, the proceeds of such sale shall be applied as follows: first, to the payment of all expenses incident to the sale, including a counsel fee of ____________ Dollars ($____________), for conducting the proceedings if without contest, but if legal services be rendered to the trustee appointed by such decree or to Mortgagee or to the party selling under the power of sale in connection with any contested matter in the proceedings, then such other counsel fees and expenses shall be allowed out of the proceeds of sale as the court may deem proper; and also a commission to the trustee in the amount of ____________ (______%) percent of the gross sales and a commission of ____________ (______%) percent of the gross sales to the auctioneer conducting the sale, and also any liens prior to the lien of this Mortgage unless the sale is made subject to such prior liens; second, to the payment of all claims of Mortgagee hereunder, whether they have matured or not, with interest thereon until final ratification of the auditor's report; and third, the balance, if any, to Mortgagor, or to any person or persons entitled thereto, upon the surrender of the Property to the purchaser, less any expenses incurred in obtaining possession.

6. Immediately upon the first insertion of the advertisement or notice of sale, there shall be and become due and owing by Mortgagor, and each of them, to the party inserting the advertisement or notice, all expenses incident to such advertisement or notice, all court costs, attorneys' fees, and all expenses incident to the foreclosure proceedings under this Mortgage and a commission to the trustee of ______% on the total amount of the mortgage indebtedness, principal and interest, then due, and such party shall not be required to receive the principal and interest only of the debt in satisfaction thereof, unless the same be accompanied by a tender of such expenses, costs, attorneys' fees, and commission.

7. If Mortgagee shall incur any expense or expend any sums, including reasonable attorneys' fees, whether in connection with any action or proceeding or not, to sustain the lien of this Mortgage or its priority, or to protect or enforce any of its rights hereunder, or to recover any indebtedness hereby secured, or for any title examination or title insurance policy relating to the title to the Property, all such sums on notice and demand shall

be paid by Mortgagor, together with interest thereon at the rate of interest of ______ (______%) percent or the maximum interest rate permitted by law, and shall be a lien on the premises subordinate to the lien of this Mortgage, and in any action or proceeding to foreclose this Mortgage, or to recover or collect the debt secured hereby, the provisions of law respecting the recovery of costs, disbursements, and allowances shall prevail unaffected by this covenant.

8. Should Mortgagor fail or neglect to pay any ground rent, taxes, assessments, public or other dues or charges levied or assessed or which may be levied or assessed on the Property or on the Mortgage Debt and interest, when due or to keep the Property in proper repair, or to keep the Property insured as agreed herein, or shall permit any lien or encumbrance upon the Property except as aforesaid, Mortgagee may make such payments or repairs or insure the Property against such loss in such an amount as may be necessary to secure the Mortgage Debt, and any sum so paid shall be added to the principal of the Mortgage Debt and shall bear interest from such time at the rate of interest above stated in Paragraph 7.

9. Should all or any part of the Property be condemned or taken through eminent domain proceedings, all or such part of any award or proceeds thereof as Mortgagee in its sole discretion may determine, in writing, shall be paid to Mortgagee and applied to the payment of the Mortgage Debt and all such proceeds are hereby assigned to Mortgagee.

10. Mortgagee may at any time renew this Mortgage, extend the time for payment of the debt or any part thereof or interest thereon and waive any of the covenants or conditions of this Mortgage, in whole or in part, either at the request of Mortgagor or of any person having an interest in the Property, take or release other security, or any part of the Property, or such other security, grant extensions, renewals, or indulgences therein, or apply to the payment of principal of and interest on the Mortgage Debt any part or all of the proceeds obtained by sale, foreclosure, or receivership as herein provided, without resort or regard to other security, all without in any way releasing Mortgagor, or any of them, from any of the covenants or conditions of this Mortgage, or releasing the unreleased part of the Property herein described from the lien of this Mortgage for the amount of the Mortgage Debt, and may release any party primarily or secondarily liable on the Mortgage Debt without releasing any other party liable thereon and without releasing the Property subject thereto.

11. Until default is made in any covenant or condition of this Mortgage, Mortgagor shall have possession of the Property. Upon default in any of the covenants or conditions of this Mortgage, Mortgagee shall be entitled without notice to Mortgagor, or any of them, to the immediate possession of the Property and to the appointment of a receiver of the Property to operate the same, without regard to the adequacy thereof as security for the Mortgage Debt, and Mortgagor shall pay all costs in connection therewith, and upon any default, whether or not a receiver be appointed, the rents and profits of the Property are hereby assigned to Mortgagee as additional security.

12. Upon default in any of the covenants or conditions of this Mortgage, any funds on deposit with Mortgagee in the names of Mortgagor or any of them, and all securities and Property of Mortgagor or any of them, in the possession of Mortgagee whether as collateral security or held in a mortgage expense account or otherwise, may be held by Mortgagee as additional security and may be applied to the payment of any sums due Mortgagee under the terms of this Mortgage.

13. The rights, powers, privileges, and discretions specifically granted to Mortgagee

under this Mortgage are not in limitation of but in addition to those to which Mortgagee is entitled under any general or local law relating to mortgages in the State of ____, now or hereafter existing.

14. Before the full payment of the Mortgage Debt, Mortgagee, in its discretion, may make advances and readvances of funds to Mortgagor and renew, modify, or extend any letter of credit to the extent permitted by law and such sums shall be secured by this Mortgage.

15. The rights, powers, privileges, and discretions to which Mortgagee may be entitled herein shall inure to the benefit of its successors and assigns, are cumulative and not alternative, may be enforced successively or concurrently, and failure to exercise any of them shall not be deemed a waiver thereof and no waiver of any one shall be deemed to apply to any other nor shall it be effective unless in writing and signed by Mortgagee.

16. The covenants, agreements, conditions, and limitations of or imposed upon Mortgagor shall be binding upon their respective heirs, personal representatives, successors, and assigns.

17. The loan secured hereby was transacted solely for the purpose of carrying on or acquiring a business or commercial investment within the meaning of ____ of the (cite, if applicable, governing commercial law statute section) of the (cite, if applicable, the appropriate state law).

18. Whenever used herein, the singular shall include the plural, the plural the singular and the use of any gender shall be applicable to all genders.

WITNESS the signature and seal of Mortgagor, the day and year first above written.

____________________________, Mortgagor

By: ____________________________

(CORPORATE SEAL)

Title: ____________________________

WITNESS:

____

STATE OF ______________, COUNTY OF ______________, to wit:

I HEREBY CERTIFY, That on this ____ day of ____________________________, XXXX, before me, the subscriber, a Notary Public of the State of __________________________, in and for the County of ____________________________________, personally appeared ____, who, being by me duly sworn, did dispose and say that deponent resides at _______________________________; deponent is the ____ of the within named Mortgagor described in and which executed, the foregoing instrument; deponent knows the seal of said Mortgagor; that the seal affixed to said instrument is such corporate seal; that it was so affixed by order of the Board of Directors of said Mortgagor; and deponent signed deponent's name thereto by like order.

AS WITNESS my hand and notarial seal.

____

Notary Public

MY COMMISSION EXPIRES:

STATE OF ______________, COUNTY OF ______________, to wit:

I HEREBY CERTIFY, That on this ________ day of __________________________, XXXX, before me, the subscriber, a Notary Public of the State of __________________________, in and for the County of ____________________________________, personally appeared ____, the subscribing witness to the foregoing instrument who, being by me duly sworn, did dispose and say that deponent resides at ____; deponent knows ____ to be the individual described in, and who executed, the foregoing instrument; that he/she, said subscribing witness, was present and saw him/her execute the same; and that he/she, said witness, at the same time subscribed his/her name as witness thereto.

AS WITNESS my hand and notarial seal.

____

Notary Public

MY COMMISSION EXPIRES:

State of ______________________

County of ______________________

RECORDED ON THE ________ day of ______________________, XXXX,

at ____________ o'clock ____-m. in Liber ______________________

of Mortgages at Page ________ and examined.

____

Clerk

Please record and return to:

(Insert name and address of Mortgagee)

Schedule A

(description of property)

Schedule B

(liens and/or encumbrances)

Operational Documents/ Worksheets— Leasing Company

Form: o-01
Disk File Name: o-01.rtf

BANK REFERENCE WORKSHEET

Form Purpose

An equipment leasing company lessee bank reference verification worksheet.

Bank Reference Form

Final Approval and Credit Information on: ______________________

Approved by: ______________________ Date: ______________________

D & B Rating: ______________________ Years in business: ______________________

Type of business: ______________________ Net worth (if known): ______________________

Bank information	*1st Bank*	*2nd Bank*
Date cleared	________	________
Name of bank	________	________
Bank officer	________	________
Checking information		
Date opened	________	________
Average balance	________	________
Rating	________	________
Loan information		
Date opened	________	________
Indiv. high amount	________	________
Aggr. balance	________	________
Unsecured	________	________
Secured	________	________
Security	________	________
Rating	________	________

Bank comments

Credit approval
Notes ____

Form: o-02
Disk File Name: o-02.rtf

MASTER DOCUMENTATION WORKSHEET/CHECKLIST

Form Purpose

An equipment leasing company master documentation worksheet/checklist.

Master Documentation Worksheet/Checklist

Lessee Name: ______________________________

Lease Application # ____________________

CREDIT: Check Off Documents Required For Approval Date: _______ Initials ________

SALES	*Req'd*	*Rec'd*		*Req'd*	*Rec'd*
Signed Lease		( )	Vendor Recourse	( )	( )
Advance Rental Check	Always	( )	Purchase Order from Lessee	( )	( )
Signed Delivery Receipt	Req'd	( )	Life Ins Policy or Assign	( )	( )
Vendor Invoice		( )	Tax Exemption Certificate	( )	( )
Personal Guarantee	( )	( )	Landlord Waiver*	( )	( )
Corporate Guarantee	( )	( )			
Corporate Guarantee	( )	( )	Mortgage Waiver*	( )	( )
Corporate Resolution	( )	( )	*Req'd For Vendor Payment		
Credit Info Obtained at Signing	( )	( )			
(Specify) ____________	( )	( )			
____________________			Other ________________	( )	( )

Sales Review

Documents	*Process*	*Complete*
Advance Rental Check	Currently dated, payable to Lessor/Agent, signed	( )
	Company name matches Lessee name	( )
	Amount matches Lease	( )
	Make two copies for file	( )
Signed Lease	No cross-outs, front and back	( )
Lease to Application	Signature name and title match	( )
	Rate and term match	( )
	Monthly rental computed properly	( )
	Lessee name and address match	( )
	Equipment description matches	( )
	Equipment location matches	( )

*NOTE:*If all documents are received except the Vendor Invoice, pass file to next step.

Performed By: ____________ Date: ____________

Documentation Checks

Documents	*Process*	*Complete*
Master Document	Sheet Required Documents as indicated above match Application approval terms	( )
	Double check all documents received and verify sales review	( )
Signed Lease	"Good signature"–Corp. Officer for Corp., Partner for Partnership, Proprietor for Proprietorship	( )
	All copies legible and complete	( )

Documentation Checks (continued)

Lease to Signed Delivery Receipt	Signer is same on both documents	( )
Personal Guarantee	Signed without a title	( )
	Home telephone number in file	( )
Corporate Resolution	Signed by Corporate Secretary	( )
	Person authorized in resolution is lease signer	( )
Purchase Order	P.O. sent	( )
	Equipment location and description on P. O. matches signed lease	( )
Purchase Order from Lessee	Made out to Lessor	
	Lease term and payments spelled out	( )
	Equipment location and description matches signed	( )
	lease	( )
Invoice to Signed Lease Application	Cost Matches	( )
	Equipment description matches	( )
	Equipment location matches	( )
Invoice	Billed (Sold) to Lessor, not Lessee	( )
	Equipment serial number included	( )
	Extensions and total correct (run tape)	( )
Telephone Verification of equipment delivery	Equipment installed and running properly—Date	
	Telephone Verification script in folder	( )

Performed By: ______________ Date: ______________

**********Lease Ready To Be Signed By Credit Manager**********

==

Lessee: ____

Lease Cost: ______________ Lease Type: ______ Term: ______ Residual: FMV ______

Lease Number: ___________ Customer Number: ___________ Sales Rep: ___________

Commencement Date: ______________ 2nd Payment Due Date: ______________

==

Booking Checklist

Function	*Date Competed*
Booked into Lease Register	______________
Thank-you letter sent	______________
Invoicing set up	______________

Invoice for 2nd payment sent	____________
Vendor Paid	____________
UCC-1 filed	____________
UCC-1 filing copy received	____________
Insurance received	____________
Lease folder completed	____________

Form: o-03
Disk File Name: o-03.rtf

NEW LESSEE WELCOME LETTER

Form Purpose

An equipment leasing company lessee welcome/thank-you letter.

Executing Parties

The lessor.

[Letterhead of Leasing Company]

(Insert name and address of new lessee)

Re: Lease Number: ____________________

Equipment Description: ____________

Dear ______________________________:

We would like to take this opportunity to thank you for calling upon us to handle your recent capital equipment lease. We are pleased to have been chosen.

Enclosed is your copy of the Lease Contract, as well as a request for insurance on the equipment. It is EXTREMELY IMPORTANT THAT THIS INSURANCE REQUEST BE FULFILLED IMMEDIATELY PURSUANT TO PARAGRAPH ________ OF THE LEASE.

All payments are due on or before the due date shown on your rent invoice. A ____ percent (______ %) late charge, with a minimum of $10.00, will be added to any late payments, to the extent allowed by law.

It is important that you understand paragraph ______ of your lease contract, which states that you as the lessee are responsible for reimbursing the lessor for all taxes, which includes the property tax related to your equipment, if applicable.

We appreciate this opportunity to serve you and trust that our business relationship will be mutually enjoyable. Please call us for further equipment that you wish to lease.

Very truly yours,

Form: o-04
Disk File Name: o-04.rtf

Tax Notification—Personal Property

Form Purpose

An equipment leasing company lessee personal property tax notification and information memorandum.

Executing Parties

The lessor.

Tax Notification

To: (Insert name and address of lessee)

From: (Insert name and address of leasing company)

Re: Personal Property Tax

In accordance with Section ________ of your lease, you are responsible for all taxes related to your leased equipment.

Personal Property Tax is charged by your state once per year. (Insert name of leasing company) is responsible for collecting this tax from you and paying it to the State.

To expedite the collection of Personal Property Tax, please fill in the information at the bottom of this tax notification memorandum. This will help us insure proper credit to your account and avoid delinquent taxes.

Thank you for your cooperation.

==

PLEASE RETURN COMPLETED FORM TO US WITH YOUR NEXT PAYMENT.

Company Name: ____

Company Address: ____

____

Lease Number: ____

County Where Equipment Is Located: ______________________________

Zip Code Where Equipment Is Located: ____________________________

Form: o-05
Disk File Name: o-05.rtf

TRADE REFERENCE WORKSHEET/REPORT

Form Purpose

An equipment leasing company lessee trade reference worksheet.

Trade Reference Worksheet/Report

Date: ______________________

Lessee: ______________________

Investigator: ______________________

Vendor/Supplier Name: ______________ Phone No.: ______________

Contact: ______________________

Principal Products: ______________________

____

____

____

Prime Supplier of: ______________________

Invoice Terms: ______________________

Open Date: ______________________

Highest Credit: ______________________

Payment History: ______________________

Discount: ______________________

Prompt: ______________________

0–30 Days: ______________________

30–60 Days: ______________________

60–90 Days: ______________________

More Than 90 Days: ______________________

Comments:

____

____

____

____

Form: o-06
Disk File Name: o-06.rtf

TRANSACTION SUMMARY WORKSHEET

Form Purpose

An equipment leasing company lease transaction summary worksheet.

Lease Summary Worksheet

For Transactions of $[50,000] or More

I. Name: ______________________________

Trade Name: ______________________________

Address: ______________________________

____

Business Type: ______________________________

II. Equipment Funding Dollar Amount: ____________________

III. Term: ____________ Months

IV. Rental:

Number of Advance Payments: ____________________

Total Advance Payment Amount: $ ____________________

Numer of Periodic Rental Payments: ____________________

Periodic Rental Payment Amount: $ ____________________

End-of-Lease Equipment Residual Dollar Amount: $ ____________________

or as a percentage of Equipment Cost: ____________________ %

IV. Purpose of Leased Equipment:

____

____

____

V. Equipment Description: ____________________

Manufacturer: ____________________

Model Number: ____________________

New or Used: ____________________

VI. Principals of Lessee:

Name: ______________________________

Title: ______________________________

Home Addresses: ______________________________

____

Social Security Number: ____________________

Background, History: ____________________

____

____

Name: ______________________________

Title: ______________________________

Home Addresses: ______________________________

____

Social Security Number: _______________
Background, History: _______________
____
____

Name: _______________
Title: _______________
Home Addresses: _______________
____

Social Security Number: _______________
Background, History: _______________
____
____

Name: _______________
Title: _______________
Home Addresses: _______________
____

Social Security Number: _______________
Background, History: _______________
____
____
____

VII. Lessee Financial Overview: _______________
____
____
____

VIII. Guaranties: _______________
____
____
____

IX. References: _______________
____
____
____

X. Recommendation: _______________
____
____
____
____

Form: o-07
Disk File Name: o-07.rtf

TRANSACTION WORKSHEET/CHECKLIST

Form Purpose

An equipment leasing company small ticket transaction worksheet/checklist.

Transaction Worksheet/Checklist

Lessee Name: ____________________

Lessor Name: ____________________

Approved By: ____________________

Guarantors: ____________________

TRW ____ Personal Financials ____________________

D&B ____ Corporate Financials ____________________

Tax Returns ____________________

Other ____________________

Suppliers/Vendors to be Paid:

Name Amount

Documents and Requirements

Name Verification: ____________________

Lease Agreement: ____________________

Schedule: ____________________

D&A Certificate: ____________________

Invoice: ____________________

Assignment: With Recourse ____ Without Recourse ____

Guaranty: Personal ____ Corporate ____

UCC Filing: Comments: ____________________

State: ____________________

County: ____________________

Fixture: ____________________

Insurance: ____________________

Lien Search: ____________________

Landlord Waiver: ____________________

Mortgage Waiver: ____________________

Collateral Pledge Agreement: ____________________

Indemnity Mortgage ____________________

Bill of Sale: ____________________

Physical Audit: ____________________

Subordination: ____________________

Form: o-08
Disk File Name: o-08.rtf

VERIFICATION AND AUDIT WORKSHEET

Form Purpose

An equipment leasing company internal transaction verification worksheet.

Verification and Audit Form

Date: ________________________

Time: ________________________

Lease No.: ________________________

Lessee: ________________________

Guarantor: ________________________

Signatory: ________________________

Telephone Number Called: ________________________

Name of Person Called: ________________________

Is All the Equipment Delivered? ________________________

Is All the Equipment Functioning Satisfactorily? ________________________

Is the Vendor Expected to Do Anything Further? ________________________

Is All the Equipment Accepted? ________________________

Where Will the Equipment Be Located? ________________________

Is Signature of the Lease and the Delivery and Acceptance Form Confirmed? ________

Do They Know the Lease Is Noncancelable? ________________________

Verifier's Name: ________________________

Opinions of Counsel

[See Form I-02g.]

Options/Rights—Lessee

Form: o-09
Disk File Name: o-09.rtf

Early Termination Right/Option

Form Purpose

Early lease termination option Rider for short-form, net finance master equipment lease agreement. This form is integrated with Lease Agreement, Form l-03.

Executing Parties

See:

Lease Agreement, Form l-03

_________________________, Lessor

Home Office Address: _________________________

Phone (   ) _______________

RIDER ____ to Schedule No. ____,dated as of _______________, to Master Agreement to Lease Equipment, dated as of _______________, between _______________, Lessor, and _______________, Lessee.

Early Termination Option

(a) Provided no Incipient Default or Event of Default has occurred and is continuing, Lessee shall have the right at its option at any time during the respective Lease Terms of the Units described below on not less than 90 days' prior notice to Lessor to terminate this Lease with respect to one or more of such Units on the ____ Rent payment date of each such Unit, or on any Rent payment date thereafter ("Termination Date"), provided that Lessee shall have made a good faith determination that each such Unit with respect to which Lessee intends to exercise this option ("Termination Units") is obsolete or surplus to Lessee's requirements. During the period from the giving of such notice to the Termination Date, Lessee, as agent for Lessor, shall use its best efforts to obtain bids for the purchase of such Termination Units by a party or parties other than Lessee or an affiliate of Lessee. Lessee shall promptly certify in writing to Lessor the amount and terms of each bid received by Lessee and the name and address of the party submitting such bid. Subject to Lessor's right to retain such Termination Units as provided in paragraph (b), on the Termination Date Lessor shall sell such Termination Units for cash to the bidder or bidders ("Third Party Purchaser") who have submitted the highest bid for such Termination Units and shall transfer title to such Termination Units to such Third Party Purchaser without recourse or warranty, except that Lessor shall represent and warrant that it owns such Termination Units free and clear of any Lessor's Lien. The total sale price realized upon such sale shall be retained by Lessor and, in addition, on the Termination Date, Lessee shall pay to Lessor the amount, if any, by which the applicable Termination Value of such Termination Units as provided in paragraph (d), computed as of the Termination Date, exceeds the net proceeds of such sale, whereupon this Lease shall terminate as to such Termination Units except as herein otherwise expressly provided. If no sale shall have occurred on the Termination Date as to any Termination Unit, this Lease shall continue in full force and effect as to such Termination Unit.

(b) Notwithstanding the provisions of paragraph (a), Lessor shall have the right at any time up to and including 30 days prior to the Termination Date, within its sole discretion, to elect not to sell any one or more Termination Units to any Third Party Purchaser. In the event Lessor elects not to sell any such Termination Units to such Third Party Purchaser, Lessee shall return such Termination Units to Lessor in accordance with the provisions of Section 8 of the Master Agreement to Lease Equipment designated above, and Lessor thereupon may retain such Termination Units for its own account without further obligation to Lessee under this Lease. In the event of the return of such Termination Units to Lessor pursuant to this paragraph (b), and provided no Incipient Default or Event of Default has occurred and is continuing, all obligations of Lessee with respect to such Termination Units, including the payment of Rent, for any period subsequent to their respective Termination Dates shall cease.

(c) Subject to Lessor's rights as provided in paragraph (b), if as to any Termination Unit the Termination Value exceeds the highest bid or in the event no bids are received by Lessee, Lessee may, at its option, upon notice given to Lessor not less than 15 days prior to the Termination Date, elect to rescind Lessee's notice of termination with respect to such Termination Unit, whereupon this Lease shall continue in full force and effect as though no notice of termination had been given by Lessee with respect to such Termination Unit.

(d) The Termination Value of any Unit shall be that percentage described on Annex A hereto of the Acquisition Cost of such Unit corresponding to the applicable Termination Date of such Unit, plus an amount of money equal to the Rent payment due on such Termination Date.

Unit Description:

[Insert unit information]

______________________________, Lessor

By: ______________________________

Title: ______________________________

______________________________, Lessee

By: ______________________________

Title: ______________________________

Annex A
to Rider __________ to
Schedule No. __________

Termination Value Table

The Termination Value of any Unit shall be that percentage specified below of the Acquisition Cost of such Unit corresponding to the applicable Termination Date of such Unit, plus an amount of money equal to the Rent payment due on such Termination Date.

Termination Date	*Percentage*	*Termination Date*	*Percentage*	*Termination Date*	*Percentage*
0	______				
1	______	26	______	51	______
2	______	27	______	52	______
3	______	28	______	53	______
4	______	29	______	54	______
5	______	30	______	55	______
6	______	31	______	56	______
7	______	32	______	57	______
8	______	33	______	58	______
9	______	34	______	59	______
10	______	35	______	60	______
11	______	36	______	61	______
12	______	37	______	62	______
13	______	38	______	63	______
14	______	39	______	64	______
15	______	40	______	65	______
16	______	41	______	66	______
17	______	42	______	67	______
18	______	43	______	68	______
19	______	44	______	69	______
20	______	45	______	70	______
21	______	46	______	71	______
22	______	47	______	72	______
23	______	48	______	73	______
24	______	49	______	74	______
25	______	50	______	75	______

76 ____________
77 ____________
78 ____________
79 ____________
80 ____________
81 ____________
82 ____________
83 ____________
84 ____________
85 ____________
86 ____________
87 ____________
88 ____________
89 ____________
90 ____________
91 ____________
92 ____________
93 ____________
94 ____________
95 ____________
96 ____________
97 ____________
98 ____________
99 ____________
100 ____________
101 ____________
102 ____________
103 ____________
104 ____________
105 ____________
106 ____________
107 ____________
108 ____________
109 ____________
110 ____________
111 ____________
112 ____________
113 ____________
114 ____________
115 ____________
116 ____________
117 ____________
118 ____________
119 ____________
120 ____________

Lessee acknowledges receipt of copy hereof.

______________________________, Lessee

By: ______________________________

Title: ______________________________

Form: o-10
Disk File Name: o-10.rtf

PURCHASE RIGHT/OPTION—FAIR MARKET VALUE/FIXED

Form Purpose

A lessee equipment purchase option letter.

Executing Parties

The equipment lessee.
The equipment lessor.

Lessee Purchase Option

[Insert Lessee name and address]

Re: Lease Agreement, dated ______________, XXXX,
by and between (insert name of Lessee)
and (insert name of Lessor)
Lease No.: ______________________

TO WHOM THIS MAY CONCERN:

With reference to the above mentioned Lease Agreement (hereinafter the "Lease"), you shall have the option to purchase the equipment described in the Lease, as-is, where-is, and without any representation or warranty, at the end of the scheduled Lease term thereof, provided, of course, that there is no default under the Lease and that you have performed all of the terms and conditions of the Lease.

The purchase price at the expiration of the Lease term shall be (insert, as applicable, "fair market value," or "a fixed price equal to $ ____________, "or "a fixed equal to ____ % of equipment cost."). However, you are hereby informed and advised that this purchase option offer is made conditioned upon your signing and returning a copy of this document to our office at the above-mentioned address no earlier than one hundred and twenty (120) days and no later than thirty (30) days from the end of the scheduled Lease term.

You will also be responsible for any applicable sales tax and agree to sign documentation reasonably acceptable to us to reflect the sale.

Very Truly Yours,
[Insert Lessor name]

By: ______________________________

Title: ____________________________

Acknowledged and Agreed to:

[Insert Lessee name]

By: ______________________________

Title: ____________________________

Form: o-11
Disk File Name: o-11.rtf

PURCHASE RIGHT/OPTION—FAIR MARKET VALUE

Form Purpose

Fair market value purchase option Rider for short-form, net finance master equipment lease agreement. This form is integrated with Lease Agreement, Form l-03.

Executing Parties

The equipment lessor.
The equipment lessee.

See:

Lease Agreement, Form l-03

______________________, Lessor

Home Office Address: ______________________________

Phone ( ) ______________________

RIDER ______ to Schedule No. ______, dated as of ______________________,

to Master Agreement to Lease Equipment, dated as of ______________________,

between ______________________, Lessor, and ______________________, Lessee.

Fair Market Purchase Option

Provided that this Lease has not been terminated earlier and no Incipient Default or Event of' Default has occurred and is continuing, not earlier than ____ days and not later than ____ days before the end of the Lease Term, or in the event such Lease Term has been extended before the end of any period for which this Lease has been extended ("Renewal Term"), first to expire under this Lease of the Units described below, Lessee may as to all, but not less than all, such Units deliver to Lessor a written notice tentatively electing to purchase such Units at the end of the respective Lease Terms, or any Renewal Terms, as the case may be, for an amount equal to the Fair Market Value of each such Unit at the end of such periods. If no such notice is delivered by Lessee to Lessor within such period, Lessee shall be deemed to have waived any right to purchase such Units. Fair Market Value shall mean the value which would obtain in an arm's-length transaction between an informed and willing buyer-user (other than a lessee currently in possession or a used equipment dealer) under no compulsion to buy, and an informed and willing seller under no compulsion to sell and, in such determination, costs of removal from the location of current use shall not be a deduction from such value. Fair Market Value shall be determined by the mutual agreement of Lessor and Lessee in accordance with the preceding sentence. If Lessee and Lessor cannot agree within 30 days after Lessee's notice of tentative election, Fair Market Value shall be determined by a qualified independent equipment appraiser mutually satisfactory to Lessee and Lessor. If Lessee and Lessor fail to agree upon a satisfactory independent equipment appraiser within 10 days following the end of the 30-day period referred to above, Lessee and Lessor shall each within 5 days appoint a qualified independent equipment appraiser and such appraisers shall jointly determine the Fair Market Value of such Units. If, within 15 days after the appointment of the last of these two appraisers, the appraisers cannot agree upon the Fair Market Value of such Units, the two appraisers shall, within 10 days, appoint a third appraiser and the Fair Market Value of such Units shall be determined by the three appraisers, who shall make their appraisals within 15 days following the appointment of the third appraiser and the average of their three determinations so made shall be deemed to be the Fair Market Value of' such Units and shall be conclusive and binding upon Lessor and Lessee. If either party shall have failed to appoint an appraiser, the determination of the Fair Market Value of such Units of the single appraiser appointed by the other party shall be final.

At any time within the 15-day period following the determination of the Fair Market Value of such Units, Lessee may deliver to Lessor a further notice finally electing to purchase such Units. If no such further notice is delivered by Lessee to Lessor within such period, Lessee shall be deemed to have waived any right to purchase such Units.

At the end of' the respective Lease Terms or Renewal Terms, as appropriate, if Lessee has finally elected to purchase such Units, Lessee shall purchase from Lessor, and Lessor shall sell to Lessee, each such Unit for a cash consideration equal to the Fair Market Value of such Unit, and Lessor shall transfer title to each such Unit to Lessee without recourse or warranty, except that Lessor shall represent and warrant that it owns such Unit free and clear of any Lessor's Lien. All appraisal fees and expenses shall be borne by Lessee.

Unit Description:
Options/Rights—Lessee

[Insert unit information]

_______________________, Lessor

By: _______________________

Title: _______________________

_______________________, Lessee

By: _______________________

Title: _______________________

Form: o-12
Disk File Name: o-12.rtf

PURCHASE RIGHT/OPTION—FIXED PRICE

Form Purpose

Fixed price purchase option Rider for short-form, net finance master equipment lease agreement. This form is integrated with Lease Agreement, Form l-03.

Executing Parties

The equipment lessor.
The equipment lessee.

See:

Lease Agreement, Form l-03

_________________________, Lessor

Home Office Address: _________________________

Phone ( ) _________________

RIDER ______ to Schedule No. ______, dated as of ____________,

to Master Agreement to Lease Equipment, dated as of ____________,

between _________________________, Lessor,

and

_________________________, Lessee.

Fixed Price Purchase Option

Provided that this Lease has not been terminated earlier and no Incipient Default or Event of Default has occurred and is continuing, Lessee may, upon not less than that number of days' notice specified below before the end of the Lease Term first to expire under this Lease of the Units described below, purchase each but not less than all the Units described below at the end of their respective Lease Terms for cash in the amount specified below. Upon payment to Lessor in full for each Unit, Lessor shall transfer title to such Unit to Lessee without recourse or warranty, except that Lessor shall represent that it owns such Unit and has no knowledge of' any Lessor's Lien relating to such Unit.

Purchase Price	*Unit Description*	*Purchase Price as a Percentage of Acquisition Cost*	*Purchase Price in Dollars*	*Number of Days' Notice*

[Insert information]

_________________________, Lessor

By: _________________________

Title: _________________________

_________________________, Lessee

By: _________________________

Title: _________________________

Form: o-13
Disk File Name: o-13.rtf

Renewal Right/Option—Fair Market Value

Form Purpose

Fair market lease term renewal option Rider for short-form, net finance master equipment lease agreement. This form is integrated with Lease Agreement, Form l-03.

Executing Parties

The equipment lessor.
The equipment lessee.

See:

Lease Agreement, Form l-03

____________________, Lessor

Home Office Address: ____________________

RIDER _____ to Schedule No. _____, dated as of ____________________,
to Master Agreement to Lease Equipment dated as of ____________________,
between ____________________, Lessor, and ____________________, Lessee.

Fair Market Renewal Option

Provided that this Lease has not been terminated earlier and no Incipient Default or Event of Default has occurred and is continuing, not earlier than _____ days and not later than _____ days before the end of the Lease Term, or in the event such Lease Term has been extended before the end of any period for which this Lease has been extended ("Renewal Term"), first to expire under the Lease of the Units described below, Lessee may as to all, but not less than all, such Units deliver to Lessor a written notice tentatively electing to extend the Lease as to such Units at the end of the respective Lease Terms, or any Renewal Terms, as the case may be, on the periodic basis described below (not to exceed the aggregate Renewal Term specified below) at the Fair Market Rental of each such Unit as of the end of such applicable periods. If no such written notice is delivered by Lessee to lessor within such period, Lessee shall be deemed to have waived any right to extend the Lease with respect to such Units, Fair Market Rental shall mean the value which would obtain in an arm's-length transaction between an informed and willing lessee (other than a lessee currently in possession or a used equipment dealer) under no compulsion to lease, and an informed and willing lessor under no compulsion to lease and, in such determination, costs of removal from the location of current use shall not be a deduction from such value. Fair Market Rental shall be determined by the mutual agreement of Lessor and Lessee in accordance with the preceding sentence. If Lessee and Lessor cannot agree within 30 days after Lessee's notice of tentative election, Fair Market Rental shall be determined by a qualified independent equipment appraiser mutually satisfactory to Lessee and Lessor. If Lessee and Lessor fail to agree upon a satisfactory independent equipment appraiser within 10 days following the end of the 30-day period referred to above, Lessee and Lessor shall each within 5 days appoint a qualified independent equipment appraiser and such appraisers shall jointly determine the Fair Market Rental of such Units. If, within 15 days after the appointment of the last of these two appraisers, the appraisers cannot agree upon the Fair Market Rental of such Units, the two appraisers shall, within 10 days, appoint a third appraiser and the Fair Market Rental of such Units shall be determined by the three appraisers, who shall make their appraisals within 15 days following the appointment of the third appraiser and the average of their three determinations so made shall be deemed to be the Fair Market Rental of such Units and shall be conclusive and binding upon Lessor and Lessee. If either party shall have failed to appoint an appraiser, the determination of Fair Market Rental of the single appraiser appointed by the other party shall be final.

At any time within the 15-day period following the determination of the Fair Market Rental of such Units, Lessee may deliver to Lessor a further notice finally electing to extend the Lease with respect to such Units. If no such further notice is delivered by Lessee to Lessor within this 15-day period, Lessee shall be deemed to have waived any right to extend the Lease with respect to such Units. All appraisal fees and expenses shall be borne by Lessee.

Unit Description	*Maximum Aggregate Renewal Term*	*Periodic Renewal Term Basis*
	[Insert information]	

______________________________, Lessor

By: ______________________________

Title: ______________________________

______________________________, Lessee

By: ______________________________

Title: ______________________________

Form: o-14
Disk File Name: o-14.rtf

Renewal Right/Option—Fixed Price

Form Purpose

Lessee fixed price lease term renewal option Rider for short-form, net finance master equipment lease agreement. This form is integrated with Lease Agreement, Form l-03.

Executing Parties

The equipment lessor.
The equipment lessee.

See:

Lease Agreement, Form l-03

______________________________, Lessor

Home Office Address: ______________________________

RIDER ______ to Schedule No. ______, dated as of ______________________________, to Master Agreement to Lease Equipment dated as of ______________________________, between ______________________________, Lessor, and ______________________________, Lessee.

Fixed Price Lease Renewal Option

Provided that this Lease has not been terminated earlier and no Incipient Default or Event of Default has occurred and is continuing, not earlier than ________ days and not later than ________ days before the end of the Lease Term, or in the event such Lease Term has been extended before the end of any period for which this Lease has been extended ("Renewal Term"), first to expire under the Lease of the Units described below, Lessee may as to all, but not less than all, such Units deliver to Lessor a written notice tentatively electing to extend the Lease as to such Units at the end of the respective Lease Terms, or any Renewal Terms, as the case may be, on the periodic basis described below (not to exceed the aggregate Renewal Term specified below) for a fixed price (as specified below) with respect to each such Unit as of the end of such applicable periods. If no such written notice is delivered by Lessee to lessor within such period, Lessee shall be deemed to have waived any right to extend the Lease with respect to such Units.

Unit Description	*Maximum Aggregate Renewal Term*	*Periodic Renewal Term Basis*	*Fixed Price Renewal Rate*

[Insert information]

______________________________, Lessor ______________________________, Lessee

By: ______________________________ By: ______________________________

Title: ______________________________ Title: ______________________________

Form: o-15
Disk File Name: o-15.rtf

SUBLEASE RIGHT/OPTION

Form Purpose

Lessee right to sublease Rider for short-form, net finance master lease agreement. This form is integrated with Lease Agreement, Form l-03.

Executing Parties

The equipment lessor.
The equipment lessee.

See:

Lease Agreement, Form l-03

________________________, Lessor

Home Office Address: ________________________

RIDER _____ to Schedule No. _____ dated as of ________________________,
to Master Agreement to Lease Equipment, dated as of ________________________,
between ________________________, Lessor, and ________________________, Lessee.

Lessee Right to Sublease

Provided that no Incipient Default or Event of Default has occurred and is continuing, Lessee shall be entitled without Lessor's consent, and upon 60 days' prior notice, to sublease any or all of the Units to any entity, including without limitation any subsidiary, affiliate, or parent corporation of Lessee, incorporated in the United States of America, but in all cases only upon and subject to all the terms and conditions of this Lease. No such sublease or other assignment of use by Lessee shall relieve Lessee of any of its obligations under this Lease.

Unit Description:

[Insert unit information]

________________________, Lessor	________________________, Lessee
By: ________________________	By: ________________________
Title: ________________________	Title: ________________________

Options/Rights—Lessor

Form: o-16
Disk File Name: o-16.rtf

Automatic Transfer of Title

Form Purpose

Fair market value purchase option Rider for short-form, net finance master equipment lease agreement. This form is integrated with Lease Agreement, Form l-03.

See:

Lease Agreement, Form l-03

______________________________, Lessor

Home Office Address: ____

Phone (   ) __________________________

RIDER ______ to Schedule No. ______, dated as of __________________________, to Master Agreement to Lease Equipment, dated as of __________________________, between __________________________, Lessor, and __________________________, Lessee.

Automatic Transfer of Title

Provided that this Lease has not been terminated earlier and no Incipient Default or Event of Default has occurred and is continuing, immediately upon the end of the applicable Lease Term title to each of the Units described below shall without any further action be automatically transferred to Lessee. Title to each Unit shall be transferred without recourse or warranty, except that Lessor shall, if so requested in writing by Lessee, represent that it owned such Unit immediately prior to the transfer and has no knowledge of any Lessor's Lien.

Unit Description:

[Insert unit information]

______________________________, Lessor

By: __________________________

Title: __________________________

______________________________, Lessee

By: __________________________

Title: __________________________

Form: o-17
Disk File Name: o-17.rtf

PUT

Form Purpose

A lessor right to force a lessee to purchase equipment subject to lease at the end of the lease term Rider. This form is integrated with Lease Agreement, Form l-03. Care must be exercised in using a put option because it can cause the lease to fail to qualify as a "true" lease for income tax purposes.

Executing Parties

The equipment lessor.
The equipment lessee.

See:
Lease Agreement, Form l-03

_______________________________, Lessor

Home Office Address: ____

Phone ( ) ___________________________

RIDER _______ to Schedule No. _______ dated as of ___________________________, to Master Agreement to Lease Equipment, dated as of ___________________________, between ___________________________, Lessor, and ___________________________, Lessee.

Lessor Sale Option

Lessor may, upon not less than 60 days' notice before the end of the Lease Term of each Unit described below, elect to sell to Lessee, and Lessee shall purchase, each such Unit at the end of such Unit's Lease Term in cash for the amount specified below. If Lessor shall make the election provided for in this Rider, the sale shall occur on the day next following the day the applicable Lease Term ends. Upon payment to Lessor in full of the purchase price indicated below, Lessor shall transfer title to each such Unit to Lessee without recourse or warranty, except that Lessor shall represent that it owns such Unit and has no knowledge of any Lessor's Lien. If Lessor exercises this option, it shall upset and prevail over any purchase, renewal, or early termination option Lessee may have under this Lease.

Unit Description	*Purchase Price as a Percentage of Acquisition Cost*	*Purchase Price in Dollars*
	[Insert information]	

_______________________________, Lessor _______________________________, Lessee

By: _______________________________ By: _______________________________

Title: _____________________________ Title: _____________________________

Participation Agreement Document

[See Form I-04b.]

Prohibited Lender Assignee Schedule

[See Form I-02h.]

Promissory Note Documents

[Also see Forms I-06a and I-07b.]

Form: p-01
Disk File Name: p-01.rtf

PROMISSORY NOTE—GENERAL FORM

Form Purpose

A promissory note.

Executing Parties

The borrower.

Promissory Note

$ ________________ ________________, XXXX

FOR VALUE RECEIVED the undersigned, ________________, a ________________ corporation (the Payor"), having its executive office and principal place of business at ________________, hereby promises to pay to ________________, a ________________ corporation, having a principal place of business at ________________ (the "Payee"), such payment to be made as provided for herein and to be sent to Payee at ________________, or to such other place as the Payee shall hereafter specify in writing thirty (30) days in advance of such change of place, the principal sum of ________________ ($________________), in such coin or currency of the United States of America as at the time shall be legal tender for the payment of public and private debts.

1. Interest and Payment.

1.1 The unpaid principal amount hereof shall bear simple interest from the date hereof at the rate of ________________ (____ %) per annum.

1.2 This Note shall be payable in ________________ (____), consecutive, equal installments, including principal and interest, as follows:

(a) The first payment of principal and interest thereon shall be due on ________, and shall be in an amount equal to $ ____________, of which $ ____________ shall be applied toward the outstanding principal balance of the Note; and

(b) The remaining ________________ (________________) monthly principal and interest payments shall be due on the 1st and the 15th of each month thereafter, beginning on ________________, in the amounts set forth on the schedule attached as Annex A hereto and made a part hereof.

1.3 If any payment of principal and interest accrued thereon is not made on or before five (5) days after the time when such payment is due and payable, then interest shall accrue on such unpaid amount from the date of nonpayment to the date of payment at a simple interest rate equal to EIGHTEEN PERCENT (18%) per annum, or the maximum interest rate permitted by law.

2. Prepayment. At the option of the Payor, this Note may be prepaid in whole or in part at any time or from time to time, without penalty or premium, provided, however, such prepayment may only be made on or after ____________ (____) months following the date of this Note stated above. Each prepayment of this Note shall first be applied to interest accrued through the date of prepayment and then to principal.

3. Modification. This Note may not be modified, or discharged unless paid in full, except by a writing duly executed by the Payor and the Payee.

4. Miscellaneous.

4.1 This Note is secured by ________________________________.

4.2 The headings of the various paragraphs of this Note are for convenience of reference only and shall in no way modify any of the terms or provisions of this Note, or the Agreement.

4.3 All notices required or permitted to be given hereunder shall be in writing and shall be deemed to have been duly given when personally delivered or sent by registered or certified mail, return receipt requested, postage prepaid, to the address of the intended recipient set forth in the preamble to this Note or at such other address as the intended recipient shall have hereafter given in writing, thirty (30) days in advance, to the other party hereto pursuant to the provisions hereof.

4.4 This Note shall bind the Payor and its successors and assigns.

4.5 The laws of the State of ______________________________ shall apply to this Note.

______________________________, Payor

By: ______________________________

Title: ______________________________

Annex A

[Insert debt amortization schedule.]

Form: p-02
Disk File Name: p-02.rtf

PROMISSORY NOTE—INTEGRATED

Form Purpose

A promissory note. This form has been integrated with Loan and Security Agreement, Form l-05.

Executing Parties

The borrower.

See:

Loan and Security Agreement, Form l-05

Exhibit B

Promissory Note

$ ______________________
(Insert here City and State where executed)

Dated: ______________________

FOR VALUE RECEIVED, the undersigned, (insert name of borrower) (the " Borrower"), hereby promises to pay to the order of (insert name of lender) (the " Lender ") at (insert address of Lender) the principal sum of ______________________ Dollars with interest on the unpaid balance thereof from the date hereof at the rate of (insert per annum Note interest rate) % per annum, computed on the basis of a 360-day year and twelve 30-day months.

Past due principal and, to the extent legally enforceable, interest installments shall bear interest equal to ____ % per annum, until paid. Principal of and interest on this Note shall be payable in lawful money of the United States of America.

This Note is issued under and pursuant to a Loan and Security Agreement (*Author's Note:* See Form 1-05 for integrated loan and security agreement form) dated ______________, as amended on ______________________, between the Borrower and the Lender (the "Security Agreement"), to which agreement reference is made for a statement of the terms and provisions thereof.

A schedule of the installment payments to be made hereunder which consists of the expected amounts to be paid by the Lessee to the Lender is set forth in the amortization table attached as Schedule A hereto and incorporated by reference herein; such amounts which are paid by the Lessee to the Lender shall be applied first to the payment of accrued interest hereon and then to the payment of the unpaid principal hereof. In addition to the payments set forth on Schedule A, on ______________________, a payment of interest only on the Note from the date hereof, in the amount of $ ______________ shall be due and payable to the Lender.

The principal of this Note may be declared due and payable prior to the expressed maturity date thereof in the events, on the terms and in the manner provided for in the Security Agreement. In the event this Note is accelerated, the unpaid principal balance shall be determined from the schedule annexed hereto.

Subject to the provisions of Section 5 of the Security Agreement, the liability of the Borrower is limited to the Units and the assigned income and proceeds from the Lease (as said terms are defined in the Security Agreement).

The provisions of this Note shall inure to the benefit of and be binding upon any successor to the Borrower and shall extend to any holder hereof.

______________________________, Borrower

By: ______________________________

Title: ______________________________

Schedule A

Annexed to and made part of Promissory Note dated ______________________

in the principal amount of $ ______________________.

PMT No.	*Outstanding Principal*	*Debt Service*	*Interest Portion*	*Principal Portion*

Form: p-03
Disk File Name: p-03.rtf

PROMISSORY NOTE—CONFESSED JUDGMENT

Form Purpose

A promissory note with a confessed judgment provision.

Executing Parties

The borrower.

Commercial Note–Time

(Confessed Judgment)

$ ______________________________

Dated: ______________________ XXXX

The undersigned promises to pay to the order of ______________________ ("Payee") the sum of ______________________ DOLLARS ($ __________) together with interest on the unpaid principal balance thereof computed at an annual rate [*Author's Note:* Select (i) or (ii)]: (i) which shall float and which is __________ percent (__________ %) above the prime rate as published in *The Wall Street Journal,* adjusted as of the first day of each calendar quarter; or (ii) which shall be fixed at the rate of ______________ percent (________ %) per annum.

Principal and interest shall be paid in (*Author's Note:* select: monthly, quarterly, or semiannual, as applicable) installments, [*Author's Note:* select "in advance" or "in arrears"] of $ ____________ beginning on the ________ day of ____________, XXXX, and each (*Author's Note:* select: monthly, quarterly, or semiannual, as applicable) period continuing on the (first) day of each [*Author's Note:* select: monthly, quarterly, or semiannual, as applicable] calendar period thereafter until the principal balance is paid in full. [*Author's Note:* An alternative could be that payments shall continue "in accordance with the following schedule:"

(Insert desired payment schedule.)

Interest shall be computed on the basis of a 360-day year of twelve 30-day months, and charged for actual days elapsed.

As used herein, "Obligations" means all indebtedness hereunder and any renewals, extensions, or modifications hereof together with any now or hereafter existing indebtedness of Undersigned to Payee whatsoever. "Obligor" means undersigned and all endorsers, guarantors, and sureties of any Obligation. As security for the full and timely repayment of the Obligations (in addition to any other collateral), the undersigned hereby grants to Payee a security interest in all monies, deposits, accounts, or credits held by Payee for or owed by Payee to the undersigned, and, in the event of default or demand hereunder or under any agreement between undersigned and Payee, such monies, deposits, accounts, or credits may be setoff and applied to payment of any Obligations.

[*Author's Note:* Delete if not applicable] This Note and all Obligations are secured pursuant to and entitled to the benefits of the terms of a certain ______________________ ______________________ dated ______________________ XXXX.

The undersigned shall be in default hereunder on the occurrence of any of the following: (a) Nonpayment when due of any payment of principal or interest hereunder or of any Obligation; (b) Any warranty, representation, or statement made or furnished to Payee by or on behalf of the undersigned proving to have been materially incorrect when made or furnished; (c) The existence of any uncured event of default under the terms of any instrument or writing evidencing a debt of the undersigned to someone other than Payee; (d) Uninsured loss, theft, substantial damage, destruction, or transfer or encumbrance without fair value in return of any of the undersigned's assets; (e) The institution by or against any Obligor of any proceeding under any provision or chapter of any federal or state bankruptcy, insolvency, or other debtor relief law whatsoever, or the appointment of any trustee or receiver for any Obligor or any of its assets; (f) Judgment against, or attachment of property of any Obligor; (g) Payee deeming itself insecure; (h) Dissolution, merger, consolidation, liquidation, or reorganization of any Obligor; or (i) Death of any Obligor. Upon the occurrence of any event of default, Payee at its option may declare any or all Obligations immediately due and payable without notice, presentation, demand of payment, or protest, which are hereby expressly waived by every Obligor. Payee's rights and remedies hereunder are cumulative, and recourse to one shall not constitute a waiver of others. The undersigned shall be liable for all costs and expenses incurred by Payee in connection with collection of the Obligation, including court costs, costs of appeal, and attorney's fees.

In the event this Note or any Obligations are not paid when due or demanded, each Obligor hereby authorizes any attorney at law to appear for them before any court having jurisdiction within the United States or elsewhere and after one or more declarations filed, confess judgment against them, jointly and severally, for the unpaid balance of this Note, any Obligations and interest, court costs, costs of appeal, and attorney's fees, such attorney's fees to be equal to twenty-five percent (25%) of the amount confessed, for collection and release of errors, and without stay of execution and inquisition and extension upon any levy on real estate, all of which are hereby waived and condemnation agreed to; and to the extent allowed by applicable law, the exemption of personal property from levy and sale is also hereby expressly waived and no benefit of exemption shall be claimed under any exemption law now in force or which may be hereafter adopted, and further authorizes any attorney at law to confess judgment against them pursuant to all of the terms set forth above for any deficiencies remaining after the collection, foreclosure, realization, or sale of any collateral securing the Obligations, or any part thereof, together with interest, court costs, and attorney's fees as set forth above.

If any part of this Note is declared invalid or unenforceable, such invalidity or unenforceability shall not affect the remainder of this Note, which shall continue in full force and effect. Any provision that is invalid or unenforceable in any application shall remain in full force and effect as to valid applications.

The undersigned warrants and represents that the purpose of this Note is ____________
____ and that it is a commercial purpose Note.

This Note is executed under seal on the date first above written and shall be governed by the law of the State of ____________________.

______________________________, Borrower

By: ______________________________

(CORPORATE SEAL)

Title: ______________________________

(Insert address of maker)

Witnessed:

By ______________________________
(Insert name of witnessing party)

Proposal Documents—Lessor

Form: p-04
Disk File Name: p-04.rtf

SINGLE INVESTOR (NONUNDERWRITTEN)

Form Purpose

An equipment leasing company proposal letter format for a single investor, firm commitment (nonunderwritten) lease financing offer.

Executing Parties

The equipment lessor.

Nonunderwriting Proposal Letter

December 5, XXXX

Secour Corporation
800 Second Avenue
New York, New York 10017

Attention: Mr. R. Babcox
President

Gentlemen:

Able Leasing Corporation ("ALC") offers to purchase and lease to Secour Corporation ("Secour") an item of newly manufactured computer equipment on the following terms and conditions:

1. Equipment Description: The equipment will consist of one (1) new computer, model no. EA-1, manufactured by IXT Computer Corp.
2. Equipment Cost: Approximately $1 million.
3. Delivery and Payment: Delivery of the Equipment is anticipated on January 1, XXXX, but in no event shall be later than March 1, XXXX. ALC shall pay for the Equipment on delivery and acceptance.
4. Lease Term: Eight years, beginning on delivery and acceptance of the Equipment.
5. Rental Program: Secour shall remit 32 consecutive level, quarterly payments, in advance, each equal to 4.4000% of Equipment Cost
6. Options: At the conclusion of the Lease Term, Secour may (with at least 120 days' prior written notice):
   A. Buy the Equipment for an amount equal to its then fair market value.
   B. Renew the lease with respect to the Equipment for its then fair rental value.
7. Tax Benefits: The rent is calculated based on the assumption that ALC will be entitled to:
   A. Five-year MACRS depreciation on the full Equipment Cost, 200% declining-balance switching to straight-line, and
   B. A corporate income tax rate equal to 35%.
8. Fixed Expenses: This is a net financial lease proposal and all fixed expenses such as insurance maintenance, and personal property taxes shall be for the account of Secour.

9. Conditions Precedent: This offer is subject to the approval of the Board of Directors of ALC and to the execution of lease documentation mutually acceptable to Secour and ALC.

If the foregoing is satisfactory to you, please indicate your acceptance of this offer by signing the duplicate copy of this letter in the space provided therefor and returning it directly to the undersigned.

This offer expires as of the close of business on December 19, XXXX.

Very truly yours,

ABLE LEASING CORPORATION

By: ______________________________

Vice President

Accepted and Agreed to on this

__________ day of __________, XXXX

SECOUR CORPORATION

By: ______________________________

Title: ______________________________

Form: p-05
Disk File Name: p-05.rtf

UNDERWRITTEN

Form Purpose

An equipment leasing company proposal letter format for an underwritten, best efforts lease financing offer.

Executing Parties

The equipment lessor.

Underwriting Proposal Letter

July 8, XXXX

White Airline Corporation
200 Park Avenue
New York, New York 10017

Attention: R. Rosset
Assistant Treasurer

Gentlemen:

Able Leasing Corporation ("ALC"), on behalf of its nominees, proposes to use its best efforts to arrange a lease for one new Martin RC-75 aircraft for use by White Airline Corporation under the following terms and conditions:

Lessee:	The Lessee shall be White Airline Corporation.
Lessor:	The Lessor will be a commercial bank or trust company acting as owner trustee ("Owner Trustee") pursuant to one or more owners' trusts (the "Trust") for the benefit of one or more commercial banks or other corporate investors (the "Owner Participant"). The Trust shall acquire the Equipment and lease it to the Lessee.
Equipment:	One new Martin RC-75 aircraft.
Cost:	For purposes of this proposal, a total cost of $28 million, plus or minus 5% has been assumed.
Delivery Date:	Delivery of the Equipment is anticipated as of November 1, XXXX, however, shall be no later than December 30, 1 XXXX.
Interim Lease Term:	The interim lease term shall extend from the Delivery Date until the Commencement Date. For the purposes of this proposal the Commencement Date is assumed to be January l, XXXX
Interim Rent:	The Lessee shall pay interim rent equal to interest-only on the total cost of the Equipment at an interest rate equal to the Long-Term Debt Interest Rate.
Primary Lease Term:	The primary lease term shall be 20 years from the Commencement Date.
Primary Rent:	From the Commencement Date, the Lessee shall make 40 consecutive, level, semiannual payments, in arrears, each equal to 4.400% of Cost.
Debt Financing:	An investment banker acceptable to ALC and the Lessee shall arrange for the private placement of secured notes or similar instruments ("Indebtedness") to be issued by the Lessor

for a principal amount equal to 80% of total Equipment cost to certain institutional investors ("Lenders") who may be represented by an indenture trustee or agent bank ("Agent"). This proposal assumes that the Indebtedness shall be amortized in semiannual payments of principal and interest at an 8% per annum interest rate ("Long-Term Debt Interest Rate"), payable in arrears over the term of the lease. In the event that the Long-Term Debt Interest Rate varies from that assumed, the rent shall be adjusted, upward or downward, so that the Owner Participant's after-tax yield and after-tax cash flows will be maintained. The Indebtedness shall be secured by an assignment of the lease and a security interest in the Equipment but otherwise shall be without recourse to the Owner Participant and the Lessor.

Insurance: The Lessee may self-insure the Equipment.

Purchase and Renewal Options: At the end of the Primary Lease Term, the Lessee may (with 180 days' written notice prior to the end of the term):

A. Renew the lease on the Equipment for its then fair rental value for one five-year period.

B. Buy the Equipment for an equivalent price and under similar conditions as rendered by a third party approached by the Lessor and agreed to by the Lessor prior to sale to that third party.

If the Lessee does not elect to exercise any of the above options, the Lessee shall return the Equipment to the Lessor at the end of the term at a mutually agreeable location.

Termination Option: At any time during the Primary Lease Term, on or after 10 years from the Commencement Date, the Lessee may (with 180 days' prior written notice) terminate the lease in the event the Equipment becomes obsolete or surplus to its needs, on paying a mutually agreed-on termination value.

Fixed Expenses: This is a net financial lease proposal with all fixed expenses, such as maintenance, insurance, taxes (other than net income taxes) for the account of the Lessee.

Transction Expenses: ALC shall pay all transaction expenses, including:

1. fees and disbursements of special counsel for the Agent and the Lenders;
2. acceptance and annual fees and expenses of the Agent;
3. fees and disbursements of special counsel for the Owner Trustee and the Trustor;
4. acceptance and annual fees and expenses of the Owner Trustee;

5. fees and disbursements in connection with obtaining a ruling from the Internal Revenue Service;
6. expenses of documentation, including printing and reproduction; and
7. fees and disbursements in connection with the private placement of the Indebtedness.

If the transaction is not consummated for any reason, the Lessee shall pay all of the above fees and expenses.

Nonutilization Fee: Once ALC has obtained equity investor commitments satisfactory to the Lessee, the Lessee shall be liable to ALC for a nonutlilization fee equal to 0.5% of the Equipment cost in the event it does not lease the Equipment in accordance with intent of this proposal.

Commitment Fee: A commitment fee of 0.5% per annum shall be paid by the Lessee to the equity investors on the outstanding equity investor commitment. The fee shall accrue as of the date investor commitments satisfactory to White Airline Corporation have been obtained, shall run up to the Commencement Date, and shall be payable quarterly, in arrears.

Tax Assumptions:

A. The Rent is calculated based on the assumptions that:

1. the organization created by the Trust will be treated as a partnership for federal income tax purposes;
2. the Lessor will be entitled to seven-year MACRS depreciation on 100% of the Equipment Cost, 200% declining-balance switching to straight-line;
3. the Lessor will be entitled to deduct interest on the Indebtedness under Section 163 of the 1986 Internal Revenue Code;
4. the Lessor will be entitled to amortize the transaction expenses over the Interim and Primary Lease Terms using a straight-line method;
5. the effective federal income tax rate of the Owner Participant is 35%; and
6. the Lessor will not recognize any income from the transaction other than from Lessee rental, termination value, stipulated loss value, and indemnity payments payable to the Lessor.

B. The Lessee shall provide necessary representation relating to the estimated economic life and residual value of the Equipment.

Tax Ruling: The Lessor plans to obtain an Internal Revenue Service ruling with respect to the tax assumptions stated above. The Lessee shall agree to indemnify for the tax assumptions above. Such indemnity shall remain in effect until a favorable ruling has been obtained.

If the foregoing proposal is satisfactory to you, please indicate your acceptance by signing the duplicate copy of this letter in the space provided therefor, and returning it directly to the undersigned.

This offer expires at the close of business on October 28, XXXX and is subject to the approval of the Owner Participant's Board of Directors and mutually satisfactory lease documentation.

Very truly yours,

ABLE LEASING CORPORATION

By: ______________________________

Vice President

Accepted and Agreed to on this

______ day of ________________, XXXX.

WHITE AIRLINE CORPORATION

By: ______________________________

Title: _____________________________

Purchase Agreement/ Assignment

[Also see Form I-04a.]

Form: p-06
Disk File Name: p-06.rtf

Purchase Agreement Assignment—Integrated

Form Purpose

Assignment of equipment purchase agreement rights to an equipment leasing company. This form is integrated with Lease Agreement, Form l-03.

Executing Parties

The equipment lessor.
The equipment lessee.

See:

Lease Agreement, Form l-03

______________________________, Lessor

Home Office Address: ______________________________

Phone ( ) ______________________________

Purchase Agreement Assignment

PURCHASE AGREEMENT ASSIGNMENT ("Assignment"), dated as of ____________, between ______________________, a ______________________ corporation ("Lessor"), and ______________________, a ______________________ corporation ("Lessee").

WHEREAS, Lessee has entered into one or more purchase agreements identified in Exhibit A hereto (collectively "Purchase Agreement"), true and complete copies of which, as amended to the date hereof, have been initialed and delivered by Lessee to Lessor on or before the execution and delivery of this Assignment, with the manufacturers or vendors identified in Exhibit A (collectively "Vendor"), providing for the purchase by, and delivery to, Lessee of the items of equipment identified in Exhibit A (collectively "Units");

WHEREAS, Lessee desires to lease rather than purchase the Units and Lessor is willing to acquire Lessee's rights and interests under the Purchase Agreement relating to the Units and to purchase the Units, all on the terms and conditions set forth below; and

WHEREAS, Lessor will, subject to certain conditions, pay for each Unit in accordance with the terms of the Purchase Agreement upon delivery to and acceptance by Lessee of such Unit for lease pursuant to the terms and conditions of a Master Agreement to Lease Equipment between Lessor and Lessee, dated as of ______________________, and the applicable Schedule identified on Exhibit A (collectively "Lease");

NOW, THEREFORE, for good and valuable consideration, the receipt and sufficiency of which is hereby acknowledged, the parties hereto agree as follows:

1. Assignment. Lessee does hereby assign and set over to Lessor all of Lessee's rights and interests under the Purchase Agreement relating to the Units, including without limitation (a) the right to purchase the Units and to take title to the Units and to be named the purchaser in the bill or bills of sale to be delivered with respect to the Units, (b) all rights to enforce claims against Vendor for damages, losses, liabilities, and expenses arising directly or indirectly out of or in connection with the Purchase Agreement or the Units, including without limitation all guaranty, warranty, and indemnity provisions contained in the Purchase Agreement as to the Units, and (c) all rights to compel performance of the terms of the Purchase Agreement.

Notwithstanding the foregoing, provided that Lessor has not notified Vendor in writing that an Incipient Default or Event of Default under the Lease has occurred and is continuing, Lessor authorizes Lessee as to each Unit during the Lease Term of such Unit to exercise in Lessee's name all rights and powers of the purchaser under the Purchase Agreement and to retain any recovery or benefit resulting from the enforcement of any Vendor guaranty, warranty, or indemnity under the Purchase Agreement or otherwise; provided, however, that Lessee may not consent to any modification of the Purchase Agreement or any documentation relating thereto without the prior written consent of Lessor.

2. Continuing Liability of Lessee. It is expressly agreed that, anything contained herein to the contrary notwithstanding, (a) Lessee shall perform, and at all times remain liable to Vendor under the Purchase Agreement to perform, all duties and obligations of the purchaser thereunder to the same extent as if this Assignment had not been entered into, (b) the exercise by Lessor of any of the rights assigned hereunder shall not release Lessee from any of its duties or obligations to Vendor under the Purchase Agreement, and (c) the performance by Lessor of any duties or obligations of Lessee to Vendor under the Purchase Agreement shall not release Lessee from any of its duties or obligations to Lessor under this Assignment

3. Purchase of Equipment; Limitation of Lessor's Liability. Lessor agrees with Lessee, subject to (a) the execution and delivery by Vendor to Lessor of a Consent and Agreement substantially in the form of Exhibit B hereto, (b) the terms and conditions of the Lease, and (e) delivery to and acceptance by Lessee of the Units in accordance with the terms of the Purchase Agreement and the Lease, to pay to Vendor the purchase cost to Lessee of each such Unit. Lessor does not assume and shall not at any time have any obligations or duties to Vendor under or by reason of this Assignment or the Purchase Agreement.

4. Further Assurance. Lessee agrees at any time and from time to time, at the request of Lessor, to promptly and duly execute and deliver any and all such further instruments and documents and take such further action as Lessor may request to obtain the full benefits of this Assignment and of the rights and powers herein granted.

5. Lessee Indemnity. Lessee agrees to indemnify and defend Lessor, its successors and assigns against any and all losses, claims, damages, liabilities, and expenses (including without limitation reasonable legal fees) which arise directly or indirectly out of or in connection with this Assignment, the Purchase Agreement, or the Units (including without limitation the manufacture, purchase, testing, operation, acceptance, rejection, ownership, shipment, transportation, use, delivery, installation, leasing, possession, storage, return, or sale of any Unit); provided, however, that Lessee shall not be required to indemnify Lessor under this Section 5 as to any matter resulting solely from Lessor's willful misconduct.

6. Lessee Warranties and Covenants. Lessee warrants and covenants that (a) the Purchase Agreement is valid, in full force and effect, is not in default, and is and will remain enforceable in accordance with its terms, except as limited by applicable bankruptcy, insolvency, reorganization, and similar laws affecting the enforcement of creditor and lessor rights generally, (b) the execution and delivery of this Assignment has been duly authorized, and this Assignment is and will remain the valid and binding obligation of Lessee enforceable against Lessee in accordance with its terms, except as limited by applicable bankruptcy, insolvency, reorganization, and similar laws affecting the enforcement of creditor and lessor rights generally, and (c) Lessee has not made and will not make any other assignment of the Purchase Agreement or any part thereof or any of its rights thereunder, all of which are free and clear of any and all liens, encumbrances, rights, or claims of third parties whatsoever.

7. Governing Law. This Assignment shall be governed in all respects by, and construed in accordance with, the laws of the State of ________________.

8. Assignment by Lessor. This Assignment and Lessor's rights, interests, and obligations hereunder may be assigned in whole or in part by Lessor without the consent of Lessee. This Assignment shall be binding upon and inure to the benefit of the respective successors and assigns of Lessor and Lessee.

IN WITNESS WHEREOF, the parties hereto have duly executed this Assignment as of the date first above written.

______________________, Lessor

By: ______________________

Title: ______________________

______________________, Lessee

By: ______________________

Title: ______________________

Exhibit A

Purchase Agreements Assigned

Vendor	*Purchase Agreement Date*	*Schedule No.*	*Description of Units*

Exhibit B

Purchase Agreement Assigned Consent and Agreement

For good and valuable consideration, the receipt and sufficiency of which are hereby acknowledged, the undersigned, a ______________________ corporation ("Vendor"), hereby acknowledges notice of and consents to all of the terms and conditions of the attached Purchase Agreement Assignment ("Assignment"), dated as of ____________, between ______________________, Lessor, and ______________________, Lessee. The terms defined in the Assignment shall have the same meanings in this Consent and Agreement, Vendor hereby confirms to and agrees with Lessor that (i) all representations, warranties, indemnities, and agreements of Vendor under the Purchase Agreement to the extent assigned in the Assignment with respect to the Units shall inure to the benefit of Lessor to the same extent as if Lessor had originally been named the purchaser in the Purchase Agreement, (ii) Lessor shall not be liable for any of the obligations or duties of Lessee under the Purchase Agreement, nor shall the Assignment give rise to any duties or obligations whatsoever on the part of Lessor to Vendor, and (iii) from and after the date of delivery of each Unit or any part thereof pursuant to the Purchase Agreement Vendor will not assert any lien or claim against such Unit or part thereof arising on or prior to the date of such delivery, including without limitation any lien or claim for any work or services performed on or prior to the date of such delivery.

Vendor hereby represents and warrants that (a) Vendor is a corporation duly organized and validly existing in good standing under the laws of the State of ______________, (b) the making and performance of the Purchase Agreement and this Consent and Agreement have been duly authorized by all necessary corporate action on the part of Vendor, do not require any stockholder or other approval, and do not contravene any law binding on Vendor or contravene Vendor's articles of incorporation or by-laws or any indenture, credit agreement, or other contract to which Vendor is a party or by which it or its properties are bound, (c) the Purchase Agreement constitutes a valid and binding obligation of Vendor enforceable against Vendor in accordance with its terms, and this Consent and Agreement is a valid and binding obligation of Vendor enforceable against Vendor in accordance with its terms, in each case except as limited by applicable bankruptcy, insolvency, reorganization, and similar laws governing the enforcement of creditor and lessor rights generally, and (d) the Purchase Agreement is in full force and effect and no default exists thereunder.

IN WITNESS WHEREOF, Vendor has duly executed this Consent and Agreement as of the ________________ day of, XXXX.

__________________________, Vendor

By: __________________________

Title: __________________________

Purchase Order Documents

Form: p-07
Disk File Name: p-07.rtf

PURCHASE ORDER—EQUIPMENT

Form Purpose

An equipment leasing company equipment purchase order.

Executing Parties

The equipment lessor.

Purchase Order No. ______________

Vendor: ______________________________

SHIP TO (Insert name and address of Lessee below

Description of Equipment Cost

[Insert equipment information]

Confirming Lessee's prior order. Do not duplicate.

Instructions to Vendor

Invoice should be mailed to ______________________ on date of shipment. INVOICES CANNOT BE HONORED UNLESS THE FULL EQUIPMENT DESCRIPTION INCLUDING SERIAL NUMBERS APPEAR THEREON.

Show on invoice:

- Sold to–
- Shipped to (Name and address of Lessee)
- Full description of equipment, model and serial numbers
- Our purchase order number

This purchase order is subject to cancellation if the equipment covered by this order is not delivered to and accepted by the Lessee on a Delivery Receipt within 30 days of the date shown below.

This purchase order is subject to the terms and conditions on reverse side which are a part hereof.

Date: ______________________________

(Insert leasing company name)

By: ______________________________

Title: ______________________________

[*Author's Note:* The following should be placed on the reverse side.]

Terms and Conditions of Purchase

1. No Changes Authorized. This purchase order must be accepted as written. Any increase in price, change in quantities, or quality of merchandise ordered or any other change in terms or conditions of this order shall not be binding on the buyer unless such change is agreed to in writing. Delivery must be in accordance with the conditions hereof and unless otherwise specifically noted thereon Vendor is to deliver the merchandise f.o.b. Lessee's address, destined as thereon indicated.

2. No Charges Authorized. No charges for crating, boxing, packing, or drayage, or for unloading, assembling, or installing any merchandise will be allowed or payable unless specified herein.

3. Inspection, Acceptance, or Rejection. All merchandise shall be received subject to buyer's inspection and acceptance or rejection. The place and time of inspection shall be determined by buyer. Merchandise which is defective or not accepted by Lessee within a reasonable time or otherwise not in accordance with this purchase order may be returned for full credit and Vendor shall assume all transportation and handling charges in connection therewith. Rejected merchandise shall not be replaced except upon buyer's specific instructions in writing to that effect. Any deposit, prepayment, or other payment made to Vendor by buyer shall either be refunded to buyer or buyer may, at buyer's option, apply the amount thereof to any other debt or obligation of buyer to Vendor.

4. Risk of Loss. Vendor shall bear all risk of loss of any merchandise covered by this purchase order until physically delivered, installed, inspected, and accepted by Lessee at the designated place of delivery, and Vendor shall further bear the risk of loss at all times on rejected merchandise.

5. Delivery to be Made to Lessee. The person, firm, or corporation to which the merchandise covered by this purchase order is to be delivered (as indicated herein) has leased said merchandise from the buyer pursuant to a Lease Agreement, and is herein referred to as "Lessee". Lessee is authorized on behalf of the buyer to receive delivery of such merchandise, to inspect, and to accept or reject same. Delivery is to be made promptly, and any delay in delivery requires buyer's prior written approval.

6. Rejection by Lessee. If Lessee shall reject or refuse to accept any merchandise pursuant to this purchase order, buyer shall be deemed relieved of any liability to Vendor under such purchase order as to such merchandise, and all obligations of buyer hereunder as to such merchandise shall upon such rejection or refusal be deemed those of Lessee, with the same force and effect as if Lessee, instead of buyer, had placed this purchase order as to such merchandise, and Vendor in such event, shall look only to Lessee with respect to any liability or obligation hereunder.

7. Cancellation by Buyer. This purchase order may be canceled by the buyer in the event the Lessee is not authorized to enter into the Lease, or the person signing the Lease on behalf of the Lessee is not authorized so to do, or, in the event that Vendor or any of its agents make any representations to Lessee inconsistent with the terms or conditions of the Lease, upon which Lessee reasonably relies.

8. No Assignment by Vendor. Vendor shall not assign this purchase order without the prior written consent of buyer. In the absence of such consent, no such assignment

shall be effective, and at buyer's option, shall effect a cancellation of all buyer's obligations hereunder.

9. Patents. Vendor agrees to and does by shipment thereof indemnify, protect, and hold harmless buyer, its successors or assigns, and Lessee and its successors and assigns against all claims. demands, damages, costs, or expenses including attorneys' fees) for actual or alleged infringements of any patent covering any merchandise hereby ordered or the use thereof.

10. Fair Labor Assurance. Vendor warrants and represents that the goods ordered hereby have been produced in compliance with the requirements of the Fair Labor Standards Act of 1938, as amended, and with all legislation and regulations, including, without limitation, those governing Fair Employment practices and Equal Employment Opportunity.

11. Warranties by Vendor. Vendor warrants that immediately prior to buyer's purchase Vendor had legal title to the merchandise, title is transferred free from any liens and encumbrances, that the merchandise ordered hereunder will be fit and sufficient for the purpose intended, that it will conform to the specifications, drawings, or samples, if any, furnished or adopted by the buyer and will be merchantable, of good quality, and free from defects in material, design, or workmanship. No part or plans made according to buyer's design will be sold to any other person, firm, or corporation. The foregoing is in addition to and not in lieu of any or all other warranties expressed or implied. All warranties shall run to, inure for the benefit of and be enforceable by both buyer and its lessee, jointly and separately.

12. Excusable Delays. Vendor will not be responsible for delays or defaults in delivery if occasioned by unforeseeable cause beyond the control and without the fault or negligence of Vendor; and buyer shall not be responsible for failure to receive or take delivery if occasioned by any like cause on its or Lessee's part.

13. Freight. If the buyer has not indicated any preference for the method of shipment, then the merchandise shall be shipped in the least expensive way.

14. Purchase Price. All quantity, cash, or other discounts granted by Vendor as a direct or indirect result of the purchase herein ordered shall be paid to buyer. Vendor represents and warrants that no payments have been made to Lessee nor has Lessee received any other consideration as a direct or indirect result of the purchase herein ordered unless the amount of such payment or the value of such consideration is deducted from the gross invoice price.

15. Title to merchandise shall pass to buyer only after physical delivery, installation, inspection, and acceptance as provided herein.

Resolutions—Corporate Lessee

[See "Corporate Secretary Certification Documents—Lessee."]

Request for Lease Quotations

Form: r-01
Disk File Name: r-01.rtf

RFQ—Deal Sheet Format

Form Purpose

An informal lessee request for leasing company lease quotations, incorporating a deal sheet.

Executing Parties

The prospective equipment lessee.

An Informal Deal Sheet Approach

Author's note: If your company leases a high volume of equipment each year, consider putting together a deal sheet format that can be filled out and attached to a simple lease request cover letter.

Here's a suggested format. If you decide to use a similar format, use the Lessee Proposal Stage Checklist (Form c-01) to ensure you've covered all issues of importance in your deal.

BRIGHT TIME COMPANY
34 Orchard Road
Rye, New York 10580

(914) 991–8900

May 2, XXXX

BY HAND

Ms. Mary Mari
Marketing Vice President
Rapid Leasing Corporation
1425 Money Drive
White Plains, New York 10604

Dear Mary:

We are planning to take delivery on the equipment specified on the attached term sheet during the last week of May. We would be interested in receiving a lease financing quote to determine if leasing is the best alternative for us. Please submit a written quote no later than May 5, XXXX.

If you have any thoughts about other structures or benefits that may be beneficial, please include them in your response. Incidentally, we will not accept a brokered transaction and are looking to you to be the actual lessor.

Our decision will be made by May 10, XXXX. The lease must be signed no later than May 15, XXXX. If you have any questions, my direct line is (914) 991-8795

Sincerely,

Roger Rogueson
Assistant Manager

BRIGHT TIME COMPANY

TERM SHEET
May 2, XXXX

Equipment:	Monitor Sentex Computer System, Model 3 with Excel Payroll Package.
Equipment Cost:	$215, 000 ± 15%
Vendor:	Monitor Computer Company
Delivery Date:	May 29, XXXX
Lease Term:	3- and 5-year
Rent Quote:	Monthly, in advance, and quarter, in arrears
Purchase Option:	10% of Equipment Cost
Renewal Option:	Maximum 1st year 25% of primary rent, thereafter year-to-year fair market rental value
Early Termination Right:	Anytime after first year of base lease term Attach schedule to proposal
Bid Due Date:	May 5, XXXX
Award Date:	May 10, XXXX

Special Provisions:

1. Transaction to be single investor, nonbrokered
2. Lease to qualify as operating lease for accounting purposes
3. Net finance lease
4. Our master lease to be used in the form enclosed. Please identify with proposal any provisions that are not acceptable.
5. A casualty value schedule must be sent with your quote.

Form: r-02
Disk File Name: r-02.rtf

RFQ—INFORMAL

Form Purpose

An informal lessee request for leasing company lease quotations.

Executing Parties

The prospective equipment lessee.

A Less Formal Request for Quotes

Author's note: In certain situations, as mentioned earlier, a less formal RFQ will do the necessary job. For example, in a $100,000 lease financing, there are fewer issues and negotiating risks. Here's an approach that can be used:

BRIGHT TIME COMPANY
34 Orchard Road
Rye, New York 10580

(914) 991-8900

May 2, XXXX

BY HAND

Ms. Mary Mari
Marketing Vice President
Rapid Leasing Corporation
1425 Money Lane
White Plains, New York 10604

Dear Mary:

We are planning to take delivery on a Monitor Computer System during the last week of May. We would be interested in having you submit a lease financing quote for our internal purchase/lease evaluation. Please submit the quote in writing no later than May 5, XXXX.

The equipment cost is anticipated to be $215, 000. We, however, need some leeway in your bid to cover a cost variance of 15%, up or down. The actual system configuration is a Model 3, Excel Payroll Processing System, sold by Monitor Computer Company. I've enclosed a copy of our vendor equipment purchase order confirmation detailing the equipment specifics. The vendor expects payment in full on the date we accept the equipment for lease.

We would like to see monthly, in advance, and quarterly, in arrears, quotes for three-year and five-year lease terms. We want a 10% purchase option and the right to renew the lease for successive one-year terms, the first term renewal rent not to exceed 25% of the original term rent and the remaining at a rent equal to the fair market rental value. We would also like the right to terminate the lease before the end of the basic term and ask that you submit a schedule of termination values beginning at the end of the first year. Incidentally, we also would like you to submit your casualty value schedule along with your quote.

If you have any thoughts about other structures or benefits that may be beneficial, please include them in your response. Incidentally, we will not accept a brokered transaction and are looking to you to be the actual lessor.

Our decision will be made by May 10, XXXX. The lease must be signed no later than May 15, XXXX. If you have any questions, my direct line is (914) 991-8795.

Sincerely,

Roger Rogueson
Assistant to the President

Author's note: The preceding letter, although still informal, tells the leasing company what is needed. It states the equipment specifics as well as the lease terms that it is looking for. And it tells when the bids are due and when the decision will be made.

It also does not indicate that a lease is the only alternative. To keep negotiating leverage highest you must leave the door open to a purchase possibility, at least as far as the leasing company is concerned.

Form: r-03
Disk File Name: r-03.rtf

RFQ—Long Form

Form Purpose

A long-form formal lessee request for leasing company lease quotations.

A Formal Request for Quotes Letter

Request for Quotations to Lease Equipment

April 12, XXXX

SunTime Corporation is issuing this REQUEST FOR QUOTATIONS (RFQ) to obtain equipment lease bids from perspective lessors. This RFQ is not an offer to contract. SunTime Corporation will not be obligated to lease the specified equipment until a mutually satisfactory written lease has been executed by all parties.

A. Proposal Request—General

In accordance with the terms and conditions specified below, SunTime Corporation wishes to receive proposals from equipment leasing companies (Lessors) to provide lease financing for certain data processing equipment.

In the evaluation of each proposal, SunTime Corporation will rely on all written and verbal representations made by each prospective Lessor and each representation will be incorporated into any and all formal agreements between the parties.

No Lessor receiving this RFQ is authorized to act for, or on behalf of, SunTime Corporation prior to the receipt of written acceptance by SunTime Corporation of a satisfactory lease proposal and then only in accordance with the specific terms, if any, of the acceptance.

B. Proposal Guidelines

1. Your proposal must be submitted in writing and follow the guidelines in this RFQ. If it does not, it will be rejected.

2. All RFQ requirements must be addressed. Specifically identify any requirements that cannot be satisfied.

3. If you can offer any additional benefits not requested in this RFQ, identify them as "Additional Benefits" and state them in a separate section at the end of your proposal.

4. You must notify SunTime Corporation no later than the Lessor Proposal Intent Notification Date specified in the Time Table below if you intend to submit a proposal in response to this RFQ.

5. SunTime Corporation may, without liability and in its sole discretion, amend or rescind this RFQ prior to the lease award. In such event each Lessor offering to submit a proposal will be supplied, as the case may be, with an RFQ amendment or a notification of our intent not to proceed.

6. Your proposal will be considered confidential and none of the contents will be disclosed to a competing Lessor.

7. You shall be responsible for all costs incurred in connection with the preparation of your proposal and any contract(s) in response to this RFQ.

8. Your proposal must be signed by a duly authorized representative of your company.

9. Your proposal must be submitted in triplicate and remain in effect at least until the Lessor Proposal Commitment Cut-Off date specified in the Time Table below.

10. Your proposal should be accompanied by (a) a copy of your most recent annual report or financial statements or appropriate bank references with account officer name and telephone number, (b) a description of any material litigation in which you are presently involved, and (c) a statement of any potential conflict of interest, and plan to avoid it, as a result of an award.

11. SunTime Corporation intends to announce its award decision no later than the Award Announcement date specified in the Time Table below.

12. Any questions concerning this RFQ, should sent in writing to:

SunTime Corporation
1823 Third Avenue
New York, New York 11020
Attn. John Peterson
Telephone Number: (212) 754-2367

Any questions and answers which we feel would be of assistance to all Lessors submitting proposals, will be promptly distributed to each.

13. SunTime Corporation may enter simultaneously in negotiations with more than one Lessor and make an award to one or more without prior notification to others we are negotiating with.

14. Any information supplied to you in this RFQ by SunTime Corporation or otherwise by any representative in connection with this RFQ is confidential and may not be disclosed or used except in connection with the preparation of your proposal. If you must release any such information to any person or entity for the purpose of preparing your proposal, you must obtain an agreement prior to releasing the information that it will be treated as confidential by such person or entity and will not be disclosed except in connection with the preparation of your proposal.

15. If you are a selected Lessor, prior to our making the award you will be supplied with a copy of our form lease document(s) for your review. Your response to the acceptability of the document provisions, with exceptions noted in writing, will be a condition precedent to any award.

C. Equipment Lease Requirements

1. EQUIPMENT DESCRIPTION, COST and TRADE-IN

a. The equipment will consist of electronic data processing equipment (Equipment) acquired from the following designated vendor(s):

Vendor	*Equipment Description*	*Cost*
StarByte Computer Corp.	(1) Model 423 Computer	$1,850,000
Buffalo, NY	(7) Model 3 Remote Ctrs.	350,000
Micro Tech, Inc.	Material Tracking System	150,000
New York, NY		
	Installation:	120,000
	TOTAL:	$2,470,000

(i) The final cost of the Equipment may vary as much as + (10)% or −(20)%, and your financing offer must permit this leeway without penalty.

b. If you can provide more advantageous financing by supplying equipment you own, have access to, or can acquire through volume discount arrangements with a vendor, please provide the specifics in the Additional Benefits section. If you intend to offer to provide any used equipment, the serial number(s), current location(s) and owner(s) must be stated in your proposal.

(i) Any equipment you offer to supply must be delivered to SunTime Corporation at 937 Secour Drive, Buffalo, New York 11342 no later than the Anticipated Equipment Delivery Date specified in the Time Table in Section D below and ready for acceptance no later than the specified Anticipated Equipment Acceptance Date. You must provide a firm delivery date commitment with contractual assurances and remedies for failure to meet such date, which should be stated in your proposal.

c. The Equipment will replace equipment under an existing lease of computer equipment and SunTime Corporation would like you to propose an additional financing arrangement which would incorporate the buy-out of that lease. The specifics of the existing lease are as follows:

Lessor: AmerLease Corp.
Lease Term: 7 Years
Lease Start Date: March 1, XXXX
Lease Ending Date: February 28, XXXX
Monthly Rent: $21,324, in advance
Lease Termination Amount as of August 31, XXXX: $397,000
Equipment: StarByte XTRA Material Tracking Computer System
Original Equipment Cost: $1,253,000
Right to Sublease: Yes
Purchase Option: Fair Market
Renewal Option: Year to Year, 90 Days' Prior Notice, Fair Market

(i) If you can provide any other arrangement that would be beneficial, such as subleasing the existing equipment to another lessee, please so indicate.

2. ESTIMATED DELIVERY AND ACCEPTANCE DATE

It is anticipated that the Equipment will be delivered and accepted for lease no later than the anticipated delivery and acceptance date(s) specified in the Time Table below.

3. EQUIPMENT PAYMENT

The Equipment must be paid for by Lessor no later than thirty (30) days following acceptance for lease.

4. EQUIPMENT LOCATION

The Equipment will initially be accepted for lease at our manufacturing plant located at 937 Secour Drive, Buffalo, New York. We must have the right to move the equipment to any location in the United States without the prior consent of Lessor, but upon providing thirty (30) days' prior written notice.

5. PRIMARY LEASE TERM

Your proposal must provide offers to lease the Equipment for Primary Lease Terms of five (5) and seven (7) years.

The Primary Lease Terms must run from the later of the Equipment acceptance for lease or payment by Lessor for the Equipment.

6. PRIMARY TERM RENTS

Rent payments must be quoted on a monthly, in advance, and quarterly, in arrears, basis.

The rent payments must be expressed as a percentage of Equipment Cost and be on a consecutive, level basis. The nominal lease interest rate must be provided for each rent quote.

SunTime Corporation shall not be obligated for payment of rent until the Equipment vendor has been paid in full.

7. INTERIM LEASE TERM

No Interim Lease Term will be permitted that requires payment of interim rent.

8. INTERIM RENTS

No Interim Lease Term rent payments will acceptable.

9. OPTIONS

a. SunTime Corporation must have the option to renew the term of the lease year to year for a total of three (3) years, on a fair market value basis. Offers providing for a fixed-price renewal will also be considered. Any fixed price offers should be included in an "Additional Benefits" section at the end of the Lessor's proposal.

b. Lessee must have the right to purchase the Equipment at the end of the Primary Lease Term and each Renewal Term for its then fair market value. Offers providing for the right to purchase for a fixed percentage of Equipment Cost will be given favorable consideration and should be included in an "Additional Benefits" section at the end of the Lessor's offer.

c. SunTime Corporation must have the right, beginning as of the end of the first year of the Primary Lease Term, to terminate the Lease prior to the end of the Primary Lease Term, or any Renewal Term, in the event the Equipment becomes obsolete or surplus to SunTime Corporation's needs.

(i) In the event of an early termination, SunTime Corporation shall have the right to arrange for the sale or re-lease of the Equipment. Any proceeds from the sale, or anticipated proceeds from the lease, of the Equipment shall reduce any termination penalty payment required.

(ii) A schedule of early termination values must be included with your proposal.

d. SunTime Corporation must have the right to upgrade the Equipment, by adding equipment or replacing components, at any time during the term of the lease and Lessor must provide financing for such upgrade for a term coterminous with the term remaining during the upgrade period at a financing rate which will not exceed Lessor's transaction nominal after-tax yield.

10. INSURANCE

The Equipment shall be self-insured.

11. CASUALTY VALUE SCHEDULE

A schedule of casualty values, expressed as a percentage of Equipment Cost, for both the Primary Lease Term and any Renewal Term(s) must be submitted with your proposal.

12. TRANSACTION FEES

Lessee will not pay financing commitment or nonutilization fees.

13. ACCOUNTING CLASSIFICATION

Preference will be given to a Lease which qualifies as an operating lease under the applicable accounting guidelines.

14. SINGLE SOURCE PREFERENCE

Preference will be given to Lessors who intend to provide 100% of the funds necessary to purchase the Equipment over those who intend to leverage the purchase with third-party debt. Your proposal must disclose your intent.

(a) In the event you determine it would be advantageous to propose a leveraged lease financing structure, it should be submitted assuming a long-term debt interest rate of 6.75% per annum. In addition, the following terms will apply:

(i) Our investment banker, Chicago First Corporation, will be responsible for securing the third-party leveraged lease debt at a rate satisfactory to SunTime Corporation, within our sole discretion.

(ii) You must provide assurance that the lease will qualify as a true lease for federal income tax purposes under the current tax rules and guidelines.

(iii) You must state whether your proposal is on a best efforts or firm basis; preference will be given to those on a firm basis.

(iv) At the time of submission of your proposal you must be prepared to identify all lease participants (with contact name and telephone number), including each identified equity and debt participant, so they may be called immediately for verification in the event you are the successful bidder.

15. BROKER DISCLOSURE

We will give a preference to lease offers from principal funding sources who do not intend to re-sell or broker the transaction. In the event that you do not intend to act as a principal and purchase the equipment for your own account, you must disclose that in your proposal.

16. EXPENSES

Lessor shall be responsible for payment of all fees and expenses of the transaction, other than Lessee's own direct legal fees in connection with documenting the lease transaction, including fees and expenses incurred in connection with the arranging, or documentation, of the Equipment Lease.

D. Time Table

SunTime Corporation will adhere to the following time schedule in connection with evaluating submitted proposals, making the award decision and negotiating the equipment lease document(s):

Action	*Date*
Lessor Proposal Intent Notification Due	
Lessor Proposals Due	
Lessor Proposal Commitment Cut-Off	
Lessor Notification of Initial Qualification	
Form Lease Document(s) Sent to Qualified Lessor(s)	
Lessor Response to Form Lease Document(s)	
Lessor(s) Selection	
Award Announcement	
Lease Negotiations—Start	
Lease Signing	
Anticipated Equipment Delivery	
Anticipated Equipment Acceptance for Lease	

Form: r-04
Disk File Name: r-04.rtf

RFQ—Short Form

Form Purpose

A short-form formal lessee request for leasing company lease quotations.

Request for Lease Quotation

The Mideastern Railway Corporation

Lessee:	The Mideastern Railway Corporation
Equipment:	Model 6 RD-10, 23,000 hp diesel locomotives (est. unit cost-$525,000), manufactured by Arcane Locomotive Corp.
Estimated Total Cost:	$3,150,000
Equipment Delivery:	February, XXXX-Two units March, XXXX-Two units April, XXXX-Two units
Equity Contribution and Commitment:	Not less than 20% of cost. The equity investor(s) must agree to buy equipment with a maximum equipment cost up to $3.5 million.
Interest Rate Assumptions:	7 3/4%, 8%, 8 1/4%
Agent for Debt Placement:	Samon & Smith Co.
Attorney for Long-Term Lenders:	Carr, Swift & Moore, subject to agreement of the long-term lenders
Structuring of the Transaction:	15-year net finance leveraged lease with semiannual, in arrears, level payments. Any other proposal format will be considered provided a bid as requested has been submitted. The lessee must have three two-year fair market rental renewal options. A fair market purchase option at the end of the initial term and each renewal term should also be provided. The lessee will give a letter stating that, in its opinion, the locomotives will have a useful life exceeding 18 years and a residual value equal to 20% of the original cost at the end of 15 years.
Delivery Cutoff Date:	The cutoff date for the equipment deliveries will be July 1, XXXX. All equipment not delivered before this date will be excluded from the transaction unless the lessor and the lessee agree to extend such date.
Expenses:	All expenses of the transaction, including rating fees and the investment banking fees, will be borne by the lessor.
Security:	The lessee's lease obligations will be unconditionally guaranteed by The Eastern Railway Company. The Mideastern Railway Company is a wholly owned subsidiary of The Eastern Railway Company. The long-term debt will be secured by an assignment of the lease. An agent bank will be selected by The Eastern

	Railway Company and Samon & Smith Co. after the long-term debt is placed. The long-term debt will be noncallable except for casualty occurrences.
Indemnification:	Preference will be given to bids with minimum indemnification. All indemnification requirements must be precisely stated in the proposal.
Interim Rentals:	All quotations must assume not more than three equity closing dates and provide interim rents from such dates to July 1, XXXX, the beginning of the primary lease term. Interim rentals will be equal to the daily equivalent of the long-term debt interest rate.
Casualty Values:	All bidders must provide a schedule of casualty values, expressed as a percentage of original cost, both for the primary lease term and any extensions thereafter. The method of calculating the casualty values must also be supplied.
Insurance:	The equipment will be self-insured.

Please mail us your proposal in writing postmarked no later than April 15, XXXX. Your proposal must be on a "firm" basis and at the time of submission you must be prepared to identify the investor source(s) so that they may be contacted immediately by telephone for verification in the event you are the successful bidder.

Schedules—Equipment

[See Equipment Schedule, Form 1-02a.]

Security Agreements

[See "Loan Documents."]

Secretary's Certificates

[See "Corporate Secretary Certification Documents—Lessee."]

Subordination Agreements

Form: s-01
Disk File Name: s-01.rtf

LESSEE CREDITOR

Form Purpose

A subordination agreement for use by a leasing company in obtaining a lessee creditor waiver of any potential claims against the leased equipment.

Executing Parties

A lessee creditor.

Subordination Agreement

The undersigned hereby waives any interest in the below described equipment currently owned by ______________________ (Lessor)

[Equipment description]

[Insert creditor's name]

By: ______________________________

Title: ____________________________

DATE: ____________________________

Termination Value Schedules

[See Termination Value Schedule, Form I-02d.]

Time Tables

Form: t-01
Disk File Name: t-01.rtf

TIME TABLE—DEAL SCHEDULE

Form Purpose

A lessee-prepared deal time table to keep an equipment lease deal on track from lease proposal to document closing.

Time Table

(Insert name of lessee) will adhere to the following time schedule in connection with evaluating submitted proposals, making the award decision, and negotiating the equipment lease document(s):

Action	Date
Lessor Proposal Intent Notification Due	
Lessor Proposals Due	
Lessor Proposal Commitment Cut-Off	
Lessor Notification of Initial Qualification	
Form Lease Document(s) Sent to Qualified Lessor(s)	
Lessor Response to Form Lease Document(s)	
Lessor(s) Selection	
Award Announcement	
Lease Negotiations—Start	
Lease Signing	
Anticipated Equipment Delivery	
Anticipated Equipment Acceptance for Lease	

Time Table Action Category Explanation

Lessor Proposal Intent Notification Due

The date when each leasing company receiving the RFQ must indicate its willingness to submit a lease offer. Typically, I set a date one week following the delivery of the RFQ to prospective bidders.

Lessor Proposals Due

The date when all lessor proposals are due. Use a date which will provide adequate lead time to have the transaction re-bid, get the equipment delivered and operationally accepted, and cover any unforeseen delays.

Lessor Proposal Commitment Cut-Off

The date through which the lessor must keep its proposal available for acceptance by the lessee. I set a date which will provide adequate time to review all proposals, with a margin for comfort.

Lessor Notification of Initial Qualification

The date when the lessee will make the preliminary lease award, subject to acceptance of the lessee's form lease documents. Set a date you're comfortable with.

Form Lease Document(s) Sent to Qualified Lessor(s)

The date when the lessee's form lease documents will be sent to the preliminary selected lessor(s) for review and comments. The date is typically one shortly following the Lessor Notification of Initial Qualification Date.

Lessor Response to Form Lease Document(s)

The date when the initially selected lessor(s) must submit comments to the lessee's form lease documents. Typically, I like to give a lessor two weeks to review the form lease agreement and respond.

Lessor(s) Selection

The date on which you will make the final winning lessor(s) selection. Set a date which will give you adequate time to review with your lawyers the lessors' form lease agreement responses.

In certain situations, in may be a good negotiation approach to select three lessors—specifying a first place, second place, and third place award and simultaneously telling all three that if negotiations break down with the first place lessor, you will immediately begin negotiations with the second place lessor and similarly, if necessary, with the third place lessor.

Award Announcement

The date when all lessors will be notified of your lessor selection decision. Typically, I set a date one to two business days after the Lessor(s) Selection Date.

Lease Negotiations—Start

The date when negotiation will begin with the winning lessor. I usually set a date three to five business days following the Award Announcement date.

Lease Signing

The date when you expect all lease negotiations to be concluded and the lease documents to be signed by all parties. The date you set will depend on the complexity of the lease financing. A simple transaction can be documented in one week, while a complex leveraged lease transaction may take three months. Seek the advice of experienced legal counsel in setting this date.

Anticipated Equipment Delivery

The date when the equipment is anticipated to arrive on the lessee's premises.

Anticipated Equipment Acceptance for Lease

The date when the lessee expects to accept the equipment for lease. This date should allow sufficient time to ensure that the delivered equipment is operationally acceptable.

Tax Indemnity Documents

[See Form I-04e.]

Trust Documents

[See Form I-04d.]

Trust Indenture and Security Agreement Documents

[See Form I-04c.]

Vendor Agreement Documents

Form: v-01
Disk File Name: v-01.rtf

Program Agreement

Form Purpose

A vendor program agreement providing for an arrangement in which a leasing company will purchase equipment leases entered into from time to time by a equipment vendor with its customers.

Executing Parties

The equipment lessor.
The equipment vendor.

Dealer Program Agreement

THIS AGREEMENT is made as of the ______ day of ____________________, XXXX, by and between Able Leasing Company, a ____________________ corporation having a place of business at ____________________ ____________________ ("ALC"), and ____________________ ("Dealer"), a ____________________ corporation, having a place of business at ____________________.

WHEREAS, ALC and Dealer contemplate engaging in a program ("Program") in which Dealer will, in the ordinary course of its business, lease personal property to retail Lessees (singularly, "Lessee"), which leases will be upon such terms and conditions as are acceptable to ALC; and

WHEREAS, the Program contemplates the sale and assignment from time to time by Dealer to ALC of such leases and all of Dealer's right, title, and interest in and to such personal property, without recourse, except with regard to Dealer's (i) representations, warranties, and covenants, and (ii) repurchase obligations, all as provided in this Agreement.

NOW THEREFORE, for good and valuable consideration, the parties hereto agree as follows:

1. Offer of Leases

(a) Submission of APS. Dealer may from time to time, offer lease application packages ("APS") to ALC for approval and, upon acceptance by ALC, the related Leases and property for purchase by ALC. The APS Dealer submits to ALC shall be in such form and contain such information and be evidenced by such documents as ALC may supply or otherwise require.

(b) Terms. The APS submitted to ALC shall provide for such rentals, rental periods, charges, and residual values, if any, as are acceptable to ALC in its sole discretion from time to time.

(c) Approval or Rejection. ALC shall not be required to approve any APS submitted by Dealer. ALC may condition approval as to any APS on the Lease containing various specified and required terms. ALC shall advise Dealer within a reasonable period of time as to whether the APS has been accepted or rejected and, if accepted, upon what conditions.

(d) Documents, Records, and Reports. ALC shall have access to all records of Dealer for any Lease which ALC shall have purchased from Dealer.

(e) The Terms, Leases, and Property. As used in this Agreement, "Lease" means the lease agreement and other related documentation which evidences the obligation of a lessee ("Lessee") to pay to Dealer the monthly rentals and other sums due for the leasing of the property, and may include the obligation, if any, of another person or persons to pay to Dealer the residual value of such property upon termination or expiration of a Lease. The term "property" shall be deemed to include all equipment, accessories, and accessions in any way attached to or pertaining to the use or operation of the leased property.

2. Assignment and Dealer's Restatement of Warranties, Representations and Covenants.

(a) Assignment. Dealer hereby agrees to sell, assign, transfer, and set over to ALC all of its right, title, and interest in and to each Lease and the property covered thereby. ALC hereby agrees to purchase each such lease and the property covered thereby as are acceptable to ALC and conform by signing and delivering an approved Lease to ALC, shall thereupon be deemed to restate to ALC with regard to that Lease all of Dealer's representations, warranties, and covenants as are provided in this Agreement.

(b) *Breach of Warranties. All Leases purchased from Dealer by ALC will reflect Leases made in the ordinary course of Dealer's business. Dealer represents that it has no knowledge of any breach by Dealer or by the manufacturer of the property covered by such Leases of any warranties or representations made to the Lessees, or of any breach by any of the Lessees of any warranties, representations, covenants, promises, or obligations of any of the Lessees to the Dealer as provided in the Lease. In addition, if a Lessee asserts against ALC a claim or defense which the Lessee may have against the Dealer which arises out of the ownership, use, possession, operation, control, maintenance, or repair of the property covered by the Lease, Dealer shall indemnify and defend ALC for the entire amount of ALC's loss, cost, and expense. The liability shall be in addition to any liability Dealer may have under Paragraph 3 below.*

3. Dealer's Further Warranties, Representations and Covenants

To induce ALC to acquire Leases, Dealer warrants, represents, and covenants and, so long as any Leases purchased by ALC hereunder remain unpaid in whole or in part, continues to warrant, represent, and covenant that, at the time of assignment of any Lease to ALC as to all acts and conditions required to be completed by or to exist at such time and, as to all acts required to be performed and conditions required to exist thereafter, with respect to that and each Lease acquired by ALC pursuant to this Agreement: (1) (a) the Lease and related documents are valid, (b) they represent the obligation of a bona fide Lessee, and (c) the documents supporting the transaction and the signatures thereon are genuine; (2) all amounts stated in the Lease are true and correct; (3) the description of the property and related accessories, equipment, and accessions is complete and correct; (4) other than the Lease, no agreement has been or will be entered into between the Lessee and Dealer or any other person with respect to the financing or leasing of the property; (5) Dealer shall have full responsibility to assure ALC receives full and complete title: (6) if the transaction involves the leasing of new or used property for which title is evidenced by a Certificate or Document to Title and with regard to which a security interest is or may be perfected pursuant to a title encumbrancing law, Dealer shall have obtained, or caused an APS to be filed for such Title Certificate or Document with ALC ownership or security interest, as applicable, duly noted thereon and/or, if appropriate, the applicable financing statement(s) or security agreements have been duly filed with the appropriate filing office(s); (7) the form, terms, and execution of the Lease and all related documentation and Dealer's activities in originating the Lease and documents supporting the Lease and the actual leasing of the property giving rise to the transaction each comply with all applicable federal, state, and local laws; (8) to the best of Dealer's knowledge, all of the information contained in the Lessee's APS submitted to ALC is true and correct; (9) ALC has been named as a loss-payee and/or second beneficiary on a policy or policies of insurance covering all such risks and with such amounts of coverage and such insurers as are reasonably acceptable to ALC, and such insurance coverage shall be in force at or prior to the delivery of the property to the Lessee; and (10) Dealer and its affiliates currently hold and at all material times shall hold in good standing, any and all federal, state, and local licenses and other regulatory approvals required to enable Dealer lawfully to originate and assign the Leases contemplated hereby.

4. Compensation

ALC shall pay to Dealer a purchase price ("Purchase Price") for each Lease purchased by and sold and assigned to ALC, as specified in ALC's approval of an APS, or otherwise as agreed upon by the parties.

5. Collection

ALC or its assignee shall collect payments on all Leases purchased from Dealer, unless the parties to this Agreement mutually agree otherwise. ALC may request Dealer to make reasonable efforts to arrange for the release or disposition of repossessed property. Dealer will not, without ALC's written consent: (1) grant any extension of time or payment; (2) compromise or settle any Lease for less than the full amount owing; (3) release, in any manner any Lessee or guarantor; or (4) sell, release, or dispose of the property or any other collateral for the Lease for less than the unpaid balance due under the Lease (including, if applicable, the residual value of the property as provided in the Lease).

Unless with ALC's prior approval, all payments on Leases which may be received by Dealer shall be received in trust and immediately paid to ALC in the form received, except for necessary endorsement(s), without intermingling them with Dealer's funds. Dealer appoints ALC and each of its officers as Dealer's attorney-in-fact, without any right of revocation and with full power of substitution, to endorse Dealer's name upon any notes, checks, drafts, or other instruments for the payment of money received by ALC which are payable to Dealer with respect to Leases. Repossessed Property and other collateral held by Dealer will (1) be held in trust for ALC and (2) not be intermingled with Dealer's property, and (3) upon notice to Dealer, be surrendered directly to ALC.

6. Nonrecourse Assignment During Lease Term; Repurchase Obligation

Dealer's sale and assignment of any Lease to ALC shall be without recourse during the entire term of the Lease, except the Dealer shall remain personally obligated: (i) to repurchase the Lease and the property covered thereby on demand of ALC if, in ALC's reasonable judgment, any of Dealer's representations, warranties, and covenants as to such Lease shall have been breached, and to pay to ALC all sums then due under the terms of the Lease as if the Lease were actually paid in full by a Lessee in default, and (ii) at the end of the Lease term, to repurchase the Lease and the property from ALC for the residual value as provided in the applicable APS for the Lease. ALC shall, upon any such repurchase by Dealer, provide such endorsement and cooperate with Dealer in effecting such transfers of title or security as Dealer may reasonably request or require.

Notwithstanding anything contained in the immediately preceding paragraph to the contrary, Dealer may elect not to purchase a Lease and the property covered thereby from ALC at the end of the Lease term and will be absolved of and from any personal obligation therefore if Dealer, within 10 days after the end of the Lease term, advises ALC of such election and pays to ALC the sum of $ ________________.

7. Additional Liabilities and Indemnities

Dealer shall promptly fulfill and perform all obligations on its part and agrees to enforce, assert, and exercise, and cooperate with ALC in so doing any right, power, or remedy conferred on it by any Lease or related document or under this Agreement. The purchase by ALC of any Lease shall not be deemed an assumption by ALC or an imposition on ALC, of any Dealer obligation under the Lease or any other Dealer agreement with the Lessee, which lease shall be and remain enforceable by the Lessee solely against Dealer. Dealer agrees to indemnify and hold ALC harmless from and against any and all loss, damage, and expense, including attorney's fees reasonable in amount, which ALC may suffer, incur, be put to, pay, or lay out by reason of Dealer's actions or omissions to act, except where specifically attributable solely to directions from ALC given in writing. ALC similarly shall indemnify and hold Dealer harmless against such loss, damage, and expense which Dealer may suffer, incur, be put to, pay, or lay out by reason of any action taken by Dealer on behalf of ALC for collection, repossession, release, or resale where Dealer relied upon incorrect information from ALC and Dealer was not negligent under the circumstances.

8. Relationship

This agreement shall not create an employer-employee relationship, it being the contemplation of the parties that all acts performed by Dealer in carrying out the provisions of this Agreement shall be those of an independent contractor. Except for acts performed by Dealer at ALC's express direction, ALC shall not be responsible for the acts of Dealer, its officers, agents, or employees.

9. Termination

(a) Dates. This Agreement shall become effective as of the date first written above, and shall remain in effect until terminated by either party on giving ninety (90) days' written notice to the other of its intention to terminate at its respective address above, or to any address which such party shall have specified on the ninetieth (90th) day after the day on which such notice is mailed by Certified Mail, Return Receipt Requested; provided however, that if any event occurs which materially affects the ability of Dealer to lawfully honor its obligation to ALC under this Agreement, ALC may terminate this Agreement effective immediately.

(b) Rights on Termination. Upon the effective date of any termination except with regard to Dealer's warranties, representations, and covenants, or any indemnification and/or repurchase liability of Dealer incident thereto or otherwise contained under the provisions hereof or the Lease, all of which shall survive this Agreement, Dealer shall have no further obligation to ALC under this Agreement except to cooperate with ALC in any action in which ALC becomes a party or if ALC requests collection assistance on delinquent Leases.

10. Forms

ALC will in no way be responsible for the validity, legality, or sufficiency of any form of Lease or other documents with the exception of forms provided by ALC.

11. Modification, Binding Effect and Governing Law

No modification, rescission, waiver, release, or amendment of any provision of this Agreement shall be made except by written agreement signed by duly authorized officers of the parties hereto. This Agreement is binding upon and shall inure to the benefit of the successors and assigns of the parties hereto. However, Dealer may not assign this Agreement without the prior written consent of ALC. This Agreement shall be construed under the laws of the State of ________________, as amended from time to time.

12. In the event of an early payout or default by Lessee, any unearned commissions, as determined by the rule of 78 payoff method, shall be refunded to ALC within 30 days of written request by ALC.

13. All commissions over ________ % shall be shared equally with ALC at the time of funding.

DEALER

By: ________________________________

Title: ______________________________

ABLE LEASING COMPANY

By: ________________________________

Title: ______________________________

Form: v-02
Disk File Name: v-02.rtf

REMARKETING AGREEMENT

Form Purpose

A vendor program agreement providing for an arrangement in which a leasing company will purchase equipment leases entered into from time to time by a equipment vendor with its customers. In this case the equipment vendor has a captive leasing company (the "initial lessor") that initiates the leases which will be sold off to a third-party equipment leasing company ("Credit Funding Corporation").

Executing Parties

The equipment lessor.
The equipment vendor.
The equipment vendor's captive leasing company.

See:

Assignment of Lease Forms

Vendor Remarketing Agreement and Reserve Agreement

THIS AGREEMENT entered into and made effective this ____ day of ____________, XXXX, among (insert name of vendor), a ______________________________ corporation, with its principal office at ______________________________ ("Vendor"), (insert name of initial lessor) a ______________________________ corporation, with its principal office at ______________________________ ("Lessor") and CREDIT FUNDING CORPORATION, a ____________________ Corporation, with its principal place of business at ______________________________ ("Credit Funding").

WITNESSETH:

WHEREAS, Vendor is engaged in and provides equipment and support services to Merchants (as defined hereinafter) with respect to electronic bank card processing; and,

WHEREAS, Lessor is engaged from time to time in the business of leasing Vendor's electronic credit card authorization and related equipment to customers of Vendor; and,

WHEREAS, Credit Funding is in the business of financing equipment leases and the underlying equipment by taking an assignment of all right, title, and interest in such leases, their noncancelable lease payments, and the equipment subject to such leases; and,

WHEREAS, (i) Vendor and Lessor desire to establish a program with Credit Funding in which Lessor will assemble and remit Leases to Credit Funding executed by Vendor's customers, providing for the lease of equipment for use solely by Customers (as defined hereinafter), and (ii) Credit Funding will review such leases and accept assignment and fund those leases which, in the sole discretion of Credit Funding, meet the reasonable independent credit standards of Credit Funding.

NOW, THEREFORE, in consideration of the foregoing, and of the representations, warranties, covenants, and agreements hereinafter contained, and to induce Credit Funding to accept assignment and fund Leases with Customers, the parties hereto agree as follows:

Article 1—Definitions

Section 1.1. Definitions. As used in this Agreement, the following terms shall have the following meanings (such meanings to be equally applicable to both the singular and plural forms of the term defined):

1.1. *Assignment Documentation* shall mean a duly executed assignment of lease agreement from Lessor acceptable to Credit Funding in its sole discretion, financing statements sufficient under the Uniform Commercial Code in form satisfactory for filing in the appropriate jurisdiction when requested by Credit Funding, and any other documents, instruments, reasonably required by Credit Funding.

1.2. *Collateral* shall mean (i) all of Vendor's and Lessor's right, title, and interest in and to all accounts, deposit accounts, money market accounts, money, and deposits which are now or hereafter held by, assigned, pledged to, or otherwise restricted on behalf of Credit Funding, its successors or assigns, (ii) any Reserve Account and the funds represented by any Reserve Requirement, all rights to payment and connection therewith, all sums or property now or at any time hereafter on deposit therein, together with all earnings of every kind and description which may now or hereafter accrue thereon, (iii) any Commitment Reserve Account and the funds, leases, and equipment related thereto and, (iv) any Security Leases, and the rights and funds related thereto or arising therefrom; and (iv) all proceeds, and interest thereon, of the foregoing.

1.3 *Commitment Reserve Account* shall be as defined in Section 4.3 hereof.

1.4. *Customer* shall mean a Merchant and any lessee, debtor, guarantor, borrower, or other person, partnership, corporation, or other entity which executes or becomes obligated to Lessor pursuant to a Qualifying Lease (or any part thereof).

1.5. *Customer Default* shall mean any breach by a Customer of any obligation, covenant, duty, condition, or agreement with respect to any Qualifying Lease including, without limitation, failure to timely pay rent or other sums when due, failure to return the equipment, or failure to keep the equipment properly insured, which breach shall occur and continue for a period of sixty (60) days following notice in writing from Credit Funding to Customer specifying the default and requesting that it be cured or fully corrected within such time.

1.6. *Defaulted Lease* shall mean any Qualifying Lease with respect to which any one or more of the following shall have occurred: (i) a Customer Default shall occur, or (ii) Credit Funding is unable to timely recover, or reasonably believes it will be unable to recover, its Unamortized Net Investment with respect to a particular Qualifying lease.

1.7. *Default Period* shall be as defined in Section 5.1 (a) hereof.

1.8. *Equipment* shall mean all equipment or machinery and other personal property which is the subject of a Qualifying lease including, without limitation, credit card authorization and processing equipment.

1.9. *Lease* shall mean a lease of Equipment by Lessor to a Customer and all other documents and instruments relating thereto or executed in connection therewith (other than Vendor's Merchant Processing Agreement), including, without limitation, any personal guarantee, corporate guarantee, certificate of acceptance (or other instrument whereby customer acknowledges acceptance of the equipment), corporate resolution, or financing statement.

1.10. *Merchant* shall mean any seller of goods, services, or both, who is a customer of Vendor.

1.11. *Obligations* shall mean (i) all sums, payments, monies, rents, and other amounts due or to become due from Vendor and Lessor to Credit Funding, now existing or hereafter arising, and (ii) all agreements, warranties, duties, obligations, and covenants of Vendor and Lessor to Credit Funding pursuant to this Agreement or otherwise.

1.12. *Present Value* shall mean the total sum of all future rent payments, due and unpaid discounted to present value using a ten percent (10%) per annum interest rate, or such other per annum interest rate as shall be mutually agreeable to the parties.

1.13. *Purchase Price* with respect to a Qualifying Lease shall mean the Present Value of the regular monthly noncancelable rent payments due and unpaid.

1.14. *Qualifying Lease* shall mean a Lease with a Customer which has been approved by Credit Funding for financing in its sole discretion, and which has been sold and assigned to Credit Funding pursuant to the provisions of this Agreement.

1.15. *Reserve Account* shall be as defined in Section 4.1 hereof.

1.16. *Reserve Requirement* shall be as defined in Section 4.1 hereof.

1.17 *Security Leases* shall be as defined in Section 4.3 hereof.

1.18. *Substitute Lease* shall mean a Lease or sublease with a Customer which replaces a Defaulted Lease upon approval by Credit Funding in its sole discretion as a Qualifying Lease.

1.19. *Unamortized Net Investment* shall mean the sum of all accrued and unpaid rent payments discounted to present value at an interest rate equal to the simple interest lease rate on the Qualifying Lease, calculated monthly in arrears, plus all rents accrued and not yet paid, and all other sums due Credit Funding or its equipment lease lender with respect to a Qualifying Lease or a Defaulted Lease, including accrued interest on unpaid rent payments.

Article II—Assignment of Leases

Section 2.1. Sale of Equipment to Credit Funding. Lessor agrees to sell and does hereby sell, assign, and transfer to Credit Funding the equipment described in each Qualifying Lease. Vendor and Lessor warrant to Credit Funding with respect to each sale of equipment (whether or not separately documented) that Lessor has good and marketable title to the equipment free and clear of all liens, claims and encumbrances; that Lessor has the right to sell, transfer, and assign the equipment to Credit Funding; and that Credit Funding is obtaining good and marketable title to the Equipment free and clear of all liens, claims, and encumbrances, except those arising through or from Credit Funding.

Section 2.2. Assignment of Lease Rights and Obligations.

(a) Lessor agrees to use its best efforts to present or cause to be presented Leases with Customers to Credit Funding from time to time in accordance with this Agreement which will qualify as Qualifying Leases whose aggregate monthly Purchase Price shall equal ______________________ dollars ($ ______________________) provided, however, Lessor will supply Credit Funding over the initial first year term of this Agreement Qualifying Leases whose aggregate Purchase Price equals at least ______________________ dollars ($ ______________________), together with such credit information, credit reports, and other documentation as Credit Funding shall reasonably request. Upon receipt of all such information, Credit Funding shall promptly approve or disapprove each Lease for funding. Credit Funding shall have the right to approve or disapprove each Lease in its sole discretion in accordance with independent credit standards acceptable to Credit Funding. Upon proper completion and delivery to Credit Funding of Assignment Documentation for each Qualifying Lease, and other relevant documentation, Credit Funding shall pay to Lessor the Purchase Price less the Reserve Requirement and less any other sums due Credit Funding from Vendor or Lessor under this Agreement. Credit Funding does not by this Agreement or otherwise assume any of the obligations of Vendor or Lessor or any other party under the leases, and Credit Funding shall not be responsible in any way for the performance by Vendor or Lessor or any other party of the terms and conditions of the Qualifying Leases.

(b) In the event Credit Funding determines that any Qualifying Lease with respect to which the Purchase Price has been paid is not as represented by the credit or documentation information supplied by Vendor or Lessor at any time prior to and including two (2) months following payment of the Purchase Price (the "Review Period"), Credit

Funding shall so notify Vendor and Lessor in writing at which time Lessor shall within five (5) business days after the receipt of such notice pay Credit Funding, or its designee, less any rent payments received by Credit Funding, or its designee, an amount equal to the Purchase Price, plus in the event of a material misrepresentation a fee equal to seventy-five dollars ($75.00) per lease.

Section 2.3. Assignment Documentation. With respect to each Qualifying Lease, Lessor agrees to execute or cause to be executed and delivered to Credit Funding, the originals of the Qualifying Leases and all Assignment Documentation prior to payment of the Purchase Price by Credit Funding. The terms and conditions of the Assignment Documentation shall supplement the terms and conditions of this Agreement. Credit Funding shall have the right, if applicable, to stamp or mark each Qualifying Lease and all Assignment Documentation to clearly and conspicuously state that it is subject to the security interest of Credit Funding, in such form and with such language as Credit Funding may desire. The originals of such Qualifying Lease and all Assignment Documentation shall be maintained in the possession of Credit Funding.

Section 2.4. Security Interest. As security for (i) the payment, and performance, of the obligations and all other present and future indebtedness, liabilities, and obligations of Vendor and Lessor to Credit Funding, whether arising hereunder, or under the Assignment Documentation, or under any other document or instrument executed in connection with the transactions contemplated hereunder or otherwise, including indebtedness of every kind and description, direct or indirect, absolute or contingent, due or to become due, now existing or hereafter arising, and (ii) Vendor's and Lessor's obligations and liabilities arising out of its covenants, warranties, and representations contained herein, or in any other document or instrument executed in connection with the transactions contemplated hereunder, Lessor hereby pledges, assigns, and grants to Credit Funding a priority security interest in the Collateral free and clear of all liens, claims, and encumbrances except those arising through or from Credit Funding. If any deposit or account constituting Collateral is evidenced by a certificate of deposit or is otherwise subject to Article 9 of the Uniform Commercial Code, the foregoing security interest shall be construed as a grant of a security interest subject, to the extent applicable, to the Uniform Commercial Code as enacted in the State of __________________.

Section 2.5. Payment of Rent Directly to Credit Funding. Lessor shall cause all rental and other payments assigned to Credit Funding pursuant to Qualifying Leases to be made by electronic funds transfer directly to Credit Funding when received, and, to that end, to have caused each Customer to sign an authorization giving Lessor or its designees and assigns the right and power to authorize such transfers to be made. If any Customer has not signed such an authorization, the lease to such Customer shall not constitute a Qualifying Lease under any circumstances and Credit Funding shall have no obligation to consider funding such lease. All electronic transfers of payments shall be made to an account designated by Credit Funding. Lessor hereby irrevocably designates Credit Funding as attorney-in-fact to direct the electronic funds transfer as to each Qualifying Lease and Lessor shall cause each Lessee to be notified of the assignment of rent payments to Credit Funding.

Section 2.6. Financing Statements. Upon written request by Credit Funding Lessor agrees to execute and provide Credit Funding with commercially standard UCC financing statements covering the Collateral, which Credit Funding is authorized to file upon receipt. Lessor agrees that it will, at its expense, execute such additional financial statements, endorsements, continuation statements, and other documents in connection therewith and do such other acts and provide such further assurances as Credit Funding may from time to time reasonably request to establish and maintain a first lien priority security interest in the Collateral free and clear of all liens, claims, and encumbrances, except those arising through or arising from Credit Funding, and preserve and protect Credit Funding's interests acquired herein. At the option of Credit Funding and upon notice to Lessor, Credit Funding may sign any financing statements on behalf of Lessor (directly in the name of Lessor or in the name of Credit Funding on behalf of Lessor) and file the same, and Lessor hereby irrevocably designates Credit Funding, its agents, representatives, and designees, as agents and attorneys-in-fact for Lessor for this purpose. In the event that any rerecording or refiling thereof (or the filing of any statement of continuation or assignment of any financing statement) is required to protect and preserve such lien or security interest, Lessor shall, at Credit Funding's written request, and at its sole cost and expense, cause the same to be rerecorded or refiled at the time and in the manner requested by Credit Funding

Section 2.7. Quarterly Accounting. Lessor agrees to provide, or cause to be provided, Credit Funding with a quarterly (or monthly, if requested by Credit Funding), accounting of all Qualifying Leases within thirty (30) days following the last day of the immediately preceding calendar quarter (or month, if applicable), commencing on ______________, XXXX.

Section 2.8. Taxes and Reporting. Lessor agrees to report, file, and pay promptly when due as required by statute or regulation to the appropriate taxing authority, indemnity, defend, and hold Credit Funding, and any of its assignees, harmless from any and all taxes (including sales, use, property, transaction, and gross receipts), assessments, license fees, and governmental charges of any kind or nature, together with any penalties, interest, or fines relating thereto that pertains to a Qualifying Lease, the equipment, its lease or rent, or other sums due thereunder. On all such reports or returns required hereunder, Lessor shall show the ownership of the equipment by Credit Funding or, if requested, its designee. Upon written request by Credit Funding, Lessor agrees to remit such taxes to Credit Funding and First Street shall remit such taxes so collected by Credit Funding to the appropriate taxing authority.

Section 2.9. Licenses, Permits, Consents, and Approvals. Vendor and Lessor have or will obtain all licenses, permits, consents, approvals, authorizations, qualifications, and orders of governmental authorities required to enable them to continue to conduct their business as presently conducted and will be duly qualified to conduct business in each and every state in which they enter into a lease transaction. Vendor and Lessor have duly filed and shall continue to timely file with the appropriate federal, state, local, and other governmental agencies, all tax returns, information returns, and reports required to be filed by them and their subsidiaries, have and will continue to pay or cause to be paid, in full or make adequate provision for the payment of all taxes (including taxes withheld from employees' salaries and other withholding taxes and obligations), interest, penalties, assessments, or deficiencies shown on such returns or reports to be due to any taxing authority, including but not limited to all sales, use, transaction, property taxes which may be due or become due for all equipment subject to a Qualifying Lease, whether assessed against Lessor or Credit Funding. All claims for taxes due and payable by Lessor have either been paid or are being contested in good faith by appropriate proceedings. Vendor and Lessor warrant that neither is a party to, nor are they aware of, any pending or threatened action or proceeding, assessment or collection of taxes by any government authority. Credit Funding reserves the right at any time to enter the business premises of Vendor and Lessor and to inspect and audit the appropriate books and records of Vendor and Lessor to verify and assure compliance with all applicable regulations and the provisions of this Agreement, including, but not limited to, sales, use, and property tax regulations.

Section 2.10. Advances by Credit Funding. At its sole option, and without any obligation to do so, Credit Funding may discharge or pay any taxes, liens, security interests (other than the lien or the security interest of Credit Funding contemplated in this Agreement or liens arising from acts or omissions of Credit Funding), or other encumbrances at any time levied or placed on or against the Collateral or Vendor or Lessor in breach of this Agreement, and may pay for insurance on the Collateral, and may pay for its maintenance and preservation. Vendor and Lessor agree to reimburse Credit Funding on demand for any such payment made, or expense incurred, pursuant to the foregoing authorizations, and such advances shall be deemed additional obligations secured by the Collateral.

Section 2.11 Commitment Paid to Credit Funding. Vendor shall pay to Credit Funding upon the execution by Vendor of this Agreement a nonrefundable commitment fee equal to __________ dollars ($ ______________). Neither Vendor nor Lessor shall be obligated to pay any other fees, including attorney's fees, or expenses in connection with this Agreement unless otherwise expressly stated herein.

Article III—Term

Section 3.1.Term. The initial term of this Agreement shall be one (1) year from the date hereof. Unless either Vendor or Lessor notifies Credit Funding or Credit Funding notifies Vendor or Lessor not later than one hundred twenty calendar (120) days prior to the expiration of the initial or any renewal term that it does not wish to renew this Agreement for a subsequent term, this Agreement shall automatically renew for additional terms of one (1) year upon the same terms and conditions. The foregoing notwithstanding, all rights and obligations of the parties herein to each with respect to Qualifying Leases assigned to and funded by Credit Funding during the time this Agreement is in force, and all representations, warranties, and covenants of Vendor and Lessor, shall survive any expiration or earlier termination of this Agreement. Notwithstanding the foregoing, Credit Funding may terminate this Agreement, in whole or in part, at any time in the exercise of its rights and remedies upon an Event of Default hereunder.

Article IV—Reserve Account

Section 4.1. The Reserve Account. Credit Funding agrees to deposit into and maintain in a restricted Reserve Account in the name of Lessor an amount equal to ten percent (10%) on Qualifying Leases calculated on the Purchase Price of each Qualifying Lease (such sum hereinafter is referred to as the "Reserve Requirement"). Credit Funding may hold back and deduct the Reserve Requirement from the proceeds due Lessor from Credit Funding for each Qualifying Lease. Credit Funding and Lessor agree that they will not withdraw or attempt to withdraw funds from, terminate, deplete, pledge, hypothecate, assign, grant a security interest, or permit a lien to attach to the Reserve Account, except those permitted pursuant to this Agreement.

Section 4.2. Distribution from Excess Funds. Credit Funding and Lessor recognize that as Customers make lease payments, the Unamortized Net Investment in its portfolio of

Qualifying Leases may decline. Provided Credit Funding has a favorable loss experience as set forth below with respect to Qualifying Leases, the amount of funds on deposit in the Reserve Account may exceed the Reserve Requirement. Credit Funding will review the Reserve Account and its loss experience quarterly, and provided that each and every one of the following conditions has occurred and is continuing, Credit Funding shall distribute to Lessor the excess funds in the Reserve Requirement:

(a) Credit Funding actual cumulative Customer default experience (without regard to recovery) has been less than the Reserve Requirement (for purposes of determining Credit Funding default experience, Substitute leases will be excluded); and

(b) No event of default has occurred on the part of Vendor or Lessor and continued uncured for a period of sixty (60) days following notice in writing from Credit Funding specifying the default and requesting that it be cured and fully corrected within such time.

Section 4.3. The Commitment Reserve Account. Lessor and Vendor agree as a condition precedent to the purchase by Credit Funding of any Qualifying Leases to assign all right, title, and interest to Qualifying Leases, and related equipment and proceeds, with a total Purchase Price of not less than four hundred thousand dollars ($400,000.00) to Credit Funding or its designee (the "Security Leases") as security for the reasonable performance by Vendor and Lessor under this Agreement. The Security Leases shall be reassigned to Lessor at the end of one (1) year from the date of assignment to Credit Funding, or its designee, if Vendor and Lessor have reasonably complied with their obligations under this Agreement.

Article V—Defaulted Leases

Section 5.1. Substitution Procedure. With respect to any Defaulted Lease, upon written request of Credit Funding, Lessor, at its sole expense, agrees promptly to perform the following:

(a) Upon notice from Credit Funding or actual knowledge on the part of Lessor that a lease constitutes a Defaulted Lease, whichever shall first occur, Lessor shall (i) take immediate steps to replace the Defaulted Lease with a Substitute Lease of equal or greater present value than the Unamortized Net Investment of the Defaulted Lease and (ii) pay to Credit Funding within ten (10) days following the receipt of such notice seventy-five dollars ($75.00). Lessor shall not be obligated to replace a Defaulted Lease with a Substituted Lease if a Qualifying Lease becomes a Defaulted Lease as a result of events occurring following two hundred and forty (240) days following the date of payment by Credit Funding of the Purchase Price (the "Default Period"). If the Present Value of the Substitute Lease exceeds the Unamortized Net Investment of the Defaulted Lease, Credit Funding will refund the excess present value to Lessor after first deducting all fees, costs, and interest due with respect to the Defaulted Lease due on the Substitute Lease. Lessor shall take all steps necessary to assign the Substitute Lease and underlying equipment to Credit Funding within sixty (60) days from such notice or actual knowledge. Upon approval by Credit Funding in its sole discretion, the Substitute Lease shall thereafter constitute a Qualifying Lease hereunder. Lessor shall only be permitted under this Agreement to make one lease substitution in the case of a Defaulted Lease.

(b) A Substitute Lease may be for the same equipment originally leased under the Defaulted Lease or for like equipment of at least equal value as the equipment under the Defaulted Lease.

(c) Lessor's obligation to substitute such Defaulted Lease hereunder shall not be subject to or diminished by any defense, counterclaim, or setoff which it may have or claim to have against Credit Funding and shall also not be conditioned on Credit Funding first having obtained a judgment against the Customer or otherwise proceeding against the Customer. Credit Funding may, but shall not be obligated to proceed in any manner against the Customer or the applicable leased equipment

(d) Upon approval and assignment of a Substitute Lease by Credit Funding, Credit Funding shall return to Lessor the originals of each lease corresponding thereto which constitute a Defaulted Lease, and all Assignment Documentation associated therewith.

(e) Should Lessor fail to substitute a Qualifying Lease or if the applicable Substitute Lease becomes a Defaulted Lease, Credit Funding may debit the Reserve Account for the Unamortized Net Investment in the Defaulted Lease. If the Reserve Account contains insufficient funds to satisfy the Unamortized Net Investment in the Defaulted Lease, Credit Funding may collect from the Collateral described in Section 1.2. hereof upon sixty (60) days written notice to Lessor of its intention to do so, and Lessor's failure to sufficiently replenish the Reserve Account within said sixty (60) days.

(f) In the event the Collateral described in Section 1.2 is insufficient to satisfy any Defaulted Lease, then upon written demand by Credit Funding, Lessor shall pay to Credit Funding such amounts within ten (10) days, as the Purchase Price of said Defaulted Lease.

(g) In the event Lessor fails to pay Credit Funding in accordance with Section 5. 1.(f) above and upon written notice to Vendor, Vendor shall pay the amount specified by Section 5. l.(f) within ten (10) days after receipt of written notice from Credit Funding.

Article VI—Vendor's and Lessor's Representations and Warranties

Section 6.1. Warranties and Representations. Vendor and Lessor hereby represent, warrant, and covenant the following to Credit Funding:

(a) With respect to each lease sold hereunder during the term of the lease, Credit Funding or its assignee, is and shall remain (except for acts or omissions of Credit Funding) the sole owner of the lease and equipment leased thereunder, which are and will remain free and clear of any lien, security interest, mortgage, charge, or encumbrance (except for a security interest granted by Credit Funding, its successors and assigns and the Lessee's leasehold rights in the equipment).

(b) This Agreement, the sales and assignments of Qualifying Leases and underlying equipment to Credit Funding (and any sales and assignment of the Qualifying Leases from Vendor to Lessor), the Qualifying Leases and all other documents now or hereafter executed by Vendor and Lessor pursuant to the terms hereof, are and shall be enforceable in accordance with their respective terms, except as they may be limited by bankruptcy, insolvency, or other similar laws affecting enforcement of creditors' rights in general.

(c) At the time of the sale or assignment of any lease and underlying equipment to Credit Funding, the equipment thereunder shall have been delivered to and accepted by the respective Lessee under the lease. The equipment shall not be or suffered to be wasted, misused, abused, or to deteriorate, except for ordinary wear and tear, and will not be used in violation of any law, ordinance, or regulation of any governmental authority insofar as it adversely affects the value of the respective lease, equipment, or the security interests granted hereunder. Vendor and Lessor will during the Default Period (or will cause the Lessees to) maintain, preserve, protect, and keep the equipment under each Qualifying Lease in good repair, working order, and condition and from time to time, will make all repairs, renewals, replacements, additions, betterment and improvements to the equipment as are needed and proper, at Vendor's and Lessor's sole cost and expense.

(d) Neither Lessor, Vendor, nor any Lessee are in default under the leases as of the date of payment of the applicable Purchase Price. The Lessees under the Qualifying Leases have no claims, defenses, setoffs, or counterclaims against Lessor or Vendor under such leases. Vendor and Lessor shall indemnify, defend, and save the Credit Funding harmless of and from all costs, expenses, losses, claims, damages, attorney's fees and expenses, suits, and liabilities arising out of or incurred by Credit Funding as a result of any claims, defenses, setoffs, or counterclaims raised or asserted by any Lessee under any lease arising by, through, or under Lessor's or Vendor's acts or omissions.

(e) With the exception of a lease which constitutes a Defaulted Lease, neither Vendor nor Lessor will repossess or consent to the return of any equipment prior to the scheduled expiration of the lease term without the prior written consent of Credit Funding.

(f) Neither Vendor nor Lessor will cause the Collateral to be sold, transferred, assigned, encumbered, pledged, hypothecated, or disposed of, without the prior written consent of Credit Funding. Credit Funding recognizes that certain Customers may sell or transfer their business and the new owner may sublease the equipment from the Customer. Credit Funding shall allow such subleases, subject to satisfactory credit review.

(g) Each lease delivered by Lessor to Credit Funding shall be the original counterpart of such lease and shall be the sole counterpart deemed chattel paper under the Uniform Commercial Code as enacted in the State of ____, and effective to transfer Lessor's rights as Lessor to be assigned herein and therein.

(h) Vendor will punctually perform and observe all of its obligations and agreements contained in any servicing or processing agreements made with respect to the Qualifying Leases. Vendor, Lessor, and Credit Funding will immediately notify the other of any default by any party under the Qualifying Leases of which it becomes aware.

(i) Lessor will not declare a default under or exercise any remedies under the Qualifying Leases or enter into or permit any cancellation, termination, amendment, supplement, or modification of or waiver with respect to such leases or give any consent or approval as to any matter arising out of such leases, and any such attempted declaration, exercise, cancellation, termination, amendment, supplement, modification, waiver, consent, or approval shall be void and of no effect unless the Lessor shall have received the express prior written consent thereto from Credit Funding.

(j) Vendor and Lessor are corporations duly organized, validly existing, and in good standing under the laws of the State of ______________. Vendor and Lessor shall do all things necessary to maintain and preserve their corporate existence.

(k) Each lease to be assigned to the Credit Funding shall be a valid and genuine lease, and in all respects what it purports to be.

(l) There are and shall not be any agreements, undertakings, or other documents relating to the leases hereinafter assigned to the Credit Funding which are not contained in such leases.

(m) Vendor and Lessor will keep true books of records and account in which full and correct entries will be made of all its business transactions, and which reflects in such financial statements adequate accruals and appropriations to reserves, all in accordance with generally accepted accounting principles.

Article VII—Termination

Section 7.1. Default by Vendor and Lessor. Vendor and Lessor shall be in default hereunder upon the occurrence of one or more of the following ("Event of Default"):

(a) Vendor or Lessor fail to pay any amount when due hereunder to Credit Funding or its assigns;

(b) Vendor or Lessor shall fail to pay or perform any of its obligations or any other obligations hereunder or shall breach or default in the due observance or performance of any other term, covenant, warranty, or representation contained herein, in the assignments of the leases to Credit Funding, or in any other document or instrument executed in connection herewith;

(c) a receiver, liquidator, or trustee is appointed for Vendor or Lessor or any of their assets or properties;

(d) any proceeding under any state or federal bankruptcy or insolvency laws is instituted against Vendor or Lessor, and such proceeding is not dismissed, vacated, or fully stayed within sixty (60) calendar days;

(e) any property of Vendor or Lessor is attached, levied upon, or seized under any judicial process which could materially and adversely interfere with the operation of Vendor's or Lessor's business;

(f) Vendor or Lessor shall file a petition for relief under the bankruptcy laws including, without limitation, a petition seeking for itself any reorganization, readjustment, liquidation, dissolution, or similar arrangement under any present or future bankruptcy statute, law, or regulation, or a petition to take advantage of any insolvency laws, or make an assignment for the benefit of creditors, or admit in writing its inability to pay its debts as they become due;

(g) Vendor or Lessor shall sell, transfer, assign, pledge, encumber, hypothecate, grant a security interest, or dispose of the Collateral, without the prior written consent of Credit Funding;

(h) any warranty, representation, financial statement, covenant, or agreement made or furnished to Credit Funding by or on behalf of Vendor or Lessor is false or misleading in any material respect when made or furnished;

(i) Vendor or Lessor default under or otherwise has accelerated any material obligation including, but not limited to, credit agreements, loan agreements, conditional sales contracts, lease indentures or debentures, or Vendor defaults under any agreement now existing or hereafter made with Credit Funding or its assignees;

(j) the breach or repudiation by Vendor or Lessor or any party to any subordination, waiver, or other agreement running in favor of Credit Funding obtained in connection with this Agreement or a Qualifying Lease;

(k) if the validity or effectiveness of any Qualifying Lease of its assignment by Lessor or to Credit Funding shall be impaired.

Section 7.2. Default by Credit Funding. Credit Funding shall be in default hereunder upon the occurrence of one or more of the following ("Event of Default"):

(a) Credit Funding falls to pay any amount when due hereunder to Vendor or Lessor; or

(b) Credit Funding shall fail to pay or perform any of its obligations to Vendor or Lessor hereunder, or shall breach or default in the due observance or performance of any other term, covenant, warranty, or representation contained herein, in the assignment of the leases to the Credit Funding, or in any other document or instrument executed in connection herewith.

Section 7.3. Notice and Right to Cure. In the event an Event of Default occurs and continues for a period of thirty (30) days following notice in writing to the other party or parties, as the case may be, specifying the default and requesting it be cured or fully corrected within such time, this Agreement may be terminated, without further notice or action of any kind.

Section 7.4. Rights Upon Default. Upon the occurrence of an Event of Default under this Agreement which is not cured in accordance with the terms herein, Vendor and Lessor or Credit Funding, as the case may be, against whom the default has occurred, may recover any amounts owing to it pursuant to this Agreement and may:

(a) terminate this Agreement without further notice or demand of any kind;

(b) seize, appropriate, apply, and set-off (as such term is defined in the Uniform Commercial Code of the State of ____) any and all items of Collateral against any amounts owing to Credit Funding by Vendor or Lessor;

(c) institute legal proceedings against the other party or parties at law or in equity; or

(d) exercise any and all rights and remedies available to it under this Agreement, the assignments of the leases and all other documents and instruments executed in connection herewith.

Section 7.5. Remedies not Exclusive. No remedy referred to in this Agreement is intended to be exclusive, but each shall be cumulative, and shall be in addition to any other remedy referred to above or otherwise available by statute, at law or in equity, and may be exercised from time to time and any number of times. In addition, Vendor and Lessor agree that they shall be liable for any and all unpaid obligations or additional sums due hereunder, before, after, or during the exercise of any of the foregoing remedies. If Credit Funding or its assignee employs counsel to represent Credit Funding, or its assignee, in any litigation, dispute, suit, or proceeding in any way relating to the leases assigned to Credit Funding (excluding enforcement and collection with respect to the Qualifying Leases), or conflicting claims of third parties to all or any portion of the Collateral, or the sums advanced or paid to Vendor or Lessor hereunder, or any provision of this Agreement or of the Assignment Documentation, or other documents arising out of the transactions contemplated herein or to enforce any term of this Agreement, the Assignment Documentation, or documents arising out of the transactions contemplated herein, then Vendor and Lessor shall pay on demand all of Credit Funding's reasonable attorney's fees arising from such services and all expenses, costs, court costs, and charges relating thereto.

Article VIII—General Provisions

Section 8.1. Notification. Each party shall promptly notify the others of any suit or threat of suit of which that party becomes aware (except with respect to a threat of suit one party might institute against the other) which may give rise to a right of indemnification. The indemnifying party shall be entitled to participate in the settlement or defense thereof and, if the indemnifying party elects (and demonstrates to the satisfaction of the indemnified party the financial ability to promptly honor its obligation to indemnity), to take over and control the settlement or defense thereof with counsel satisfactory to the indemnified party. In any case, the indemnifying party and the indemnified party shall cooperate (at no cost to the indemnified party) in the settlement or defense of any such claim, demand, suit, or proceeding.

Section 8.2. Indemnification. In addition to such obligations of indemnification as may be provided elsewhere in this Agreement, Vendor and Lessor as a unit and Credit Funding hereby also agree to indemnify, save, and keep harmless each other and their successors and assigns from and against any and all losses, damages, penalties, injuries, actions, and suits, including litigation costs and attorney's fees of whatsoever kind and nature directly and indirectly arising by reason of breach or default of any term, condition, representation, warranty, or agreement set forth in this Agreement or by reason of any improper act or omission to act in relation to the subject matter of this Agreement. The foregoing indemnity shall continue in full force and effect notwithstanding the expiration or earlier termination of this Agreement.

Section 8.3. Disclosure. Each party shall promptly notify the others of any action, suit, or proceeding, facts or circumstances, or the prospect or threat of the same, which might materially adversely affect that party's ability to perform this Agreement. Each party represents and warrants to the others that there are no suits, actions, or legal, administrative, arbitration, or other claims or proceedings or government investigations which are pending or which have been made against that party or its parents or affiliates, or its officers, directors, or employees or, to the knowledge of that party, threatened against Vendor, Lessor, or Credit Funding, as the case may be, or its parent or affiliates, or its officers, directors, or employees, which might materially adversely affect the financial condition of Vendor, Lessor, or Credit Funding, or its ability to observe or perform its obligations under this Agreement.

Section 8.4. Compliance with Laws. Each party hereby represents and warrants to the others that it is familiar with the requirements of all applicable laws and regulations and covenants and agrees that it will comply with all such laws and regulations, as well as all other applicable laws and regulations in the performance of this Agreement. The parties each agree to comply with all applicable statutes, rules, regulations, orders, and restrictions of the United States of America, foreign countries, states and municipalities, and of any governmental department, commission, board, regulatory authority, bureau, agency, and instrumentality of the foregoing, and of any court, arbitrator or grand jury, in respect of the conduct of its business and the ownership of its properties, except such as are being contested in good faith.

Section 8.5. Relationship of the Parties. The parties acknowledge and agree that in performing their responsibilities pursuant to this Agreement they are in the position of independent contractors. This Agreement is not intended to create, nor does it create and nor shall it be construed to create, a relationship of partner or joint venture or any association for profit by and between Vendor or Lessor and Credit Funding. Neither Vendor nor Lessor are agents of Credit Funding, and Credit Funding is not an agent of Vendor.

Section 8.6. Further Assurances. Within five (5) business days following written notice by Vendor or Lessor or Credit Funding, as the case may be, each party shall produce and make available for inspection by the others, or its officers and agents, at the business premises of the other, such books and records of Vendor and Lessor or Credit Funding, as the case may be, shall deem reasonably necessary to be adequately informed of the business and financial condition of Vendor and Lessor or Credit Funding, or its ability to observe or perform its obligations hereunder. Vendor agrees to execute and deliver such other or additional documents as may be requested by Credit Funding from time to time hereafter which are necessary or desirable to effectuate the intent of this Agreement.

Section 8.7. Assignment, Benefit, and Binding Effect. This Agreement may not be assigned or transferred by Vendor. Credit Funding may freely assign or transfer its rights and privileges hereunder. This Agreement shall be binding upon Vendor, Lessor, and Credit Funding, and shall inure to the benefit of and be enforceable by the Credit Funding successor and assigns (hereinafter "Assignee"). Any Assignee of Credit Funding may reassign its rights and interests hereunder.

Section 8.8. Continuation of Corporate Condition. Vendor and Lessor represent and warrant that neither shall, where Credit Funding's rights and interests are diminished or impaired: (i) merge into, consolidate with or be acquired by an unrelated entity, or sell or otherwise dispose of all or substantially all of its assets or any of its assets except in the ordinary course of its business; (ii) make any material change in capital structure or operations which might in any way adversely affect the ability of Vendor or Lessor, as the case may be, to make payment or perform its obligations to Credit Funding hereunder; or (iii) knowingly enter into or continue to be a party to any transaction, which materially or adversely affect its business, operations, assets, or conditions (financial or otherwise) or Vendor's or Lessor's ability to make payment or perform its obligations to Credit Funding hereunder. Vendor's and Lessor's principal place of business and chief executive office is at ______________________________. Vendor and Lessor will notify Credit Funding promptly should the location of such principal place of business and chief executive office change.

Section 8.9. Notices. All notices, requests, demand, and other communications hereunder shall be in writing and shall be deemed to have been duly given if delivered or mailed by certified mail or confirmed facsimile transmission;

if to Vendor:

with a copy to:

if to Lessor:

with a copy to:

if to Credit Funding:

with a copy to:

Section 8.10. Waiver. None of the parties shall be deemed to have waived any of its rights, powers, or remedies hereunder unless such waiver is approved in writing by the waiving party and signed by a duly authorized officer of the waiving party. No course of dealing between the parties hereto any failure or delay on the part of Credit Funding or Vendor or Lessor in exercising any rights or remedies hereunder shall operate as a waiver of any rights or remedies of Credit Funding or Vendor or Lessor, and no single or partial exercise of any rights or remedies hereunder shall operate as a waiver or preclude the exercise of any other rights or remedies hereunder. No modification or waiver of any provision of this Agreement and no consent by Credit Funding or Vendor or Lessor to any departure therefrom by Credit Funding or Vendor or Lessor shall be effective unless such modification or waiver shall be in writing and signed by duly authorized officers of all parties, and the same shall then be effective only for the period and on the conditions and for the specific instances and purposes specified in writing. No notice to or demand on Credit Funding or Vendor or Lessor in any case shall entitle Credit Funding or Vendor or Lessor to any other or further notice or demand in similar or other circumstances.

Section 8.11. Amendments. This is the only Agreement between the parties. The terms and conditions of this Agreement may be altered, modified, or waived only by a written agreement, signed by all of the parties to this Agreement.

Section 8.12. Construction. The captions contained in this Agreement are for the convenience of the parties only and shall not be construed or interpreted to limit or otherwise define the scope of this Agreement. This Agreement shall not be deemed to have originated with any particular party hereto.

Section 8.13. Counterparts. This Agreement may be executed and delivered by the parties hereto in any number of counterparts, and by different parties on separate counterparts, each of which counterpart shall be deemed to be an original and all of which counterparts, taken together, shall constitute but one and the same instrument.

Section 8.14. Time is of the Essence. The parties agree that the time is of the essence as to all rights, obligations, and duties under this Agreement.

Section 8.15. Additional Documents. Subsequent to the execution of this Agreement, the parties agree to execute and deliver such further documents, instruments, certificates, or notices as any other party shall reasonably request which are necessary or desirable to effect complete consummation of this Agreement.

Section 8.16. Nonexclusivity. The parties hereto acknowledge that this Agreement is not exclusive and any party may market or fund leases and leasing programs separate from this Agreement with other persons.

Section 8.17. Severability. In the event that any part of this Agreement is ruled by any court or administrative or regulatory agency to be invalid or unenforceable, then this Agreement shall be automatically modified to eliminate that part which is affected thereby. The remainder of this Agreement shall remain in full force and effect

Section 8.18. Survival. All representations and warranties shall survive the execution and termination of this Agreement. Each representation, warranty, and covenant of Vendor and Lessor contained in this Agreement or Assignment Documentation shall be deemed remade by Vendor and Lessor as of the time of acceptance by Credit Funding of each Qualifying Lease and payment of the Purchase Price by Credit Funding and shall be deemed remade by Vendor and Lessor as to each Qualifying Lease.

Section 8.19. Governing Law and Jurisdiction. This Agreement shall be interpreted and construed in accordance with the laws of the State of ________________. The parties expressly agree that any suit between the parties in connection with this Agreement shall be filed and venued in the County of ______________________ located in the State of ______________ with respect to any dispute, proceeding, or action arising from this Agreement.

Section 8.20. Legal Authority. Each of the parties represents and warrants to the others that all consents and approvals necessary to the validity of this Agreement have been duly obtained, and that this Agreement does not conflict with any provision or any document or agreement binding that party or its property or affairs. Each party hereto further specifically represents and warrants to the other party hereto that: (i) the making of this Agreement is duly authorized on the part of such party and that upon its due execution by the other party hereto, it shall constitute a valid obligation binding upon, and enforceable and against such party in accordance with its terms; (ii) neither the making of this Agreement nor the due performance hereof by such party shall result in any breach of, or constitute a default under, or violation of, such party's certificate of incorporation, bylaws or any agreement to which such party is a party or by which such party is bound; and (iii) such party is duly incorporated and in good standing in its state of incorporation and is in good standing in any jurisdiction in which it owns properties or is carrying on business (except Credit Funding shall not be deemed to be carrying on business in any jurisdiction by virtue of its purchase of Qualifying Leases from Vendor).

Section 8.21. Entire Agreement. This Agreement represents the entire understanding among Vendor, Lessor, and Credit Funding with respect to the matters contained herein.

IN WITNESS WHEREOF, each party has caused this Agreement to be executed on its behalf by its proper officer thereunder duly authorized, as of the date first written above.

(Insert name of Vendor)

("Vendor")

By: ______________________________

Title: ____________________________

(Insert name of initial lessor)

("Lessor")

By: ______________________________

Title: ____________________________

Credit Funding Corporation

("Credit Funding")

By: ______________________________

Title: ____________________________

Addendum

Parties agree and understand that insurance obligations referenced in Paragraphs 1.4 and 2.10 may be imposed. Credit Funding shall exercise its best efforts to avoid the imposition of insurance costs. In the event insurance is deemed necessary by Credit Funding, and Credit Funding intends to enforce its right under a Qualifying Lease to require the lessee to purchase insurance as specified in the Qualifying Lease, then in the event the lessee does not purchase such insurance the failure to do so will not be deemed a Customer Default if (i) Vendor or Lessor provides on behalf of the lessee the applicable insurance at its own cost, or (ii) Credit Funding provides the applicable insurance and Vendor or Lessor reimburse Credit Funding in full for the cost of providing such insurance, provided, however, in no event shall Vendor or Lessor be required to pay in excess of nine dollars ($9.00) per Qualifying Lease per year during the term of such lease for such insurance cost.

(Insert name of Vendor)

("Vendor")

By: ______________________________

Title: ______________________________

(Insert name of initial lessor)

("Lessor")

By: ______________________________

Title: ______________________________

Credit Funding Corporation

("Credit Funding")

By: ______________________________

Title: ______________________________

Addendum

[illegible]

Worksheets

[Also see Forms o-05 through o-08.]

Form: w-01
Disk File Name: w-01.rtf

WORKSHEET—LEASE PROPOSAL EVALUTION

Form Purpose

A lease proposal summary response sheet to enable a lessee to easily evaluate lessor offers. Typically, leasing company offers have different formats. Digging through each can take work. To simplify your job, you can include with your RFQ a Summary Response Sheet for the lessor to complete and return with its proposal. The sheet should list, in an orderly and clear fashion, every key review item so a quick look will tell you whether the proposal is in the ball park.

This summary response form must be tailored to your company. You can use the Lessee Proposal Stage Checklist, Form c-01, to identify what should be included for your particular needs.

See:
Request for Lease Quotations, Forms r-01 through r-04
Lessee Proposal Stage Checklist, Form c-01

Proposal Summary Response Sheet

Leasing Company Information:

Name: ______________________________

Address: ______________________________

____

Deal Contact: ______________________________

Telephone No.: (______) ______________________________

Equipment Cost (+ 15%): ______________________________

Lease Term: Lease Rate Factor: (As a % of Cost)	Payment Mode (i.e., Monthly, In Arrears, etc.)	Interest Rate (Nominal)
3 Years	______	______
5 Years	______	______

Purchase Option (Check One) _____ FMV _____ Fixed Price (_____% of Equipment Cost)

Renewal Option (Check One)

______ FRV, for ______ Years, Every ______ Year(s)

______ Fixed Price [______% of Primary Rent, Every ______ Year(s)]

Early Termination Option (Schedule of Values attached ______ Yes, ______ No)

______ Not Available

______ Available, Beginning the ______ Year of the Lease Term

Upgrade Financing Option (______ Yes, ______ No)

State Future Lease Rate Determination Basis IF Upgrade Financing Not Fixed at Award (i.e., Adjustment So Lessor Can Maintain Nominal After-Tax Yield, Pre-Tax Yield, etc.) ______________________________

____

Casualty Schedule Attached (______ Yes, ______ No)

Transaction Structure (Check One)

Single Investor ______

Leveraged Lease ______

Lessor Offer: (Check One)

Brokered ______ (______ Best Efforts, ______ Firm)

Principal Lessor ______

Lessor Financial Statement Attached (______ Yes, ______ No)

Index

[Form file names appear in brackets, providing access to the disk files by adding the extension .rtf.]